Vampire

THE REQUIEM

a Modern gothic Storytelling game

"Would you like to dance?" she asked me. I died that night. It was cold, winter, but though the outside cold never touched us, the inside cold eclipsed the warmth of the fire blazing on her terrace, growing outward to meet the chill of the season on its own terms. We danced, my hand on the small of her back, yet she led me nonetheless. The music came from… somewhere. Strings. A piano. That was all. I never saw the players, though I heard their tune. It was a strange piece to dance to: a dirge, almost a requiem. The wind moved the curtains. We danced and she moved in close, as if to kiss my neck. It was not a kiss, however, but the sweetest damnation. She took my life, then, and I felt the vitality ebb from my throat in a crimson bloom. And then she gave it back.

I had spent eight years becoming a doctor. Fresh from medical school, I took a job under a friend of the family, a fellow doctor. Only a year into my practice, he invited me to a party hosted by one of his patients. A special patient, he said, one of the few upon whom he still paid house calls. It was to be a formal affair, a white-tie party visited by the upper echelon of society.

I was beside myself. After all, I was no more than a young, inexperienced sawbones; I might as well be a quack or charlatan as far as society was concerned. I arrived nervously but on time, and it was there that I met the men and women - no, those others - who would be my fellows in the eternal pageant that I was oblivious would follow.

I remember lady Moltis, a beauty from somewhere in Europe but who had a reputation as a black widow (only after my death would I learn the significance of that statement). Mr. Audelia was a queer man who never looked anyone in the eye and whose body curled in upon itself at his extremities. Mr. Bennett seemed rustic, but my hostess assured me that he had power and money far beyond the suggestion of his simple facade. Mr. Maxwell had arrived from Chicago and was rumored to be either one of its rising stars or its fallen scions, depending upon to whom I spoke. A woman named lindsay, was a scandal, having never taken a husband in life and who comported herself with little of the propriety that the rest of the women maintained.

Little did I know then that this was no true party, but a panoply of monsters. Even my hindsight fails me, for when I spent those precious few moments with Miss lindsay, I recall none of what happened, but I know now that the liaison was far more than mere attraction (and that the stain at my wrist probably didn't come from a pinching cufflink).

Another night, another victim; that's how I look at it. Motherfuckers don't want to die, all they have to do is stay out of my way. "Though I walk through the valley of the shadow of death, I will fear no evil," yeah, because I'm the wickedest sonofabitch you're gonna find down here.

I don't draw the line at just normal people, either. I'll kill my own kind if I need to. What the fucking "Kindred" need to understand is that there's nothing more important than the place you call your own. Oh, I'm sure they have some fancy word for me and my kind. I know their titles and offices and all that bullshit make a big deal out of who's responsible for what and who needs to keep who in line, and motherfuckers like me are the reason for it all. Someone comes beating down your door at just a few minutes past sunset, you know you're in trouble. Still, making it on your own is part of what this is. I didn't sign on for a bunch of new rules when my goddamn sire Changed me. Shit, that's half the reason I cut off his head and drank his soul along with his blood.

Respect, that's what I'm saying. It's about respect. God knows the fucking Kindred aren't going to give you any. You have to take it or make your own.

You don't know terror, whelp. All that stuff you're talking about? That's just being afraid. Growing up in your safe little suburbia, how would you ever know real terror? And now the power of the Blood makes you feel ever more invincible. Now that you're among the Damned, real terror will find you. You can pray that it doesn't, but it will. It found me. Horror — actual, visceral horror — is here in our precious city. I never want to see it again, but that's part of the terror, isn't it? I can't control it. All I can do is hope that that *thing* never wants to see *me* again.

She says she's a prince. I thought that maybe that was some kind of cultural anachronism or linguistic mistake. We don't have "princes," and even if we did, a woman isn't the right gender for a prince.

"You have been wrong before, have you not?" she asked me. "Our kind has different rules. Your kind, now." The invisible orchestra went sotto voce.

Later that night, we received a visitor. My mistress sat in a chair on the terrace. I was told to wait in the bedroom, but I saw and heard the whole affair from the window that overlooked the patio.

The strangest sort of man spoke before her. His skin was translucent. I expected to see his veins beneath it, but they were so pale I could discern them only by willing my senses to greater acuity. His veins were empty, and if any blood were in them, it did not move. I could not hear his heart beat. He looked up at my window and his eyes were black orbs, no pupil at all.

"I bid you good night, my Prince," he said, once his attentions turned back to the woman who killed me.

I have been wrong before.

Impossibly quickly, she was in the bedroom, having bid the visitor farewell only seconds before. Her hands on my waist. My lips on her lips. I have been so very wrong before, and surely will be again.

Not all of the monsters hide themselves so prettily as that party's guests, however. Since becoming one of the Damned, I have had the grave misfortune of meeting some truly horrific members of our kind. I have met those who would return the world to the nights of kings and vassals, those who steal children from poor homes and either slake their thirst upon them or offer them in fiery sacrifice to gods whose names are better left unspoken. I have met fervent zealots who gorged themselves on blood in the name of some Biblical figure, and I have spoken with members of an Old World cult who cavort beneath nacreous moons and believe that this state is merely one stop along the way to... something else.

I have seen all kinds among us, to be sure: penitent souls and unabashed terrors, scheming aristocrats and sullen revolutionaries, godless scoundrels and those who accept no masters other than themselves.

Truly, the world of the Damned, this midnight processional, is both rich and wayward. We are trapped in prisons of ourselves, fighting ever against the bloodthirsty creature inside all of us, but having to let it free now and again so that it doesn't overwhelm us in neglect. I consider myself one of the more reserved among this Danse Macabre, and I — well, suffice it to say that I have committed sins for which no just God would pardon me. Yet I continue to rise each night, for even in my doubt and sorrow, I cannot help but think that there is some purpose to all this.

I do what I want when I want. Take tonight — went to the bar. Call me a drunk-ass fool, but I like the way booze made me feel when I was alive, and I like it now, though I have to take my whiskey from the vein with plenty of Old Red mixed in. Women, though... not too many women drink whiskey. The ones who do are rough old bitches, stinking of cigarettes and sweat and the BO of whatever shitbag rolled off of them that evening.

So I picked one of the hags at the bar and made with the small talk. Those beasts love when you talk tough. Give them some story about cracking some asshole's arm or putting your thumb in someone's eye and they're yours for the night. Don't go too far, though. Even they're not psycho enough to get off on some fiend who kills people and drinks their blood.

Anyway, I'm working this bitch in a booth at the bar and some fucking flunky comes in, one of the bootlicks to some bigshot Kindred in town who's always nosing around in everyone else's business. You know the kind — the ones who want to keep tabs on you to make sure you're not somehow fucking shit up for them.

Like I said, you have to take respect or make your own. I get up from the booth and walk over to this little cocksucker, picking up a pool cue along the way. His eyes get all squinty as he sees me coming over and he opens his mouth like he's going to say something smart but then CRACK. Right in the fucking mouth, with all the juice these dead muscles of mine can put out. Asshole's jaw breaks clean. I can see two fractures. Individual teeth are falling out.

Fuck him. Back to the booth, where dinner awaits. I can smell that she's excited, too, the dirty old whore, and you know what I mean by "excited."

It was in a cellar in the ethnic part of town, the neighborhood where it's so old that all the early owners have moved to better locales and sold their families' original homes to other interests. The neighborhoods have ghettoized, some Jewish, some Armenian, some Czech and some even I can't determine. A house stood above the cellar, but my guide intimated that the cellar did not connect to the house proper and that, indeed, the home's owners were unaware of it hiding beneath their own basement.

My guide was one of those unfortunate souls who had tasted the Vitae of a Kindred but was not himself Damned.

Who, exactly, plied him with that blood wasn't my business. All I know is that he and he alone knew where this *thing* was that had been plaguing my restless sleep, and I recognized him only because he had been haunting those dreams as well.

A shoddy wooden door separated a small room from the rest of the nitrous-walled cellar. The guide carried only a single, guttering candle; he pointed me to the door. Cautiously, carefully, I opened that door, and chill air laden with the stench of rotting flesh surged from within. The feeble light from my guide's candle barely penetrated the darkness beyond the door, or else in that instant I might have suffered seeing even more of it. I remember amniotic, slick fur and a dozen baleful eyes all opening and focusing on me at once. As I stood there gaping, I heard the baying of a hound, though far more guttural than any beast I knew. Moreover, the baying came from *below* where we currently stood.

I slammed the rickety door, knocked my guide aside, and hurtled recklessly back up the rough steps. I careened wildly into the night, vowing to forget what I... hadn't truly seen, but more *felt*.

Bah! Now, you think me weak? Too many habits of the living are left in your face. It shows your thoughts. I've only sparked your curiosity about it, haven't I? Even as I confide this wisdom, still you are merely afraid of it. You don't know real terror, yet.

Credits

Concept and Design: Justin Achilli, Philippe Boulle, Bill Bridges, Dean Burnham, Ken Cliffe, Conrad Hubbard, Mike Lee, Chris McDonough, Ethan Skemp, Richard Thomas, Mike Tinney, Stephan Wieck, Stewart Wieck and Frederick Yelk

Second-Stage Concept and Design: Justin Achilli, Bill Bridges, Ken Cliffe, Chris McDonough and Frederick Yelk

Third-Stage Concept and Design: Justin Achilli, Bill Bridges, Ken Cliffe, Conrad Hubbard, Chris McDonough, Mike Tinney, Aaron Voss and Frederick Yelk

Additional Conceptual and Design Assistance: Carl Bowen, John Chambers and Matthew McFarland

Vampire: The Requiem is inspired by **Vampire: The Masquerade**

Vampire: The Masquerade was created by Mark Rein•Hagen

Written by: Ari Marmell, Dean Shomshak and C. A. Suleiman

World of Darkness created by Mark Rein•Hagen

World of Darkness co-created by Stewart Wieck

Additional Material: Justin Achilli, Carl Bowen, John Chambers, Matthew McFarland, Sarah Roark, Matthew Rourke and Greg Stolze

Developer: Justin Achilli

Developmental Assistance: Bill Bridges and Ken Cliffe

Editor: Carl Bowen

Art Director: Pauline Benney

Layout & Typesetting: Pauline Benney

Interior Art: Samuel Araya, Daren Bader, Tim Bradstreet, Brom, Avery Butterworth, Pauline Benney, Shane Coppage, Marko Djurdjevic, Fred Hooper, Travis Ingram, Alex Maleev, Ken Meyer JR, Mark A. Nelson, Michael Phillippi, Jeff Rebner, J S Rossbach, Mattias Snygg, Rich Thomas, Joshua Gabriel Timbrook, Andy Trabbold, Conan Venus, Cathy Wilkins

Cover Design: matt milberger

First- and Second-Stage Playtesters: Chastain Addington; Alan Alexander; Demian Anderson; Sara Anderson; Nils-Johnson Andreasson; David Bergkvist; Kraig Blackwelder; James Luke Boswell; Cassandra Brackett; Ryan Brandos; Daniel Byström; Ben Chism; James Comer; Chris Cowan; Tara De Blois; Corey Dixon; J. Entsminger; Gala Ferriere; Kevan Forbes; Douglas A. Forsyth; James Ganong; Fred Grass; Jasmine Marie Gribble; Brent Halstead; Aaron Harmon; Robert Holmberg; Conrad Hubbard; Julian Hubbard; Charles Kelley; Steve Kenson; Bishop Lewis; Terje Loklingholm; Chad McGrath; Mario Meo; Krister M. Michl; Albert Mowatt; Robin Nair; Mike Nudd; Corey Ovendale; Matthew Petosa; Chris Renfroe; Mattias Renmark; Steven Sharpe; Malcolm Sheppard; Kearsley Shieder-Wethy; Dean Shomshak; Jeff Skagen; Justin Smith; Ted Sunnerton; Helen E. Taylor, Ph.D.; Joseph Turner; Jarett Underwood; Rachel "Bunnie" Winter; Jim Zubkavich

Third-Stage and In-House Playtesters: Justin Achilli; Charles Bailey; Andrew Bates; Philippe Boulle; Carl Bowen; Bill Bridges; Chad Brown; Dean Burnham; Brad Butkovich; Raphael Castle; John Chambers; Mike Chaney; Ken Cliffe; Lisa Eidson; Brian Glass; Paul Gregory; Conrad Hubbard; Terrence James; Becky Jollensten; Katie McCaskill; Chris McDonough; Matt Milberger; Ben Monk; DeCarlo Murray; Rebecca Schaefer; Mike Tinney; Aaron Voss; Adam Voss; Frederick Yelk; Diane Zamojski

Acknowledgement

Thanks to the visionaries who broke boundaries and redefined roleplaying with the previous incarnation of **Vampire**: Mark Rein•Hagen, Stewart Wieck, Steven C. Brown, Tom Dowd, Andrew Greenberg, Jennifer Hartshorn, Robert Hatch, Lisa Stevens, Josh Timbrook and the unsung contributors whose names were never mentioned but who nonetheless know who they are. We couldn't have done it without the trail you blazed before us.

Special thanks to you, whether you're joining us again after 13 years of thrills and chills or just showing up for the first time. Game on!

WHITE WOLF GAME STUDIO

1554 LITTON DR.
STONE MOUNTIAN,
GA 30083
USA

Table of Contents

Introduction

Every night stands out as singularly

as each separate note in a composer's opus.

When we hear the composition, though,

we do not examine each and every note.

We experience it in sum.

This is the key to avoiding the malaise of eternity.

Let each night, each note, stand out

in the greater body of the Requiem your life has become.

— Charlotte Gaudibert, *Aequitas Fatalis*

Dead, your Majesty. Dead, my lords and gentlemen. Dead, Right Reverends and Wrong Reverends of every order. Dead, men and women, born with Heavenly compassion in your hearts. And dying thus around us every day.

—Charles Dickens, *Bleak House*

Vampires: blood-drinking creatures of the night. Horrors born of darkness, whose sole purpose in life — unlife, actually — is to slake their unholy thirst on the blood of the living. Without doubt, vampires are monsters.

Monsters, though, need not always be unthinking, unfeeling terrors empty of remorse, or even compassion or other human traits. Indeed, vampires can exceed their deathless curse, themselves becoming antiheroes or even heroes.

Then again, some vampires truly remain monsters.

This is the purpose of **Vampire: The Requiem.** What you hold in your hands is a Modern Gothic Storytelling game, a roleplaying game that allows you to build chronicles that explore morality through the metaphor of vampirism. In **Vampire,** you "play the monster," and what you do as that monster both makes for an interesting story and might even teach you a little about your own values and those of your fellows.

A Modern-Gothic World

The setting of **Vampire** borrows greatly from gothic literature, not the smallest amount of which comes from the "set dressing" of the movement. Key to the literary gothic tradition are the ideas of barbarism, corruption and medieval imagery. This World of Darkness can be said to be our own seen through the looking glass darkly.

With regard to barbarism, the world of the vampires is like our own, but with a significant upturn in violence and decay. The streets are more brutal, with the desperate eyes of the unfortunate ever watchful for someone more privileged from whom they can steal something to make their own bleak lives more comfortable. Gangs are more active and violent; vagrants are bolder or they obliviate themselves even more. Even those with vast resources are more fearful of those who would harm them — or more jealous of those who rival their own wealth or power. Their actions can turn fierce with the slightest provocation.

Corruption goes hand in hand with the idea of barbarism. The world is nasty and brutish, and anyone who can get ahead had best avail himself of the opportunity. This is a world of indulgent clergy, avaricious businessmen, cops looking for a payoff and gangsters who have no other options than crime. Even those who don't fit into such neat iconic archetypes face corruption of their own, such as an unwed mother who finds herself addicted to drugs and sells her child for a few grams of crank, or an otherwise honest journalist who finds out that his brother has become a bloodthirsty creature of darkness and must keep the secret for kinship's sake.

Medieval imagery adorns all of the visual elements of the setting, and it can even bleed over into other aspects. Buildings soar heavenward, supported by flying buttresses, gilded when the architects can afford it and studded by gargoyles that scare away evil spirits that are all too real. Streets have fallen into disrepair. Even cities themselves are like medieval bastions, isolated from the outside world, xenophobic and cut off. Anachronisms abound, from antique decorations in otherwise ultramodern buildings to forgotten catacombs beneath bank vaults and subway tunnels. Honest-to-goodness castles might exist in the World of Darkness where none stand in the real world. Moss and vines cling everywhere. Torches and candles light hallways and anterooms. Walls bear breaches, cracks or other signs of disrepair. *Ars moriendi* punctuate works of art. A sense of dread and fear looms visibly on the face of every passerby.

Is it so strange, then, to believe that such a world hosts the Damned, as well?

A Timeless Curse

Most vampires believe that their kind didn't just pop into existence one night to scare a cowering mortal populace. Most of the Kindred, as vampires call themselves, believe, at least metaphorically if not literally, that vampires have existed for as long as they have had men upon whom to prey, and that they have followed mortal civilizations since humankind first formed them. Others believe in a vampiric genesis not unlike that of Adam in the Bible, and that the Kindred have been chosen by whatever power makes the decision to let them stalk the night. Still others believe that vampires are part of the natural but hidden order of the world, attaching vampiric origins to pagan beliefs and ancient mythologies. Many vampires don't care at all, believing the mystery to be as demonstrably unknowable as the question of mortal life's origin. Whatever the case, whatever the truth, it is known that vampires have preyed upon the world since ancient times. Kindred society's admittedly fallible memory marks the undead as active during the height of the Rome, if not before. Even those unreliable stories suggest that Kindred activity might have existed further back in time.

Tradition and Breaking from It

The Kindred, the unique vampires of **Vampire: The Requiem**, have certain differences from the vampires you have encountered throughout literature and popular culture. This game assumes that most stories involve a group of vampires — a coterie of Kindred — as opposed to the more solitary stalkers of seminal fiction. From the Dracula of Bram Stoker's novel to Lord Ruthven of John Polidori's "The Vampyre," the undead are often depicted as lone figures. On the other hand, the vampires beneath the Theatre des Vampyres in Anne Rice's *Vampire Chronicles* functioned as a group, as did *The Lost Boys* and the nomadic fiends of *Near Dark*.

None of those visions of vampires really serves the purpose of **Vampire: The Requiem**, however. Those groups of vampires are inherently antagonistic in their stories, while the solitary vampires don't really accommodate the group dynamic of Storytelling games. As such, for the sake of the game, we've adapted the cultural notions of the vampire to one more suited to a troupe of players. We've added our own mythologies and social structures to the mix, the better to highlight the highs and lows of the undead condition. Our — *your* — vampires have the selfishness of the solitary predator, but also the social urges of creatures who fear the malaise of being left to their own company for eternity. The result is a conspiratorial blend of horror and suspense, a truly gothic mixture of madness, corruption, sensuality, mistrust and violence, all set against a backdrop of livid moodiness.

Clans

Each Kindred is a member of a clan. A clan is a group of vampires who all share common characteristics. Popular Kindred mythology suggests that all vampires are assumed to have descended from one common Kindred, the founder of that clan, though no one knows who those founders might be. When a vampire Embraces a new Kindred, the progeny is of the same clan as the progenitor. Certain "sub-clans" of vampires also exist, known as bloodlines, but a vampire can never change her clan.

Covenants

Covenants are like clans in that they are distinctions of vampires. The difference between clan and covenant, however, is that one chooses his covenant. If clan is family, covenant is political, philosophical or even quasi-religious membership. Indeed, some vampires choose to belong to no covenant at all, acknowledging no authority higher than themselves.

Myths and Facts

Where does **Vampire**'s mythology diverge from popular belief? Where do the conceits ring true? The following statements outline real-world legends of the undead, clarifying their truth or falsity in the World of Darkness.

Vampires must sustain themselves on the blood of the living: Fact. For the Kindred, the act of feeding becomes highly sensual. The vessel feels ecstatic when it happens, and the feeding vampire undergoes a heady rush as well. Certain vampires sustain their undeath by drinking the blood of animals, but rarely for long, as either their tastes or the needs of their cursed bodies force them to seek human blood.

Vampires are "immortal": Myth and fact. Although vampires do not appear to age, and some survive for centuries, the Kindred use the word "undead" rather than "immortal." Vampirism is a curse, not a blessing. It does carry with it great power, but the state of being a vampire also brings with it numerous detriments, not the least of which include the internalized rage of the Beast and feeding on human blood.

A vampire's prey becomes a vampire: Myth. You do not *necessarily* become a vampire if you're bitten or killed by a vampire. It takes a conscious act of will, known as the Embrace, to create a new vampire. Indeed, a vampire leaves little to mark her passing if she is careful. All a vampire must do to hide the wound left by her feeding is to lick it when she's done.

Vampires have every manner of supernatural power, such as turning into animals, flying and wielding the strength of a dozen men: Fact. While these powers are not universal, vampires have unique abilities known as Disciplines, which can grant individual undead capabilities such as these and more.

Vampires can have sex: Fact. While the act of feeding replaces all physical urges, vampires can still indulge in sex and even take pleasure from it. Curiously, however, the emotional aspect of sex vanishes after the Embrace. A vampire might enjoy the physical sensation of sex, but no more than she enjoys a particularly savory smell or the touch of a luxurious fabric.

A wooden stake destroys vampires: Myth. Vampires aren't destroyed upon being staked, they're held in stasis. A vampire's body slowly withers and turns inward while trapped in this state, desiccating and becoming ever more corpselike.

Vampires don't show up like normal people on camera or in mirrors: Fact. Vampires show up with their features obscured in photographic media (including video footage) and in mirrors. They can temporarily counteract this effect, but the "default" is a sort of occlusion. The same is not true for voice recordings; vampires' voices are captured normally on those.

Sunlight burns vampires: Fact. As part of their curse, vampires recoil at the touch of the sun, its vital rays scorching their undead flesh. Vampires typically spend the daylight hours in the cold sleep of undeath, and only the most resolute can shake off the weight of the day's forced slumber for even a short time.

Garlic and running water repels vampires: Myth. Such notions are nothing more than old wives' tales, cultural biases or perhaps the banes of certain bloodlines of Kindred.

Vampires are repulsed by crosses and other holy symbols: Myth — almost. While such is not generally the case, the devout sometimes do affect the Kindred with miraculous aspects of their faith.

Vampires' souls are as dead as their bodies after they become undead: Myth and fact. While a vampire might believe that he feels an emotion, what he actually feels is the echo of mortal emotions that the remnants of his soul apply to his current experience. That is, a vampire who feels angry might indeed be angry at the subject of his ire, but the resonance of the emotion actually comes from some situation the vampire dealt with in life. This condition results in many strange situations. A vampire who has never experienced a given emotion before becoming Kindred might be emotionally confused, while a vampiric artist might create a work of "art" that is awkwardly devoid of any true emotional insight.

Theme and Mood

While each story you and your troupe tells will have its own unique theme and mood, **Vampire** itself has a certain theme and mood built into it. While you can certainly play against type or push the overarching themes and moods into the background, they are present nevertheless.

Theme

Many Kindred define their existence as an unanswerable riddle: "A Beast I am, lest a Beast I become." This idea makes morality the core theme of **Vampire**. What will a vampire do now that she's become a vampire? Will she exult in the Beast's passions? Will she fight to retain her ties to what she knew in her mortal life? Is her unlife a lie, played out falsely under the pretense that she never became a vampire? Is her unlife a hellish maraud through the dark side of evil wiles indulged? Most Kindred's unlives fall somewhere in between. That's the crux of the riddle, however. How much leeway does a vampire allow her Beast in order to acknowledge it and yet keep it from overwhelming her?

Mood

In some senses, **Vampire**'s mood corresponds to key elements of the setting. The world is grim and brooding, with shadows hiding ugly secrets and terrible threats. Play this up as much as you wish — make the game a fount of boundless angst if you choose. On the other hand, secrets and espionage are part of the setting, so a conspiratorial mood is also very appropriate. Optimally, a blend of the two serves the game best. A certain amount of woe regarding the Kindred condition highlights the game's personal horror and gothic roots, while schemes and secrets give the world a degree of creeping horror above the personal level, revealing the true depth of its malignance bit by bit, much like a darkening sky blanketing the world in night.

How to Use This Book

This book is broken up into numerous chapters, each covering a certain set of topics that relate to the information as it will be used over the course of the game and in your chronicle.

This **Introduction** exists to give you a quick bit of exposure to the world of **Vampire**'s Kindred, as well as a few ideas on what the game is designed to do.

Chapter One concerns itself with a greatly in-depth look at Kindred society as well as the world in which the Kindred hide. It examines everything from covenants and customs to domain politics and hoary secrets of the Danse Macabre, the never-ending struggle between Kindred for supremacy.

Aspects of character are the focus of **Chapter Two**, from details regarding creation of an alternate persona to the characteristics of the clans to the mechanics of the Kindred's unholy powers themselves.

The game's systems and dice-rolling concerns make up **Chapter Three**. These mechanics govern all of the aspects of chance that occur during the course of a story, handling everything from characters threatened by frenzies spawned by the Beast to suffering physical damage to losing one's Morality and sanity, and even more.

Advice is offered to the Storyteller in **Chapter Four**. This includes everything from suggestions on how to handle the setting to considerations when structuring a chronicle. The chapter includes a variety of pre-made antagonists for use in stories as well.

Appendix One comprises bloodlines and new Disciplines. One of the features of **Vampire: The Requiem** is a customizable lineage system by which characters can create their own unique broods and families of vampires, as well as the unique powers to which they lay claim. This chapter includes a few of the bloodlines that are already assumed to be a part of the setting, as well as systems by which players and Storytellers can generate new ones.

Finally, a sample setting makes up **Appendix Two**. This chapter includes a host of plot threads, secrets — oh, and some common knowledge, too! — regarding the domain of New Orleans, a stronghold for the covenant known as the Lancea Sanctum.

Sources and Inspiration

Vampires have been part of people's storytelling traditions for hundreds of years. **Vampire** obviously concerns itself with the gothic tradition and a familiar modern setting, so certain sources are more influential than others. The "Additional Inspirations" sections, below, include titles that don't necessarily feature vampires but that are thematically or dramatically suitable for consideration.

Fiction

The Vampire Chronicles by Anne Rice. One of modern fiction's most popular entries in the vampire genre, these books are probably more widely read than their seminal forerunners. The first three titles in the series are the most suitable for **Vampire**, as later books in the series grow more epic in scale and more involved with the stranger fringes of the supernatural world.

Dracula by Bram Stoker. This is the one that started it all, drawing on real-world history and Eastern European lore to make the vampire a contemporary monster.

"The Vampyre" by John Polidori. This short story arguably marked the first modern usage of the vampire as a sentient creature (as previous incarnations of vampires were little more than blood-drinking corpses). Possibly homoerotic, this story came out of a group of friends that included Lord Byron (upon whom the Vampyre, Lord Ruthven, is modeled), Percy Shelley and Mary Shelley, who made no small contributions to the gothic and romantic movements themselves.

"Carmilla" by Sheridan LeFanu. A wonderful example of the idea of vampires hiding among their prey, Carmilla (or Millarca, or...) moved in and out of the lives of her prey, coming back and reinventing herself as their memories left her depredations behind. "Carmilla" has sexual overtones in the same manner as Polidori's "The Vampyre," further establishing the vampire as a sensual metaphor.

Additional Inspirations

Fear and Loathing in Las Vegas by Hunter S. Thompson, *Trainspotting* and *Filth* by Irvine Welsh, *The Bonfire of the Vanities* by Tom Wolfe, *The Unburied* by Charles Palliser, *The Great Gatsby* and *The Beautiful and Damned* by F. Scott Fitzgerald.

Movies

Nosferatu, either the original F. N. Murnau version featuring Max Schreck or the Werner Herzog version featuring Klaus Kinski. For weird, unsettling vampires with their own strangeness and derangements, you can't beat the tale of Count Orlock.

Shadow of the Vampire starring John Malkovich and Willem Defoe. Speaking of weirdness, this movie depicts the filming of the original *Nosferatu*, casting many elements of the production into question. Was the movie cursed? Did the supernatural really plague the crew? Was Schreck *really* a vampire himself?

The Lost Boys starring Kiefer Sutherland, Corey Haim and Corey Feldman. While it occasionally lapses into lampoon and camp, this is a horror movie at heart, especially in regard to its treatment of the vampires. It almost single-handedly establishes the modern vampire as a hip, cool and countercultural icon, much like the rebels and antiheroes of the romantic movement.

Near Dark starring Lance Henriksen and Bill Paxton. Want to be scared to hell by vampires who don't have any moral accountability for their actions? See this movie.

The Hunger starring Catherine Deneuve and David Bowie. Bringing the vampire-as-sexual-metaphor notion to the big screen, this is one of the most sensual vampire movies ever made. It also opens with a cameo performance by Bauhaus, for those who like a bit of musical counterculture with their film.

The Tom Cruise/Brad Pitt film adaptation of Anne Rice's *Interview with the Vampire* deserves mention, as does Francis Ford Coppola's *Dracula*, but both works are mentioned in the fiction section.

Additional Inspirations

Dangerous Liaisons, Blade Runner, Mulholland Drive, The Manchurian Candidate, The Sixth Sense, Croupier, Casablanca, Amadeus

Music

It gets touchy here: So many bands that are popular at any given moment vanish without a trace shortly after their popularity peaks. As such, we'll just touch on a few musical genres and discuss their applicability, listing a few key performers and composers.

Classical: Any elder who has spent over a century among the undead probably has a greater knowledge of classical musical than popular music. With its intricate arrangements of instruments and careful composition, classical music is the archetypal sound of both refinement and conspiracy spanning centuries. As you might expect, requiems are excellent examples of these types of music, as well. Recommended composers include Beethoven, Bach, Dvorak and Mozart.

Punk: Punk's original sound rose out of a desire to rebel against the status quo and be seen and heard doing it. While punk hasn't aged particularly gracefully, it has at least retained its hooky pop sensibilities, losing only the irony of such accessibility. Punk bands not to miss include the Sex Pistols, the Damned, the Misfits and Black Flag.

Goth: It doesn't get any more vampiric. Lyrics about bats, blood and vampires flirt with religious, pagan or even blasphemous overtones, all put up against a bombastic wall of sound that's heavy on percussion and discordant guitars. Key goth bands (even though many of them deny it) include the Sisters of Mercy, This Mortal Coil, Faith and the Muse, Switchblade Symphony and Bauhaus.

Additional Inspirations

Hey, who are we to tell you what music to listen to? No doubt you have your own musical tastes and your own ideas for using a certain song to highlight your **Vampire** experiences. You needn't even confine yourself to "vampire music." A certain Johnny Cash or Public Enemy song might suit a certain story or chronicle far better than Concrete Blonde's "The Bloodletting" ever could.

Caesar has his due, yet even Caesar is but king among Men.
— The Testament of Longinus

Chapter One:
Society of
the Damned

1

Seeing that Christ was dead,

the soldiers did not break his legs.

One of the soldiers, however,

pierced his side with a spear,

and blood and water flowed out.

A drop of Christ's blood fell upon the soldier's lips,

and he wiped it away with his hand

Yet the next day, he slept past the sunrise,

and roused from his slumber only at nightfall

And after tasting Christ's blood,

he thirsted for more.

I know.

I know because I am that soldier.

— The Testament of Longinus

Evil gains work their punishment.

— Sophocles, *Antigone*

Try though they might, the Kindred are not, and never can be, truly a part of mortal society. Regardless of their feelings, their wishes or their intentions, vampires are always separate from those around them. They are wolves amid the sheep, and their very nature prevents them from ever forgetting or ignoring that fact. No matter how much one of the Kindred might love a mortal and wish to stay with him, the Blood calls constantly. The Beast threatens a frenzy that all too often results in the violent death of those held dear. The Kindred inability to stand beneath the gaze of the sun separates them irrevocably from the greater portion of the culture, the society and the *life* that surrounds them. They are provincial creatures who think almost solely on a local level, because the greater portion of the world is well beyond their reach.

Mortals create communities, almost despite themselves. They portion off nations, celebrating cultures that have evolved over centuries, if not millennia. They are all a part of something greater than themselves, even if they fail — or choose not — to acknowledge it.

The Kindred, however, are bound for the most part to the cities that the kine — the living — have created, and each of those cities is a distinct and separate domain. The Kindred have no nations, no overarching government; the local ruler is the only ruler. Although a vampire retains a sense of identity or memories from her mortal life, she does not belong. She is no longer a part of whatever greater body with which she identified. Rather, any loyalty or sense of belonging she has is limited to local circles: fealty to the Prince, membership in a covenant or clan. These are the only connections the Kindred can truly maintain, the only cultures of which they are truly a part, and it is upon them that the entirety of their society is built.

The Embrace

It begins with death — a torrid rush of blood spilling from the throat or wrist of the victim. At the right moment, the vampire tears her own skin and places a few drops of precious Vitae on the lips of the victim. The dark magic works its blasphemous miracle then. The vessel dies… and yet he doesn't. While his natural processes cease, his sire's Vitae infuses him with the force that sustains him beyond death. This is the Embrace, the first step from existence as a mortal into the gothic world of the Damned.

What is the secret? What causes vampires to rise from beyond their natural life, to consume the blood of their erstwhile mortal fellows? Even the most erudite of the vampiric race do not know. Origin stories trace vampirism back to the Bible, to pagan ways and witchcraft, to the infamous Vlad Dracul, to the Devil himself and to any number of other sources. Every culture in the world has vampires in its mythology, and likely among its populace as well. "The Kindred condition" is an utter mystery, with an unknown number of members but no shortage of would-be prophets and philosophers with their own dogmas, theories and heresies as to the meaning or genesis of damnation.

If anything is certain, it's that the Embrace is not some kind of blessed immortality. Existence as a vampire is a curse, and quite possibly a curse handed down by God Himself. While being one of the undead certainly has its advantages — Disciplines (the mystical and eldritch powers of the Damned), deathlessness, the potential to transcend mortal boundaries — the drawbacks easily outweigh them. The price of undeath is steep, as foolish romantics infatuated by the myth of the vampire occasionally learn. One is forever apart from the world into which he was born, unconsciously shunned by it. Indeed, he can only pretend to be a part of it, and even that for only a short while, as the vampiric state forces him to prey on that world. It is his sustenance now, rather than his company. Never again shall a vampire see the light of the sun without feeling it burn him. Never again will he know the vital pleasures of life. The Requiem is a forced ostracism that may literally last forever. No wonder, then, that so many of the Kindred blind themselves to it with their petty schemes and rivalries. Their endless war, the Danse Macabre, might be the only way to escape their damnation, and even then, it is only a distraction and not true redemption.

The Requiem

It is curious, if not unfitting, that the most common name for unlife among the Kindred is a musical reference, the Requiem. The word itself means a mass or musical composition for the dead. In some cases, a requiem is a dirge. In other cases it is a chant intended for the dead's repose. In still others, it is a gesture of respect.

No surprise, then, that the word has taken on its own meaning among the Kindred. The word has connotations of its own, suggesting that the Kindred must have adopted it in a more enlightened or sophisticated time. Tonight, however, all but the most cloistered Kindred knows that the word bears its own specialized meaning. The Requiem is the Kindred's unlife, the grand, doomed waltz through which every one of their kind dances every night, urged on by metaphorical strains of music that represent the hidden powers that guide, manipulate and inspire them.

But Why?

The reasons for Embracing are many and varied, and every Kindred who exists in the world tonight probably has a host of her own for why she'd Embrace a childe. First and foremost is loneliness, as becoming Kindred imposes a state of isolation that many vampires seek to combat. Of course, the Embrace creates another Kindred — who is then himself alien and isolated, continuing the desperate, doomed cycle. Some Kindred Embrace to preserve a mortal's talents, only to find that the Embrace renders that childe unable to reach the apex of her living abilities. Other Kindred Embrace out of a sense of duty or to prevent disaster, such as when accidentally killing a vessel and then "saving" her with the curse of undeath — whose existence will then possibly doom other mortals on down the road. The trend is inevitable but irreversible. Despite its intentions, the Embrace never causes anything but damnation, as it brings another vampire into the world.

Whatever the reason, no vampire is Embraced recklessly or without some degree of thought on the part of the vampire making a new childe. Creating a Kindred requires an act of immense will, and even a vampire who says she created a childe "just because" certainly hides her own reasons.

The Danse Macabre

If an individual vampire's existence is the Requiem, the way she interacts with her fellow Kindred is the Danse Macabre, through which any number of individual Requiems play, conflict, resolve and end.

To many Kindred, the Danse Macabre has negative connotations. Relationships between Kindred are forced, at best, as vampires are seemingly designed to be solitary predators. The Embrace doesn't completely deny the urges the individual knew as a mortal, however. Inevitably over the course of undeath, all but the most withdrawn yearn for contact among those who might be able to understand them. Is it so unnatural to seek fellowship among others who have experienced the same pains and sorrows inflicted upon them (and inflicted by them) throughout the Requiem?

Indeed, the notion has undeniable risks. Although the Embrace doesn't strip the Man from the individual, it leaves its own mark, that of the Beast, the urges and wiles of the facet of personality inside all Kindred that requires blood to survive and doesn't care who it hurts to fulfill that goal. When Kindred come in contact, they innately fear or see each other as a challenge. Indeed, all Kindred vie for limited resources and secrecy, and other Kindred threaten both. In a world where Kindred must skulk and kill to survive, how trustworthy is any other vampire?

The Requiem weighs on the Kindred soul. When one knows he will never truly die, he has no sense of urgency. Over the course of forever, what can sustain a vampire's interest, or even a Kindred of a hundred years' unlife? In the interests of fighting off their own timeless malaise, the Kindred plot and scheme against each other. Once they've exhausted all of the sources that legitimately brought joy or interest to their unlives, many turn to treachery in hopes of provoking any response at all from their jaded emotions.

This last, then, is the true Danse Macabre, the "dance of death" orchestrated by vampires to elevate themselves above their peers socially, politically or even physically. It is a dangerous dance, punctuated by vampiric traps, scheming elders, ambitious neonates and ruses that can take decades, centuries or even millennia to come to fruition. The Kindred potentially have forever to concoct their master plans and hatch their vendettas — they have no need to rush. For many vampires, revenge is best when left to grow cold, prompting another turn in the Danse Macabre in response. Thus the cycle continues indefinitely.

The Danse Macabre is at once a saving grace and a resignation to damnation, for it distracts the Kindred from their nihilistic, introspective Requiems, but only by causing conflict that jeopardizes those very Requiems.

Clans

A clan is a vampiric lineage. The Kindred acknowledge five clans, and all Kindred belong to one clan or another. The most widely accepted theory regarding clans is that they are like "families" of vampires. Members of clans all inherit certain mystical commonalities, from acumen with certain Disciplines to traditional shortcomings for their particular type. One of the failings of the "families" theory is that none of the clan progenitors are reliably known, and only a few are guessed at with any degree of confidence. Certainly, the clans came from somewhere — but where? In a modern context, only two Kindred are known to have no clan, and they haven't reliably demonstrated that they've been able to Embrace over the course of their Requiems. These vampires, the legendary Dracula and the Roman centurion Longinus are responsible for the creation of certain covenants, not clans, but might they be on a path toward clan creation themselves? And if the origin of clans doesn't lie with certain progenitor vampires, from what source do clans originate? If Longinus and Dracula have no clan, who's to say that other, more secretive Kindred haven't also suffered the curse in the same way?

Tonight, the influence of the clans is felt almost everywhere. The five clans have a presence throughout the Western world, or so it is believed. The Kindred definitely came to the New World along with the early colonists, suggesting that these vampires are European in origin, or that they grew out of the civilizations that first populated the world and followed the movements of mortal men. Oral histories and sparse records indicate that some vampiric presence existed among the tribal cultures of North America before its colonization, but whether these creatures were members of clans or solitary, unique beings — or even if they were truly vampires at all — cannot be determined. While information on the Far East is fleeting, members of the five clans are known to be active there, as they are in Africa, South America and much of the Middle East. Still, little is known about how indigenous culture shapes the understanding of clans in all these regions, and anyone attempting to study the phenomenon is probably wise to take no presuppositions with him.

A bloodline is like a clan, but its characteristics are not so universal. It might help to think of a bloodline as a "sub-clan." Not all vampires are members of bloodlines. Each bloodline has a parent clan from which it distinctly diverges, yet claims descent. Kindred scholars have no reliable estimates of how many bloodlines exist in the world tonight, because bloodlines can arise at any time and few of them would stand up to be counted, even if some formal roster of them were made.

Daeva

The Daeva are emotional, sensual and desirable. Sexual predators and sensual hedonists alike populate the ranks of these succubi-seducers.

Among Kindred historians, the Daeva are suspected of being one of the oldest clans of the Damned. Their moniker suggests a Persian mythological origin, and their abilities suggest that they could be related to the demons from which they take their name. A few ancient writings suggest that the progenitor of the line was a Kindred known as Aesma Daeva, but vampiric scholars debate whether this individual was actually undead or the writings merely draw comparisons to the Persian demon of lust and anger.

The name "Daeva" predates the commonly accepted origin point of Kindred society, generally understood to parallel the ascension of Rome. Certainly, some incarnation of the Daeva existed before then, but whether they had their own society or were merely a rabble of lust-crazed revenants is unknown. After the rise of Rome, the Daeva had become an inextricable part of Kindred society, and vampiric history shows that they were very active in the Camarilla, the first known social contract of the undead.

Gangrel

The Gangrel are primal, hardy and savage. They embody the myths of vampires turning into animals or otherwise changing form (wolves, bats, mist).

Many Kindred believe that the Gangrel clan is an old one, but due to the Gangrel's bestial nature, few records exist that can connect their origins to any specific time period. While the murky pre-history of the Kindred contains any number of legends about bestial vampires, not all of these tales coincide with the hallmarks of the Gangrel.

Geographically, the Gangrel seem to hail from what is tonight Eastern Europe, where they came in contact with the nascent Camarilla and were reluctantly drawn into that society. As Rome's holdings moved westward, so, too did the Camarilla and thus the Gangrel. Historians also theorize strong Gangrel roots in what is modern Scandinavia. Since those early nights of society, the Gangrel have chosen the outlying borders of domains for their own territories. As such, Gangrel are often seen as pioneers, eking out an existence where domains will later form, or as scavengers, clinging desperately to territories and refusing to yield once domains have fallen.

Mekhet

The Mekhet are quick, discreet and wise. Legends of vampires hiding in shadows, preying secretly on victims, and even learning secrets no one else but the keeper is supposed to know probably refer to Mekhet activities.

Some of the oldest Kindred known to the vampiric world are members of Clan Mekhet, though most spend their time harrowed by the cold sleep known as torpor. While most are predisposed toward solitude, some have traveled with mortal armies and are even suspected of forming undead mercenary factions of their own. As with most other clans, nothing verifiable is known about the progenitor of the Mekhet line. Many stories depict reclusive Mekhet cult-leaders or masters of schools of stealthy soldiers, so the clan might have origins that abut the Pharaohs or philosopher-kings of the Classical or Ancient worlds.

The name Mekhet itself gives some clues as to the clan's origin, as it is an Egyptian word for "amulet." Some of the most venerable elders certainly bear features that might be described as Egyptian, while a few have classical Hellenic complexions, which isn't surprising, considering Greece's proximity to Egypt. The commerce between the Egyptians and Greeks, and later the Romans, corresponds with the legendary travels of members of this clan, as well as their formative role in the nascent Camarilla. Since that time, the Mekhet have traveled wherever shadows have fallen, wherever secrets lay hidden, and wherever Kindred call upon others to give them counsel.

Nosferatu

The Nosferatu are stealthy, strong and terrifying. Their very presence unnerves people, whether by physical ugliness, foul stench or nebulous personal malignance.

Studies of Nosferatu legend suggest that the clan is relatively young, possibly originating not too long before the rise of Rome, and possibly among the peoples it conquered. Certainly, the Nosferatu were active among the clans of the Camarilla, but proof of their presence before then is spotty at best. And yet, claims occasionally surface about very old Kindred who, if not Nosferatu, are strikingly *like* the Nosferatu. Whether these vampires are indeed members of the same clan, are Kindred of some "proto-clan" that became the Nosferatu, or are entirely unrelated can only be guessed at.

Legends of the *nosferatu* are historically heaviest in central Europe, particularly in Germany, northern Italy and eastern France. Early records describing what seem to be broods of Nosferatu also originate in modern Poland, Slovakia, Hungary, Romania, Bulgaria and Greece, with some indication of presence in north Africa as well. Like the Gangrel, Nosferatu tend to either seek out territories before or after most of Kindred culture bothers with them. Unlike the Gangrel, though, the Nosferatu adapt relatively quickly to the presence of other vampires, relying on their monstrous nature to make a place for them in the society of the Damned.

Ventrue

The Ventrue are regal, commanding and aristocratic. Vampires as everything from Eastern European lords on the mountain to gentrified nobles to modern corporate raiders belong to this clan.

Surprisingly, the Ventrue are understood to be the youngest of the clans, almost certainly originating in Rome itself, probably in tandem with the formation of the Camarilla. While their history is relatively short (in vampiric terms), it is also distinguished, as the Ventrue are made to rule. Although none remember the name of the first Ventrue, various vampiric histories do ascribe the origin of the clan, which was believed to once be a covenant, to a single female vampire. A darker history implies that this Kindred was not the first of the Ventrue line, but that she consumed the soul of her own sire, and in so doing founded a new bloodline that rose to the status of a proper clan.

As might be surmised, the Ventrue have historically been strongest in Europe, from which they grew into North and Central America, but their presence elsewhere in the world has been relatively minor. As a clan, their numbers are probably fewer than those of any other clan, but such things vary by domain, as one vampire community might consist of nothing but Ventrue — likely all the preeminent Kindred's progeny.

Coteries

Decades and centuries ago, when cities were smaller and technology far less advanced, the Kindred could afford to remain solitary predators, moving alone through the massed ranks of humanity. Tonight, the world has changed. Both mortal and Kindred populations are substantially larger than anyone could have dreamed even a few score years ago. Kindred, particularly young ones with no political clout and minimal influence in the mortal world, need allies in ways their elders never did at their age. Combined with the lingering desire for companionship left over from their mortal days, this need inspires modern Kindred to gather in small social groups called coteries.

The coterie, which normally consists of anywhere from three to six Kindred, with a few unusual groups growing as large as a dozen, has existed as an ideal for hundreds of years. In ages past, coteries tended to assemble for a specific purpose, such as the taking of an important road and the construction of a lair, or perhaps defending a domain against outside aggression. The notion of a coterie that assembles and remains together for long-term goals, or even more strangely for social purposes, seems alien and artificial to most elders tonight. Their positions in society are already secure, their havens well hidden from enemies and unsuspecting kine alike. They dismiss the formation of coteries as youthful foolishness, or even worse as the behavior of animals.

For those Kindred not considered elders, however, coteries are just common sense. Some modern coteries do assemble for a particular goal, as they did in years past. It might be an

objective that members wish to achieve, or they might be assembled at the behest of a Kindred leader, faction, their sires or by any others with the authority to demand some service of the group members. In most cases, coteries are purely social constructs, with no purpose other than the long-term benefit and mutual protection of their membership. They provide allies and support that young Kindred haven't yet managed to find anywhere else. At the very least, such community provides someone to watch one's back, to aid in the hunt and to corroborate any accounts that might have to be given to elders or authorities — advantages not be underestimated in the world of the Damned.

That said, coteries aren't happy bands of friends rollicking through a domain. The mistrust endemic to all Kindred doesn't end with the formation of a group. Coteries are subject to the same internal squabbling, double-dealing and, on occasion, outright betrayal as any other Kindred institution, especially owing to the fact that most coteries are cosmopolitan with regard to members' origins. In fact, almost every coterie ever formed is temporary; even if it lasts decades, it eventually falls apart. The more time that passes, the more opportunities for advancement by betrayal (or at least abandonment) come up, and eventually some member is almost certain to succumb to temptation. Even on the off chance that nobody leaves or turns against the group, Kindred tend to grow increasingly paranoid as they age. Considering the sort of society in which they "grow up," this reaction isn't unreasonable. What it means, however, is that beyond a certain age, most vampires aren't willing to trust their former coterie-mates, even if nobody has engaged in any direct treachery. Those coteries that don't tear apart due to dishonesty or ambition inevitably separate out of mistrust that someone will turn traitor.

Exceptions exist, of course. Some elders still operate in, or at least maintain contact with, their former coteries, if only to maintain longstanding networks of contacts, allies and the like. These long-lasting groups are rare, though. For the most part, elders continue to mistrust the notion of coteries — even those who, in their youth, were members of one — and, by extension, they often mistrust those fledglings who form them. In fact, though few admit it, many elders fear the spread of the coterie phenomenon, concerned that it will provide future rivals with a base of power they themselves cannot exploit.

Dead Cultures

The society of the Damned is a mysterious and alien thing. After all, Kindred nature — the innate paranoia, distrust and animosity that vampires often hold toward one another, to say nothing of their constant squabbles over hunting territory — would seem to suggest that they were intended to be lone hunters.

Some believe that Kindred society exists now as it has for thousands of years. Legend has it that vampires once ruled as kings and that their feudal domains have simply passed down through the centuries. Of course, no vampire who walks the Earth tonight, or at least none known, can truly recall the details of events so long past. The memories of those Kindred who have slept away the decades grow uncertain, dreams intruding on reality, and none of them can truly know what *was* from what they simply *believe* to remember.

Some Kindred, particularly among the neonates, believe that their society is a more recent development, at least in historical terms. They maintain that only in the modern era, when hiding from the kine has truly become difficult thanks to rapid communication and other technological advancement, has Kindred isolation from humankind become complete. Only now, they claim, has the need for a separate society developed.

The primary purpose of Kindred society, Kindred philosophers believe, is regulation. Kindred gather not merely in physical proximity, but socially, under a local government because enough of them recognize the need to police their own. Were the Kindred to dwell in the crowded cities with no overt authority, nothing would prevent the indiscrete or foolish from waging war with one another openly, feeding indiscriminately or otherwise threatening each other's vitality. A figure known as the Prince (or whoever represents the local government) is an enforcer, first and foremost.

Beyond this, Kindred claim that their kind cleave together socially for reasons far more personal and ingrained than the need to protect themselves from each other. Kindred society grants its members something they could never have among mortals: a sense of belonging, of community. Vampires might despise the greater portion of their fellows and their Prince or governor — and a great many do — but this is nevertheless their community, their city. Where mortals turn to family, the Kindred have clans. Where mortals form nations and cultures, the Kindred have covenants. These social constructs allow the Kindred to feel as though they're a part of something, to counter the extreme isolation that they would otherwise suffer for all eternity.

The Kindred are still outsiders, proponents of this idealized state, but at least their domains and clans and covenants allow them to be outsiders together.

Many elders, of course, consider such theories a heap of mealy mouthed, revisionist, self-indulgent effluvia spewed by idle childer with no knowledge of the way the world works. As they cannot provide any evidence for their conservative, "society has always existed thus" attitudes, however, elders aren't likely to silence the social theorists any time soon. And thus the Danse Macabre continues on one more front.

The Covenants

A covenant is a social unit of vampires. Each is an artificial group comprising Kindred with similar philosophies, ideals, political aims and even religious notions. Vampires can usually belong to only one covenant at a time, as members are somewhat exclusionary about their principles, but Kindred sometimes leave one covenant to join another, evade notice of membership in multiple covenants, or actively concoct false identities with which to spy on other covenants. Some vampires belong to no covenant at all. While all of these groups receive greater treatment elsewhere in this book, it helps to familiarize yourself with some of their basic notions.

The Carthians seek to reconcile Kindred society with modern governmental structures and social systems. In any number of cities across the world, the Carthian experiment is in some stage of its inexorable cycle, running from naïve idealism to "the revolution eats its children."

The Circle of the Crone venerates a variety of female figures as an amalgamated creator of vampires, the Mother of all Monsters. Regarded as pagans by some of the more conservative Kindred factions, the Circle relies more on holistics and redemption than on the penitence and guilt of other ideological covenants. Its members are sorcerers and blood witches.

The Invictus is the aristocracy of the night. Neofeudal and corrupt from within, it is nonetheless a powerful covenant that draws strength from tradition. The Invictus claims to trace its roots back as far as ancient Rome, if not before.

The Lancea Sanctum looks to Biblical history for its spiritual outlook. The covenant seeks to influence Kindred society with the strictures of Longinus, who was believed to be a progenitor turned into one of the Damned by the blood of Christ. The covenant practices a magic that draws on elements from Biblical times, when God's will was manifest.

The Ordo Dracul is a neo-Victorian faction not unlike a secret society. It commands mystical knowledge and rituals that allow members to transcend their vampiric state. The covenant claims descent from the historical Vlad Tepes — Dracula himself.

Kindred who belong to no covenant at all are known by many names, but among the most universal are "the unaligned" or "the unbound." They have no formal structure, and many just want to handle the Requiem on their own terms, rather than those of covenants or other institutions.

The Body Count

So how many Kindred are there? If they've got a society, they must exist in pretty substantial numbers, yet they've managed to keep themselves more or less hidden from the majority of the mortals around them.

The truth is, Kindred numbers vary from city to city. In most small cities, the proportion of undead to mortals tends to be relatively low: One vampire per 100,000 or more mortals is not uncommon. In large cities, the ratio is usually nearer one vampire per 50,000 mortals. In some cities that seem to draw the Kindred for whatever reason — cities such as New York, London, New Orleans and Chicago — the ratio can be substantially higher. Most Princes don't particularly keep track. As long as the population doesn't grow so high that people take notice of the predators among them, numbers don't matter.

If one were to take a worldwide average, the ratio is probably around the one-to-50,000 mark. It fluctuates so thoroughly from domain to domain that one should never assume that any given population corresponds to that figure.

A Gilded Cage

Perhaps the single greatest reason vampire society has developed as it has is the Kindred's unbreakable tie to the city. The undead are bound to the cities of the kine as tightly as they are to the Blood itself. For them, the city is really a cage, gilded though it might be, and the Kindred could no more abandon it than they could become vegetarians.

It would be foolish, of course, to suggest that Kindred never travel. If they did not, they could never have spread as humanity has, and they would still be restricted to select areas of the Old World. Despite all the reasons not to, reasons that have literally shaped Kindred society as it's known tonight, travel is sometimes necessary (or simply the best of a list of bad options). It's not that Kindred don't travel, it's that they don't travel casually.

What is it, then, about cities that holds the Kindred as though their feet were nailed to the floor? Why does each city exist as its own fiefdom, with little if any congress between it and its neighbor?

Staying Near the Well

Perhaps the most obvious reason for the Kindred to gather in cities, and to remain there, is the simple fact that that's where the people are. Ultimately, no matter what sort of religious, cultural or mystical face the Kindred wish to put on it, blood is all that matters. It's at the core of everything they do. While hunting is never a sure

thing, a Kindred can be relatively certain that, with a reasonable degree of care and effort, she can find someone on whom to feed in a city without attracting too much attention. Cities have slums, clubs, drug dens, hospitals and, if it comes down to it, dark alleys. Even when Kindred can find people elsewhere, they don't always present a viable opportunity for feeding.

Certainly, it might be possible for a particularly hardy or desperate vampire to eke out an existence outside an urban center. A rustic town of 500 people out in the middle of nowhere might provide enough Vitae to support a particularly careful Kindred for a short time. In a population of that size, however, someone would eventually discover his depredations when he inevitably loses control and frenzies. At best, the vampire has a frightened, angry population of mortals on his hands, all of whom move on or look for the culprit with shotguns. At worst, the elaborate charade that hides the Kindred from the world's awareness is compromised, at least on a local level.

Some few vampires take the idea of escape a step further and attempt to survive in the wilds, feeding on animals. Many give it up after a relatively short time, though. Not only do they face a relative paucity of available blood, Kindred eventually reach the point at which animals are no longer sustaining. Why scavenge and scrounge in the yard when they can simply stay nearer the table and feast?

In addition to the difficulties involved in feeding, existing outside a city invariably leaves a Kindred subject to the other hazards and difficulties inherent to travel.

The paradox of the Kindred is that they possess both the solitary nature of the predator and the social leanings of humans. They gather in groups, though their competitive and aggressive nature often renders such gathering dangerous, or at least uncomfortable. They compete against one another — plotting, scheming, backstabbing — yet they find themselves unable to function in other environments. Even if the Kindred could easily acquire blood outside the urban sprawl, few would be willing to leave cities behind, for both Kindred and mortal society supports them.

The Kindred gain most of their power and strength not from their own innate abilities, but from the influence they wield in the mortal world. No matter how old or powerful a vampire is, someone is always older and stronger. Why risk one's own potentially eternal existence, miserable as it might be at times, when one can manipulate pawns into taking those risks instead? Rare is the Kindred without some influence, or at least a few contacts, whether in government, business, organized crime or in some other potentially useful element of kine society. And for the most part, those connections are all within the city because that's where the people are.

A Kindred without his contacts is, to a large extent, helpless. He certainly has his innate powers — the strength and abilities inherent in the Blood and his undead nature — but so do his enemies, and he no longer has any help on which to call.

Even Kindred society serves as something of a safety net, as long as everyone involved is willing to follow the rules. For the most part, any given vampire is unlikely to attack another openly within the city. All but the most desperate Kindred think twice before blatantly violating the Traditions of their kind or the local law for fear of reprisal from the Prince and other authorities. Away from the reach of the Prince, however, all bets are off. For the Kindred, anything beyond the city limits is lawless territory, lacking any supreme authority to whom grievances can be brought. As most wise Kindred stay inside their cage, those who do not have no undead allies on whom to call, just as they have few or no mortal pawns.

PLAYING THE DANSE MACABRE

The need to build up both mortal influence and Kindred allies is a vicious cycle that constantly feeds into itself. Young, unattached Kindred who are new to the Requiem quickly find that they need some degree of leverage in order to make a place for themselves in the world of the Damned. Maybe a fledgling vampire has accidentally angered another neonate, someone holds a grudge against her sire, she needs to convince an elder to allow her to feed in his territory, or maybe she simply runs across someone who dislikes her covenant, clan, bloodline or hair color. She needs allies among the other local Kindred, or at least something to offer or with which to threaten her rival. The greatest asset most Kindred truly have to offer one another is access to their ties and connections in mortal society. Certainly, some particularly skilled Kindred provide other services, and a Prince can offer territory or other special privileges, but influence is the currency with which most Kindred barter. One elder with leverage at the local airport might agree to smuggle something for another, if the other will use his own contacts to make sure that the police don't break up the first's drug-trafficking operation. Without some measure of influence in mortal society, most Kindred have little to trade.

So the young vampire discovers that she must develop mortal allies and contacts if she wishes to cultivate Kindred allies. The more Kindred allies she has, however, the more attention she draws. The enemies of her allies become her enemies. Other Kindred who might have left her alone suddenly see her rising in power and decide to cut her off at the knees before she becomes dangerous. Suddenly, her allies aren't sufficient. She needs more connections, more influential sponsors. For that, she needs to develop more contacts and influence in kine society.

Despite the amicable-sounding name they have chosen for themselves, the "Kindred" don't particularly see themselves as family unless they're forced to do so. The bonds of friendship are all but nonexistent among vampires, and those relationships that do form against all odds rarely survive as long as those who enter into them. Kindred who attempt to remain aloof, who try to avoid entangling themselves in mortal or Kindred affairs, usually find that society won't permit them to sit the game out.

And so it goes, an endless loop ensuring that few Kindred ever manage to haul themselves out of the quagmire that is the modern city.

The bonds of clan, bloodline or covenant also provide ample ties to make common cause between vampires. Kindred who dwell among a large population of, or in a region dominated by, their clanmates and covenant members have an undeniable social and political advantage over those who do not. These social bonds are, almost by definition, found entirely within cities. Leaving them all behind might seem like a liberating notion to young Kindred, as they wouldn't have to worry about upsetting their brethren, angering elders, hunting on the wrong ground or speaking to the wrong person. Too many Kindred have found, however, that the inherent difficulties of surviving away from population centers are greater than expected, and they have no assistance on which to call.

Loneliness

One of the most ingrained reasons to remain in cities is loneliness. Kindred are no longer mortal, but the transition is relatively recent for most. Not even the eldest can fully shake the last lingering traces of what they used to be. Predators tend toward solitude by nature, but people are gregarious in the extreme, and the Kindred's waning sense of community, of belonging, helps tie them to their remaining Humanity.

Vampires certainly feel lonely as often or as easily as mortals do (if not more so), and some who remain apart from the masses too long discover they can no longer blend in when they attempt to return.

Some young Kindred have recently attempted to survive in the wild as coteries, rather than as individuals. Doing so goes a long way toward alleviating the loneliness of such isolation, but many of these coteries run into difficulties finding enough sustenance upon which to feed. It's hard enough for a lone Kindred to feed herself on animals and the occasional hitchhiker. For a group, the task is extremely challenging in the long run.

Elysium

One of the most ancient and honored surviving Kindred customs, and one whose importance many modern neonates drastically underestimate, is that of Elysium. In essence, a Prince may declare specific locations of his city to be Elysium, places free of violence, safe for all Kindred. Most official Kindred business takes place in Elysium. The Prince's court is most frequently held in one such location, and most young vampires who need to speak with a leader or elder come to Elysium to seek them out. Politics and intrigue are as common here as rats on the street outside, with debate and negotiation heard as frequently as casual gossip. Many elders spend entire nights here, and while neonates are welcome (most of the time), they are expected to remember their place.

Most areas of Elysium are cultural or artistic centers, conducive to intellectual pursuits and the sense of calm reflection that most Princes hope to maintain. Such places include everything from theaters and opera houses to museums and galleries to university halls and libraries. As more Princes come to accept the ways and conveniences of the modern world, and as young Kindred ascend to positions of power, the number of nightclubs and restaurants declared Elysium grows as well. In any case, wherever an Elysium is, attendees are expected to dress and comport themselves appropriately, for the sake of the secrecy, if not simple courtesy.

While refreshments are often provided at Elysium, especially during court or other formal gatherings, such is not always the case. It is considered bad manners to show up to Elysium hungry, as not only does doing so lead to short tempers and potential violations of the laws of nonviolence, but most Princes discourage or even forbid hunting within several blocks of Elysium. After all, these locations are centers of Kindred activity. If hunting were permitted in the region, it would only be a matter of time before the number of strange occurrences and deaths attracted attention. Kindred who bring guests to Elysium — be they blood slaves, mortal retainers, new childer, vampires from outside the city or even local Kindred who simply were not specifically invited to a given event — are responsible for their guests' behavior, and they can be punished severely for violations committed by companions.

Any sort of physical or mystical confrontation is strictly forbidden within Elysium (though social conflict has risen to both an art form and outright war). Violators of this rule are inevitably banished or executed posthaste. When tempers flare beyond words, the Prince, Sheriff or Master of Elysium might ask those involved to leave and cool off elsewhere in hopes of heading off an explosion that would result in violence and punishment. Elysium is strictly neutral ground, and Kindred are expected to leave their conflicts — or at least any physical continuation of them — outside. That said, elders are experts at holding grudges, and while a neonate might get away with mouthing off to an elder while inside, he'd better have reliable transportation home and learn to sleep with one eye open. Many Kindred conflicts that have eventually erupted in violence began with a single misspoken word in the corridors of Elysium.

Havens

Any discussion of Kindred safety and security from zealous enemies must eventually turn to the concept of the haven — at once a vampire's resting place, personal domain and private inner sanctum. A haven is the place (perhaps the only place) where a vampire can reliably find shelter from the sun while she sleeps the day away. Due to the Kindred's inhospitable relationship with the sun, the selection and administration of one's haven can often be (or quickly become) one of the most important aspects of a young vampire's unlife.

The vast majority of neonates do not begin their unlives with an established haven of their own. As a rule, mortals do not keep their domiciles in a condition well suited to a vampire's needs, so the Embrace often forces an immediate change of environs upon a newly created fledgling. More often than not, a Kindred's sire provides his new progeny with a haven, even if only temporarily. Once a neonate has grown accustomed to the rules of his new existence, he may then — often with his sire's assistance — procure a haven of his own somewhere in the domain. Once in a while, the neonate merely returns to his former, mortal residence with the intent of renovating, and indeed, some types of homes need surprisingly little work in order to become functional havens. Most of the time, though, the sire advises against such a move, as it invites questions from one's former life and generally complicates a young vampire's existence unnecessarily.

A SIRE'S HOSPITALITY

A strange, unofficial tradition has arisen over time concerning havens, and it is one that has caused no small measure of ill will between sires and childer over the centuries. The tradition is seen most often among the Ventrue clan, and many believe that the custom's origins can be traced back to an ancient Eastern European mortal convention. Regardless, some Kindred follow a tradition that says a sire is responsible for housing his progeny until such time as that protege is released into the world. After all, they argue, once a neonate has a haven of his own, he technically has his own personal domain, and many old-fashioned sires do not believe that childer are entitled to the rights of domain until such time as they are released. Therefore, the waiting period for receiving a haven of one's own can be much longer than a neonate expects, depending on his sire's sense of convention. Many bitter neonates are quick to point out the fact that being beholden to one's sire for protection from the banes of one's existence, as well as for one's political station in vampiric society, puts one's entire unlife in the sire's hands, and that's just how many sires like it. Thankfully, this tradition is practiced less and less frequently as time marches on, and tonight, few sires would even want their fledgling childer dwelling under the same roof with them for years on end.

A haven itself is a very personal affair. Given the sheer amount of time a Kindred must spend within — at least 12 hours a day, for all eternity — a haven can become the only thing its owner will see in any real sense as his own. One does not have to be aesthetically obsessed to appreciate a level of personalization in the home, and even the most Spartan vampire eventually develops some sense of individual style (or at least efficiency) in the design, decoration and layout of his haven.

Technically speaking, a haven is nothing more than a vampire's home. At least, that's all it has to be to fit the definition. As such, there exist just as many different kinds of havens as mortal domiciles, or even more, considering the options at a vampire's disposal. The average mortal can't stand living under extreme weather or pressure conditions, but such considerations mean very little to the undead. Some Kindred (especially the Gangrel and some Nosferatu) enjoy the solitude offered by inhospitable surroundings, and they elect to make havens in areas deep underground, atop dizzying heights or even underwater. Others opt to blend in as much as they can, preferring the warm comforts of modern high society to the cold comforts of the grave. Daeva and Ventrue in particular are known for their rarified tastes in havens (and all associated trappings), and some well-to-do Kindred maintain lavish homes and penthouse suites that would make the wealthiest mortal green with envy.

Security, of course, is of paramount concern, and Kindred possessed of any degree of material resources usually spare no expense in making sure that a haven is well protected from both the sun and from daytime intrusion. Such security might come in the form of high-tech alarms, a bank of cameras, pressure-sensitive floor plates and the like, or it can come merely from locale. A haven buried deep underground or in an old vault is going to be very secure by nature alone, without any further security measures.

Domains of the Dead

Without a doubt, isolation and the attitudes and practices spawned by it have resulted in the current forms of vampiric government, culture and society. While humanity has developed enormous countries, world-spanning faiths, multi-national cultures and even the tentative beginnings of what might one day grow into a world community, the Kindred have been left behind, as unchanging as they are undying. Exceptions certainly exist, but for the most part, when it comes to government and sociological development, the Kindred never left — or at the very least, have returned to — far more primitive times.

No Kindred domain is governed exactly like any other, but the vast majority of them resemble the feudal nations of ages past. This doesn't mean that the Kindred ignore modern conveniences or dress like the cast of a Shakespearean tragedy. It does mean that their power structure is usually hierarchical and largely inviolate.

Consider the details. A given city is isolated by Kindred standards. It's a walled sanctuary with barbarians roving about outside the gates. The population usually consists of Kindred of drastically different ages, influence and power. And, perhaps most importantly, no higher authority exists outside the city. Nobody can step in and tell the locals they're doing it wrong.

Add all this up, and the result is a "government" in which anyone strong enough to take and hold power is, by default, entitled to it. In most cases, this is a single vampire, usually one of the eldest and most powerful in the city. The standard term for the Kindred who rules a given domain is gender-neutral "Prince," though many choose alternate titles that more accurately reflect their personalities and styles of rule. A few cities are ruled by allied groups of Kindred, and an even smaller number actually attempt to emulate more modern political styles of governing, but these cities are by far the exception, not the rule.

By and large, the Kindred have no choice but to accept the dictates and leadership of a given Prince, no matter how tyrannical his reign is or odious his laws are. After all, what are the other options? Petition for help? To whom? No higher authority exists. Overthrow the regime? Odds are, no single faction in the city has the strength to wrest power from the Prince, else it would have happened already. One might be able to rally several different factions, multiple powerful elders or simply a great portion of the Kindred population behind the goal, but for this tactic to work a great many Kindred with their own ambitions and fears must put aside their differences and work together. This simply doesn't happen often enough to provide much hope. The only way such is likely to occur is if the Prince is so truly horrible and abusive that nearly every vampire in the city believes that she has something to gain by ousting him. Sometimes a single powerful elder does succeed in scheming her way to authority, ousting a weaker Prince in the process, but doing so requires years of machinations, numerous alliances and many decades of experience.

So if no appeal is available and revolution is unlikely to succeed, what's left? Leave the city, begin anew somewhere else? The Kindred are acutely aware of the hazards of that course of action. For the great majority of Kindred, the only way to survive is to keep one's head down, grin and bear the current Prince no matter how awful he is, and hope one night to accumulate enough personal power and influence to take steps at that time.

It must be said, though, that not all Kindred Princes are sadistic, iron-fisted tyrants. Few Princes rule so absolutely that they can do everything they might want. Other elders most likely dwell in their domains. Certain vampires (known collectively and individually as the Primogen) may advise the Prince, but that doesn't necessarily mean they share all his goals and desires. Few Princes are so secure in their positions that they can afford to completely ignore the wishes of their cities' elders. This isn't necessarily a good thing — no guarantee exists that the desires of other elders are any better for young Kindred than those of the Prince — but the need to make occasional concessions is still the only check on the Prince's power, other than the Traditions (see p. 74).

Many domains take the feudal model further still. One way the Prince has of both mollifying the other elders and delegating responsibility is by parceling out portions of his city and granting them to other Kindred as personal feeding grounds. Only a very few Princes parcel off an entire city. Most focus only on the best areas: downtown, specific slums, hospital districts, club and bar areas. (In many cities, an area of this sort is called the Rack.) If the Prince grants such a territory to an elder, that elder then decides who, if anyone, may feed there. This grants the elder substantial power, as many Kindred rely on Racks for easy feeding. If they wish to continue hunting in those areas, they must offer favors or concessions to the current landholder. Of course, some Kindred choose to ignore the fact that the territory is no longer open. Many get away with it, but a vampire caught poaching on another's territory can be taken before the Prince and judged as a criminal.

DEPENDENT DOMAINS

Precisely how much power individual elders have over those in their territory varies city by city. In some domains, they have very little. They might offer to trade feeding and haven rights for boons or services, but anything beyond that is considered stepping on the Prince's toes.

In other cities, elders rule their territories almost as domains within domains. Here, an elder may set his own laws and enforce his own dictates, as long as they do not blatantly contradict those of the Prince. This is particularly common in cities where an elder is very nearly as powerful as the Prince himself. In some cases, the Prince doesn't even grant territorial rights to the elder in question. Rather, she goes to him and says, "I'm claiming this portion of the city for my own. Do you care to dispute it?" Weak Princes (at least in comparison to other local elders) sometimes accept such arrangements as a means of avoiding conflict.

For more information on such situations, see "Subinfeudation" on p. 35.

So, as in a feudal kingdom, the domain is divided into smaller territories, each of which is metaphorically ruled by its own landowner, who has power over those who would hunt or dwell in his territory. That power, however, still ultimately belongs to the Prince, who might withdraw his grant or offer it to someone else. Thus does a wise Prince placate those who would otherwise be his enemies, while at the same time granting himself leverage over them for future use.

In some cities, the process continues further still. Those who control a given territory might subdivide it further, granting portions of their own holdings to favored childer or allies. Doing so works only in the largest cities, of course, and not always in those. When it does, the local rule often has three or even more layers, resulting in a chain of authority that even the Byzantine-minded Kindred can find confusing.

Rule by Fear

Niccolo Machiavelli wrote, when speaking of the wielding and maintaining of political power, "…one ought to be both feared and loved, but as it is difficult for the two to go together, it is much safer to be feared than loved, if one of the two has to be wanting." This is a theory by which the Kindred, who are largely incapable of loving one another as mortals understand the term, have ruled for as long as any surviving vampire can remember, and possibly many centuries more. It is fear, after all, more than any other factor that holds Kindred society together.

In most cases, any social or political action the Kindred take is motivated by fear. The Prince fears losing power, so she cracks down on those who rebel against her word. Elders fear the loss of status, so they squabble among themselves to tear down their enemies while exalting themselves in the Prince's eyes. Neonates fear the tyrannical political machine, and they react either by becoming part of it or by striking against it in hopes of changing the system before the system catches up with them. Covenants as a whole fear mortals and young Kindred. The Invictus fears savvy young Kindred who can react to the modern world better than staid elders can, and it fears staid elders who have had decades or even centuries to hoard power and influence. The Lancea Sanctum fears the changes and secular nature of the modern world. The Carthians fear the current power structure. The unbound fear being bound by the laws of others. The Circle of the Crone fears, or so it seems, the very nature of the Kindred condition. The Ordo Dracul fears that which it cannot quantify or understand. All of the Damned fear being cut off from access to blood or being forced to leave their home cities.

It would not be wholly inaccurate to say that the Kindred who would be Prince must simply make herself the most feared, more than she must be the most powerful or the best connected or the eldest. This, then, is why the majority of Princes are far more despotic than, perhaps, their situations require. They know that it is only their subjects' fear that keeps them in line. Some Kindred are loyal to their Prince due to some personal attachment, however, or perhaps in repayment for past favors. As always, the rare exception does exist.

Anachronism Ascendant

Some young Kindred, particularly those who are not particularly familiar with the feudal model, are utterly confounded by the shockingly outdated nature of Kindred society. Even when established in a context they can understand, it makes for a horrifying juxtaposition with the comparatively progressive modern world from which they have been drawn. Kindred society has various cliques, all of which tend to cling together and snub anyone outside their own incestuous ranks. It has a proliferation of petty grudges, backstabbing and overblown squabbles over minor or even imagined slights. And, like many factionalized populations, vampire society is ruled with an iron fist by one individual (or, in a few cases, a cadre) who has managed to become the most popular, largely by manipulating everyone else's fear of being left out or seen as different.

Needless to say, the society of the Damned is far from perfect. The fact that such vicious and barbaric customs ring true even in general terms goes a long way toward showing how petty and deadly many Kindred personal and political struggles can be.

Another factor shaping and steering Kindred society, and one that ties back into the notion of rule by fear, is the proliferation of vendettas and feuds among the undead. The Kindred have developed the ability to hold and inflate a grudge to an art form, and most of them never forget even the most minuscule slight. Part of this is physiological. As the Kindred cease to age, so too do they often cease to grow mentally and emotionally. Therefore, a vampire of 200 probably knows a great deal more than she did when she was 20, but she is unlikely to be any more mature or truly any wiser. And as the majority of modern Kindred are Embraced at the prime of life — and therefore relatively young — few of them ever develop the maturity that would have come with but another decade or so of actual living.

Perhaps the greater part of it, however, comes back to fear. Kindred respond to minor offenses by holding grudges and working to humble or destroy the one who slighted them because they are scared of doing otherwise. They fear losing face, and therefore status and power, in the eyes of their compatriots, so they must show that they can give better than they receive. They fear appearing weak before those who slight them, thus inviting further and ever-escalating scorn and political attack. Certainly, the infamous Kindred capacity for rage enters into it as well, but fear is, ultimately, the strongest motivator.

These grudges often greatly influence the entirety of society. Factions in a given city, and even entire domains, have struggled and engaged in cold wars with one another purely over an incidental remark or some other minor

transgression by one party against another. Many elders seek their positions and offices for no other reason than to wield power against rivals.

These disputes often leave the realm of the personal and grow to far-reaching proportions. A feuding vampire might call upon clanmates or fellow covenant members for support, and while not all of them respond, a few usually do. He might involve allies in the city power structure, which transforms the struggle into a political one, even if political power was not the initial subject of disagreement. It's an open question as to whether the conflict between covenants, which so concerns and even defines those groups in the modern nights, truly began as cultural disagreements at all, or if they were spawned from personal feuds that swiftly got out of hand.

Government Activities

The previous description of Kindred domains as usually feudal can give the impression that they're all similar in construction. In truth, while the practical result is the same more often than not, the specifics of government differ from city to city. Discussed here are just a few of the near infinite possibilities for governmental models found across Kindred domains. All the descriptions assume rule by a single individual, a Prince or the like, but rule by Primogen or other council is also a possibility. Plenty of other types of Kindred governments exist; those listed here represent some of the most common (or, in the case of the democracy, the most frequently attempted and failed). Although the forms vary wildly, the ultimate results — a dictatorship swayed by the powerful few, with little to no recourse available to those beneath — are almost universal.

Remember also that all these governmental models apply *to Kindred society only*. No Prince on the face of the Earth is so powerful that he has the mayor, police chief, and the local congressman all dancing to his tune. No entire city answers to the whim of a vampire. Even were such a thing possible, it would inevitably lead to a Masquerade breach, for someone would eventually notice something amiss. Powerful Princes and other Kindred leaders likely have substantial influence among the mortal elite. They are necessary contributors to a mayor's campaign, or they can lean on certain lobbyists who in turn lean on the city council. The Kindred must remain hidden, and even the most brutish Prince knows that his touch must be light indeed when applied to the mortals who dwell within his domain.

DRESSING THE PART

Note that when one of these descriptions says a court or assembly "resembles" something from the past, it doesn't mean the Kindred involved dress in cloaks, hose and powdered wigs. While some truly eccentric or anachronistic elders might maintain the look they preferred back in their mortal days (at least in private), most aren't too many years behind the modern fashion. Dressing as an obvious anachronism is a great way to attract attention, and the Kindred know all too well that

attention can bring their whole kind low. Whether he calls himself a Prince, an Archbishop, a CEO or a Don, the ruler of a given domain is far more likely to wear Armani than ermine.

Feudal Monarchy

One of the most common societal models, and the one considered the "default" when discussing a city about which details are unknown, is also the one that most closely resembles the medieval kingdom. A single ruler holds absolute power and makes no attempt to hide that fact. His word is law, enforced by other elders to whom he has chosen (or, in some cases, been forced) to grant titles, authority or territory. Princes of these sorts of domains often hold formal courts and usually decree various laws limiting the movement of other Kindred through their domains, and they demand that all newcomers present themselves for approval. These courts often involve substantial pomp; a Seneschal announces members or petitioners as they arrive, titles that would never see use on the streets are wielded and bestowed, and so forth. This sort of government is found most frequently in Invictus- and Ordo Dracul-dominated cities, but also forms a significant minority among those domains ruled by the Lancea Sanctum and particularly tyrannical Circle of the Crone domains.

The Boardroom

The result of modern sensibilities, this sort of city is run almost like a corporation. The Prince sits in a position much like a board chairman, with other elders in power serving as co-executives. The ultimate result is largely the same as that of the more obvious feudal system, but the Kindred involved like to appear more enlightened. Most decisions are made by a vote of the ruling elders (unless the Prince chooses to overrule them, of course), policies are decided in committee, and the elders make at least a show, if not an honest practice, of rewarding loyalty and ability among underlings. Unlike a true corporate board, presiding vampires rarely have the power to vote their chairman out, and those below them cannot often look forward to a death or retirement opening up a managerial position. Both the Invictus and the Carthians make frequent use of this governmental model.

The Diocese

The Church has influenced both mortal and Kindred history more than any other single entity or organization in the West, and many Kindred model their domains on Church hierarchy even tonight. To uninformed outsiders, this system often appears identical to a feudal system with new names. The Prince — who usually takes an ecclesiastical title such as Archbishop or Cardinal — rules absolutely, assisted by a council of advisors (variously called Priests, Bishops or the like) who serve as enforcers and landowners. The vast majority of Church-modeled domains tend to swing toward one of two extremes. Many of them — particularly those dominated by the Lancea Sanctum (and, to a lesser extent, the Circle of the Crone), who make greater use of this system than any other covenant — truly do enforce a rule by religious doctrine. They demand observances and certain behaviors of those who dwell in their domains, or at least of those who would hold offices therein, and truly believe the faith they espouse. At the other extreme are those Kindred who seek to use the trappings of faith and the beliefs of others for their own ends. In these domains — usually found in cities held by the Invictus, the Ordo Dracul, the Circle of the Crone or the unaligned — the overt religious nature of the government is either deliberately mocking, or meant to inspire a loyalty among faithful Kindred that leaders themselves do not honestly share. In either domain, merely questioning the rule of leaders is often a greater crime than in more overtly feudal domains, for the "criminal" does not merely challenge a secular authority, but the rule of God (or Longinus or the Crone or whoever). These domains usually hold official functions with as much pomp as do monarchies, but such gatherings are usually devoted to religious pursuits, including prayers and hymns or rituals and ceremonies, rather than celebrations of the rulers themselves.

By the Kindred, For the Kindred

Found almost exclusively within Carthian domains (though some of the unbound have tried it, and some Invictus Kindred have tried to appear as though they try it) are those recent attempts at imitating modern governmental systems. These Kindred want to take the lessons of mortals to heart, to eliminate rule by the eldest or most powerful under which they've always suffered, and to grant all Kindred an equal say in what happens to them, or at least an equal opportunity to attain power. To date, few of these attempts have lasted, as those Kindred who do obtain power eventually decide they don't care to give it up when their brethren tell them they should. Those few cities that do still remain often resemble the worst aspects of mortal government. They are mired in rules, regulations and red tape designed to prevent any single vampire from wielding too much power, and they are paralyzed by squabbles among various officials, all of whom are convinced that their own vision for the city and government is the way to go. Their courts usually resemble either chaotic public forums or very orderly (and difficult to obtain) private meetings with high officials.

Common Law

While the Traditions (see p. 74) form the basis for all Kindred law, they do not represent the extent of that law. Every Kindred domain has its own rules and regulations. Some have more than others, some enforce them more severely than others, and some are downright bizarre, the results of an eccentric or insane Prince. They all have them, though. Some of the most common laws, those found in many domains, are listed here.

Presentation

Many Princes demand that any Kindred newcomers to their cities present themselves formally at court. This is partly to make sure that the Prince has a solid grasp on

chapter one

who's in his city at any given time, and partly to make sure that the new arrival understands who holds power and what she's supposed to do while she's there. Of course, following this custom can be difficult, since new arrivals rarely know how to find the Prince in order to report, but that, frankly, is their problem. In domains with this law, Kindred who go for more than a few nights without presenting themselves are likely to be dragged before the Prince upon being caught. If the Prince is understanding, he might simply issue a warning. Just as likely, he banishes the offender from the domain without allowing any time to prepare, which is tantamount to a death sentence.

Clan, Covenant or Bloodline Restrictions

In some cities, the powers that be have a particular aversion to one particular clan, covenant or even familial bloodline and have decreed that group a pariah. In these domains, merely being Nosferatu or Carthian or whatever is a breach of the domain's social contract. A member of said group is forced to leave the city, but some truly vicious or hate-filled Princes call blood hunts on fugitives.

While a city might be dominated by a single covenant, almost no city belongs entirely to one faction over the others, and most contain members of at least three or four, if not all five, of the major covenants. Even more rare, almost to the point of nonexistence, is a city where one specific clan holds absolute power.

Feeding Restrictions

Some Princes declare certain types of mortals off-limits to the Kindred population. The restricted type can be anything as narrowly defined as a single family ("None shall touch the descendents of Philip Danforth, for he once saved my life when I was mortal"), a profession ("I need the police to hold back the criminal gangs employed by the unbound"), or even an entire demographic ("As I am a Catholic, and I believe that only we have seen the true way, you shall not touch any of the faith, that we may spread the Word to others"). Of course, the Prince's reasons for declaring any particular group off-limits might well be entirely selfish — maybe he himself feeds only on that type, and doesn't want the competition — but that doesn't make the law any less valid. Violators of such laws are usually banished, but some are slain.

Title, Rank and Position

So who holds all the power in Kindred society? What, really, defines a Prince or a member of the Primogen or a Sheriff? Are they all the same? What do they really do?

Presented here are the primary ranks and positions found throughout Kindred domains. Not every city has one of these positions — in fact, the smallest of communities might have only two or three of them — but they are common enough that all are worth discussing. Note that while each position is listed by its most common title, all of them are known by various terms throughout the world.

Prince

The single most important and ubiquitous figure in Kindred politics, the Prince normally rules her city with nearly absolute power. Some are weaker than others, of course, and some are mere figureheads for powerful Primogen or other elders. For the most part, however, any given Prince holds that position for no other reason than that she was strong enough to take it in some way. She might be a consummate politician who attained her post by accumulating favors from all the other elders, and who now manages her domain through diplomacy and compromise. Alternatively, she might be a veritable warlord who gained power by intimidating or "disappearing" her rivals, and now maintains power through the simple expedient of slaughtering anyone who questions her. Most Princes, of course, fall somewhere in the middle, but nearly all boast some advantage or trait that keeps them on top.

Of course, a Prince must do more than bark orders and issue death sentences. Her job is not merely to govern, but to regulate. A Kindred domain is a boiling pot, full of personal and sectarian conflicts, petty grudges and endless political maneuvering, all topped with the innate and inescapable violence of a race of predators who feed on blood. The Prince's job is to keep a lid on that pot — or, perhaps more accurately, to be the lid on that pot. The reason most Princes eventually become dictatorial is that they must keep so many powerful and easily agitated vampires in line.

Note that in some rare cities, normally those largely dominated by the unaligned and the Carthians, the Prince may attain power through means other than sheer personal ability. Such a Prince might be selected by local elders. The Carthians have even attempted open elections. Most often, such Princes are either overthrown by more powerful Kindred or themselves become tyrants to make sure they are not overthrown.

Other Titles

While Prince is the most common term by far, Kindred leaders refer to themselves as Cardinal, Bishop, Archbishop, Don, President (usually in the case of those rare elections mentioned earlier), Sultan, Lord, Duke or whatever title strikes their fancy, depending on the nature of their government. A few self-styled "Queens" exist, but most Kindred leaders avoid use of the title King.

Seneschal

The Prince's right hand, the Seneschal is responsible for many of the night-to-night details of running a government. While the Prince concerns himself with conflict in the city and making certain the Masquerade goes unbroken, the Seneschal makes sure that things run smoothly in the government itself. He is responsible for keeping track of the Prince's assets (and possibly those of the Primogen or other ruling bodies). He makes schedules and appointments and handles the many logistics required so that no elder feels that another is given preferential treatment. The Seneschal holds substantial power in the domain, for he often decides whose petitions are passed on to the Prince, who receives a court audience, and in what order. In some few but noteworthy domains, the Seneschal's power is so complete, and he is so much better informed of happenings among the elders than the Prince himself, that it's actually a tossup as to who is the true ruler.

Other Titles

Although Seneschal is the most frequently used term by far, the position is also sometimes referred to as Amanuensis, Chamberlain, Majordomo, Secretary and, in some of the most informal domains, simply as an assistant.

Herald

The Herald is the Prince's mouthpiece. When the Prince makes a decree, the Herald's job is to make sure that all of the city's Kindred hear of it (assuming it's meant for all ears…). When the Prince convenes an unscheduled court, the Herald is responsible for alerting those who must attend. The Herald hands down judgment, represents the Prince in proxy when she cannot (or will not) make a personal appearance, and otherwise serves as something of a "secretary of state." The Herald is assumed to speak with the Prince's voice at all times. Some treacherous or ambitious Heralds use this fact to direct other Kindred to their own liking, making suggestions that others assume (incorrectly) carry the weight of the Prince's orders. Some Heralds who were less subtle than they believed have been executed for this very thing, so most wise Heralds remain more or less honest.

The Herald is a position that is often absent in small cities. In many such cases, the Seneschal (or less frequently the Sheriff) handles these duties in addition to his other responsibilities.

Other Titles

In addition to Herald, this position is sometimes called Minister, Runner, Mouthpiece, Spokesman or Secretary (not in the domains where the Seneschal bears that last title, of course).

Primogen

If a single position can be considered to be nearly as ubiquitous and representative of Kindred politics as the Prince, it is the Primogen. The Primogen (singular as well as plural) officially serve as the Prince's advisory council on matters of policy. The precise nature of that council varies from domain to domain. If the Prince is both strong and especially tyrannical, the Primogen might be little more than a formality, a conclave of elders who serve to rubberstamp whatever the Prince wishes to do. In most domains, they serve as true advisors, and most wise Princes try to take that advice into account whenever possible, not merely because the advice might be good, but to avoid angering an entire group of elders. Some Primogen are powerful enough (or the Prince they advise weak enough) that they can actually overrule the Prince on certain matters. A few Primogen actually rule their cities, either through a figurehead Prince or openly as a governing body.

The precise size and nature of the Primogen varies. Some are informal, meeting in shadowy back rooms when the situation requires, arguing out whatever issue brings them together. Others cleave to a schedule and procedures for speaking, often appearing much like a governing board, a congress, an old-fashioned Greco-Roman senate, an ecclesiastic council or any other form of organization imaginable. Said councils can range from a mere three or so vampires in small communities to large advisory bodies, which may consist of a dozen or more Kindred.

For the most part, the Primogen consist of those local elders who have sufficient power to claim a seat. Also common are those Primogen who decide among themselves whom to admit into their ranks. More rarely, a Prince might select members of his advisory council, but this occurs only in cities where the Prince is especially strong and the Primogen especially weak. Most Primogen contain a mix of members of various clans and covenants, though some are more homogenous, depending on the domain. That is, the Primogen in a city largely dominated by Carthians is likely to have more Carthian members than any others, and the Primogen in a city where the Gangrel are persecuted is unlikely to have many Gangrel members.

Other Titles

The vast majority of these councils (and council members) go by the title Primogen, but they are sometimes known as Boards, Circles, Senates, Tribunals or simply as advisors.

Priscus

A Priscus (or Prisci in plural) is the informal "head" of a specific clan in a domain. This position is not an official one in the local governmental structure. Rather, it evolves organically as a single powerful Kindred takes responsibility for his clanmates. This can be a choice he himself makes, to seek power, or it might result from others of his clan coming to him with problems. As an informal position, the Prisci have no institutional power or rank. That said, the position does convey a substantial amount of status, and because it's usually powerful and well-respected Kindred who attain the position, the Prince and other elders are wise to at least consider their opinions. Many Prisci also sit on the Primogen, but the two bodies are not synonymous; not all Prisci are Primogen, and not all Primogen are Prisci. Many cities have no Prisci, and many more have Prisci for some clans and not others.

Whip

Perhaps one of the strangest of Kindred positions, the Whip is as informal a position as the Priscus. She is responsible for "inspiring" her clanmates to present a united face on major issues and to make their voices heard on local issues, to make sure that the other clans take them seriously. She is both a leader and a taskmaster, a figurehead and a bully. Many Kindred make the mistake of thinking of the Whip as an assistant to the Priscus. In point of fact, the two positions are independent, and oftentimes at odds with each other. A Whip succeeds only as long as she has sufficient power or leverage to force her clanmates to do as she wishes. Whips exist only in those cities with fairly large populations of a given clan, and even then only if a particular member of that clan feels the need to take the position.

Other Titles

Whips are often referred to, informally and angrily, as taskmasters, slavers, headmasters and many other far less polite terms.

Harpy

Unusual in that it is both an official and unofficial position, the Harpy is, at its simplest level, a member of the "Kindred elite." Harpies represent a who's who of Kindred affairs, the celebrities and fad-starters. Other Kindred look to Harpies to see who's in and who's out, and what positions and opinions are popular this season. A well-known Harpy can sway public opinion faster with a biting comment than some Princes can with a solid decree.

Harpies who attained their influence and position unofficially, through nothing more than personal power and charisma, are often more respected than those who are appointed by Prince or Primogen. An unofficial Harpy probably calls things as he truly sees them, whereas an appointed Harpy is usually believed (accurately or not) to be a shill or even propagandist for the Prince.

Sheriff

A combination police investigator, enforcer and inquisitor, the Sheriff is responsible for enforcing the Prince's laws and dictates, for bringing outlaws before the Prince for judgment and — at times — for carrying out sentences. Some Sheriffs truly believe in the rule of law and believe that they serve their society and fellow Kindred by keeping the city as orderly as possible. Others love the position for the power it offers, as they are permitted to bully and push around other vampires, even those who would normally be too dangerous to touch. Some Sheriffs are clever, subtle investigators, while others are little more than bruisers with rank.

Other Titles

While Sheriff is the most common title, the position is also sometimes called Reeve or Constable.

Hound

Quite simply, the Hound is the Prince's (or Primogen's) muscle. If the Sheriff is a policeman, the Hound is an assassin or a leg-breaker. He doesn't investigate, he doesn't question. His job is to punish anyone he's told to punish. In some instances, the Hound and the Sheriff are at odds due to their overlapping responsibilities. In other cities, the two are combined into a single position. While the Hound might be asked to carry out the official and public chastisement of a lawbreaker, that duty more often falls to the Sheriff. The Hound is normally employed when the Prince wishes to skip over normal (and possibly public) procedure.

Other Titles

In addition to Hound, such an enforcer is often called Assassin, Archon, Scourge or Templar.

Master of Elysium

In essence a combination master of ceremonies and groundskeeper, the Master of Elysium is responsible for maintaining a city's Elysium, ensuring its readiness for court or other official functions, cleaning up afterward and making sure that word of specific Elysium-related events reaches those who must attend. The Master of Elysium is also responsible for enforcing the custom of nonviolence at such gatherings, and he often works hand-in-hand with the Sheriff or Hounds for such purposes. In many cities, the duties of Master of Elysium fall on the Seneschal or Herald. In particularly large cities, more than one Master of Elysium exists, perhaps even one for each declared Elysium.

Subinfeudation

While the feudal model upon which Kindred society is based has its roots in similar historical mortal practices, only the most oblivious Kindred would refuse to acknowledge that governmental feudalism is all but dead in the world of mortal politics. Some of the realities that brought feudalism to an end in the mortal world plague the Kindred world. Unlike many mortal governments, however, the Kindred have found a way to work around such problems.

Quite simply, cities are too big, populaces too large, and minutiae too overwhelming for a single Prince to truly rule an entire domain. Only in the smallest communities can a solitary Prince hope to lay sweeping claim to all of a domain. As a result, the process of domain subinfeudation occurs, which is the breaking down and parceling out of different sub-domains, each of which becomes the responsibility of a "sub-Prince" who answers to the true Prince's ultimate authority. Such figures of authority are known as Regents, and their sub-domains are known as tenurial domains.

For all intents and purposes, a Regent is a Prince in everything but name, with a single, significant difference. The Regent has no praxis in his tenurial domain, no claimed "right to rule." Rather, a Regent is awarded his position by the Prince herself, who can unmake a Regent just as easily as she made him. Appointment to a Regency is almost always accompanied by a formal oath of subservience, particularly among the Ventrue and in domains with a powerful presence of the more traditional covenants such as the Invictus or Lancea Sanctum. Even among more "progressive" clans and covenants, Regencies do not come lightly, and the wise Prince ensures loyalty through some vow, contract or other defined agreement.

How much power a Regent has over a tenurial domain depends on the power of the city's Prince and why the Prince assigns the domain in the first place. One of the benefits of the Regency is the ability to set one's own rules, as long as they also enforce the Prince's dictates. Of course, some Princes specifically restrict the actions of their Regents (such as, "You may not designate an area Elysium" or "Only the true Prince may grant the right to Embrace"), but the title itself comes with near autonomy unless the Prince specifies otherwise.

Regents come in all varieties. Some are themselves loyal or respected elders, gifted with certain domains in which the Prince acknowledges their status, influence or expertise. Prisci and Harpies are prime examples of candidates for this sort of Regency, but one does not necessarily beget the other. Other Regents are upraised ancillae or even neonates who are tasked with the upkeep and maintenance of certain tenurial domains (whether as reward, opportunity, trial or punishment). Some Regents are important figures among their own clans or covenants, granted tenurial domains to reflect that status much as a Church bishop or archbishop might have been granted political territory in mortal history. Deposed Princes who haven't been sent to their Final Deaths upon a new Prince's claim of praxis often find themselves made Regents, either to prove their loyalty to the new regime or so the new Prince can keep an eye on them. Granted, these last instances are rare.

Tenurial Domains

A great many Kindred tend to confuse the concepts of tenurial domains and feeding grounds (see p. 81). Indeed, the two are often intertwined, though one doesn't necessarily encompass the other. A tenurial domain is simply an area ruled by a specific Regent, inside a larger region. For instance, a particularly powerful elder might claim a specific neighborhood, and the Prince of the city might legitimize the elder's claim. The Prince might do so because he wants the elder in his debt, or it might simply be that the Prince doesn't have the power to challenge the elder. In other circumstances, the Prince of a small city might retain power even after her erstwhile domain is annexed by a larger city and thereby made tenurial.

Alternatively, the Prince might grant a favored servant or ally tenurial rights over a small area. The Prince wins all ways. He makes the smooth running and customs enforcement of a part of his domain someone else's responsibility, he grants a favored ally enough power to make her grateful, and he has the ability to strip that power away at a single word if the underling proves treacherous or otherwise dangerous.

At other times, the Prince doesn't really intend to grant the Regent quite so much power, but only "feeding rights" to a given territory. Shrewd Kindred are able to transform feeding rights into true power by trading permission to feed for favors or even further subinfeudation. (After all, the Regent has every power of a Prince in her tenurial domain.) Wise Princes take advantage of the opportunity to let others shoulder the responsibility for running portions of the city. Less wise and more fearful Princes attempt to curtail the development of all such domains. Most of these would-be tyrants are ousted from power when the Kindred beneath them grow sick and tired of the lack of opportunity.

Unconventional Domains

Hand in hand with the evolution of tenurial domains came the advent of less tangible notions of domain. Whereas a Prince might once have granted an ethnic ghetto or prestigious neighborhood to a Regent, some Princes now grant dominion over spheres of influence under the auspices of domain, both their own and tenurial. A Prince who acknowledges one of his subjects' sway among the authorities might grant "law enforcement" as a tenurial domain. A Kindred who owns significant property among trading ports might be granted rights to "the docks," both as a geographical region and in reference to shipping commerce.

These sorts of domains are just as valid as any other tenurial domain, but are harder to be wary of. After all, when one steps into a region known to be the territory of another Kindred, he knows he crosses a physical, tangible line of demarcation. On the other hand, how far does a grant of an unconventional domain go? If the health-care infrastructure of a city is one Kindred's tenurial domain, does that include hospitals (surely), independent practitioners (maybe), and even drug stores (likely not)? Unless the Prince specifically outlines the extent of the Regent's domain — which makes for awkwardly wordy titles and occasionally incenses the Kindred who's ostensibly being honored with the grant — boundaries remain vague.

Unconventional domains are a double-edged sword. The Regent arguably has to be more vigilant in his tenure's dimensions than a Kindred granted domain over a physical region. After all, how can a Kindred granted tenurial domain over "the police" be sure that somewhere in that organization, someone's not answering to another one of the Damned? Further, if other Kindred recognize the tenure too broadly, the esteem can work against the Regent, as those excluded from the domain can use the Regency as an example of a stranglehold over a particular aspect of unlife and rally others against the Regent. A Regent of Fine Arts would likely face significant opposition, as would a Regent of Finance. This isn't to say such things don't happen, but rather that those positions are either embattled or held by Kindred with such enormous personal power that they can maintain broad tenurial domains.

Territorial Dispute

Occasionally, trouble arises between the Prince and his Regents, and more frequently between Regents themselves. A rare few Regents are so powerful that they can pass laws in opposition to the Prince's decrees or at least refuse to enforce the Prince's decrees. Domains occasionally overlap, as well, especially when unconventional domains come into conflict with geographical ones. For instance, if a crime occurs in a Regent's neighborhood, is that her issue or does it fall under the auspices of the Regent of Law Enforcement?

In many of these cases, the only clear winner is the Prince, as the resources that rival Regents devote to foiling each other take their attention from him. Indeed, if things turn ugly and one of the Regents ends up meeting Final Death, that leaves a potential position open for another Kindred's reward.

As might be expected, conflict over tenurial domains is common. It rarely escalates beyond the boundaries of grudges and vendettas, but such feuds can be bitter and long-lived, as with any interaction between Kindred. Indeed, some cities have been plunged into veritable civil war over domain disputes, but most savvy Princes know to step in and reevaluate their Regents before things become so dire.

Society High and Low

While many of the Kindred's actions seem to be politically oriented, that's certainly not the full extent of their interactions with each other. Indeed, the bulk of Kindred interactions occur in social venues, but as is the case with such relationships, the outcomes are not so rigidly defined. The Kindred power structure is formalized. The Kindred social structure has many more facets that can't possibly be explained in a single book.

Kindred Requiems are curious things — as noted before, vampires are solitary predators, yet they crave the social contact that keeps their deathless loneliness at bay. Every Kindred has some reason or another to attend social functions. For the Daeva, the sensuality of such contact is first and foremost. The Ventrue enjoy opportunities to display their grandeur and munificence. The Gangrel certainly enjoy cutting loose under the right circumstances. And even the Mekhet and Nosferatu need to emerge from the shadows and forget that they're monsters, if only for a short time.

The following are just a few examples of the many ways in which Kindred gather and meet without the formalities of domain politics imposing themselves. Of course, what happens in these venues can certainly affect politics (and only the most naïve Kindred think such things happen only rarely), but at least those politics aren't the order of the night in every exchange between Kindred.

Nightlife: The Damned are no strangers to the dance clubs, bars, lounges, pool halls and numerous other places where mortals go to enjoy themselves. For most Kindred, visiting such places serves two purposes. It allows them to seek prey who are comfortable in their own element, and it allows that longed-for contact with someone other than themselves.

Cultural Events: To be sure, any time an art gallery shows an exhibit, an opera or ballet is staged, a museum hosts a ceremony, or any other affair that represents the uniqueness of the human condition takes place, the Kindred are there, drinking in its magnificence and making their own known. These needn't even be high-society affairs, as art shows can take place in starving artists' bohemian galleries, and not every play is a Broadway production.

Parties: What better way to forget the pain of Damnation than to celebrate something — anything — else. From lavish soirees hosted in grand hotel ballrooms or private mansions to warehouse parties, underground raves and countercultural festivals, a party can be a grandiose affair or a reckless revel. Some Kindred even throw their own parties of varying sizes, with socialites hosting nigh-Victorian engagements, lowlifes rousing the rabble and everything in between. Among parties hosted by the Kindred, sometimes mortals are invited and sometimes not, depending on the scale and purpose.

Religious Ceremony: In nights long past, churches formed the center of communities. While these faithless times make that less common, it is still true that a community that prays together stays together. In those domains that host strong

religious or spiritual presence among covenants and individuals, centers of faith form the basis of relationships and interactions that eclipse their clerical foundation. The anointing of a new childe, for example, or the formal adoption of a new member into a religious covenant can serve to draw Kindred of many stripes together. Indeed, some religious ceremonies involve mortals, whether as sacrifices, or more openly, such as with blood cults or groups that blend mortal and Kindred dogma.

Salons: Salons are usually intellectual affairs, where invited Kindred gather to discuss a particular idea. In some cases, the matter to be discussed might be a new philosophy, point of debate or emerging new theory. Other salons reinterpret classical or even ancient ideas. Salons can be formal, high-society affairs akin to their historical namesakes, debates only the smallest step away from political gatherings, or even informal rants where a Kindred with a pet passion puts it forth to whomever will listen. Salons usually bring great prestige to their hosts — when they come off well, that is.

Elysium: Not every gathering of Elysium is a political affair convened by a Prince with matters of policy to discuss. Some are purely social, venues where Kindred can meet and not have to worry about the... unpleasantness that occasionally occurs among their kind. Most sites of Elysium in a given city are open (to the Kindred only, of course) at any time after dark, maximizing the number of places where Kindred can congregate in relative safety.

The Danse Macabre

Throughout their long history, the Kindred have engaged in an endless struggle — the coldest of cold wars, fought in the shadows of mortal society. This internecine conflict is known as the Danse Macabre, and it nightly threatens to tear the entire race of the Damned apart.

This secret war of the Kindred's is both the beginning and the end for the undead. As a race, they are destined to blood and violence, yet their survival depends on peace between them. They are consumed nightly by the possibility that the war will one night consume them, and they toil ceaselessly in fear of having to forever struggle against their own kind. The conflict is perhaps the greatest, saddest paradox of the Kindred world, and as such, it is a fundamental aspect of unlife among the Damned.

Deus Vult

Perhaps ironically, Christianity signaled the dawn of the Danse Macabre. Factionalism spread like wildfire through the mortals of Europe and the Holy Land, and for the first time, parallel ripples of dissonance emerged from Rome herself. Emerging from the wake of the events of the Crucifixion, the "Childer of Longinus," as members of that covenant insist on calling the earliest recorded vampires, were hardly content to sit huddled in their candlelit chambers, speaking prayers to a father whose very actions had damned them, while wordlessly and thoughtlessly accepting everything their sires had taught them. No, the world was changing, and with it changed the

undead. Some vampires likened Christ's resurrection to the mockery of their own, and many fell to bickering about the nature of his divinity. Indeed, some blasphemous Kindred even suggested that Christ was either some kind of vampire or Longinus, himself! And, naturally, these and other social fissures only further entrenched elders and sires.

During the Dark Ages, what had long been seen as a heretical movement grew to become the order of the night. Many believed that God had forsaken the world entirely, and they left their ancient traditions behind in favor of the whims of appetite and petty egotism. Hostilities between Kindred reached an all-time high as sires struggled to keep childer in line amid an endless sea of darkness and fire. Several religious orders emerged among the Kindred, each possessed of a different slant on the nature of the Damned and their place in God's world. Many vampires latched onto the fringes of the Church and its scions, and the Damned were some of the most active supporters of the early to mid-Crusades. Indeed, God Himself became the foil that vampires would use upon one another, each more deftly than the last, in the name of either power or righteousness. And when their impious temerity was uncovered? More bloodshed, to "right" the wrongs.

All their bluster came to a head during the burning times of the holy Inquisition. Vampiric infighting had grown so great, the Kindred's arrogance so complete, that they drew the attention of the mortal world. Although the effect was the widespread violation of the First Tradition, the greater cause was the growing violation of the Blood-borne prohibition against kinslaying and a decrease in the overall level of respect and love for God (or anything resembling Him).

After the fires of the Inquisition died down, the Kindred looked around to find that their numbers had dwindled, their fortunes had crumbled to the ground, their society had shattered and new factions rose almost nightly. When they looked upon what their conflict had wrought, they neither learned from what they saw nor endeavored to trace the disaster's origin back to its root. Instead, the Kindred all secretly blamed one another for the downfall of the system, and the species as a whole turned inward. Where there had once been overt moves and periodic salvos into the domains and affairs of other Kindred, there were now hidden schemes and patient plans that took years to unfold. The Damned still moved against one another, and they still engaged in the Danse Macabre, but now they savored it more, learning the art to a carefully played game. The Kindred were a patient breed — when one's mentor is undeath, patience is the first lesson one must learn — and they learned how to put that patience to use.

The Blood Will Tell

The coming of the Industrial Age saw a nearly paradoxical dichotomy emerge in the world of the Kindred. Cities expanded at astronomical rates, and with each technological advancement came more opportunities for influence in the mortal world. By the same token, however, the localization of power and money made each new resource that much more prized among the undead. Territory in cities became a serious issue, and for the first time, political groups emerged as major factors in Kindred society. The times called for some major adaptations in the ways the undead did things, but as is endemic to a selfish and predatory species, very few Kindred took up the mantle of responsibility with the intent of making sure that everyone adapted together.

Even with the expansion of the mortal world, the Kindred continued to play their local games of love and hate, point and counterpoint. The nature of vampiric existence no longer allowed for extensively planned movements of units or forces across multi-national battle maps. Vampires were no longer generals governing legions of childer and blood thralls, ready to sail off to battle at a moment's notice as a few had been in earlier times. They were humanoid jackals, territorial scavengers with nothing but their food and land. And at the end of the night, each vampire was a prisoner of that land, whether he called it home or not. And when faced with that realization, many vampires tried to make themselves the wardens of their prison homes, each bucking for superiority over the other inmates. Only when one was the warden could he be sure of how the prison would operate from night to night.

This notion in particular, the concept of control, is central to the Danse Macabre as it is known tonight. Through the passing of years upon years, many Kindred feel the reins of control slip ever so slowly from their clutching talons. Despite their temporal power, they must sit by, unable to build or create or evolve as they once did, watching while the world moves on around them. So they seek to amass as much mortal power and influence as possible in the hopes of feeling vicariously through their connections to modern reality. They vainly seek a glut of material power

hoping somehow to make up for the spiritual and creative impotence of their existence.

To make matters worse, other Kindred are often the only barometer by which an out-of-touch vampire can measure his own surrogate success. If his brothers and sisters of the night do not fare very well, then logically, he must be truly successful. The entire system feeds on its own illogic until, at a certain point, only the struggle for dominance remains. Some Kindred even see this existence for what it is and claim that it is the only way that their accursed kind can progress with any peace through the ages. After all, they reason, only when one has control over everything does one not need to resort to diablerie or kinslaying. The Danse Macabre, they dare claim, is actually the salvation of the Kindred race! Needless to say, many vampires would disagree vehemently, but it does go to show the degree to which the undead try to rationalize what they have become.

The Fog of Eternity

Some modern neonates are surprised to learn just how little is known for sure among their kind. Like many others before them, they make the mistake of assuming that creatures who exist forever must likewise remember forever. The shock is even greater for those Embraced in the last three decades, due to the prevalence and availability of information in the world. Upon being informed of just how old the Kindred truly are, many grow eager — giddy, even — to find really old vampires and pick their brains about people, places and events of ages past.

They quickly come to learn, however, that history is an inconstant companion for the Kindred. Even if a single (formerly) mortal mind could conceivably retain all that it saw, all that it learned and all that it experienced over a period of centuries, the very physiology of the Kindred form forbids such clear and detailed recall. A vampire's blood increases in potency the longer he stays awake and active in the mortal world, and the more potent a vampire's blood, the more difficult it is for him to remain at ease with the world around him. Potent Blood is demanding, indeed. It calls out for the Vitae of other Kindred — an urge potentially leading to the terribly sinful act of diablerie. Failing that, it calls out for sleep, so that the blood at least has a chance to thin over time and return the vampire to a semblance of his more composed self. To make matters worse, certain vampiric activities can cause a Kindred's blood to concentrate prematurely, thus leading to further mental distortion, frustration and anguish.

This fact alone would call into question any elder vampire's ability to remember specific details of centuries past, but the Blood is neither the only nor the greatest contributor to the eternal inconstancy of history where the Kindred are concerned. When an elder finally does succumb to the call for rest, she enters a state known as torpor, a comatose sleep during which her vampiric essence thins out. While in torpor, the Kindred does not need to feed to keep her unnatural form in its static state. She merely sleeps, rejuvenating her body while her blood returns to more manageable levels.

The difficulty comes in the quality and nature of torpor-induced sleep. Being in torpor is akin to lying prostrate through a decades-long waking dream. Visions, memories and images of events past (and possibly even future) plague the blood-addled mind of the torpid Kindred, and that's just a mild torpor experience. For some, torpor is a protracted nightmare, fraught with horrific visitations of past atrocities and failures. Imagine all the most intense qualities of a powerful drug high, combined with the lucid displacement of the deepest sleep, and the result is what every passing hour of torpor is like. Now, try to imagine such a mental state stretching on for 50 years. How about 100 years? The results can be harsh.

Not even the strongest mortal mind could withstand such psychic duress for more than a few days, let alone years. Waking from such a state would leave the average mortal psychologically scarred, if not entirely catatonic. And yet, the Kindred must endure this punishment regularly and repeatedly in order to survive the passage of centuries. Is it any wonder, then, that their concept of time and the sequence of events is a little bit (or in some cases more than a little bit) distorted? Indeed, some are simply too weak to bear the brunt of the mental onslaught of repeated torpors. Their minds eventually shatter from the strain, leaving them incapable of rising of their own volition. It is whispered that hundreds if not thousands of such Kindred lie beneath the Earth's surface, their sanity stripped from their undead minds like husks from corn. Some believe that these insane Kindred will rise one night

and be like unto an army against the Damned society from which they were driven.

Wise Kindred take steps to make sure that their precious thoughts and memories stay fresh, and more importantly, fixed. Many use journals and other mundane means of recording events and dates, while others resort to more drastic and often mystical means. One group in particular, a faction known as the Agonistes, has taken it upon itself to catalog some of the knowledge that has been lost to Kindred over time and in torpor, while simultaneously looking for ways to ameliorate the worst of the great sleep's effects. So far, the scholars of the Agonistes have made little headway in the latter objective, but they have made such advances in the former as to be "in demand" around the world. Indeed, many elder Kindred, in expectation of impending torpor, summon one of the Agonistes to oversee his transition, as well as to assist in various other record-keeping tasks. The group takes the "confidentiality" of patrons' activities and memories very seriously, and there have been few accusations of impropriety to date.

The Way of All Flesh

It is, therefore, both in and against Kindred nature to plot, scheme and ultimately bring to ruin the unlives of their own kin. It is both fate and personal choice. Even those who seek to bring about a better world for their kind (or at least a subset of their kind) merely further the mistaken beliefs and ideals that lead to greater Kindred calamity. Some believe it is simply the way of things: God's will, inherent spiritual evil or the most natural aspect of an unnatural species.

Others see the way the Danse Macabre is going and legitimately fear for the future. In recent years, more evidence emerges about the vampires of old — the long-forgotten elders who might have been the original progenitors of the modern clans. Elders of advanced age are feared greatly, and rightly so, and the most common position to take is one of wishful thinking. Pretend it's not a threat, and it will go away.

Just the same, puppets and sinners continue to bring news to the scattered domains of the Kindred. Stories of another burning time yet to come, when a reckoning shall fall upon the wayward Damned. Some believe that various harbingers of some great accounting will rise, that the prophecies in various Kindred holy or occult texts will come true, that Longinus or the Crone will take an accounting of the sins of their lines, that Dracula will return to find his covenant in disarray and enact a culling or that only the purest of the pure will remain safe from whatever form this portentous justice takes. Many still study the old ways and texts, searching for signs and omens of when this dark time might arrive. They believe in the words of prophets and madmen among the Kindred, and God help those who have forsaken them. Others believe the stories to be nothing but rumor — another political ploy hatched from among the distempered minds of the young and foolhardy. Others believe that some concordance among all the myriad tales, or the cryptic nature and format of the stories themselves, indicates the return of a bloodline or covenant known as the Moirai — one believed long dead yet still spoken of every night in hushed whispers.

What is agreed upon, at least by those who have stopped to pay attention, is that the Danse Macabre is headed into yet another era. Advancements seen in the last 30 years alone have allowed Kindred-versus-Kindred conflict to blossom into never-before-seen arenas. Young and savvy vampires use the Internet as often as they use any other tool of manipulation and deceit, and with the advent of fiber optics, digital networking and a host of other inventions, the possibilities are endless. Never before has there been so much potential in the art of war, and despite the quiet nagging of what remains of the vampiric conscience, it all sounds pretty good to the average vampire.

And so, childer continue to plot and scheme against their sires, and sires continue to plot and scheme against their childer and their rivals. The covenants continue to plot against each other, and the unaligned continue to buck the authority of them all. The Carthian experiment shows no sign of slowing down around the world, for good or for ill, and beside it all, the Circle of the Crone remains, vigilant and secretive. The stage is set for the next act in the Danse Macabre, and all the players have taken their places. There isn't a doubt in their minds that they are ready for the play that awaits.

After all, they've played these roles before.

In Vitae Veritas

While possessed of many curious properties, the Blood of the Kindred reacts in special ways to that of other vampires. Details as to why this happens are unknown. No blood-specialist or vampiric hematologist has studied the phenomena extensively enough, and no mystics understand the nature of the Curse so well. Certainly, though, these situations occur often enough and widely enough to be known to all Kindred.

Predator's Taint

Vampires instinctively know other Kindred upon sight, as the Beast seems to call to other Beasts in its vicinity. Hackles rise, fangs distend and a sense of fear or territoriality overtakes a Kindred upon meeting another vampire for the first time. The urge is primal and bestial — the Kindred with more potent blood sees the interloper as a threat to his superiority, while the vampire with less potent blood instinctively feels a desire to flee this greater predator. Both Kindred potentially risk frenzy at the overwhelming surge of instinct, the aggressive vampire feeling the urge to attack the lesser to assert his dominance, and the "subordinate" vampire feeling a pressing urge to flee. Kindred of equally potent blood both feel the desire to attack each other and settle the matter of primacy once and for all. True, such compulsions abate once two Kindred are familiar with each other, but the initial experience can be terrifying — or perversely thrilling.

The Sweetest Sin

The blood of the Kindred is both savory and sweet, scintillating the tastes with its heady, forbidden flavors. Those who consume the Vitae of the Kindred, especially older Kindred, find that they long to taste it again. While the Damned would never stoop so low as to suggest that their blood is addictive, the reality defies their semantic pride. Dependencies can develop, longings make themselves felt, and full-blown addiction is certainly not out of the question.

As a result, the sharing of blood between Kindred is looked down upon by Kindred society as a whole. Although it is occasionally forgiven in light circumstances, such as a lover's tryst or another symbol of affection, those who make a habit of drinking other Kindred's Vitae are looked upon as degenerates at best and potential diablerists at worst.

The Vinculum

Part of the Kindred's ill regard for tasting the blood of other vampires is the Vinculum, sometimes known as the blood bond. Those Kindred who consume the blood of another single vampire three times become subjected to a unique state of emotional control. This Vinculum creates a powerful but artificial love for the vampire from whom three draughts are taken.

A thrall is any being currently under the influence of a Vinculum. The vampire to whom a thrall is bound is called the regnant or domitor. In social situations, the term thrall is applied to bound Kindred, as most undead think of bound mortals solely as ghouls, mortals who have tasted the Vitae of the Kindred (see p. 80). This is not, however, an entirely accurate delineation. It is possible to have a mortal thrall who is not a ghoul, as mortals who have tasted Vitae do not automatically become ghouls. Those who do retain the powers and traits of the ghoul only so long as Kindred Vitae remains in their system, but the power of the Vinculum far outlasts any such limits. Rumor has it that the Vinculum can subvert the will of even the wildest supernatural entities, but little hard data has come forth to verify this.

Thralls are not complete slaves of their masters, but they come close. They constantly feel the artificial love, affection and loyalty imposed by the bond, even if they simultaneously hate their domitors for demeaning or enslaving them. Among those who are weak-willed, naïve, mentally unstable or even willing, the blood bond creates a feeling of singular devotion. Most Vinculums result in this condition, as most thralls subjected to them either know what they're getting into or have some turgid notion of their relationship with their domitors-to-be. Ghouls who see their masters as dark angels, Kindred lovers expressing their devotion to each other through mutual blood bonds, even wayward "blood dolls" who readily give of their own blood to please their undead patrons.... All of these at least initially enter into Vinculums willingly (or at least without resentment afterward). Others aren't so enthusiastic, as with unbound Kindred brought to heel under a Prince through the Vinculum, or truculent childer forced to bond themselves to their sires "for their own good." It truly is a blasphemous love, for it is unnatural and the conscience often rebels against it. Thralls are normally incapable of blatantly disobeying or working against their regnants, but some are sufficiently strong willed to sabotage their masters in more subtle ways.

Some very rare coteries attempt to overcome the inevitable growth of mistrust between members by engaging in a web of Vinculums. Reciprocal bonds wouldn't work to hold a coterie together; rather, it would engender loyalty between pairs. Instead, these coteries engage in a practice that some Kindred youth have rather crudely dubbed a "circle jerk." That is, one neonate bonds herself to another, who bonds himself to a third, who bonds himself to a fourth, who in turn bonds herself back to the first. The amount of trust required to enter into such an arrangement is incalculable, and the results are inevitably painful for those involved, as they must spend much of their time watching the object of their affections fawn over someone else. Many coteries that attempt this process eventually tear themselves apart out of obsession and petty jealousy. Those few that manage to make it work are indeed remarkably cohesive.

Kindred Covenants

If the clans represent family and perhaps culture among the Kindred, and cities are their domains, then the various covenants represent the closest vampiric equivalent to nations, political parties and even religions. The covenants form a cornerstone of undead society and — as far as is possible to determine given the Kindred's rather hazy view of their own history — are ancient traditions that have been part of the vampiric world for hundreds of years. The covenants that are (supposedly) oldest hold a more respected "pedigree" than others, but none is truly modern. Even those young vampires who believe that Kindred society as it exists tonight is a relatively recent development admit that the covenants almost certainly predate the Industrial Revolution in some form or another.

The covenants serve as nations, for they provide the Kindred with a sense of community that they can find nowhere else. Kindred are Embraced into a clan, with no say of their own. Like many mortals, even if they feel a loyalty to their blood and their family, they often differ with one another in their opinions and beliefs. They are, for the most part, trapped in their home domains, and their loyalty toward the local regime is usually purchased with fear and enforced by ambition. Covenant allegiance, however, is something over which Kindred have personal control. They are drawn toward factions that espouse doctrines in which they can believe (or at least to which they don't object). Here, more than anywhere else, they are likely to encounter other Kindred who share at least some of their ideas and objectives.

The covenants serve as political parties, for they provide ambitious Kindred with built-in support. Most covenants seek as much influence in the local Kindred power structure as possible, either to advance their own goals or to simply prevent rivals from gaining power. For the most part, politically active Kindred would rather have a fellow covenant member in power than any other rival (though many would certainly rather hold the power themselves, when at all possible). A vampire with many elder allies working to aid his ascendance has an undeniable advantage over rivals with less support.

Perhaps most strangely, the covenants even serve as a religious body for some members. While some of the covenants — the Lancea Sanctum and the Circle of the Crone specifically — are overtly religious in their makeup, all of the factions have strongly held beliefs and attitudes that often reach the level of dogma. While some young Kindred flit from ideology to ideology, either in search of a place to belong or trying to figure out their own attitudes, many other vampires cling so completely to the doctrines of their chosen covenants that they are unable to comprehend any other viewpoints. While only a few covenants declare outright that their way is mandated by Longinus, God or some other higher power, most of them claim zealots who certainly seem to act that way.

Further distinguishing them from clans, covenants have a fluid membership. A Kindred's clan never changes, but a Kindred's covenant may. Certainly, it is difficult to forswear one's covenant and join a new one, but doing so is not impossible. An expected lack of trust often accompanies such behavior, but only the most severe members of either the renounced or the new covenant stoop to leveling (unsubstantiated) claims of treachery against a convert. In many cases, a Kindred's philosophies simply change over the course of the Requiem. Most covenant members would rather lose a dilettante whose heart doesn't truly belong to the cause any longer than have her lack of faith undermine the rest. Granted, those who repudiate all covenants usually lose significant esteem in the eyes of erstwhile peers, but sometimes a Kindred just grows… away.

Such being the case, it is with raised eyebrows that the Damned allow others of their kind to move from one covenant to another. Oddly, neonates and under-accomplished ancillae have the easiest time of it, as their lack of tangible ties to covenants at low levels occasionally allow them to escape notice. Some Kindred even count themselves as members of multiple covenants — but only until they're found out and forced to stop playing all sides against the middle. More accomplished Kindred have difficulty changing sides, usually because of the contacts they've made or secret knowledge they've accumulated as a member of their original covenant. Highly visible "defections" are usually the source of much gossip, and more than once have been the foundation for ill will or even bloody vendetta.

The covenants are not necessarily in constant conflict. Most cities contain members of all of the major groups (or at least a few), and Kindred governments operate effectively with officers and advisors from multiple factions. Like rival churches in ages past or political parties in modern mortal government, the covenants often manage to coexist, yet they rarely agree on any salient points.

Still, the simple fact that these covenants exist at all inevitably leads to discord. Even those few Kindred who don't want power for themselves understand why it's in their best interests to make sure that fellow covenant members hold as much authority as possible. Every faction wants to be in control, and every covenant has different views on how the Kindred should rule (and even behave). In most cities, this conflict is covert, taking the form of political maneuvering, espionage, sabotage, bribery, blackmail and the occasional assassination. In select domains, this ongoing cold war heats up and covenants engage in open conflict (as open as possible for the Kindred). Much like mortal gang warfare, these conflicts are usually short — the longer a war rages, the harder it becomes to protect the Masquerade — but exceedingly bloody. Such conflicts usually do not end so much as they simply fade out as one or all parties involved grows too exhausted to continue. The shaky peace that appears to result, as the covenants are forced through attrition to coexist once more, often lasts only until one of them regains sufficient strength to begin the process anew.

COVENANTS AROUND THE GLOBE

The Kindred exist everywhere humanity builds cities and extends cultures. Vampires cover the globe, and while their numbers are few in comparison to those on whom they feed, their population is not so small that it can easily be regimented into neat factions. The covenants described here differ somewhat — and potentially significantly — from domain to domain. That is, a member of the Invictus in London probably shares most of the primary attitudes of a fellow Invictus in Detroit, but they likely differ on a great many of the details.

More importantly, other covenants beyond the major ones exist in various regions throughout the world. The factions described here are the largest or most powerful, at least in the West, but others exist in other cultures, in smaller communities and in Third-World nations. The covenants here represent the majority of Kindred, and the greater portion of Kindred power, but they do not account for the entirety of either.

It's important to note that, while members of a given covenant tend to agree on certain basic principles, and often ally with one another against outside rivals, plenty of tension and enmity exists between members of a single covenant. In fact, in those cities where any given covenant dominates, intra-covenant rivalry is actually more common than inter-covenant rivalry. Invictus Kindred compete with others in the Invictus, Carthians struggle with rival Carthians, and so forth. A vampire's covenant allegiance is a good indicator of certain political and philosophical beliefs, but anything else is questionable.

The Camarilla

In nights long past, all of vampire society united under one common banner, at least as far as the Western World was concerned. This organization was known as the Camarilla, corresponding roughly to a later Spanish word meaning "power group" or a cabal of confidential advisors. The Camarilla's might was unchallenged — anywhere Imperial Rome held sway, so did the Camarilla. It is even

suspected that many Kindred customs that survive to this very night had their roots in Camarilla structure, such as the notion of Princes who govern autonomous domains. While proof of pre-Roman vampirism is rare or incomplete, almost all Kindred accept that pre-Roman vampires probably existed. They are commonly understood to have been savage, monstrous and completely disorganized. If anything, their "society" was probably little more than scattered, vague domains populated by a single vampire and any broods he chose to foster. The now-defunct Camarilla was the first successful attempt at a true Kindred society.

As the Roman Empire collapsed, however, so did the support structures of the Camarilla crumble. As Kindred require the blood of mortals to keep them vital, they rely on mortal society as a foundation for their own. With Europe fragmenting into isolated, feudal domains during the Dark Ages, Kindred society had little choice but to do the same or fall entirely into the barbarism of old.

The nature of the Kindred themselves hastened the ruin of the Camarilla, as well. Ever scheming and jealous, few vampires who rose to prominence in the Camarilla social order did so out of a sense of altruism or justice. The Kindred then as now craved power and influence, and such could be obtained by crippling rivals' access to the same.

It comes as no surprise, then, to see that from the remains of the shattered Camarilla came several different factions, each espousing a different policy or philosophy upheld by like-minded elders and charismatic demagogues. Where once a single organization had stood, a handful of distinct covenants emerged from the bleakness of the era. This development even set the standard for later covenants to distinguish themselves from established Kindred society.

Many of these covenants perished through the centuries, destroyed by opposing factions, absorbed into similar ones, rooted out as heretics or simply abandoned as invalid. Vampires cast about for covenants with which they could align themselves in hopes of achieving power, but they remained ever wary that those factions would demand too much in return or limit them too greatly with dogma.

As history progressed, two groups of European Kindred formed an alliance. As mortal society's strength hailed from the twin pillars of the Church and the state, these covenants formed their own version of the balance between temporal and pious power. The Lancea Sanctum, a dire and evangelical covenant claiming a Biblical origin for vampires, rose to claim a position of prominence as the spiritual leader of the Kindred. Its counterpart, known as the Invictus (a reference to the group's Roman origins), positioned itself as the vampiric nobility. In domains where the alliance was powerful, the Invictus served as political ruler of the Kindred, while the Lancea Sanctum made sure residents were duly worshipful of God and mindful of a vampire's place in the world.

The alliance between the Invictus and the Lancea Sanctum was an effective model and was easily hidden among the layers of mortal society it emulated. The allegiance experienced great success, and it soon spread across Europe not unlike the feudal model from which it drew its structures.

Not all Kindred supported the alliance's supremacy, however. Many old domains that harbored Kindred who observed pre-Christian and even pre-Roman rites and mythologies dissented. Although they never formed a unified front, given that their beliefs and geographical locations were too disparate, an undercurrent of rebellion occasionally prevented the alliance from taking hold in numerous places. Magic drawn from the Old Ways held the Lancea Sanctum's dark miracles at bay, and the pagans held their own in many cases. These faiths survive tonight as a loose coalition of factions, rarely organized but definitely powerful, and with their own spheres of influence. United only by common belief in a female progenitor or patron of the race of Kindred, the covenant known as the Circle of the Crone cultivated power through appeal to less overwhelming policies than the alliance's conquering tactics.

Another Kindred covenant eventually reared its head in Eastern Europe, fronted by an infamous and popular leader drawn from the ranks of the mortal nobility. This covenant's founder claimed that no vampire had Embraced him, but that he had been abandoned by God. Thus forsaken, he became one of the Damned. Teaching a philosophy of vampiric transcendence, this leader and his followers, the Ordo Dracul, upset the balance of power between the Invictus and the Lancea Sanctum and rushed in to seize what it could in the resulting instability. The idea of transcendence appealed to many Kindred, and thus the ideals of the Ordo Dracul took root and spread outward. From the covenant's foundation sometime during the 15th or 16th century to the nights of the 21st, the Order continues to grow in power and increase in influence.

Time passes externally for the Kindred, even if their own bodies remain locked in stasis. To many vampires, the feudal model upon which the alliance had built its power was an anachronism by the 18th century. As the mortal world rallied to the cause of new forms of government, many young vampires adapted new systems of politics to the society of the Damned. These Carthians don't always agree on what sort of political system is best, but they find common disillusionment with the outdated modes of governance to which so many other Kindred cling unquestioningly. Such philosophy finds a home especially in the New World, whose own sovereignty was won from the clutches of aristocratic nations. The Carthians believe that it can be won for the vampiric order as well.

As the modern nights unfold, a strange state of balance exists. In the Old World, many domains still honor the rule of the alliance. Here and there, small pockets of resistance cleave to the ways of the Circle of the Crone, while the Ordo Dracul still reigns in Eastern Europe. In the New World, however, something much more resembling an equal footing exists. The Carthian cause attracts new followers, especially among the young, who have never known noble rule and who have no reason to suspect one exists as the world of the Kindred opens up to them. The Invictus and the Lancea Sanctum still wield power, but the alliance is far more tenuous. Individual domains often belong solely to a Lancea Sanctum Prince or an Invictus Prince, with little effort made to preserve the customary relationship that survives between the two in the Old World. The Ordo Dracul and Circle of the Crone each has no small support, too, though their New World incarnations are steeped less in the traditions from which they hail and more in the mindset of viable (if somewhat arcane) alternatives to the undying atavism of the crumbling alliance.

It is under these circumstances that modern vampires find themselves Embraced. Covenants that have long been allies fragment, while new alliances form nightly to oppose the existing powers that be. The Lancea Sanctum and the Invictus are strange bedfellows — except where their differences have driven them to factional war. Seemingly opposed covenants such as the Circle of the Crone and the Carthians feud over ideology — except when they bury the hatchet to face mutual oppression. The world of vampires is truly gothic, with barbaric anachronisms still in place where they had been centuries if not millennia before. At the same time, technology and the world's cultural Zeitgeist manifests in a spirit of rebellion that offers a chance to cast the old shackles aside and replace them with new and exciting ideals. The world is at once medieval and modern, and the society of the Damned embodies every aspect of that paradox.

On occasion, a group of historians, unification-minded Kindred or downright conspirators makes some effort at reestablishing the Camarilla as it was in the nights of old. To date these efforts have been doomed to failure, fracturing under the weight of whatever high-minded (or underhanded) politics spawned the idea. That's not to say that some future attempt at consolidation wouldn't work, just that it has yet to.

To the Lady Tanit Pene Baal and the Lord Baal Hammon,
that which this new childe of the night has vowed, because she has heard his voice and blessed him.
— A Circle of the Crone Embrace prayer

THE CARTHIAN MOVEMENT

Undeniably the youngest of the major Kindred covenants, the Carthians are fire-eyed reformists, eager to bring the establishment to its knees if that's what it takes to facilitate positive political change. If the unbound are the irritable loners and individualists, then the Carthians are their politically motivated counterparts, the Young Turks who seek to shake up the status quo with the honesty of their passion and the ingenuity of their ideas. Due to the prevalence of young Kindred in the modern age, the Carthian Movement sees quite a bit of support worldwide.

OVERVIEW

Carthians are full of ideas. They see brave new possibilities and models for Kindred self-rule that they believe were heretofore unimagined before they arrived on the scene, and they long to share those ideas with others — especially with those whom they believe keep the covenant and its ideas down. Few stop to wonder whether the existing status quo (whatever and wherever it might be) has endured for a reason. Most are content to challenge it for the sake of trying to accomplish something positive in a world as bleak as the Kindred's.

If the Carthians have a single enemy among the Damned, it is calcification. Change is vital to all social systems. Therefore, many Carthians fear the elders of their kind. This is not because they think elders pose a direct threat, but because elders are the most stagnant members of their race, the least capable of hearing or accepting new ideas. For this reason, many sub-movements of the Carthian cause have some strict policies about who can and can't join, as they fear their dreams might become the target of some elder's crusade.

For the most part, they're right. Most elder vampires have little to no interest in seeing a bunch of neonates summarily rearrange the power structure that's been in place for centuries, and in so doing strip elders of their patiently cultivated power and influence. Vampires are nasty, predatory creatures who only grow nastier and more predatory with age, and few elders appreciate this latest "fad" among neonates. As a result, the Carthian Movement has become the scapegoat of choice for powerful elders. Were it not for the presence of some great minds within the Movement (as well as a few elders of other covenants), the faction might well collapse under the weight of tradition. All the same, the Movement has met with at least limited success in some areas, and much like a persistent union, the Carthians have begun to show some marked gains simply by remaining patient and playing the game as it must be played. Their democratic notions aren't loved by everyone, but what the Carthians lack in wisdom and support, they tend to make up for in passion and unity (though they, too, indulge in their fair share of fractiousness and infighting).

MEMBERS

The Carthians embody the youngest generation of Kindred, even more so than the unaligned. The vast majority of self-proclaimed Carthians are neonates, with a smattering of wily ancillae who have either achieved some measure of power or satisfaction from their efforts as part of the covenant, or who are simply too afraid to abandon the faction after so many years and relations forged (or destroyed). Once in a while, the rare elder emerges with ties to the Carthian Movement, but by and large elders simply scowl at the very idea of it all.

When a vampire comes to the Carthian cause, he typically does so out of a genuine desire to see some radical changes implemented in the secret world of the Damned. As might be expected, the most numerous (and vocal) clan in the Movement is the Mekhet, many of whom are drawn by the opportunity the covenant presents. Many consider the covenant to be the last and best chance for positive relations between Kindred and kine, and as such, a few are willing to do anything to make sure the Movement thrives and survives. While most Ventrue normally shy away from anything Carthian, a number of Nosferatu and Daeva can be found at Carthian gatherings — the former out of appreciation for a venue in which fear can motivate, and the latter out of a vampiric desire to involve themselves in the affairs of others.

PHILOSOPHY

The foundation of the Carthian Movement is the notion that vampires needn't accept the status quo unthinkingly. While these Kindred recognize that they're being Embraced into a world with its own secret history and traditions, they don't feel that they have to accept that history and those traditions simply because someone older than them says they do. Rather, they believe that every man can and must have a voice, in death as he did in life, and that voice must be heard in order for peace or justice to prevail in the system — any system.

This philosophy revolves around two core concepts that give the cause its fire.

Power to the People

The first and most important tenet of the Carthian cause is that any model of government that works for mortals is applicable to Kindred. Democracy in particular is the cornerstone of Carthian thinking, because it gives each individual a say in the affairs and administration of the people as a whole. Socialism is a popular model, too. Due to the relatively small scale of vampire society, many consider socialism more feasible for Kindred to adopt than it might be for mortals. Carthians detest the notion of rule by divine mandate (perceived or otherwise), and they strive to convince those in power that existing structures should be examined thoroughly, and then modified or torn down as necessary in order to create a better world for all Kindred. Needless to say, few vampires in positions of power are immediately agreeable. They understand vampiric nature, perhaps all too well, and know that even when Carthians "succeed," the result is often little more than the undead equivalent of a labor union, and such artificial contrivances are inherently dangerous to Kindred society.

Change Is Necessary

If part of the curse of undeath is stagnation and stasis, then the Kindred must be willing to change and adapt to the times if they are to endure. Dismissing new ideas out of hand simply because they are not what has been done before is the folly of ignorance, and such folly drives the Carthians to bloody tears. If they, at so young an age, can recognize the truth of vampiric existence, then why can't the elders of their kind? Or is it that those elders have long since forgotten? Whatever the case, the Carthians take it upon themselves to remind their hoary sires and grandsires that no kingdom is forever, and that in time, change comes to every thing in every system — whether it's desired or not.

RITUALS AND OBSERVANCES

While the Carthians are considerably less ritualistic than either the Lancea Sanctum or the Circle of the Crone, they still have their share of sacred practices. More often than not, Carthian "rites" revolve around politics, and what starts as a debate can easily turn into a ritual depending on the Kindred involved.

The Chain

At almost every Carthian gathering, at some point in the evening, some Kindred (usually the Prefect) steps forward and requests that everyone present take part in a long-standing custom that Carthians call the Chain. The entire rite (such as it is) is over in a matter of moments, so even the most turbulent of Kindred usually acquiesce to their involvement. The idea is simple. All the Carthians present gather in a circle, and following a few inspirational words from the Prefect, each passes a single artifact that is esteemed by the local

Carthians to the Kindred beside him, thus forming a symbolic chain representing that what one Kindred does affects all others. The symbolism is blunt but effective. Each vampire in the circle is beholden to the next and responsible for another, but not directly. In this way do the Carthians remind themselves of their outlook, common goals and objectives. Artifacts can be anything, such as a relic of a fallen Carthian leader, an effigy of an enemy or a personal possession of someone soon to be drawn into the Carthian ranks.

Independence Day

The Carthians, being fans of democracy in all its forms, hold a special fondness for Independence Day. The term can be misleading, however, seeing how the celebration day itself is not always on the American holiday, the fourth of July. In countries other than the United States, such as Mexico and France, Carthian vampires typically celebrate on the same date mortals do, so the fifth of May is nearly as common a date of observance, for example. In actual Carthian-dominated domains, the Kindred celebrate the night their dream of a new world came to pass. The victory of an alternate political model is both rare and wondrous in the world of the Damned, and the Carthians revel in remembering the night of its advent. When free to do so, Carthians can get quite rowdy, and their parties are truly legendary.

TITLES AND DUTIES

Unlike the other covenants, whose titles often coincide with those of standard positions of authority, the titles of important figures in the Carthian Movement denote levels of responsibility and respect, rather than true authority.

Prefect

The Kindred in charge of much of the night-to-night running of Carthian operations in a given city is known as the Prefect. In most every case, the Prefect is elected (in whatever form that takes) by a majority of other Carthians, with the exception of any active Myrmidon, who traditionally abstains from such voting. The Prefect is at once the spokesperson for the Movement in his domain, the "chair" and organizer of Carthian events, and the one responsible for making sure that no single faction member's actions jeopardize the others. The Prefect must therefore have some public relations savvy, as it is to him that the Prince inevitably turns when a Carthian is suspected of some wrongdoing. While the Prefect carries considerable sway among his confederates, he is not their leader in either name or truth, and most prefer the relationship that way.

Myrmidon

The majority of incarnations of the Carthian experiment involve Kindred getting together and democratically parceling out both feeding rights and potential dispute resolutions. As such, the need quickly arises for an entirely "neutral party" to help maintain order and restore peaceable negotiations to the table, when necessary. A Carthian known as a Myrmidon fills this role. Although the Myrmidon works very closely with the Prefect, he is not the Prefect's "right-hand man," despite appearances to the contrary. Rather, he is the one who often acts as intermediary between two quarreling Carthians or between a Carthian and a non-Carthian of no political importance. Given the Prefect's duties to the cause, the Myrmidon can and often does end up acting as the one enforcing the Prefect's duties, simply by virtue of the fact that nobody else could do it without cry of foul.

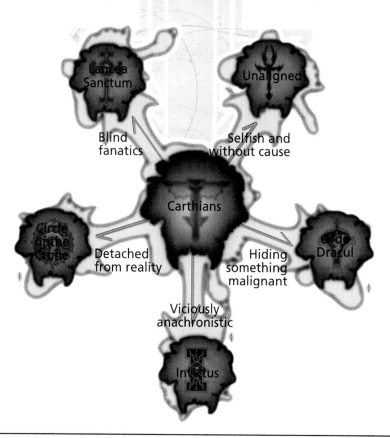

THE CIRCLE OF THE CRONE

Few vampires outside the Circle of the Crone have anything even approaching a complete understanding of the group's secretive beliefs and behaviors. As a covenant, the Circle is as devoted the Carthians, more tightly organized than the Invictus, and as often as not, more feared and misunderstood than the Lancea Sanctum and the Ordo Dracul. For many neonates, these mysterious Kindred are the "bogeymen" of vampire society — those who gather in sequestered cabals, where they practice ancient and eldritch rites in reverence to bloody gods and goddesses of cultures forgotten or shunned. These are the vampires about whom elders warn their childer: the political outcasts, iconoclasts and, to some, heretics of the Damned.

OVERVIEW

The Circle of the Crone decries what are the most widely accepted creation myths of the vampire. To these cultists, the Lancea Sanctum's progenitor is not to be revered, worshipped or even heeded. Nor is the Ordo Dracul's nigh-mythical founder anything but a grand ruse. Instead, the Circle of the Crone claims a more naturalistic origin for vampires, that they have always been a part of the world, spawned in the dark places where mortals fear to tread and where guarded suspicion yields to open fear. Their origin stories invoke such names as the Russian witch Baba Yaga, the horned god Cernunnos, the Thracian goddess of moon and magic Bendis, the animal-god Pashupati, bull sacrifices in the name of Mithras, and the bloodier incarnations of the Morrigan. Members of the Circle of the Crone occasionally even incorporate elements dating before Lancea Sanctum dogma into their philosophy through Lilith, the first wife of Adam. Acolytes, as members of the Circle are often known, reject vampiric notions of penitence entirely. Instead, they take a more organic approach to unlife, one that allows for all creatures — even the living dead — to continue to learn, grow and find enlightenment over time. While much of Kindred tradition places emphasis on guilt and penance according to the Judeo-Christian model, the Circle of the Crone sees itself as outside that framework.

Members of this covenant maintain that the primary lesson to be learned from whatever origin of the undead any given Kindred espouses is that a vampire, though damned to an eternity of unlife, is no more or less a victim than he chooses to be. Empowerment and enlightenment are both well within the reach of any creature, vampire or otherwise, who is truthful and dedicated enough to attain them. Although the Circle is primarily a vampiric phenomenon, its ideology extends beyond the worldly borders of the Kindred plight and is attractive to non-Kindred as well. As such, the Circle boasts some of the most extensive and unusual contacts among other, similarly inclined creatures, including mages and even werewolves.

As might be expected, Acolytes are none too popular with the fervent Lancea Sanctum, which takes great offense at the Circle's "corruption" of its dearly held ideals. Some truly hardline Kindred, especially those in power in conservative domains, go so far as to outlaw the practice and spread of what they call "demon worship," and they lay heavy penalties down upon those caught in violation of the decree. Most of the time, however, even the most stalwart Prince or Archbishop satisfies himself with making sure that those around him are free of any Acolyte heresy, thus cutting off any potential threat at the source.

MEMBERS

The Circle of the Crone boasts a diverse collection of Kindred among its adherents. Members of every clan and those of any age are drawn to the Circle's particular ethos, and the covenant is certainly stronger because of it. If the covenant is weak in any one demographic, it is likely in the number of Ventrue who share in its beliefs. The Ventrue are childer of tradition, and among the more conservative members of the clan, tradition suggests that core Acolyte

C. Wilkins

ideology is foolishness at best and heresy at worst. Conversely, the Gangrel (who are known for their disregard of both mortality and Kindred convention) are perhaps the perfect fit for the covenant's mindset. Many Acolytes do indeed hail from the ranks of the Savages, who can find a symbolic resonance between their nature and those of the many gods and spirits in the Circle's pantheon.

Given the relatively radical nature of their philosophies, Acolytes are understandably preoccupied with the continued growth of their membership. In recent years, many have begun to actively seek converts, particularly from among the downtrodden and dispossessed of Kindred society. This search often leads to the door of unaligned Kindred, many of whom are somewhat more tolerant of Acolytes than they are of the Lancea Sanctum or Invictus. And there are others who view the Acolytes' ideology as compatible with their own political outlook. As a result, the Circle's missionary efforts have been rewarded, and the number of former independents who have become members grows with each passing night. After all, if vampires are real, who's to say that the blood gods and deities of the Old Ways aren't?

PHILOSOPHY

At the core of Acolytes' belief sits the Crone, a sort of vampiric mentor and lover of mythological "monsters" during various stages of history and among innumerable cultures. Obviously, reverence for the Crone is the source of the Circle's name, and she is by turns an amalgamation of spirits or gods from whom vampires originated, or a literal figure not too vastly different from the Lancea Sanctum's own progenitor. Acolytes revere the image and teachings of various mother-goddesses, who, according to a variety of mythological and religious texts, was cast out of the company of fellow gods for seeking to better herself by consuming the blood of those whom the gods had made in their image. Through trial and pain, the Crone managed to uncover the secrets of creation, and to survive the harsh wasteland that was life outside the gods' own paradise. All on her own, the Crone is said to have created form, shape and beauty out of the barren nothingness that lay beyond the ken of men and gods, and her Circle seeks to emulate her experience so that it too might achieve her wisdom and power.

Branching out from this core precept are two underlying themes.

Creation is Power

Vampires of this covenant are perhaps the most honest with themselves about what they believe to be the truth of the Kindred condition. They recognize that the Requiem tears them from the natural world and suspends them in a state of eternal stasis, forever unable to create life. For those who let the truth of this realization destroy them, existence becomes an unending spiral of manipulation toward destruction, with resources being allocated merely to fuel the perpetuation of the cycle. Creation, then, becomes both the source of true power and the only way a static creature can otherwise remain a vibrant part of the earthly order. Some Acolytes practice this ideology in small ways, tending gardens or breeding animals, while others take the broader view, seeking instead to create things of lasting beauty or utility such as art or invention. Whatever form it takes, all Acolytes strive to emulate creation in their own way.

Tribulation Brings Enlightenment

Acolytes believe that any creature can overcome its own weakness and moral failings by continually testing its physical, mental and spiritual limitations. Only through ongoing tribulation can one's consciousness expand, and thus true understanding be reached. Cultists empower themselves by alternately exciting and challenging the senses, and through the newfound comprehension that results, they finally transform the static nature of undeath into the miracle of creation. Many cultists take this to a literal level, engaging in bouts of flagellation and other self-abuse that would make a mortal's stomach churn. Others simply put their bodies in new and difficult situations so that they may better understand themselves and their fears and limitations. Whatever the motivation, the results are undeniable: Those who endure are tempered by their experiences, making them ever more capable of enduring whatever comes next.

RITUALS AND OBSERVANCES

The Circle of the Crone is a rigidly ceremonial covenant. It claims a variety of different special rites, many of which are unique to the Acolytes of a given coterie or domain. Of those that see more widespread observance, three stand out.

The Crone's Liturgy

One of the most frequently heard recitations at cultist gatherings, this observance takes the form of passages read from various accounts of mythology or creation stories. The Liturgy has become the ceremonial opener (or closer, depending on the domain) for the regular meetings of assembled Acolytes. The passages themselves tell the tale, or in some convocations sing the song, of the Crone's perseverance through adversity after banishment from the company of the gods. The text has a lyrical quality to it, due to the action-reaction nature of the Crone's life, and many Acolytes have taken to employing the Greek method of call and response when reciting the Liturgy. (This has the effect of making everyone present feel involved, as opposed to just the speaker.) As most passages are fairly long, most Acolytes prefer to limit each recitation to whatever sub-section of the Liturgy is most appropriate to the subject or subjects of the meeting at hand.

The Winnowing

Acolytes claim a great many holy nights, adapted from the mythologies with which they most closely associate, and they tend to observe them with great sincerity and respect. The most important event to the covenant at large is an annual rite known as the Winnowing. The night itself falls upon a different date every year, and is dependent upon a whole host of variables, including the alignment of the stars and the phase of the moon. On the whole, though, it usually falls some time around the winter solstice (not dissimilar to the Celtic Yule,

though with notably less connection to male divinities). On this night, Acolytes take stock of the trials they have bested, the pains they have endured and the things they have either created or destroyed in the intervening year. Since these matters are specific to each cultist, this ritual is always a highly personal one, and it is usually conducted in absolute silence under starlight. During the rite, each participant offers some of his own Vitae to the ground, in the hopes of cleansing his spirit before the coming year. The rite concludes with the Hierophant placing a wreath of laurel around the head of each participant, to represent the reestablishment of each Acolyte's connection to the natural world, both within and without.

Other holidays associated with the Winnowing and observed in their unique formats punctuate the Circle's calendar. The Feast of Samhain (October 31) represents the Crone saying farewell to the world in preparation for winter, and is celebrated with much revelry and orgies of blood. Latha Lunasdal (near August 1) commemorates the time of year when the nights grow longer than the days, and when the Kindred may claim more time as their own. Those Acolytes who choose to Embrace often do so on Walpurgis Night (February 25) in observance of the custom of fertility associated with that holy day. The Pyanepsion Noumenia (September 26-27) marks the honoring of the Crone herself, and is celebrated in all manners, from vampiric celebrations that resemble wild marauds to contemplation on what it means to be a creature of the night.

Crúac

The Circle of the Crone holds the mystical ways of Crúac, the "bloody crescent," in high regard. A form of ritual magic, Crúac draws as much on shamanic systems of belief, druidic practice and even arts that resemble "black magic" in its performance. This magic is uniformly sanguinary in its practice, involving blood sacrifices at the very least and occasionally mortification of the flesh, scarring of the vampire's body or even the death of a ritual victim for its most powerful effects. As fearful as the practice's trappings are, none who has seen its powers in action can deny its effectiveness. Those outside the covenant might deride Crúac as "witchcraft," but Acolytes themselves would never stoop to using such base terms for their spiritual sorcery.

TITLES AND DUTIES

The ritualistic nature of the Circle of the Crone seems to lend itself to a hierarchy of titles and roles, each fulfilling some unique niche or aspect of the covenant's esoteric dealings, but such is not the case. In fact, only a single "official" title sees very much use throughout the covenant. The rest are either titles pro-tem, city-specific titles or simply convenient descriptors for duties that almost any Acolyte might fulfill.

Hierophant

In domains where the Circle of the Crone has a significant enough presence to warrant it (that is, in cities with three or more members), the wisest take on the equivalent role of high priest. Such a spiritual leader is called a Hierophant, and is charged with a number of duties to his fellows. The Hierophant is responsible for calling meetings to order and for leading various rites and rituals (such as the Crone's Liturgy). The Hierophant also oversees the induction of new members to the Circle, and no Acolyte may be granted full status without his leave. "Hierophant" is also a term of respect, and even elders who no longer lead rituals may continue to bear the title as a "badge of office" or a sign of enlightenment.

Among the Hierophant's responsibilities is the actual formation of dogma observed by the covenant in a given domain. For example, some Hierophants call extensively upon the Celtic pantheon in interpreting the Kindred condition, while others invoke "demons" who are actually nature spirits in certain Eastern European followings. Still others might have an outlook that draws heavily on Judeo-Christian myth, substituting Lilith for the Crone, while other groups see themselves as incarnations of the Native American *wendigo* or *manitou*. Still others blend a variety of religions into their own unique view of the Kindred. This body of dogma almost always grows organically over time, incorporating new Acolytes' beliefs, changing when the covenant's tastes dictate, or taking into account new information or discoveries. More so than any other covenant, the policies of the Circle of the Crone morph and adapt, and the responsibility of keeping it all cogent rests in the hands of the Hierophant.

The Chorus

The chorus is not an actual title in the covenant, but rather a descriptor for a certain type of member. The chorus is the collective "new converts" to Acolyte ideology, and a probationary member of the Circle. Few would-be converts are capable of grasping the often painful truth of the Acolytes' mindset, so most new members go through a period of "apprenticeship" during which they slowly acclimate to existence in the Circle of the Crone. As a point of order, covenant secrets such as Crúac are never revealed to the chorus, and they are watched just as much as guided for the duration of their probation. This introductory period exists as much for the chorus' security as the covenant's, for once members are fully inducted, there is truly no turning back.

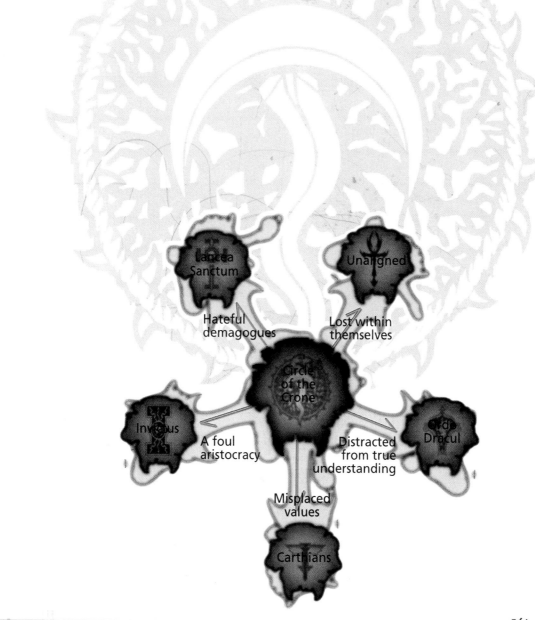

the circle of the crone

The Invictus

In the eyes of those who don't understand it — and, admittedly, of some who do — the Invictus is the despised aristocracy of the undead, the gentry who did nothing to earn their position but who would do anything to maintain it. They're the landlord, the overseer, the dictator. The Invictus might not truly hold much more authority across the domains than the other covenants do, but it makes such a big deal about what power it does have that many Kindred often associate it with the highest offices. The Invictus often tries to portray itself as among the oldest covenants, with or without justification. Oldest or not, the covenant is certainly tenured. It has vast interest — and influence — in mortal affairs, and many outside the covenant see it as the guardian (sometimes excessively so) of the Masquerade.

Overview

To an extent, the common perception of the Invictus is accurate as far as it goes, but it leaves the greatest depths of the covenant unexamined. The so-called First Estate is, at its heart, still rooted in the feudal system. It was purportedly during some stage soon after the collapse of the Roman Empire that the Invictus developed into what it is tonight, cementing a dogma that its elders claim (accurately or not) actually predates the fall. Call it divine right, the natural order, rule by the strong or whatever you like — the Invictus operates entirely as a system of linked monarchies. Everything is about power. Those who don't have it want it, while those who have it want to keep and increase it.

To hear the Invictus tell it, the covenant represents a meritocracy. The Kindred with the greatest skill, the greatest ambition and ultimately the greatest claim to leadership eventually rise to dominance. In the process, they are tempered, learning to deal with all manner of impediments, political, social or martial. If the Invictus is ruled by Princes, they are Princes of their own making.

It's a nice conceit. In many select regions, it's even true. For the most part, however, the First Estate is like any feudal government — those at the top stay there, and those at the bottom are crushed. If personal strength determines political power, how can young Kindred possibly advance? After all, their elder rivals already have the advantage of decades if not centuries of head start. They're stronger. They're wiser. They're far more experienced in the political arena. And unlike mortal aristocracies, in which the up-and-comers could count on positions eventually opening up, Invictus elders aren't likely to die naturally anytime soon, and those who fall to torpor have time to set their allies and pawns up to take their place. The Invictus, then, represents the pinnacle of achievement for the aristocracy: the illusion of equal opportunity without the reality of it. Many young Kindred aren't fooled, but many others are — and just enough of the young really do manage to carve out their own niche to make the covenant appealing. After all, despite the apparent dearth of opportunity, the Invictus really is one of the most powerful and influential factions. Sure, it's hard to move up the ladder, but if you can, you're going to be far more powerful than, say, someone of equivalent standing among the Carthians or some would-be tyrant among the unaligned.

The Invictus claims to have popularized the use of many of the common titles and ranks in Kindred society, particularly that of Prince. In all ways, the covenant thinks in terms of aristocracy, or at least gentry. In the Old World, the image remains of the noble holding court. In America, that image has evolved in some regions into industrial barons and old-money families, an unofficial yet no less effective elite. In either case, one thing remains the same — those who have it, have it, and those who don't, don't.

Ultimately, then, the Invictus exists in part to maintain order among the Kindred. Like any aristocracy, the First Estate suffers in lawlessness. Only through an ordered existence and the rule of law can the leaders of the covenant maintain their power. With the possible exception of the Lancea Sanctum, which has religious motivations for its actions, the Invictus is the most draconian covenant when it comes to enforcing the letter of the Traditions and Kindred law. It maintains the illusion of freedom and opportunity within the covenant, cloaking its tyrannical system in metaphors of "government by the fittest," in hopes of appealing to those outside its ranks, but the group is truly more concerned with keeping order among its own ranks. If the masses don't behave, then all the power the elders have built upon their backs must crumble.

And that, of course, leads to the First Estate's unstated (but hardly secret) second purpose: not merely maintaining order, but keeping the elders who already hold power in charge of that order. Let them speak all they want about expanding the rule of law and the noble cause the Invictus represents. At the end of the night, it's all about Princes, Primogen and other elders keeping themselves at the top of the pile by stepping on the heads of those beneath them.

Most disturbing of all to young Kindred, be they members or potential members, is the nagging thought that the Invictus might have the right of it. Horrific as it sounds, this notion of keeping all power in the hands of a select few undying elders, one must ask the question: If not them, who? Who else would have both the knowledge and the power necessary to fill such a position and to keep a covenant of inherently selfish predators functioning? If the Invictus' oppressive and tyrannical nature has lasted this long, maybe that's because it works.

Members

For what should be fairly obvious reasons, the Invictus often appeals far more to elder Kindred than to neonates. In the incestuous political arena that the Invictus favors, age and experience are of far greater value than anything youth might offer. Young Kindred outnumber elders, and they have a much better grasp on the changes the modern world has brought about. Many elders face those facts with a dread akin to that inspired by open flame, and the notion of a government specifically designed to keep the established strong and their childer weak is one that appeals immensely.

That said, a surprising number of ancillae and even neonates belong to the Invictus. In some instances, this is purely a matter of the Embrace. Traditionally, childer are obligated to serve their sires' interests, at least for a time. More than any other covenant, the Invictus enforces an astonishing degree of servility. The offspring of many Invictus Kindred remain in the covenant, first out of duty, and then because they have either managed to eke out some status for themselves, or because they know no other way.

Other neonates join out of sheer ambition or self-confidence (or arrogance). True, most young Kindred have little chance of any real advancement, but the luckiest and most capable few do indeed manage to make their mark, to obtain positions of power or to even carve out their own little fiefdoms. It might be challenging to advance within the ranks of the Invictus, but the rewards for doing so are great.

The Invictus makes it easy for them. After all, the covenant wants as many members as possible. Not only do more members equate to a wider base of power, but even the most fearful elders acknowledge that they need young vampires to understand and take fullest advantage of the modern world. Of course, as with all lords, what Invictus elders really want are servants and vassals, not equals. Kings don't build roads, they inspire and command others to do so. The larger a king's retinue and army, the more power he holds, and the Invictus desires to hold all the power. Members of the covenant actively seek out other Kindred for membership, expounding the strengths and benefits of the covenant while glossing over the rather substantial downsides.

No procedure or test exists for joining the Invictus. A prospective member must often take an oath of loyalty before either a covenant or local official (a Prince, Primogen or a lesser "patron," for instance). Of course, the covenant has members and the covenant has *members*. A new recruit can expect to be carefully observed for years, possibly even decades, before other Invictus members even deign to listen to him or allow him access to any sensitive information.

Given all this, the two common threads that run among almost all Invictus members, elder and neonate alike, are burning ambition and a belief in the rule of law. Those who are unwilling to work for every scrap of power — and, perhaps

more to the point, to be constantly on guard against their rivals who do the same — have no place in the courts and corporate boardrooms of the First Estate. Those who aren't prepared to operate within the unspoken rules, to play the games of politics and trading of favors, will never acquire enough allies to succeed (or, perhaps, even survive).

Philosophy

If the Invictus is devoted to a single philosophy, it must be the notion that power among the Kindred must remain in the hands of those who are worthy of wielding it. In and of itself, that's not unreasonable. The Kindred are a violent, paranoid, ambitious race. If their society is to have any hope of survival and secrecy, someone has to be in charge. Where other covenants differ with the Invictus' philosophy is largely in the notion of what "worthy" actually means.

The Invictus believes in keeping as much power as possible in its own hands, and in constantly acquiring more. A good member is one who either advances his position in society, or who aids other Invictus Kindred in advancing theirs. Apathetic or ineffective Kindred are tolerated only as lackeys and pawns.

The covenant's overarching philosophy has spawned several other guidelines, all on the level of unwritten rules. That is, nobody's going to write them down, but everyone who's been in the covenant more than a short while knows better than to casually ignore them.

The Invictus Must Be Respected

Without a doubt, the Invictus prefers to announce its presence, yet it isn't stupid about it. Members of the First Estate are experts at backroom deals and covert schemes, and they keep a secret as well as anyone. If the Invictus holds power in a region, though, it wants the Kindred to know that it's in charge. Doing so inspires others to flock to its banners; after all, everybody likes being where the power is. Making a public show also helps squash any opposition to the faction's local goals, since many Kindred are reluctant to take on a member of so powerful a covenant while they would have less objection to challenging, say, a Carthian leader. Finally, displays of power are simply a social convention. The Invictus is extremely hierarchical and very formal. Its members often demand the respect and status they feel they're due. Many Invictus Princes and other leaders who choose to hold formal courts announce their covenant allegiance without ever saying the word "Invictus."

The Invictus, alone among covenants, considers itself to be an actual entity, worthy of admiration. The Carthians tend to eschew oaths of fealty, and the Lancea Sanctum and Circle of the Crone swear oaths to higher powers such as a god or spirit, first and foremost, with obedience to the covenant second. The Invictus alone not only demands oaths of loyalty to local covenant leaders, but considers them paramount above any and all other allegiances.

It's probably this practice that creates the illusion that so many Princes are Invictus. Because Invictus leaders often make such a point of their covenant affiliation, more so than those of other covenants, the First Estate is associated with the position.

Mortals Are Power

While all the covenants understand the need for the Masquerade, the Invictus focuses most heavily on not merely infiltrating but manipulating and influencing mortal society. In the covenant's quest for political dominance, it wastes no opportunity — and six billion kine represent quite an opportunity. Most elder Kindred of all covenants wield some amount of influence in local affairs or among businessmen, but when one pictures the vampire sitting at the heart of a web of corporate, political, criminal and social connections — a rare but extant stereotype — one probably pictures a member of the Invictus.

Rituals and Observances

The Invictus has few covenant-wide observances. As a whole, the First Estate is concerned more with traditions of general behavior than with specific activities. Still, certain social customs and mores have survived to the modern era, though they have become such a standard part of the Invictus Requiem that many Kindred no longer recognize them as such.

Oaths of Fealty

Due to its largely feudal structure, nearly every layer of interaction within the Invictus has a corresponding oath of fealty or loyalty. Followers swear oaths to leaders, childer to sires, thralls to regnants. And this, of course, doesn't even count the oaths that Invictus-aligned city officials often demand from all their subjects, Invictus or otherwise. Rare indeed is the Invictus Kindred who does not labor under at least three or four oaths.

Recitation of Lineage

Despite its claims that leaders are made, not born, the Invictus puts substantial social stock in its members' parentage. The farther back a member can recite her blood, the more respect she is offered. Descent from a particularly notable Kindred confers great status in the covenant. Descent from a notorious ancestor, or an inability to recite a vast portion of one's lineage, is grounds for scorn. Being able to claim membership in some of the more respected bloodlines (such as the so-called Mithraic Ventrue) is very nearly the equivalent of royalty, and the Invictus maintains a healthy regard for any bloodline or family capable of distinguishing itself from the parent clan by word or deed.

Formality of Presentation

Most Invictus Princes hold very formal courts and rule very structured (so much as they can manage it) domains. Whether a domain is ruled like a corporate boardroom, an old South plantation or a literal feudal court, it almost certainly has formalities and procedures that must be observed. Invictus Kindred, on average, make use of more of the local titles described previously in this chapter than members of other covenants do, precisely because of their preoccupation with position and formality. Many Invictus Princes have a Seneschal announce arriving guests by name, title (if any) and lineage (if known). They insist on specific forms of address and possibly even styles of wardrobe from those who attend their courts. They might even insist on a certain degree of refinement when it comes to social interaction at court (vulgar jokes and coarse language could be forbidden). Mouthing off to a Prince, a Regent or any other elder is grounds for severe chastisement, and more than one neonate with a "You can't tell me what to do!" attitude has found himself subjected to a Vinculum, banishment or even been faced with the sunrise when initial warnings proved insufficient.

In some cities where the Invictus wields a majority of the power, this formality extends even beyond Elysium. Kindred in such domains are expected to keep very close track of social status among all those with whom they interact, and to act accordingly. In such a city, failing to show proper deference to one of higher status can result in punishment, and showing too much deference to one of lower status results in substantial mockery and loss of face. Harpies hold nearly as much power in these cities as the Primogen, for they can grant or rescind social status at whim.

Old-Fashioned Communication

As an offshoot of the formality issue, many elder Invictus insist that most of their correspondence be conducted through the use of messengers or written letters. Telephones and email are considered gauche, the tools of an unlettered and ill-mannered youth. (Additionally, many elders are rightfully concerned that they don't know enough to protect themselves from outside eavesdropping.) Most elders aren't foolish about this protocol. When it comes to vital news or emergencies, they don't object to receiving a call or an email (though even then, Princes often prefer their Seneschals or other servants to receive the information and then deliver it in person). Using these techniques for any other purpose, however, is grounds for a social snubbing at the very least. (Some young Kindred claim that this "tradition" actually exists only so that elders aren't forced to reveal how uncomfortable and incompetent they are with modern appliances. They rarely make this claim in front of their elders, though.)

Monomacy

Tradition states that, in years gone by, the Invictus used formal duels, contests and trials by ordeal to settle otherwise unsolvable disputes. These duels and ordeals are known collectively as Monomacy. Some members of the covenant believed, as did many mortals in the Middle Ages, that God stepped in and ensured that victory went to the righteous party. Other members simply wanted a means whereby elders could settle personal issues without dragging pawns and even entire domains into the conflict. By the modern nights, the Invictus has largely abandoned its claims of divine right — even the most devout souls have difficulty believing that God takes a direct hand in duels — but it is still practiced by the staunchest supporters of the First Estate when a just cause arises.

Titles and Duties

Kindred who don't fully understand the Invictus are often surprised to discover that the covenant actually has relatively few official titles and positions. What these outsiders don't realize is that the Invictus doesn't feel it needs many new titles, because it considers the standard offices described previously to be its own creations. Most officers hold the same approximate rank in the local

Invictus as they do in the domain's government. That is, an Invictus Prince is likely the leader of the local Invictus, as well. Invictus Primogen and Prisci hold power in the city and covenant. An Invictus Sheriff likely enforces order in the local Invictus as well as in the domain as a whole.

In fact, only two titles that do not correspond to political positions are commonly found in Invictus domains.

Inner Circle

In some domains where the Invictus is not fully in control, or at least where many domain offices are held by members of other covenants, the covenant needs a body of leadership that does not consist entirely of officers of the city government. This is called the Inner Circle. Its members can be anyone, from the Prince and some of the Primogen to Kindred who hold no official position in the city at all. They set policy for the local Invictus and are always on the lookout for opportunities to advance their own positions. Strongly Invictus-dominant cities rarely have an Inner Circle. An Inner Circle exists only where the city government and the faction power structure are not one and the same. Further, this Invictus-specific "sub-Primogen" is possible only in the largest domains, where the Kindred population can support such a gathering.

Judex

Sometimes members of the Invictus come into conflict with one another. Under such circumstances, most members agree that turning to outsiders (such as city officials) for resolution is a poor idea, as it makes the covenant appear divided. Monomacy is reserved for only the gravest disputes, since few elders are willing to put their unlives on the line just to settle a disagreement. Most cities with more than the tiniest Invictus presence therefore have a Judex. Her job is, quite simply, to rule on disputes between Invictus Kindred. Once the parties involved agree to such mediation, the Judex's ruling is binding, even over those Kindred who would normally hold greater authority (such as a Prince). Judices are chosen from among city officials (in Invictus-dominant domains), members of the Inner Circle or, at worst, from among the most respected Invictus present. Some cities have a standing Judex, and the position is usually filled by a candidate on whom the Prince and Primogen can agree (or whom the Prince can force the Primogen to acknowledge). Other domains choose their mediators on a conflict-by-conflict basis. Tradition states that the Judex in such instances must be chosen by a respected Kindred who has no obvious ties to either party. Doing so is often more difficult than it sounds, and many such domains have adopted the custom of allowing a Judex, as his final act, to appoint the next Judex, well before anyone knows what problem may arise next.

Lancea Sanctum
Trustworthy but sanctimonious

Unaligned
Cults of the self

Circle of the Crone
Refuse to accept their place

Invictus

Ordo Dracul
Disciplined but deluded

No respect for tradition

Carthians

The Lancea Sanctum

To members of the Lancea Sanctum, the self-proclaimed heralds of undead morality, their origin defines everything they are and everything they do. Indeed, the modern sobriquet "Sanctified," by which the covenant is sometimes known, incenses many elders and traditionalists of the covenant, who prefer to use the Latin "Lancea Sanctum" when referring to the collective covenant. They are the religious and even moral backbone of the Kindred, yes, but they are also self-appointed priests and inquisitors. The most inhuman of an inhuman race, they exalt the role of predator. Universally respected yet universally feared, this covenant constantly seeks power over all Kindred everywhere, not for political rule, as the Invictus does, but to enforce the dictates, attitudes and even thoughts that they believe have been handed down to them from their originator Longinus, and by extension from God Himself.

The catechism of the Lancea Sanctum is that they are the ideological descendants of the Roman centurion who used his spear to prod Christ on the cross. According to the covenant's dogma, some of Christ's blood dripped onto the soldier, and this blood gave the centurion eternal life. It also carried with it, however, divine retribution, and though Longinus' act revealed Christ's divinity, it did so after an act of faithlessness on the soldier's part. Thereafter, Longinus was cursed to live eternally, but he could walk only at night and subsist only on the same blood that had proved his undoing. As the creation myth blends into covenant philosophy, vampires are a form of "original sin," though God allows them to exist, and indeed even charges them with the task of representing the risks of His divine displeasure.

Overview

Perhaps one of the single most fundamental differences between the Lancea Sanctum and the Invictus is that members of the Invictus want to be the rulers of all Kindred while members of the Lancea Sanctum believe that their covenant already does rule in all ways that matter. The fact that its members claim dominance over fewer domains than the Invictus does is of no concern. They speak for God and represent the pinnacle of what the undead should be. Clearly, in the final analysis, true power is theirs.

If the Invictus represents the nobility and aristocracy, then the Sanctified are the priests, bishops, paladins and the religious and spiritual advisors. (Members of the Invictus occasionally refer to the Lancea Sanctum as the Second Estate, in extension of their own metaphor, itself a perversion of the historical first and second estates.) Most of the covenant's members take their role as

ecclesiastical guides to their fellow undead very seriously. Many of the Damned — the Lancea Sanctum prefers the older and more severe term to the more recent "Kindred" — advise Princes and other leaders on religious and moral matters. They discuss theological ramifications of decisions, and point out how a proposed action or an alleged crime violates (or fails to violate) the Traditions as interpreted by Longinus. Some members of the Lancea Sanctum take their duties further still, counseling younger Sanctified on what it means to be a vampire, educating them about the mythology and spirituality of the race, and even advising them on how to be more effective predators. This, they feel, is part of their duty as decreed by their founder — to ensure that all of the faithful understand their place in God's creation.

And if this were all the Sanctified did, it's unlikely the Lancea Sanctum would wield the fearsome reputation it has acquired. The Sanctified are determined that all their brethren should follow Longinus' philosophies. And more specifically, that they should all follow the Lancea Sanctum's interpretation of those laws. The covenant does not merely advise, it enforces. Its members do not merely preach, they demand. Members of the faction are known for their zealotry not only because Longinus himself was cursed by God, but because they maintain that violence and bloodshed are perfectly acceptable means of conversion.

The Lancea Sanctum is not mindless in its devotion to covenant principles, however, or at least most of its members are not. Violence is not necessarily their first resort. It is far better to convince other vampires of the wisdom and righteousness of their cause than to cut down a potential brother or sister. Nor is the covenant anxious to deplete its own numbers in hopeless or unnecessary conflict. In domains where other covenants hold clear dominance, the Lancea Sanctum is often willing to work with them. Sanctified members advise the current leadership in hopes of both steering its decisions and gaining their own status. They also circulate among the Kindred on the streets, preaching their message of a better way, drumming up support for future activities. The Sanctified are as patient as a cult of the undead can afford to be; violence is not to be avoided, but neither is it to be engaged in without purpose. Once the Lancea Sanctum has determined that bloodshed is the best route to an objective, however, God be merciful to anyone who stands in the way.

Of course, as frightened as many Kindred are of the Lancea Sanctum, they can take comfort in the notion that mortals have it even worse. The Sanctified have a reputation for being vampires in the truest sense of the word. They are not the mindless, bloodthirsty vandals who represent the worst of the unbound. Nor are they the brooding erstwhile generals of the Invictus, sending followers to their deaths on a whim. No, Sanctified are so frightening because they are so matter-of-fact, even reverent, about their vampiric nature. Ever since the covenant's founding in the nights following Longinus' curse, one of their fundamental precepts stated that the true Sanctified must fully acknowledge that he is no longer mortal. Vampires occupy a higher level. They are predators, feeding on mortals as those same Canaille do upon cows and sheep. To be true to the teachings of Longinus and the purposes of the Almighty, a Sanctified has to be a predator and no longer even pretend to be one of the kine from which he came. The Lancea Sanctum has no particular love of cruelty (or at least most of its members do not), nor do their beliefs or laws permit them such wantonness. They simply treat their prey as no better than animals, and this cold ruthlessness is often far more disturbing than any random outburst of conscious malice.

FROM *THE TESTAMENT OF LONGINUS*

One: That though you are Damned, your Damnation has purpose. It is the will of God that you are what you are, and the will of God is that the Damned exist to show the evils of turning from Him. The evil become Damned; God has taken those worthy of His love to His own side.

Two: That what you once were is not what you now are. As a mortal is a sheep, so are the Damned wolves among them. That role is defined by nature — wolves feed on their prey, but they are not cruel to them. The role of predator is natural, even if the predator himself is not.

Three: That an ordained hierarchy exists. As man is above beasts, so are the Damned above men. Our numbers are fewer so that our purpose is better effected.

Four: That with the power of Damnation comes limitation. The Damned hide among those who still enjoy God's love, making themselves known only to exemplify fear. The Damned shall make none of their own, for such is a judgment of soul that is the purview only of God. The Damned shall suffer yet more should they slay a fellow to take his soul from him.

Five: That our bodies are not our own. Our purpose is to serve, and when we stray from that purpose, we are to be chastened. The light of the sun excoriates; the flames of a fire purify fleshly evil. The taste of all sustenance other than Vitae is as ash upon the tongue.

Members

Unlike the Invictus, which appeals more to elder vampires than young, or the Carthians, who tend toward the reverse, the Lancea Sanctum projects an equal appeal to undead of all ages. What an elder looks for in the covenant, however, is often not the same as what interests a neonate.

Most elders join for religious or spiritual reasons. Some come to the Sanctified seeking enlightenment and understanding.

They have walked this Earth for many mortal lifetimes and have come to see that they — and their race — must have some higher purpose. They believe that God must have had some reason for making them what they are, and that Longinus' philosophy offers them at least the first few steps on a path toward answers. Others join the covenant not to seek answers, but to provide them for others. Religious zealots often believe that the entire world would be better off if everyone simply turned to their own way of thinking, and the fanatics of the Lancea Sanctum are no exception. Many elders join (or remain with) the Sanctified not for their own sake, but for the sake of others. They would make all vampires everywhere understand what they are, what they should be and what they must do. They'll all be better off, then — and those who must suffer and die in the process, well, it's all for the best of reasons.

Of course, it would be foolish to imply that all Sanctified who seek the conversion of the entire undead race do so for altruistic reasons. Some want to convert their brethren only to exalt their own position. Surely God or at least their superiors in the covenant will eventually reward them. All they must do is prove themselves worthy by converting just a few more nonbelievers.

The majority of young vampires who are drawn to the covenant are enticed not by any deeply held religious convictions, but by a lack of those selfsame convictions and of any other solid sense of identity. The Lancea Sanctum, more than any other covenant (except possibly the Circle of the Crone), allows and even demands members to accept what they are. For a neonate seeking direction in something so drastically different from mortal life — casting about not only for someplace to belong but for someone who can provide answers for "Why?" and "How?" — few things are as comforting as being told that it is acceptable to be a monster. Even if the newcomer doesn't believe it yet, being told that she has become something greater than she was is comforting in an unlife otherwise punctuated by new and alien urges.

Obviously, these are generalities, not hard-and-fast rules. Many neonates do indeed join the covenant because they already hold certain religious convictions, and many elders seek the same sense of belonging that attracts childer. And, of course, Sanctified of all ages join simply out of ambition, as advancement is often easier among the Lancea Sanctum than in other covenants.

New members of the covenant are required to make many gestures of commitment to Longinus, to God and to the goals of the faction. They engage in many rites and rituals, and undergo trials to test their fortitude and faith. These tests consist of everything from torture to theological debate. Trials aren't necessarily used to determine whether a recruit may join the Lancea Sanctum, but those who make a good showing earn the respect of their new fellows. Those who do poorly face months if not years of derision and mockery, often sufficient to drive a new member away.

Philosophy

The Lancea Sanctum believes, quite frankly, that its members are the chosen of God. Sanctified are not inherently superior to other vampires, but exalt themselves by accepting the teachings of Longinus wholeheartedly. One night, all vampires will come to worship God and venerate Longinus as the Sanctified do. The Lancea Sanctum maintains that it is the duty of all good and faithful Sanctified to hurry that night along. Thus do they constantly proselytize, seeking converts to their way of thinking long past the time that other covenants might give up and move on.

Longinus himself occupies the position of Dark Prophet. While he is not the "first of the undead" according to sect beliefs, he was certainly one of the first to be something other than a self-motivated monster, little more than an animal. With Longinus arose a code of ethics. His act of prodding Christ with the spear is more important than the man or vampire — Longinus' import follows that act, not vice versa. He is a "sin eater," representing the evils that man commits in the absence of faith, and his punishment is its just repayment.

This philosophy leads to a strange dichotomy of beliefs that rivals the most extremist and even bizarre of mortal faiths. The philosophical precepts governing members of the Lancea Sanctum — or at least those members who truly believe in what they do — seem almost mutually exclusive, yet the covenant has managed to hold them together for what might be centuries or even millennia.

Commandments and Traditions

The first and foremost rule the Lancea Sanctum observes is that the Traditions are absolute and inviolate — mostly. The covenant seeks to encourage all vampire society to adhere strictly to those precepts, for only by doing so can the Lancea Sanctum honor its progenitor and bring the rest of the undead closer to understanding him.

At the same time, however, most Sanctified are pragmatic, and their leaders know that the covenant will never succeed at its divinely appointed task if they allow themselves to become weak. Sanctified therefore Embrace childer, though it flies in the face of the Traditions. They prefer to convert other vampires where possible, but they know that the covenant would atrophy without the occasional infusion of new blood. Similarly, the Lancea Sanctum does not hesitate to kill those who threaten its objectives (though again, Sanctified would often prefer to convert or at least circumvent such enemies where possible). Murder, too, is permitted because the covenant could not survive otherwise. Strangely enough, true believers among the Lancea Sanctum do not claim that they are exempt from the Traditions they break. Rather, they maintain that they willingly risk God's displeasure for the sake of the larger community, much as Longinus himself was cursed for making the mark on Christ that proved his divine nature. They accept whatever judgment is finally levied upon them for doing so.

The Lancea Sanctum will not, however, choose to violate the Tradition of Secrecy, at least not in the sense that it lets mortals know exactly what vampires are. Members of the covenant understand as well as any others how vital the Masquerade is for the survival of the race, and thus the satisfaction of their divine charge. Of course, violent members, having taken philosophical lessons of superiority over the kine to heart, consider killing witnesses to vampiric acts an acceptable means of maintaining secrecy. Covenant leadership frowns on such brazen behavior and has been known to chastise or dispose of Sanctified who draw too much attention. They know, however, that

C. Wilkins

to rein in the entirety of the young generations would vastly curtail their recruiting power — assuming they could do it at all — so they grit their teeth and make every effort to clean up after careless childer.

Guidance

All Sanctified are worthy of spiritual guidance. True believers in the covenant's cause never turn away any vampire, of any affiliation, who seeks aid or advice on religious matters. In fact, covenant law prohibits members from refusing any such petition. Obviously, this stricture allows for reasonable interpretation. A Sanctified need not invite a known enemy into her haven with open arms, nor must she stop in the middle of a gun battle to comfort a companion who's having a crisis of faith. Where possible, however, the Lancea Sanctum serves the entirety of vampire society as priests and advisors, and it is through this reaching out that the group gains many of its most faithful adherents. Even if conversion is not viable, the covenant believes that by providing aid it can only bring other vampires that much closer to God.

Conversion

Those who will not voluntarily open their eyes must be forced to see. Violence is never the first choice, but if the undead refuse to come to the Lancea Sanctum, and if the Sanctified believe they can do so with minimal danger to their own standing, they have no qualms about shedding blood. Strictly speaking, conversion by the sword is impossible. A vampire can easily claim to have converted, and then flee at the first opportunity. Those who do not die can afford to wait for their chance. In regions where the covenant holds dominance, the Lancea Sanctum can enforce its laws and the Traditions with the most dire and horrifying of penalties. Other vampires in the territory might not actually believe as the Lancea Sanctum does, but by God they're going to act as though they do! And who knows, maybe when they've been forced to behave like Sanctified for long enough, they'll see the wisdom in such an unlifestyle.

Rituals and Observances

Few organizations, be they Kindred or kine, can match the Lancea Sanctum for sheer quantity of rituals. As the primary religious faction among the undead, the Sanctified have a rite, an observance or a tradition for many aspects of the Requiem. It would be impossible, even in many times the space available, to describe them all. Presented here, then, is a small selection of some of the more important or common rites and traditions. It's important to note that while these practices are observed wherever the Sanctified can be found, they often differ in detail from domain to domain or even from coterie to coterie. Like all religious ceremonies, they are defined as much by their performers as by their intended meaning. The specifics given here are therefore standards, not necessarily universal. Note that the use of the term "Priest" in these descriptions represents a formal position, not the more general concept that all Sanctified should "serve as priests" to their brethren.

Theban Sorcery

To hear the Sanctified tell it, its members are capable of no less than miracles themselves. In truth, the Lancea Sanctum does possess a potent form of spiritual magic, though whether it performs literal miracles is up for debate. At some point after the covenant formed — purportedly in the third century AD — some of its members followed a Roman army into Thebes ("Thebias" according to fragments of a journal supposedly recovered from the march). There, a legion of Christian soldiers was drawn from the local ranks. When members of the covenant accompanied the Theban legion on its march to Gaul, one of their number brought with her the secrets of this magic, which she claimed to have learned from an angel on the journey. To this night, the covenant studies and practices this sorcery, which it uses to demonstrate its power, "prove" its chosen nature, and to punish transgressors against its dictates.

Creation Rite

The induction of a new childe to the Requiem is a powerful event for the Sanctified. On one hand, it symbolizes the continued growth of their covenant and the birth of another disciple of the faith. On the other, it is a violation of the very Traditions that the Lancea Sanctum has sworn to uphold. The Creation Rite, then, is a combined celebration of the new childe and an act of penance for his sire. It must be conducted as soon as reasonably possible after the childe is Embraced, ideally at the very time of that Embrace. A Priest or other high-ranking member of the Lancea Sanctum conducts the rite, which involves substantial prayers and litanies recited by the Priest and the sire. The childe is then anointed (described below), and blessed with a burning brand. The brand does not touch the flesh of the childe. Rather, the Priest waves it over her not unlike the Catholic christening. The sire, however, is exposed to the brand, which is placed directly against his chest. Contact lasts only a moment, but crying out or lapsing into a fear frenzy from the flames is a mark of shame. Only when this rite has been completed is the childe considered "truly" Sanctified, and a childe whose sire holds up well is accorded more respect than one who does not.

Multiple variations on this rite exist, as few Lancea Sanctum domains and coteries operate in exactly the same fashion. Some Creation Rites involve the sire exposing herself to the rising sun or to night-long sessions of flagellation with barbed whips. One particularly dangerous variation involves the childe (after being blessed) staking his own sire and then setting one of her extremities alight. The purpose is for the childe to let his sire burn just long enough to leave a wound, yet not so long as to risk Final Death. If the childe performs well, the sire is lauded for her choice. If the childe does not perform well, the sire usually isn't concerned with anything else said on the topic.

Anointing/Blood Baths

Used whenever a Sanctified obtains a new rank or position, the Anointing, which must be conducted by a Priest or recognized covenant official, involves little more than a recited litany, a series of formal responses offered by the supplicant, and the drawing of any one of several religious symbols on the supplicant's head. The drawing is done in blood, and the supplicant is forbidden from washing it off until the next night. (Recently Anointed Sanctified do not frequently go out among kine.) This ceremony is why many Lancea Sanctum officers, officials and agents are referred to, collectively, as the Anointed.

Among some young Sanctified, the Anointing assumes a more primal form. They celebrate such events not with a simple touch of blood but with what is called a Blood Bath. The Blood Bath serves the same purpose, but the subject (often along with the other participants) is literally drenched in blood. Those who do not enter frenzy are accorded great respect, while those who succumb are mocked for their lack of control. Elder Lancea Sanctum members consider the Blood Bath a corruption of an ancient tradition, but as long as young Priests do not conduct it in such a way as to threaten the Masquerade, critics bite back their distaste and "let the whelps play."

Midnight Mass

Led by one of the highest Lancea Sanctum officials in a city, a Midnight Mass is simply that: a prayer service to God, held in the dark of night. Some truly devout Sanctified domains hold such a mass several times a week, but they occur only once or twice a month in most Sanctified-dominated cities. All covenant members in the region are expected to attend on at least a semi-regular basis. Many other rites, rituals and celebrations, often including Creation Rites and Anointings, occur at Midnight Mass.

Others

Among the dozens if not hundreds of other rites not listed here are the Fire Dance (a ceremony popular among young Sanctified in which they dance around or even through fire to prove that they can master the vampiric weakness), the Mysteries (a yearly festival of celebration and thanksgiving that all local Sanctified are expected to attend), and acceptance and allegiance rites (trials and sworn oaths when first joining the covenant or a particular coterie). In addition to those rites that are more or less universal, domains and even individual coteries often have their own rites, developed internally and not shared with the rest of the faction.

Titles and Duties

As with the Invictus, many of the Lancea Sanctum's titles overlap with local positions of authority. Many do not, however, and those that appear common often have a unique take on them.

Bishop

The religious leader of the Lancea Sanctum in a domain is called the Bishop. The Prince may rule the city, but the Bishop is the highest authority where the Lancea Sanctum is concerned. Many Bishops hold other positions in the city power structure (such as Regent, Seneschal or Primogen), even if that power structure is not Sanctified-dominated, as most Princes are wise enough to recognize the substantial power a Bishop holds.

Bishop duties include all those of a Priest, but he is also responsible for managing the local activities of the covenant as a whole.

Archbishop

This is simply the title that most Sanctified Princes choose for themselves, as Archbishop fits the Lancea Sanctum mentality far better than the secular title of Prince. The Archbishop, surprisingly enough, is usually not the same person as the Bishop, as the responsibilities of running a city usually do not leave time to serve as Bishop as well. The Archbishop does outrank the Bishop, however, so he can overrule the Bishop when necessary.

Cardinal

In those few cities where a single leader is powerful enough to serve as both Archbishop and Bishop, she often chooses to take the title of Cardinal. Cardinal isn't a "formal" covenant title the way the other two are; it's really just a vaunted way of saying, "I hold greater office than any two of you. Who would dare challenge me for it?"

Priest

A Sanctified responsible for the spiritual teaching and guidance of other vampires is known as a Priest. Some Priests serve as advisors to their local government. Others serve as Priest to a specific coterie (and many coteries larger than three members have one). This position is largely informal, but occasionally has the formal recognition of Lancea Sanctum leaders behind it.

Inquisitor

Answering only to a Bishop or Archbishop, an Inquisitor is responsible for hunting down heresy, disobedience and treason within the covenant. He has power to investigate anyone or anything, and all wise Kindred fear him. Although he technically has only low rank, his authority while conducting an investigation borders on absolute. In cities where a separate Sheriff exists, these two are often at odds. If an Inquisitor is not supported by the local Prince, he had better be careful how he handles relations with other covenants. The Inquisitor may find himself isolated in accusations or charges levied against vampires of other followings.

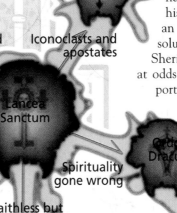

THE ORDO DRACUL

The curse of vampirism is but an obstacle, a hurdle before achieving true power. Granted, it's a daunting hurdle, and one that most Kindred are ill equipped to even see as surmountable. For those with the necessary devotion, tenacity and intelligence, the Ordo Dracul, the Order of the Dragon, can provide the means. The vampires of the Ordo Dracul run the gamut from dogged fundamentalists with just as much zeal as any fanatic to coldly secular theosophists simply seeking the means to destroy an enemy. The covenant as a whole welcomes both mentalities, for both have much to teach.

This faction claims an infamous founder — Vlad Tepes, Dracula himself. Dracula is noteworthy because he acknowledges no sire. According to Dracula's account of becoming a vampire, God turned His back on him, and in order to punish him for his wicked acts, God cursed him with undeath. The most widely accepted story of Dracula's origin is that God punished Vlad Tepes for his abuse of faith in mortal life. According to certain historical records, Tepes was appointed as a "defender of Christianity," a charge he then used as a means of advancing his own political agendas and as an excuse for atrocities. In addition to all his crimes against humanity, Dracula ultimately put his own desires before his holy oath, the act that Damned him.

The veracity of these statements remains unproven, of course, not the least obstacle to which is that Dracula himself hasn't been seen in over a century. Legends of Dracula also ascribe to him strange circumstances. By knowledgeable members of Kindred society, he is suspected of siring a very few childer — but if Dracula wasn't Embraced himself, what clan could he possibly be, and what does that make his get? By other accounts, he has never sired childer at all, or those he has sired are somehow "failed," little more than hideous horrors doomed to slake their thirsts in a constant state of mindless rage.

Indeed, the organization that has grown up surrounding Dracula's teachings is easily as enigmatic as its founder.

OVERVIEW

The Order's roots are something of a matter of debate — even within the covenant itself. It is undoubtedly one of the youngest of the major Kindred factions. The Dragons, as they are fearfully (or hatefully) known, have records of apprenticeships as early as the 16th century. With the advent of the printing press, the covenant was better able to disseminate the vast amount of archaic and arcane writings that members require in order to learn and perform their transcendental studies. The covenant experienced a sudden jump in power and membership during the Industrial Revolution, then another in the late 19th century, then yet another in recent decades. It is believed that the covenant grew to power in Eastern Europe, its philosophies traveling with the development of transportation technology, but just as credible theories place the group's origins in Victorian London and even early New York.

The Ordo Dracul reveres its founder, but in a very different way than, say, the Lancea Sanctum honors Longinus. The Dragons believe that the curse of vampirism can and should be surpassed, that the Embrace is a judgment that can be overturned and even exceeded. Nothing, *nothing*, is permanent, the Order argues, not even the lingering undeath that all Kindred experience. Of course, no known vampire has ever escaped the Requiem through the Order's rites (at least not in a manner that others would find satisfactory; it's quite possible to reduce oneself to a pile of ash or a torpid wretch through an ill-performed observance). Regardless, Kindred are perfectly willing to admit that such things take centuries, if not millennia. Some crucial piece of knowledge must yet be missing, and with the world growing smaller and more integrated as technology uncovers more of it, that knowledge won't be long in coming.

In that regard, the Ordo Dracul is much more comfortable with the modern world than the Invictus is, though not nearly so comfortable as the Carthians are. Technology isn't something to be feared, but another tool to be used, and since the covenant prizes mental evolution as much as spiritual progression, elders who wish to retain their standing must shake off the inertia of years and learn how to use a telephone or a scanner. Hidebound traditionalists aren't overtly snubbed (after all, they might know something useful, and it doesn't pay to burn bridges), but they do tend to be left alone in their havens to experience the Requiem and perform their research in solitude.

The search for knowledge is a commonly stated goal of the Order, but it's deliberately vague. Members of the Ordo Dracul are interested in knowledge, true, but that has more to do with the kind of personality the covenant attracts than with its actual goals. The Dragons seek information about the truth of the vampiric condition, and to that end, they enjoy talking to other Kindred about their experiences, their feelings upon receiving the Embrace, how their bodies have changed, and how their attitudes toward morals have progressed. (The

Gangrel in particular interest the Order, and those Savages who join the covenant quickly become some of their most respected members.) The Dragons seek to establish patterns in God's plan, in the curse of undeath and in any other facet of the Requiem that will lead them to the answer they seek — how to transcend the limits of vampirism.

The Ordo Dracul has a hierarchical structure unique to it, known internally as the Dragon's Tongue. The Order involves numerous rites and initiations, the completion of which symbolizes the member's passage from one "circle of mystery" or level of achievement to the next. Progression through the hierarchy seems to correspond to mastery of the Coils of the Dragon, but whether this is true or simply a non-member's misunderstanding remains uncertain. This structure also serves to protect the covenant's secrets. The Ordo Dracul is loath to let anyone, even low-ranking members, leave the faction. The higher one's rank in the covenant, the more she has invested and accomplished and, thus, the more reluctant she will (theoretically) be to leave. Still, defections and renunciations do occur, and with more frequency than the Order would have outsiders believe.

MEMBERS

The Ordo Dracul doesn't need to proselytize. While it welcomes new members, it isn't as open as the Invictus because its strength depends on the intelligence of its Kindred, rather than on their loyalty. The Order isn't out to overthrow the existing status quo or to enforce it, nor does it mean to adhere to an ancient set of laws or to venerate a god. Its members seek simply to move beyond, and that attracts a certain class of vampire. Kindred who are dissatisfied with their lot but who attribute that dissatisfaction to a spiritual or mystical state rather than to a political or temporal one make good candidates for the Ordo Dracul. Vampires who believe in some sort of origin for the Kindred, but who lack the zealotry or dogma necessary to join the Lancea Sanctum do so as well. The most accomplished Dragons of the Order tend to come from those Kindred who are open-minded and realistic before the Embrace. They see what they have become and do not immediately accept that the Requiem is the ultimate end of their existence. These sorts of Dragons are the cream of the crop.

Most, however, join the covenant to cheat the curse of undeath, pure and simple. The lure of the group's high rites draws all clans, and even members of the Lancea Sanctum have been known to leave their covenant, thus committing unthinkable blasphemy, to join the Ordo Dracul. The reverse is also true. Occasionally a member of the Order decides that the ceremonies she observes are sins against nature or a higher power and resolves never to call upon her hard-won knowledge again, passing the rest of her nights in quiet penance for her dabbling in forbidden mysteries. The Order has even noticed that certain specific areas of study induce this response more than others, and these texts and formulae offer a tempting target for young Dragons looking to make names for themselves.

The Ordo Dracul boasts members from all clans. The covenant hasn't seen that any one widespread lineage has any particular advantage over another. Of course, a given bloodline might spawn members of the Order as one sire trains his

childe in the ways of the covenant, and that childe does likewise, but on the whole, the Dragons look past clan when considering members. The decision process has more to do with temperament and intellectual ability. While not all or even most members of the Ordo Dracul are bookish or scholarly, the vast majority are literate and educated at least moderately well.

The hardest part about joining the covenant tends to be finding members who trust other Kindred enough to be willing to teach. That in mind, the first task a prospective Dragon has is to get a potential mentor to notice her. Investigating the Ordo Dracul (which means asking questions of vampires who are experienced enough to know something about the covenant), experimenting with the vampiric form and with the various Disciplines, and trying the limits of the Requiem are good ways to go about gaining attention. If an entire coterie wishes to attempt to find a mentor, its members' chances improve dramatically. The Order approves of this approach for a number of reasons. Aside from the obvious advantage of having peers with which to trade ideas, a coterie can protect itself better than a lone vampire can, from both enemies and potentially disastrous mystical errors. Also, although the Order's elders never mention it, a bit of healthy competition is ultimately good for the covenant, as it weeds out members who are only in it to cheat undeath for its own sake.

Once a prospective Dragon finds a mentor, the apprenticeship period begins. This period never really ends. Because all members of the Ordo Dracul are meant to learn constantly, all members can teach constantly. The Order observes "graduation" ceremonies of the most elaborate kind. Indeed, it relishes the fact that even an elder might still be able to learn at the feet of a wiser and more powerful member of the Order (a fact that frightens the other covenants more than they'd ever admit).

Just as it performs graduation ceremonies, the Ordo Dracul also performs initiations as a covenant (though individual mentors might elect to test would-be pupils privately before fully introducing them). It becomes clear within the first few weeks of training whether a student has the right mettle to learn the Coils of the Dragon, which the Dragons regard as the first necessary step in joining the covenant. If the pupil cannot learn at least the basics of this esoteric body of ceremonies — and the reasons for doing so range from simple lack of intelligence to an unwillingness to surrender their souls to spiritual study — the mentor simply stops the training. The pupil might continue to practice what she has already learned, but advancement without instruction is profoundly difficult.

PHILOSOPHY

The Ordo Dracul is as much a religious society as a secular one, but only insofar as the vampiric condition cannot be explained without the existence of God. According to members' beliefs, Dracula was himself cursed by God, much as the Sanctified of the Lancea Sanctum claim that their progenitor was. The difference, of course, is that Dracula became a vampire long after many other vampires had already existed in the world. The Ordo Dracul doesn't require the fanaticism of the Lancea Sanctum or the Acolytes, because its tenets do not demand it.

The Dragons' philosophies are as rigorously tested as any of their ceremonies, so they work their miracles without worship or reverence to a higher power. Respect, they feel, is enough.

To the uninitiated, the philosophy of the Ordo Dracul is a mire of theosophical and even neo-Victorian postulation. Some Kindred liken the order to a secret society such as the Masons or the Golden Dawn, and such speculation isn't far from the truth. One cannot argue the facts, though — those who achieve rank in the Order certainly gain benefits and are able to perform acts that other vampires cannot.

The main tenets of the Order of the Dragon are as follows.

Nothing Is Permanent

Members of the Ordo Dracul know better than to consider themselves "immortal." Vampires do indeed die, and without benefit of plotting enemies or slavering werewolves. All it takes is a fire burning out of control or a miscalculation in determining the exact time of sunrise, and centuries of unlife and experience can come to an end. But the Dragons don't look at this fragility as a vulnerability. They regard their condition as mutable. After all, they reason, if God had truly wished for vampires never to change, He wouldn't have made the means of their destruction so readily available, and He certainly wouldn't have given any of them ability to change their forms. As such, the Order looks at sweeping change, even change that seems to harm more than it helps, as ultimately beneficial. A building burns, a plane crashes, the Prince of a city falls, covenants scheme, werewolves attack, and the Ordo Dracul simply reminds its members that nothing lasts forever. This isn't a bleak, fatalistic lament so much as a challenge. "What can we take away from this change?" If nothing else, every change is a reminder that change is possible.

Change Must Have a Purpose

Central to transcending the vampiric condition is an understanding of why it is necessary to do so. The Order looks at the Requiem as a challenge more than a curse, but its members never forget or deny that it *is* a curse. In researching and realizing the Coils of the Dragon, and thus changing themselves on a fundamental, mystical level, the Dragons work toward their ultimate goal of leaving their vampiric shells behind.

This tenet has a broader application, as well. Every action has a reaction, and until a Dragon can understand the reactions that a given course causes, she is discouraged from taking action at all. This lesson is reflected most keenly in the Order's spiritual power. The Coils of the Dragon distinguish members from their peers very quickly, providing a superb object lesson in the nature of causality. The more power you gain, the less power you understand. Young members of the covenant, eager for the benefits that the Coils can grant them and enthralled with the notion of going beyond the limits of their state, don't usually understand that paradox. Many Ordo Dracul mentors regard it as the harshest, but most necessary lesson of the Requiem. If every action isn't guided by purpose, it soon spirals into entropy and eventually destruction. The Order doesn't believe in causing foolish chaos and then shirking responsibility for its actions by saying, "Change is good."

Rituals and Observances

The most important relationship in the covenant is that of the mentor and pupil. Rites and practices vary greatly among mentors. While one might keep lessons extremely informal, another might treat her pupils like novitiates in a monastery, forcing them to copy manuscripts or perform menial tasks for most of the night and instructing them in the ways of transcendence for only the last hour before sunrise.

The covenant as a whole does observe a few important rituals, however, and some individual teaching methods have become widespread enough to mention.

Titles and Duties

As mentioned previously, the mentor-student relationship is the backbone of the Order of the Dragon. Many members introduce themselves as their mentors' protégés (if a mentor is well respected), and an elder Dragon with an especially promising student might even reverse the compliment, calling herself "[so-and-so]'s master."

Not all members of the Ordo Dracul are constantly embroiled in the process of learning, however, and the covenant has great respect for those who take up the other duties that the Dragons consider important.

Guardians

Among the reverent Ordo Dracul, the Guardians are responsible for looking after the aforementioned mystical sites. The covenant has several reasons for wanting to keep other beings out of these nexuses. First, an uninformed fool with a bit of mystic talent but no proper training (by which the Dragons mean any magical being who is *not* a member of the covenant — the Lancea Sanctum and Circle of the Crone in particular) could potentially destroy the site's power and wreak havoc on an entire area. In fact, vampiric urban legend perpetuates tales of ill-performed rites on a particularly powerful site, courtesy of covens of mortal wizards, Lupine shamans and satanic cults. Second, places of power are valuable resources, and when the Order possesses one, that is both an asset for itself and an asset denied to rivals. As counterpoint to this, the Ordo Dracul knows that many of the other covenants of Kindred would destroy such sites rather than let the Dragons make use of them, or at least make them bargain for access. Third, such mystical sites are always changing, and while they normally change over the course of years or decades, sometimes magic takes a great leap forward and the Order likes to know about such events as soon as possible. Finally, the covenant asserts that some sites are truly symbolic or spiritual and deserve protection from defilement as well as from simple destruction.

Guardians are usually those Dragons with a bent toward martial prowess and stealth. They are rarely prepared to end their unlives in pursuit of their duties, however. After all, nothing is permanent, and throwing away an unlife over something that might change in a mere 50 years is just foolish.

Kogaion

Every city with a significant Order presence has a pre-eminent Guardian known as a Kogaion. He protects the city's maps of ley lines and nexuses, the locations of its greatest mystical treasures (if not the treasures themselves), and a roster of all Dragons in the area. Most often, the Kogaion memorizes this information or records it in riddles, codes and dead languages to keep it from falling into enemy hands. The title itself seems to be of Thracian origin, meaning "the magnificent's head." A new Kogaion is elected only when an old one dies, steps down or becomes untrustworthy (and being declared untrustworthy requires a statement to that effect from at least seven other Kogaions). Being declared a Kogaion is one of the greatest honors of the covenant, but it also effectively cuts the vampire off from other members of the Order. Everyone respects the Kogaion, but since she is an obvious target for enemies of the covenant, no one wants to associate closely with her. Kogaions are frequently hermits, sought for consultation and advice but very rarely for long-term apprenticeships. Kogaions also tend to be frighteningly powerful with regard to the Coils of the Dragon… though some simply believe they are.

The Sworn of Dracula

Little is known of the Sworn — from the outside, they appear to be sub-factions or sub-covenants within the Ordo Dracul. A few Kindred suspect that the Sworn of Dracula number three distinct groups, each of which is associated with some higher branch of the Dragon's Tongue. Most vampires outside the covenant don't even know the names of the Sworn, though three distinct titles do seem to be consistent where the Order grows to any appreciable numbers: the Sworn of the Axe, the Sworn of the Mysteries and the Sworn of the Dying Light.

The Coils of the Dragon

Central to the Ordo Dracul is the philosophy of transcendence, the desire to rise above the limitations of the cursed vampiric form. Learning the Coils of the Dragon allows a Kindred to "cheat" certain aspects of the Requiem. For instance, a vampire might be able to slow his mystical metabolism, consuming less blood than normal when he rises each night. Another aspect of transcendence might allow a Kindred to slake his thirst on animal blood, no matter how potent his own blood is. By defeating these incarnations of vampirism, the Order believes it is on the right path toward eliminating or escaping vampirism entirely — with the goal of attaining the next level, whatever form that takes.

The Dragon's Tongue

A forked line of progression, the Dragon's Tongue is the structure through which covenant members progress as they learn more secrets and master greater aspects of their condition. While comprehension of the hierarchy by those outside the covenant is cloudy at best, it appears that all members follow a single path of progression up until a certain point, after which the member chooses a specialty to follow. Various members of the covenant lay claim to numerous titles, but whether these are actual functions and responsibilities or mere honorifics has yet to be ascertained by outsiders. The Dragon's Tongue is an oblique concept. It is distinct from the Coils of the Dragon, but knowing the Coils of the Dragon seems to be requisite for advancement in the Dragon's Tongue. In layman's terms, the

Dragon's Tongue seems to roughly equate to rank while the Coils of the Dragon are similar to capability or potential.

Finding the Wyrm's Nests

The world is constantly in flux, on levels that not even the Kindred can perceive. Long ago, the Ordo Dracul noticed that certain places hold magic better than others. These areas, variously called "nexuses," "holy sites" or "dragon nests" by different cultures, don't stay static. They migrate as flows in the mystical energies of the world push them. Likewise, new sites of power spring up every year. The Order has determined that many places that mortals consider haunted or cursed (or blessed) are simply the result of this energy being "washed" into a new locale. Every few years, then, the Dragons re-draw the mystical maps of the world, plotting sites and the current of mystic power toward them (sometimes called "ley lines"). This practice takes place over the course of weeks and months, normally beginning with the week preceding the winter solstice, as it gives the map-makers the most time to work. A certain amount of reverence, if not outright ritual, accompanies these mapping efforts. The mystical cartographers are treated with the utmost respect, and being sent to verify the existence of a nexus is considered something of an honor among the Order. It's generally accepted that any mystical artifacts discovered at such an investigation remain property of those who find them (after the covenant has a chance to catalog and examine them, of course).

Following the Dragon's Tail

A teaching technique that has become popular as mortal populations increase, Following the Dragon's Tail is meant to illustrate that no change happens in a vacuum.

The mentor accompanies her student on a hunt, and instructs her to kill one mortal in the course of feeding (not usually a problem, especially if the student has taken well to her studies). The mentor then instructs her to follow the innumerable chains of events that death causes. Who does the mortal leave behind? What does her obituary say? Does anyone mourn her? Who shows up at her funeral? Does a police investigation ensue? How much effort do the police put into it? Do other vampires become involved? Reportedly, the first Kindred of the Order to enact this lesson still follows the effects that the murder he committed had on mortal society… more than 200 years later. In less formal terms, a member of the Ordo Dracul said to be "following the dragon's tail" takes care of loose ends, or plots some scheme and attempts to predict results for every stage of the plan.

Honoring the Mentor

Not required, but certainly not discouraged, the practice of annually honoring one's superior(s) among the Ordo Dracul hierarchy has become commonplace. Every covenant member who chooses to partake in this custom has a different method of showing reverence, and of course it very much depends on the mentor in question. For some teachers, a gift (books, a favored type of vessel, an archeological find stolen from a museum) is best. For others, a demonstration of what the pupil has learned in the past year makes the best present. Coteries of Dragons who study under the same mentor sometimes collaborate on a way to honor their teacher… but just as often they compete to decide who can elicit the most appreciation from her.

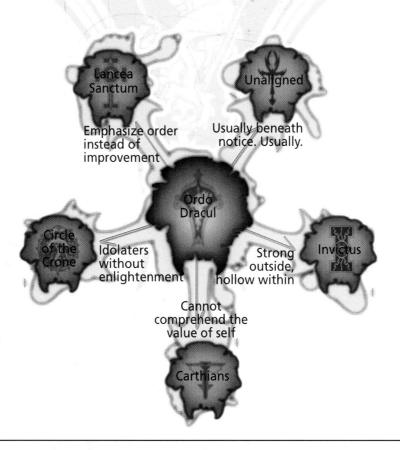

The Unaligned

When one hears a vampire refer to the existing Kindred order as the "despised aristocracy of the undead," the speaker is probably one of these free-thinking spirits — those whom the vampire world has dubbed somewhat misleadingly as one of the "unaligned" or "unbound." They are the rebels, outlaws and iconoclasts of vampire society, those who freely (and often intentionally) flout the so-called rule of the elders among their kind. Independent Kindred can also simply be apolitical vampires, those who acknowledge only their own authority but who don't necessarily make a grand show of defiance against Princes and Regents. There are as many reasons to renounce the entire notion of covenants as there are Kindred among the unbound, everything from paper-tiger rebellion to acknowledging no greater authority than the self to free will to downright bizarre mystic philosophies and even heresies.

The unaligned are fiercely independent, and many would sooner face the rising sun with a smile than spend eternity in submission before another creature of the night. While they do not truly compose a covenant, the unbound are often overlooked individually and considered in a collective rabble with others of their mindset, despite the fact that they have no shared organization. Still, enough commonalities occur that they can be discussed as a phenomenon, even if their status as a formal covenant is nonexistent. If a vampire disdains the prevailing governmental structure but doesn't belong to any structured covenant of her own, the rest of Kindred society almost always considers her one of the unaligned.

Overview

"Independent" Kindred resent or otherwise don't buy into the neofeudal establishment that is modern Kindred society. They've been around as long as any of the covenants, if for no other reason than by virtue of the fact that as long as there is a political movement going on, someone will oppose or take no interest in it. In nights past, some politically independent vampires were occasionally known as "anarchs" or "autarkis," a reference to their disregard for ironclad laws and orders among the Kindred. Those vampires cared nothing for the proclamations and decrees of heavy-handed Princes, and to a great extent, wished nothing more than to be left alone. In those nights, the unaligned were considered foolish, but ultimately harmless, as long as each individual member was smart enough not to jeopardize himself and his kind through his lawless actions.

The spread of an informal unbound sympathy would change all this. Many lawless, practically careless Kindred did much to shake up the world of vampire society in a very short time. Lines were blurred, boundaries crossed and dreadful decisions made, all in the name of independence from the established order, and that was the part that caused a stir. Although what passes for an unaligned "movement" has since settled down a bit (or at least retreated to the shadows of the domains in which such Kindred are found), the damage wrought upon the unbound was done. Tonight, more than a few elders among the covenants have taken the actions of particularly truculent unaligned as representative of the gestalt… or at least capitalized on the aftermath thereof in an attempt to clamp down on such rogues.

Members

Just as the Invictus is plainly attractive to elders, so too is unaligned existence a magnet for the young and downtrodden among the Kindred. Neonates make up the preponderance of the unbound, and new believers discover independent urges with every passing night. Many would-be unbound renounce their affiliations following eye-opening or humiliating experiences in one of the covenants. Sometimes this occurs early on, with a bitter neonate loudly claiming independence for succor and release. Other times, the taste for freedom attracts ancillae who tried for decades to play the vampiric political game but were simply outmaneuvered or disgusted by the toll it took on them over time. The independents probably see more "converts" than any of the covenants, which is yet another reason why these outcasts are often held in such low regard by the established covenants.

Although a great many unaligned Kindred are neonates or young ancillae, this is not to say that no elders renounce sectarian ways. A number of older Kindred, primarily those of the Mekhet and Gangrel, prize the unbound for their freedoms, and might even seek to turn their influence toward uniting local unbound under a common banner in hopes of forming a neo-covenant that advances their own agendas. In fact, these few manipulative elders are responsible for the hostile attitudes that certain cells of independents harbor toward more formalized groups of Kindred. This isn't to say that every elder goes independent in hopes of building a private army. Many elders among the unbound are quite content simply to ignore social strictures that they personally find distasteful. In the eyes of many "established"

Kindred, with elder power comes responsibility, and interpersonal pressures occasionally force into covenants those elders who would be more satisfied if they were freed from such duties.

Philosophy

The guiding philosophical principle behind the unaligned mindset is the fundamental conceit that every vampire — like every man — is free. Regardless of clan or age, no Kindred should be forced to bow like some lowly serf before the feet of a provincial undead governor. Not surprisingly, the unbound find the notion of vampiric titles and duties contemptible. They recognize no "Prince" to whom they should show self-effacing obeisance, and they regard the entire notion of formalized social debts as wholly unnecessary. Each of the Damned is, practically by definition, an individual, removed from the brotherhood of mankind and thrust into solitude for all eternity. The unaligned tend to feel that vampire-kind needs no phony system of forced indenture to make sure that each Kindred keeps his word and honors his promises. As alone as they are, vampires realize that all they truly have is their word — without the aid of unnatural and artificial hierarchy — and they act accordingly. Those who don't are weeded out naturally, and not by the arbitrary will of an elder.

This sole idea forms the approximate basis of the independent ideology, but like any solid foundation, it embodies itself in a number of night-to-night practical principles. These trends of the unbound mindset give individual Kindred a sense of self, while providing a necessary grounding in the realities of unlife.

Again, note that these aren't formalized codes of belief among the unbound. Each independent Kindred is her own Prince, or at least wishes to be. These are simply the most common points of agreement among a non-covenant of ruggedly individual vampires.

Vampiric Nature Is Solitary

To the unbound, the twin notions of freedom and individuality — as they pertain to vampiric existence — have their roots in the simple truth that vampires are solitary creatures. The soul of a Kindred is solitude. It is shut out from the world it knew before the Embrace and forced to survive the Requiem as a wolf among the flock, dipping in and out of the fringes of mortal society while never truly integrating with it.

The same applies to the new world into which a Kindred is thrust upon his Embrace. While many view vampire society as a sub-level resting beneath and within mortal society, the unaligned tend to reject this view on the whole. To them, the notion of a "vampire society" is a shamefully forced contrivance, a deliberate attempt by power-hungry elders to enforce structure and order where there is none. Vampires are bestial, undead predators. Forcing them to coexist under fabricated pretense is a recipe for disaster. Only by respecting the natural Kindred state — that of isolated, independent equality — can harmony be found among the Damned.

Power Corrupts

The unaligned are no fools (by and large). They tend to see how terribly power corrupts among the living. Compound the problem with undeath, literal bloodthirst and the prospect of an eternity of the same, and the result is disaster waiting to happen. The unbound can believe that the Kindred are the last creatures who should be in a position to wield great power over themselves, let alone over one another. They're called "the Damned" for a reason, and the Damned should not be leading the Damned. That's a caravan that can only travel straight to the gates of Hell, and the unbound know better than to fall into such an ill-fated line. Better that each vampire concern himself primarily with his own progress along his own road.

This is not to say that independent Kindred eschew power and influence. They are still vampires, and many feel that the only way to fight fire is with fire. Even those who don't can still appreciate the benefit of amassing great amounts of wealth or sway in various mortal circles. The important distinction is how and in what manner their power negatively affects those of their kind. Being aware of one's solitary nature does not mean pretending that other Kindred don't exist. This very mistake has earned more than one well-intentioned unbound her share of trouble. The trick is to learn how to balance the acquisition of power with the legitimate needs and desires of one's neighbors. And, of course, the acquisition of vampire-specific power and influence is considered dangerous ground among the unaligned, which is why many prefer to stick to mortal spheres of influence.

The Blood of Christ gave sight to my blind eyes.
Though Octavian cleft my tongue and pulled my teeth, I still bade him to abandon his idols.
I have been buried and returned; I have been stricken down yet returned to my feet.
If these are not miracles, what are they?
Yet if they are miracles, why does the Lord grant them to me, a vessel of sin?
— The Testament of Longinus

Belial's Brood

Not every covenant is as fully structured as the rest. Indeed, some covenants are local phenomena or simply too small to merit the elaborate systems that the larger ones have in place. With Belial's Brood, however, covenant law is unnecessary because, "Do as thou wilt shall be the whole of the law."

A loose confederation of Satanists, demon-worshippers and overt miscreants, Belial's Brood claims that the origin of the Damned is literally from Hell itself. Vampires are not their own unique species, they are "demons" given mortal form or devils who have found passage from the Pit's sulfurous depths to the surface of the world. The purpose of the Damned, in the opinion of this covenant, is to indulge the dark urges that the Beast imparts.

The Brood is truly a hellish faction of Kindred. Members exult in their wickedness, inflicting pain and misery with no remorse and even less discretion. While Belial's Brood is about, buildings burn, mortals die under overturned cars, and shocked victims covered in blood stagger down streets before collapsing. The Damned should be the Beast incarnate, they preach. Vampires serve none but the Devil himself!

Belial's Brood rarely survives long in any given domain. Its behavior is antithetical to the continued existence of the Kindred, both under literal and interpretative understandings of the Masquerade, so few Princes suffer its ilk to establish havens or stay in their demesnes. Even if Princes didn't rally entire domains against them, members of the Brood would probably bring their own Final Death about sooner rather than later. Their overt acts and blatant wickedness tend to earn them the attention of witch-hunters, mortal authorities and other groups who don't want the demoniacal murderers threatening them.

The truly remarkable aspect of Belial's Brood is that, even with all right-thinking Kindred efforts to stamp them out, the same Satanic ideology survives to take root elsewhere. Belial's Brood is seldom sophisticated enough to remain secret or hidden for long, and Princes who have destroyed cells to their last member are often surprised to see the phenomenon return a score of years later. The group's chaotic philosophy is too manic for the covenant to truly have a center anywhere, but if that's the case, how does the same sectarian philosophy keep resurfacing if the covenant's many enemies are so vigilant in rooting it out and destroying it?

C. Wilkins

VII

One "covenant" among the world of the undead has no name. Although this faction comprises vampires, those beings seem to hate all Kindred who are not part of their mysterious order, and literally attempt to destroy them on sight. The notion of this group as a covenant might even be mistaken, as it is unknown whether the group is a true covenant, its own insular clan or just a particularly zealous cult. "Seven," the name by which other Kindred recognize the sect, comes from occasional iconography that its vampires leave behind after particularly heinous or noteworthy attacks — the Roman numeral seven.

By all accounts, members of Seven are few, and not every city harbors their genocidal population. What they lack in numbers, however, they make up in fervor and burning hatred of the Kindred. A few of their organization have been captured by other vampires, and from their testimonials (most gleaned under pain of torture or through supernatural means), more than a few shuddersome details arise. Members of Seven reportedly do not suffer the same pangs of possible frenzy upon seeing other undead for the first time. They can, however, identify other vampires on sight, as they claim to be able to see "the mark of the Betrayer" upon the Kindred. Even the artificial understanding of the group's "name" is a murky translation at best. When asked under supernatural compulsion to speak the truth, these creatures cannot define what they are, and probes into their minds yield only mental images of the Roman numeral "VII" or a character from what seems to be an unknown alphabet that the vampire so questioned cannot properly explain.

C Wilkins

Despite the mysteries of their origins and purposes, one thing is certain: Members of Seven are fanatical in their drive to destroy other vampires. Seven believes it is the lost legacy of a king who was wronged centuries or even millennia ago, and that its purpose is to destroy the Damned. Only by removing the taint of the Kindred from the world can they achieve their "Sabbath," which they understand as the ability to reclaim that lost kingdom. Details differ. Some members believe that the kingdom shall emerge from a mystic curse, while others believe the kingdom is metaphorical, and they are the chosen workers of God's will to remove the scourge of the Kindred from the world. Without a doubt, Seven is made up of vampires. Its members consume blood just as do any other undead, and the true nature of their fanatical mission remains unknown.

Whatever the cause of its caustic hate for the Kindred is, Seven isn't stupid. It knows that the world at large sees no difference between it and its hated foes, so it practices what amounts to a Masquerade as well. It doesn't blindly leap into conflict if it feels it would be doomed — it chooses its fights carefully so that it can gain as many advantages as possible. Given its relatively small numbers, overt conflict with groups of Kindred is rare, but not unheard of. Assassinations, murders and stealth tactics are more suited to the covenant's capabilities, but considering Seven to comprise nothing but fiendish skulkers sorely underestimates its abilities. Too many Kindred have met their end at the claws of a coterie of Seven after thinking the killers destroyed.

Kindred Mythology

Undying, blood-drinking predators with abilities that defy the laws of science as mortals know them, the Kindred are creatures of myth, legend and folklore. Most mortals would undoubtedly be surprised, then, to learn that vampires themselves have their own myths and legends. That, in fact, the greater portion of Kindred history is known only in the blurred and distorted form of myth. Mortal civilization by and large understands its past far better than the Kindred do their own.

It seems illogical, at first glance. The Kindred are, for all intents and purposes, undying. Surely, some of them experienced these historical events firsthand. Mortals must rely on written records and archaeological evidence to piece together bits of the past, but it should be possible for the Kindred to simply ask someone who was there. Shouldn't it?

No. As the Kindred age, they find they need far more potent blood to survive, until they can finally feed only on other vampires. This inevitably drives the Kindred into torpor, either voluntarily, with the intention of slumbering long enough for the blood to thin, or involuntarily, due to simple lack of available sustenance.

During torpor, the Kindred dream. Whether it is due to some mystical link through the Blood that connects all the undead, or something inherent in the vampiric mind, all Kindred tend to experience similar dreams. That is, they experience all they have done and all they have seen over and over again. The images continue, unending, inescapable — and ever-changing. The Kindred dream of events past, but never see them exactly as they were. At the end of a mere two or three decades in torpor, a vampire has a slightly skewed memory of his entire Requiem. After centuries of slumber, an elder's memory might bear little more than a coincidental resemblance to historical fact.

This means that for every Kindred who witnessed an event firsthand, there exists a slightly (or not so slightly) warped accounting of that event. No single Kindred can possibly know the entire truth of a specific era or occurrence. Nor can outside investigation ever piece together the actual truth from many different events, as each Kindred is absolutely certain that his version of events is the correct one and is highly unlikely to accept anyone else's as more accurate.

The Kindred must therefore turn to mythology, ancient beliefs and written records passed down through the ages and generations, even as mortal writings have been. Some of these records contain elements confirming the memories of many elders, sufficient commonalities to suggest that at least some of those memories are partially accurate, as with the beginnings of vampiric society in Rome. Others come from times and places that no modern vampire can claim to have witnessed, thus forming the only surviving record. As to whether they should be believed, well, only the most shamelessly naïve individual would hope that the Kindred might ever come to universal accord on that score.

These ancient texts are essentially the basis for various Kindred religions or at least creation myths, as the Bible, the Koran and others form the basis for many human faiths, and are exceptionally difficult for some Kindred to accept. The Kindred relationship with faith is an odd one. Their existence serves as sufficient proof, at least to most of them, that something must exist beyond the realms of science. Most vampires do believe that, yes, some sort of God or higher power must exist. To attribute to Him an innate benevolence and sense of order, however, as most religions do, is something else entirely. Few vampires truly accept what they are, or even the very existence of their race. Can this be the work of a kindly deity, one who wants only what's best for His creations? Many Kindred believe in God, in some form or fashion. Not so many of them consider Him worth worshipping, however.

Consider as well the inherently deceptive and manipulative nature of the Kindred. Rare is the vampire who hasn't made lying and deceit a common practice. So what if *The Testament of Longinus* says this is true, that is not, and that the Kindred should behave thus? *Rites of the Dragon* says the exact opposite. Who's to say who actually wrote any book that puts forth an origin for the Damned? The Kindred have nothing but the word of other Kindred to trace any rumor or writing back to a given source. Few Kindred accept even the most minute piece of information at face value if it was given them by another vampire. Why should something so major as the origins, beliefs and even purposes of their race be any different? Of course, as with many things in the Requiem, the final arbiter is the Blood itself, which enforces the Traditions more thoroughly and efficiently than any institution ever could.

Thus are the majority of Kindred divided into distinct camps. The Lancea Sanctum and its long-time partner in the post-Roman alliance, the Invictus, believe that *The Testament of Longinus* represents the truth, or at least a good approximation of it, and the Sanctified modify their behavior and religious beliefs accordingly. (It must be said, however, that the Invictus pays these beliefs lip service at best when they come into conflict with members' own interests. Most of the time Invictus Kindred seem not to care at all.) The Ordo Dracul has its own writ, *Rites of the Dragon*, that, while it doesn't rule out the possibility of the Longinus theory, certainly doesn't require it to make its own position valid. The Circle of the Crone rarely bothers with formal works of vampiric origin, relying instead on oral traditions far older than either the Sanctified's or the Dragons'. Others reject such postulation on the origins of their kind as utterly meaningless, fiction or propaganda penned by manipulative elders for their own inscrutable purposes. Very few vampires fall into the middle ground. As a whole, Kindred tend to either believe strongly in one myth or none at all.

Mythology, Faith and Kindred Behavior

The faith espoused by Kindred who do find one of the many theories particularly poignant or resonant is so prevalent that it has spawned many of the vampire laws, acknowledged and obeyed even by those who don't accept a given philosophy's dogma as gospel. For instance, the three formal Traditions by which almost all Kindred society operates are mandated and spelled out in (purportedly) Longinus' own words as well as those of the now-defunct Camarilla. Many local traditions are also inspired, though less directly, by passages from the *Testament*. (See p. 74 for more on the Traditions.) The Masquerade in particular is often touted as a prime example of Longinus' wisdom and foresight. His followers maintain that if the progenitor could foresee the need for the Kindred to hide from mortals, even back when the living did not outnumber the undead to nearly the extent they do now, then surely his other commandments are equally wise.

On the other hand, many regional groups of the Circle of the Crone draw precepts from cultures and mythologies that existed long before the Crucifixion, or entirely independently of it. Their own theologies have developed concurrently with the same limitations of the Kindred form that members of the Lancea Sanctum experience. To their mind, even if Longinus did exist, his only claim to fame was setting his commentary down in written form, not explaining the genesis of the Kindred.

Likewise, the Ordo Dracul doesn't deny the Longinus theory but rather corroborates it, if its own creation myth is true. If Dracula's entrance to the Kindred world happened without a sire, so could Longinus'—and so could that of anyone before them whose name or deeds the Kindred themselves do not remember.

Further muddying Kindred's proof of origin are the clans. Whence did they take their names? Who were their progenitors? Did they all hail from the same place, or did they arise independently, mingling only in the relatively recent memory of a world that is far older than anyone suspects? Clans obviously predate the covenants, but do they all hail from the same period?

These questions have no answers, of course, just like those seeking the origins of the Kindred themselves. None of the matter is eminently provable — or so it has been to date. Certainly Kindred with faith, drive or the burning desire to *know* ceaselessly research the origins of their kind. Hidden temples in forgotten lands, domains older than history acknowledges, abandoned havens beneath cities ruined long ago. All of these and more house relics that have the potential to answer the ultimate question of why the Kindred exist. Then again, they may simply engender a different question… or perhaps the answer was never meant to be known.

Reasons and Rationale

The Lancea Sanctum, of course, is the most closely and obviously linked to the creation story of a messianic founder. Members of the covenant usually interpret *The Testament of Longinus* in its most literal sense, and Sanctified Priests often carry copies of passages, if not the entire text itself, for conducting rituals. The covenant's warriors often quote from *The Testament of Longinus* before (or even during) battle, enhancing their reputation among the other factions as fervent champions.

The Invictus' interpretation of its origin is less rigid but no less important to the covenant. The elders of the First Estate use frequent passages from *The Testament of Longinus* — references to rule by eldest, accomplishments of some clans over others, and the like — to justify their position as leaders of the Kindred community. It is nothing less than divine right that they rule their domains and will eventually rule others. It is unlikely that few believe in this canon with any degree of true faith, but faith certainly was the hallmark of the era from which more than a few elders hail, and belief in a higher power answers many questions that an unnatural, deathless existence provokes.

The Carthians (and, to some degree, independent Kindred) often share a somewhat cynical interpretation of the origin of the species. Namely, that it is a tool used by those in power to oppress those who are not. This isn't to say that no members of the covenant believe in a creation myth, or that they don't believe in it devoutly. A great many of them do. They simply believe that the Kindred can't necessarily explain who the first vampire was, or that even if a single Kindred proved the origin of the species, it came as a result of divine intervention. Longinus most likely did not even scribe "his" book itself, and even if he did, systems of order that worked at the dawn of civilization are simply inapplicable to the modern world. They point to various other mythologies, particularly those upheld by local Acolytes, and their own inapplicability to the modern state of the world, as proof that the Kindred cannot afford to remain static and must change with the times despite their inherently unchanging natures.

The Circle of the Crone, naturally, goes its own way in an almost limitless number of old mythologies and new amalgamations of existing and new ones. *The Testament of Longinus* is little more than a corruption of the older ways, much as the Church adopted pagan rites and observances into its own body of holy days. In covenant members' eyes, the abuse and impious invocation of *whatever* faith they choose to invoke is a travesty perpetrated upon the Kindred by blasphemous elders. They cannot ignore the faiths or philosophies of other Kindred, for they have shaped so much of Kindred society, but many consider them the epitome of everything that's wrong with Kindred both past and present. Other Kindred believe that vampires have existed since Creation, that they were part of God's plan from the beginning. More shamanistic or even necromantic vampires often believe that the first Kindred were spirits of the dead who, due either to hostile sorceries or some sort of spiritual turmoil, could not depart their bodies after death.

For the Ordo Dracul, the question represents both power and limitation. Many of the mysteries mastered by the covenant certainly have their echoes in the times reflected in the various creation myths, but the group as a whole is a bit more secular than many of its counterparts. The Coils of the Dragon and Order philosophy don't rely on passages from any document, much less one that requires supplication to a power higher than the self. All mythologies contain their share of wisdom, true, but in an era of miracles performed by creatures as mysterious as the Kindred, who's to take any account purportedly written by any of them at face value? *Rites of the Dragon* can be taken literally or figuratively, and the result is still the same.

Of course, groups far smaller than the great covenants shape themselves according to the precepts of the largest of their kind. Just as all religions have their factions and cults, so too do the Kindred divide themselves further still. Some vampires, fanatics even among the Lancea Sanctum, spend every waking moment behaving only as they believe the *Testament* commands them to, accepting its authority even over that of the local Prince or Archbishop, or even insisting that Longinus was the first vampire, historical evidence to the contrary. Many Invictus vampires, for whom religion would otherwise be a minor concern at best, congregate with those who share their interpretations of convenient philosophies as a means of finding common ground among potential allies. Some religious groups, often derided as doomsday cults by other Kindred, are drawn together solely by their belief that the ancient Kindred progenitors will arise some night and destroy the Kindred race. Of course, no evidence exists to indicate that such an event will ever occur, let alone that it might happen soon. Most Kindred tend to view these covenants with much the same exasperated disdain that the average mortal views people carrying "The End Is Extremely Fucking Nigh!" signs on street corners.

Still others are determined to find some sort of scientific rationale for the existence of the Kindred. These last are normally found among fairly young Kindred, and many shift from such a belief system when they finally accept what they are and what they can do.

Coteries, factions, clans, covenants (at least on a local level) and even entire domains often ally with, or oppose, other such groups based solely on religious doctrine. These disagreements rarely erupt into open conflict, but when they do, they are no less fanatical and no less violent than any religious wars among mortals.

It's important to note, at this point, that most Kindred mythology is not a replacement for religion, but rather an addition. Acolyte mythologies add to or adapt from extant pantheons observed by mortal cultures. Those Kindred who honor Longinus as an object lesson also believe in the God of the Abrahamic religion. Kindred are usually observant of their own faiths and philosophies as well as Buddhist, Christian, Hindu or Muslim beliefs, rather than instead of.

Golconda

One concept that appears only briefly in both *Rites of the Dragon* and *The Testament of Longinus*, but more frequently in other texts (including the *Rakta Veda* and *The Cycle of Demeter*) is the notion of Golconda. According to myth, Golconda is something of a vampiric state of enlightenment, in which a Kindred perfectly balances the needs of the Beast and his Hunger with his conscious mind. A Kindred in Golconda does not frenzy, does not succumb to Rötschreck, and can even access abilities that are normally available only to vampires of surpassingly potent blood. Some legends even suggest that a vampire who attains Golconda can become mortal once again. The specific details have not and probably could not ever be set down, because Golconda, as a state of being, is not only rare, it's unique to those who achieve it. The exact effects of this higher state of vampiric existence likely vary from one vampire to the next.

Few Kindred tonight believe in Golconda, considering it at worst a myth or mistranslation, and at best an indicator of how religious Kindred should conduct themselves, as opposed to an actual goal to be achieved. Still, a select few Kindred strive to find this legendary perfect state of balance, seeing in it the promise of redemption, or at least escape from an eternity of need — a state of being that certainly sounds an awful lot like redemption.

To those who see beyond the pleasant-seeming connotations of Golconda, a frightening consideration lies beneath the surface. A vampire in this state doesn't necessarily become "nice." Indeed, almost the opposite might be true. A vampire who achieves Golconda might well be one of the most fearsome creatures another Kindred could hope to meet, as her soul is in a perfect state of balance *with regard to vampirism*. Golconda

might not be a state of natural serenity, but could instead elevate one to the status of a consummate predator. In nature, a wolf and shark are both in tune with what they are, and a creature with more cognitive ability than these killing machines might be more terror than saint.

PROPHETS AND ORACLES

No discussion of vampire mythology would be complete without a mention of a particular group of Kindred occultists, scholars and prophets who might be little more than myth.

They are called the Moirai and are said to be a bloodline unto themselves, though from which clan they might descend is open to serious speculation. (Common mythology ascribes their lineage to either the Mekhet or the Daeva, but more obscure legends link them to other clans, or even to a Kindred familial group now long forgotten.)

It is said that the Moirai have somehow kept records from before the nights of Christ, that they have found some way to resist the dreams of torpor and have maintained their elders' memories of ages past. They possess hidden libraries of occult lore to arouse the envy of any Mekhet or Dragon. And strangest of all, it is said they have the gift of prophecy and oracular vision. They know not merely the past, but also the present and future of every Kindred to walk the Earth. Supposedly far more common in ages past, they were deemed mad by other vampires due to their visions and prophecies, and allegedly exterminated. Indeed, few Kindred awake tonight earnestly claim to have knowingly met anyone of this mysterious bloodline, and most vampires consider them long gone or a myth that never existed at all.

And yet, some Kindred maintain that the Moirai were true prophets. Surely they would have seen their own end coming, and surely they would have taken steps to hide themselves away, where none could ever find them....

The Traditions

Vampire society, such as it is, would have fallen under its own weight long ago were it not for the ties that bind it together. Like any society, the Kindred world survives on the rules established and agreed upon by its residents. Vampire "laws" are even more essential to the society they concern because of the nature of that society. The Kindred are manipulative killers whose mutual survival depends on their ability to get along well enough to remain sufficiently hidden from the eyes of their prey. As conservative covenants are fond of saying, lawlessness among the undead is perhaps the greatest threat facing the Kindred tonight.

As a result, the Kindred have a body of vampire laws known as the Traditions. The three most important of these laws are curiously universal, given that no common origin story is accepted for the Kindred. They are immutable rules of the Blood, passed down as liquid truth by way of the curse of undeath, and are hardwired into the very physiology of the Damned. Upon the Embrace, each Kindred knows each of these laws intuitively.

Beyond the Traditions are the less official, more fallible customs that arise within Kindred society over time. After weathering centuries upon centuries of at least nominal adherence, a few of these customs have become unofficial traditions of their own. Some of these latter-day laws are provincial in outlook or unique to a particular clan or region, while others are observed only within a particular covenant of Kindred. Three of them in particular are considered nearly as important as the Traditions themselves, but without the fundamental connection. They merely serve to further gird and bolster society as the Kindred know it. Each of the Traditions gave rise to one such custom, and each is discussed after the relevant law.

A great many of the Kindred take the Traditions to heart. Others justify them beyond "That's how things have always been," while still others accept them blindly as part of the Kindred condition. Kindred who have studied such things often suggest that though these physiological conditions have existed for as long as the Kindred themselves have, the actual wording of the Traditions as they are understood tonight was one of the efforts of the now-defunct Camarilla. This is the most widely accepted theory. Particularly fervent members of the Lancea Sanctum, unsurprisingly, sometimes claim that the actual codification of these customs is part of Longinus' original dogma. Other scriptural, quasi-religious or philosophical wordings also exist, such as those held by the members of the hoary Circle of the Crone and the Ordo Dracul, but the core ideas of the Traditions remain unchanged. True "heretics" against the laws of all Kindred were few and far between in the early nights of the Damned. Despite their differences (and they had many), most of the Kindred were in agreement about what was and was not a good idea for their kind, especially when their own bodies told them it was so. They might disagree on theory or implementation, or even on basic precepts, but few argued with the wisdom of such incontrovertible laws.

THE FIRST TRADITION: MASQUERADE

Do not reveal your true nature to those not of the Blood. Doing so forfeits you your claim to the Blood.

THE SECOND TRADITION: PROGENY

Sire another at the peril of both yourself and your progeny. If you create a childe, the weight is your own to bear.

THE THIRD TRADITION: AMARANTH

You are forbidden from devouring the heartsblood of another of your kind. If you violate this commandment, the Beast calls to your own Blood.

The First Tradition

Arguably the single most important aspect of Kindred society worldwide is the first Tradition: that of the Masquerade. Without it, the existence of vampires among the Canaille would quickly come to light, putting the unlife of the entire race in jeopardy. Given Kindred feeding habits, the world of mortals would never understand or permit their continued presence. It would be a pogrom the likes of which has not been since the fiery nights of the Spanish Inquisition, when mortal witch-hunters first proved how unity and faith were a match for even the undead.

Before the dawn of the modern era, this Tradition was significantly less enforced, and in some cases, even scoffed at by the more haughty (and foolish) among the undead. Vampires of old could freely roam their demesnes, flaunting their damnation before the terrified mortals who huddled in the dark at their feet. No phones existed with which the kine could call for help, with nobody to call even if there were. Once upon a time, the Damned truly were lords of the night.

But it is a different time now, a different world. Mortals could not run in fear of the predators among them forever. As the living world grew and advanced, the world of the undead shrank. Tonight, it is a small world, indeed, for the Damned — but only from the outside. Although the planet itself is largely unchanged, the mortals upon it are smarter, more advanced and more numerous than ever before. And now, the advent of the Internet and wireless communication has brought each mortal that much closer to the rest, putting the entire Masquerade at risk with but the touch of a button. The Damned, as powerful as they are, have never been so exposed or vulnerable.

Given this precarious state of affairs, breaching the Masquerade is usually viewed as one of the most grievous transgressions one of the Kindred can commit. Depending on the Prince, more damaging breaches can be viewed as grounds for the Final Death of the transgressor, and a number of Princes have amassed no small amount of notoriety for their unwavering enforcement of this rule. This, then, has become a source of heated debate in Kindred circles, due to the subjective nature of such determinations. Some Princes are not above using the Masquerade as justification for the removal of political opponents, and those who displease a Prince must be careful about how they act in public and what company they keep.

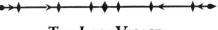

THE LOST VISAGE

Despite the terrible fate that would befall the Kindred were their existence to be uncovered, the Masquerade continues to hold fast. Part of the reason lies in the fact that the Curse itself has given the Damned a means by which they can better uphold the Masquerade (and, thus, hide themselves from mortal scrutiny). Upon receiving the Embrace, a fledgling vampire's reflection begins to fade away. After rising for the third night in a row as a vampire, the change is complete, resulting in a sort of blurry occlusion of the Kindred's image in any reflective surface or medium. Therefore, vampires' features do not appear in photographs or on video (though vocal recordings are unaffected). Kindred can counteract this aspect of the Curse through an effort of will (which "solidifies" their image in any reflective surface), but the effect usually lasts only for a brief duration. A vampire's visage may be filmed or recorded during this time, but in most cases, the image will blur immediately thereafter. The potency of a Kindred's blood seems to factor into just how long his image remains on photographic media, with less robust Vitae indicating a longer duration. Exceptions do occur every now and then, but Kindred scholars are at a loss to explain why or under what circumstances they'll repeat.

Domain

Another long-standing tradition is the right of domain. In nights past, when they were more spread out than they are now, Kindred staked claims to vast amounts of territory. When disputes arose, the results were often bloody, as the undead squabbled with one another over slights both real and perceived. Over time, civility demanded that the notion of domain become a universally respected aspect of Kindred society. Vampires needed to come to some basic accord, if for no other reason than to avoid infighting and unnecessary destruction of their fellows. The accord that was reached (informally and over time) was the right of domain.

According to the tradition, a vampire may claim a given area — one that is not already under the purview of another Kindred — as his personal domain. Within that domain, his word is law among the undead, and he can expect not to be challenged. If another vampire wishes to stake a claim to some part or all of the domain, he must either negotiate the terms under which the owner will cede control or else take the entire domain by force. This situation was the norm for centuries upon centuries of Kindred existence, and though it, too, often led to infighting and kinslaying, the custom itself was largely respected.

Come the modern era, the old ways have seen a significant pattern shift. As the Kindred huddle together in increasingly more claustrophobic environs, the concept of domain has split and polarized into two extremes. Tonight, the Kindred recognize only two definitions of domain (as per the traditional sense). First, there is the notion of domain in the larger sense; the domain of a Prince, for example, which generally includes one city or metropolitan area. The Prince is the final arbiter of all issues arising within this area, including who will and will not receive feeding grounds and official protection. Within the larger domain, however, exists the smaller "individual" domain, the modern remnant of the old ways. Each vampire's personal haven benefits, as per custom, from the protections established by this tradition. Therefore, even though a given Kindred's haven may be situated within the larger domain of the Prince, that Kindred might still invoke the customary protections of tradition. A vampire's home is his castle — even if that castle sits on the lands of a powerful elder liege. Only in the most savage domains will a Prince attempt to claim one of his subjects' personal havens once those havens have been granted and established.

The Second Tradition

The Second Tradition is the one that causes perhaps the most debate, confusion and consternation among the Kindred.

According to the wording of the Tradition, no vampire may create a childe. And yet, look how many Kindred exist! It is, perhaps, the greatest paradox of the Kindred as a species (at least to those who keep faith with the Traditions).

The Kindred world cannot even agree as to the origins of the Tradition itself. To this very night, no satisfactory answer has been put forth to the simple question of, "Why?" If whatever figure responsible for the creation of the undead was so adamant about ensuring the earthly lack of propagation of the Damned, why did it create one itself and give it the ability to propagate? Many speculate that the first Kindred, cursed to forever walk the night alone, grew lonely, as all creatures do, and that he took for himself a mate, as many creatures do. Some maintain that it is this mate, the world's second vampire, who betrayed his or her sire's wishes and created the first actual brood of the Damned. Some consider this first brood to be the true progenitors of the modern Kindred. In most cases, those who believe in various origin stories yield the principle that God (in whatever form) intended for the first Kindred to suffer in solitude, a lesson the Damned have had to learn through betrayal and loss.

Whatever the Tradition's origins are, the fact remains that its message has been corrupted in the time since. While few Kindred would deny that it is wrong (or at least complicated) to perpetuate the race of the Damned, many take issue with how the Tradition is enforced tonight. Many among the unbound (and a few members of formal covenants) believe that the Curse itself is enough to limit the numbers of new undead in the world, naturally and without need of politics or hierarchy. For their part, the Carthians generally take the stance that the issue should be one for the entirety of Kindred society to debate and decide upon, rather than be the purview of an outdated Tradition. Naturally, some in the Invictus believe in the right of the "elder" of a domain to decide upon such matters, and the Sanctified point to key passages of *The Testament of Longinus* as proof of their claims. The Order of the Dragon sometimes Embraces for the sake of bestowing its secrets upon an apprentice in order to perpetuate its knowledge. Of all the Kindred, followers of the Circle of the Crone are perhaps the most defiant of the Tradition, and are occasionally known to create new childer as part of their sacred beliefs.

THE SHAKEN WILL

Every time one of the Kindred plans to create a childe, he intends to willfully violate one of the understood commandments of the Damned. Like the Masquerade, this edict is an aspect of the Kindred condition, and it cannot be summarily ignored by vampires. The act of damning another to undeath is a strain on the Kindred soul, requiring the sire to invest a significant amount of will over the course of the Embrace.

Tutelage

A societal by-product of the Second Tradition, the tradition of tutelage has its roots in antiquity, when the Kindred's numbers were fewer and the social system more rigid. In such times, if a vampire was going to violate Kindred physiology by propagating the numbers of the Damned, he was expected to make sure that his progeny understood all the rules and customs of the Requiem (not the least of which was the Second Tradition, itself). Siring progeny is merely the bestowal of responsibility, granting one vampire the right to take a considerable burden upon his own shoulders. Until such time as the new vampire is released from his sire's tutelage, his education (or miseducation) is the responsibility of the sire. There is no "village" among the Damned. It takes an individual to raise a neonate, and any mistakes the young one makes until he reaches the time at which his sire releases him need not be forgiven by society at large. Otherwise, what would be the point of releasing him in the first place? This same rationale is often abused by controlling sires as justification for the excessive periods of indenture or servitude they require of their progeny: "I can keep you safe only as long as I don't release you." Needless to say, some childer would rather take their chances with the Prince.

From the moment of his release, a childe's sins are his own to endure. No ill may befall the sire as a result of the childe's deeds (except in a looser social sense). As such, the childe no longer benefits from the sire's protection, at least not in any official societal capacity. He is his own Kindred and must stand as such. Such, however, is also the benefit of release. Once a childe is on his own, he is no longer beholden to the whim, desire or name of his sire. For good or ill, he is now free.

The Third Tradition

Given the predatory and deceitful nature of the Kindred, the third and final "commandment" — the prohibition against the diablerie of other Kindred — is the one most often violated and warped to serve the interests of the individual. Indeed, this single law has been the cause of more controversy in and around the halls of power than any other, and its interpretation and administration are two of the most fiercely contested issues facing the Damned tonight.

As with the Second Tradition, the phrasing of this tradition is the primary cause of complaint, as well as the primary justification for use and abuse. Many believe that the original intent of the law was to give sires the right and responsibility to destroy the childer they had made (in violation of the Second Tradition) when those childer ran afoul of those same Traditions. Destruction, however, does not necessarily entail the consumption of the destroyed Kindred's soul. Those who destroy their enemies utterly often claim to drink their fallen foes' essence "to be sure" that those enemies never return, though this practice is at once primitive and false, at least in the context of modern Kindred society.

Mortal death is both inevitable and necessary, but only God Himself may judge those He has cursed. Therefore, the Kindred condition inhibits the finality of diablerie in all its forms. According to some versions of *The Testament of Longinus*, Longinus' final words to the collected brood he left behind were a simple but sobering warning: "Teach your progeny to heed my word, and tell them to likewise teach their own. When my line can no longer contain the blood it spills — the night the broods of your broods can no longer hear their brothers'

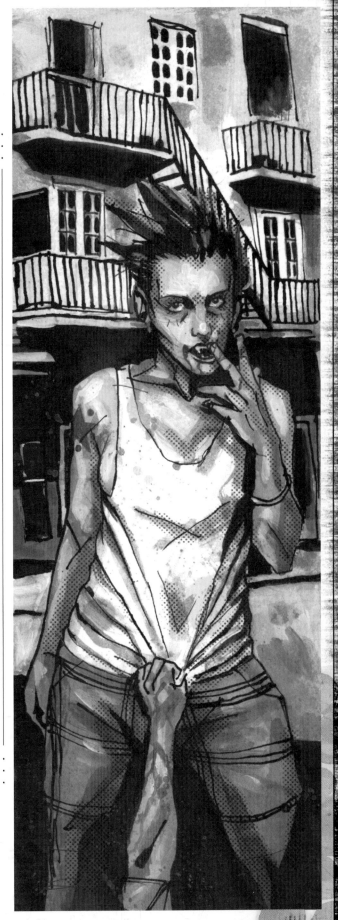

heartsblood cry unto them from the ground — that is the night when all hope for you is lost."

As a parenthetical result of this passage, many Kindred use the words of the *Testament* as support for the custom of the Lextalionis — the blood hunt in modern parlance. These Princes claim the title of "elder" mentioned in the text and use it to invoke the "right" of destruction upon any Kindred who sufficiently rouses their ire. They rarely perform the deed themselves, of course, for the act itself is damaging to the spiritual strength of a vampire. Thus has the custom of involving every Kindred in the domain in the hunt arisen (rather conveniently) over time. In many domains, all Kindred are expected to do their part in consummating a blood hunt.

THE LOST *HUMANITAS*

As with the first two Traditions, the Third Tradition is thoroughly hardwired into the psyche of all Kindred. In fact, most Kindred agree that the prohibition against diablerie is one of the most fundamental aspects of being Damned, due to the steep toll exacted on all those who violate it. Each time a vampire consumes the soul of another vampire, his morality erodes significantly. The corrosion of the self is automatic, as with cold-blooded murder it is assumed that the killer feels no immediate remorse about the act. (If he did, he wouldn't have committed it.)

Deference

A natural outgrowth of this tradition is the custom of vampiric respect. When the race as a whole endeavored to bring itself up from savagery with the notion of domain (and the rights granted therefrom), the next step was to ingrain the idea that every aspect of the existence of Kindred domains must be respected. From this effort arose the notion that a vampire should present himself whenever he travels into the domain of another vampire. After all, one doesn't really respect the tradition of domain if one hunts on another's land without permission. One doesn't have to actively challenge the rightful claim of another vampire in order to disrespect both the domain and its owner.

Of course, even this seemingly well-intentioned tradition has its controversy. Modern Princes invoke this code as a means by which to keep track of who is and who is not within their demesnes at all times, by asking that each visitor or would-be resident present himself upon entering. Once the visitor does, the Prince either acknowledges him — in which case he may remain in the domain (under the Prince's protection) — or refuses to acknowledge him — in which case, he is expected to depart the domain at his earliest possible convenience and sometimes sooner. As a result, it is this tradition that has come to be ignored the most by young Kindred, many of whom don't even know of its existence (usually because they were not properly educated after their Embrace).

One of the most common reasons for these violations is the gray area that defines visitors and would-be residents. Kindred who just pass through often feel no obligation to stop just so they can potentially put themselves at risk by coming before the local Prince. Only those who intend to remain for any length of time are required to present themselves, and some feel that it is up to personal interpretation just what a "length of time" might involve. Some Princes have been known to specify a duration (in terms of nights), so that there is no confusion when the Prince's Scourge or Sheriff brings newcomers forward for questioning. As a result, this practice tends to complicate already complex social dynamics while further widening the gulf between elder and neonate.

Technically, this tradition applies to only those who intend to hunt within a domain. If a vampire can establish that he'll not be a drain on the domain's resources (by demonstrating access to a private blood supply, for example), then he could argue that the tradition doesn't apply to him on any practical level and that presentation before the Prince is merely a social courtesy. Obviously, this situation does not arise very often, and when it does, most Princes aren't thrilled with the idea of being snubbed by the letter of the law. To them, it is better to just present one's case during rather than instead of presentation.

For a less formal interpretation of the tradition of deference, see "Presentation" on p. 32.

THE MARK OF DAMNATION

Many wonder about the true nature of the Curse, given the way the Traditions interact with it. The Traditions are tied so closely to the vampiric condition that each one actually carries with it a physiological expression. The Tradition of the Masquerade is reflected in the fact that no Kindred appears in any recording device or reflective surface unless he wishes to be seen that way. The Second Tradition, the prohibition against the profligate creation of vampires, manifests in the difficulty with which vampires create new progeny. A considerable investiture of personal will and energy is required to even consider violating the decree.

Perhaps most interestingly, however, is the third restriction, the Tradition prohibiting the destruction of another Kindred with the intent of consuming his heartsblood and soul. Unlike the physiology of the first two Traditions, which are preventive in nature, the true weight and message of the third manifests only after it has been violated. Some suspect that the prohibition is tied to the divine or diabolical origin of the Kindred. Obviously, the element of personal choice remains for the undead. By the same token, removing the onus of a decision to kill from vampires would, some might argue, defeat the purpose of vampires in the first place. Historical accounts of vampires, even among the Kindred, depict them as cursed for the terrible and selfish decisions they have made.

No, the Third Tradition's power manifests after a vampire has already made the choice to engage in diablerie, the Kindred's name for this act. Upon consuming the soul of another vampire, one's own sense of moral control — the spiritual compass that keeps a being from falling to his Beast — wavers considerably. He is not pained by the experience, and indeed, he might even relish the newfound "freedom" he sees in no longer being as restrained in his behavior and outlook as he once was. But this illusion is the nature of the Curse. The vampire has made his choice, and by forcing him to regret that choice, the higher power responsible for vampires would encourage the idea that personal choice was not the issue's crux.

To this night, many believe that the telltale black streaks in a diablerist's aura do not come from any lingering effect the victim's heartsblood may have on the killer's soul, but are rather a spiritual reflection of the mark of damnation. Due to the First Tradition, vampires cannot be branded upon the forehead or otherwise visibly marked for their crime. No, it is a far more secret and subtle mark that exposes them to their brethren for the monstrosities they truly are.

The Blood Hunt

Sometimes, when a Kindred outlaw is considered too dangerous to be allowed to survive, and the Prince's own agents prove unequal to the task of locating and capturing or executing the criminal, the Prince is forced to resort to the ancient Kindred tradition of Lextalionis, the law of justice stating that those who violate the laws must die, and all Kindred of a domain are responsible for carrying that sentence out. This results in the blood hunt, when all (or at least most) Kindred of a domain set out to locate and destroy a specific quarry.

Only the Prince or other city leaders can formally call a blood hunt (though some Primogen or Prisci have the political strength to do so over the Prince's head). Other elders occasionally attempt to call a hunt, with greater or lesser success. The blood hunt is a powerful political tool, and a vampire must have matching influence to use it. If the Kindred evoking Lextalionis has sufficient clout or personal power that local vampires will respond, and he can do so without the Prince coming down on him, he may call the hunt. If he doesn't, he often won't survive to repeat his impertinence, nor will many of those who answer his call.

Failing to participate in a blood hunt, particularly one called by a Prince, is not normally a crime, except in the most extreme circumstances, but it frequently results in a loss of status in the eyes of the court. Actively aiding and abetting a subject is a crime, however, and it can result in banishment or execution.

The Masquerade is still paramount during a blood hunt, of course. Indeed, the Kindred spread out across the city in something not unlike a police dragnet, coordinating their efforts (at least officially) with the Sheriff or other representative of the Prince. The hunters converge on suspected sightings, and things often get quite messy if and when the quarry is finally run to ground. The hunt is rarely carried out openly, with Kindred racing down the streets leading barking dogs, guns held aloft. While some Princes prefer to retrieve the subject intact, most blood hunts contain a provision stating that no participating Kindred will be charged or punished if the subject is slain or, in the case of truly dangerous criminals or truly desperate Princes, even diablerized. In this fashion, the Prince skirts the issue of the Third Tradition — after all, he himself is hardly guilty of diablerie if a subject carries it out.

The Kindred use all the tools at their disposal when engaging in a blood hunt, including influence in the mortal world. Police might put out an APB on the subject, he might find himself on "no fly" lists at airports, and his financial accounts might be frozen. In recent nights, some Kindred have begun using the Amber Alert system — a coordinated barrage of radio announcements and electronic roadside signs intended to alert the public to a kidnapping or missing child — as a means of slowing a fugitive's escape. A few truly powerful (or foolish) Kindred even use connections in the local religious community to attract Church-sponsored vampire-hunters, which is an exceedingly risky move.

Ultimately, very few criminals ever escape a blood hunt unscathed. They are either tracked down and slain or manage to flee the city, which is often a death sentence in and of itself.

Technically, a Prince is not supposed to call a blood hunt for personal reasons, only when a truly heinous lawbreaker is on the loose. Some Princes are better about following this tradition than others, and a few of the most dictatorial ones actually use the hunt as a means of squashing dissent. Sure, it flies in the face of tradition, but who are the Kindred going to complain to? That said, some Princes have found the calling of an unnecessary blood hunt to be the spark that finally triggers revolution among their subjects, so even the most tyrannical Kindred ruler doesn't invoke the Lextalionis lightly.

Very rarely, if a fugitive is considered an enemy of a specific covenant, a blood hunt might extend to more than once city. For instance, all the Invictus-dominant cities in a specific area might exchange information via email and phone in an attempt to run a criminal to ground. For the most part, however, a blood hunt is strictly a local thing, and no hunt that has expanded beyond the borders of a single domain has ever lasted more than a few nights. Multiple cities simply cannot maintain cooperation for longer than that, especially since each Prince has her own issues to deal with, the wishes of her covenant notwithstanding.

Strains of the Requiem

These overarching concerns of the Kindred condition aside, the world of the Damned is complex even in the minutiae. Whether or not an issue involves Kindred from one Prince's domain to the next is not the question. Myriad small concerns potentially face every vampire from the moment she rises at nightfall.

Slaves to the Blood

It's a simple, fundamental fact that no vampire, however determined or powerful, can escape: The Blood is all. It defines everything the Kindred are, and ultimately everything they do. It also defines many of their relations with mortals and the Kindred around them.

Vessels

By its most basic definition, a vessel is simply a source of Vitae. The vast majority of the time, Kindred use the term to refer to mortals, but those elder Kindred who can feed only on the blood of other vampires use it to refer to undead fodder as well. Mortal vessels are often called "Licks" by young Kindred.

As much as the Kindred might prefer to deny it, vessels are often far more than merely a covered dish. The act of feeding is extremely intimate, perhaps the most intimate experience either participant will ever have. For the subject, the vampire's Kiss brings exquisite pleasure, comparable to or even greater than the pinnacle of sexual release. Some mortals become literally addicted to the experience and — if they can ever piece together precisely what happened through hazy memories and the cloak of the Masquerade — they even seek out vampires, or the particular Kindred who fed on them, in hopes of repeating it. For the undead, the act of feeding is the sum total of who and what they are, the very purpose for which they exist. Mortals simply cannot comprehend the need the Kindred feel, and thus cannot imagine the satisfaction, relief and release the Kindred experience in fulfilling that need.

Thus, while some are able to separate the experience from the individual, many Kindred become emotionally attached to their vessels. They return to the same specific people over and over, growing ever closer to them. Sometimes, if the individual is properly cooperative, this behavior can result in the formation of a herd, but it's also dangerous, as it increases the vampire's risk of exposure. These Kindred are often extremely protective of their stock, even to the point of challenging anyone else, mortal or vampire, who threatens them.

Herds

A herd is a group of vessels, usually but not always mortals, from whom a vampire can feed regularly with no (or at least minimal) difficulty. A herd might be a group in the literal sense of the word, an assembly of Licks who gather for whatever reason. It might be a religious cult that worships the Kindred as an angel, members of a bondage club who consider biting and blood drinking kinky, or any other assembly in which the Kindred can hide or pass off her activities. On the other hand, a vampire's herd might be scattered farther abroad, consisting of multiple unconnected but willing vessels across the city. Some herds might not involve people at all, instead being composed of multiple accessible animals. Some Kindred even consider access to stores of donated Vitae in blood banks or hospitals to be part of their herd in the loosest sense.

Not all Kindred have herds, but those who do find it much easier to hunt. Few vampires have herds so large that they can afford to feed from them all the time, so most hunt anyway, but it's always good to have them available to fall back on when one is in a hurry or otherwise unable to hunt. As with lone vessels, many Kindred develop a reciprocal attachment to members of their herd, due to the emotional power of the Kiss.

Thralls and Regnants

Kindred society treats thralls differently depending on the domain. In some cities, elders use their thralls as proxies, and a thrall is considered to speak with her master's voice at court and on other matters of import. In other domains, thralls are messengers and pawns but are not permitted to wield any of their domitor's authority. In some particularly dictatorial domains, Kindred are not even permitted to subject one another to the Vinculum without the Prince's permission (though secret trysts and abuses of the system surely occur). In any event, a regnant is held responsible for the activities of his thrall and may be punished along with the thrall if the servant misbehaves.

Ghouls

Far more common than Kindred thralls are mortal ghouls, kine who have been imbued with the mystic power of Kindred Vitae. In mortals, the blood of a vampire spawns not merely the artificial love represented by the Vinculum, but also substantial physical strength and stamina. The ghoul does not age as long as at least some Kindred blood remains in her system, and old or strong-willed ghouls can even develop some other Kindred Disciplines beyond brawn and hardiness.

Ghouls are quite common in some Kindred domains, and are often considered essential servants. A vampire might choose a ghoul for a specific skill or position the mortal possesses, or he might select a mortal simply out of some obsessed affection. Kindred use their ghouls as messengers, bodyguards, soldiers, proxies at court, fronts through which they can influence mortal institutions, butlers, drivers, menservants, travel planners and daytime security — potentially anything the Kindred himself cannot or would prefer not to do himself. Given the quantities of blood ghouls require to maintain their abilities, most vampires have only one or two such servants, and only a very rare few Kindred can maintain more than a handful. As with Kindred thralls, some ghouls bitterly resent the tasks they are forced to perform, but few have the willpower to protest, let alone rebel.

Rumors suggest that some few ghouls do manage to escape their bonds, whether through the Final Death of their masters or by other means. These ghouls typically become rogues, seeking out vampires from whom they can acquire blood. These ghouls serve adopted Kindred briefly and then depart for greener pastures, or physically assault vampires for their precious Vitae. Rogue ghouls are sufficiently rare that most Kindred never worry about them — many doubt they even exist — but when they find occasion to travel in groups, they *can* be dangerous to lone neonates or even elders who aren't prepared to deal with them. A handful of ghouls sometimes find themselves subjected to a Vinculum by a subsequent vampire, but many don't, either becoming true rogues on their own, or meeting their end in the process of seeking "unattached" blood to support their ghoul states.

Regions and Territories

The average Kindred domain is not a single, monogamous entity. As cities have districts and neighborhoods, so too do the Kindred divvy up their domains into smaller regions. Many of these divisions are entirely artificial or political in nature, but that makes them no less real, and the petty lord of a tiny territory granted her by the Prince might punish trespassers or violators more strictly than does the Prince himself.

The Barrens

The Barrens are those areas of the city unfit for or otherwise absent of human habitation — and, by extension, Kindred habitation. These regions include industrial wastelands, certain abandoned buildings, graveyards and the like. Some truly desperate Kindred hunt the Barrens, hoping to encounter the occasional homeless person or lost tourist. For the most part, however, "beating the Barrens" is an expression that has come to mean that a Kindred is horribly down on her luck and attempts desperate and largely doomed measures.

Some Princes have been known to grant the Barrens to other Kindred as personal feeding grounds as a form of public chastisement for wrongdoings that were unworthy of more serious punishment. More than just a humiliation, this "award" can lead to worse problems for the unfortunate Kindred down the road. As lord of the Barrens, she is now responsible for everything that goes wrong there — and as the Barrens attract only those Kindred in desperate straits, things go wrong with remarkable frequency.

The Rack

The opposite of the Barrens, the Rack is that portion (or those portions) of a domain most suitable for hunting. It includes bars, nightclubs, high-crime neighborhoods, crack houses, brothels, homeless shelters — basically, any place where the kine are distracted or discomposed, where strange behavior can be hidden or passed off, and where mortals go missing on a frequent basis. Hunting the Rack is nearly effortless, and any "accidents" are easily disposed of. Many Kindred treat the Rack as fine restaurant or wine cellar, where they can go if they seek a particular "vintage" of Vitae. Sooner or later, all sorts of Licks pass through the Rack.

In those domains where the Prince parcels out feeding grounds, elders are in constant competition for the right to the Rack. Most Princes refuse to grant anyone exclusive rights to the Rack, preferring to make it available to the entire city. Others keep such feeding rights for themselves, demanding favors from any who would hunt there. Still others choose to offer portions of the Rack as territory to favored allies, granting them substantial power among lesser Kindred.

Because the Rack attracts so many Kindred, and because vampires are at their least alert when feeding, many potential Masquerade breaches occur there. The very nature of the region often covers such violations naturally — people expect odd behavior from meth-heads, for instance — but wise Princes and Sheriffs have eyes and ears in the Rack at all times. These agents watch for any breaches to stop them before they occur, or move swiftly to cover them up.

Feeding Grounds

As rewards for service, or bribes to those whose power the Prince wishes to either exploit or mitigate, many Princes grant portions of their city to other Kindred. In these territories, only the "landholder" is permitted to hunt. She may, of course, grant permission to hunt to anyone she chooses, but those who poach in her territory are considered criminals. Most Princes demand that any such lawbreakers be brought before them, but some permit a landowner to levy her own punishment. Needless to say, this is rarely a good thing for the poachers.

Hunting rights over a particular region do not necessarily convey any additional political power. In practical terms, however, many Kindred parlay control over territory into a web of substantial influence. Obviously, if a vampire holds title to an unimportant area, there's not much he can do with it. On the other hand, a Kindred who holds the rights to a portion of the Rack, or an area of town where many vampires make their havens, has considerable influence. She can demand favors or tasks in exchange for permission to feed in her territory, and many Kindred agree if the price is worth the privilege.

Security

Given the precarious nature of the Kindred in the scope of the World of Darkness, the issue of security is paramount. While the tacit arrangement among all Kindred addresses some of this concern, a great deal more remains. After all, no such arrangement, tacit or otherwise, exists between the Kindred and the natural world around them. Indeed, it can be said that the greatest threats to the security of the Damned come not from the Danse Macabre, but from the realms of the ordinary, the routine and the mundane.

The Damnable Hunt

As powerful as they are, the Kindred play a most dangerous game. It is their lot to hunt among the kine, to prey on and feed from the mortal world. Yet they must also realize that they are not always as wolves among a flock of sheep, but are often as jackals among a pack of wild dogs. The individual dog is (usually) no match for the scavenging jackal, but should the entire pack turn its attentions toward the predator in its midst….

Such is the case with the Kindred among the kine. If the eye of Man was to turn its baleful stare upon the monsters skulking in the shadows, the resulting pogrom would very likely wipe the Damned from the face of the Earth. Therefore, in this most dangerous game, the most powerful assets in Kindred hands are the complementary tools known as ignorance and belief. These weapons do more to keep vampires safe than any combination of unholy powers ever could.

In the world of the kine, ignorance truly is bliss. In the world of the Kindred, it is power. The bid to keep humanity at large ignorant of vampire existence is known as the First Tradition, the Masquerade. The Kindred condition itself mandates that this must be the single most important goal of the race, lest discovery shatter the existence of mortal and Kindred alike. Whoever created vampires clearly intended for the Damned to be a part of the world, but that entity also clearly intended for them to remain forever separate from those upon whom they prey. Such is the nature of the Requiem. And so, each scion of the Kindred line endeavors to make sure that mortal ignorance remains a top priority of unlife.

The flip side of this, and the weapon that helps the Kindred ensure continued ignorance, is belief and the nature thereof. Ironically, it was belief that nearly spelled doom for the Kindred during the burning times of the Inquisition, but not long thereafter arrived the Age of Reason (and the subsequent Industrial Revolution), which turned belief itself into the very tool with which the Kindred might reinforce the Masquerade. By cultivating belief in logic, science and reason, the Kindred subtly support humankind's weaning itself from belief in the supernatural. In the modern era, the mortal world views the existence of the undead as an unthinkable notion. Vampires are things of fancy — big-screen entertainment or novel fare, at best, and the ramblings of frightened children or pathetic lunatics, at worst. And why? Belief in reason has stolen from them the capacity to fathom even the possibility of the existence of the undead.

Despite these brilliant campaigns, however, despite all the considerable resources devoted to maintaining the Masquerade worldwide, mistakes happen. Even vampires get sloppy on occasion, and when they do, the results are nasty. Sometimes it's a careless feeding error. A slip of the mind, where a vampire forgets to lick a wound he's made, thereby beginning the chain reaction of curiosity leading to investigation leading to action. These occasions, while certainly not desirable, are often at least manageable given the resources of many Kindred domains. But sometimes a careless error leaves witnesses — mortal witnesses — and in almost every case, it leaves such witnesses with two of the most damning banes of the undead: hatred and a little knowledge.

Arising from "mistakes" such as these is the phenomenon known as witch-hunters. Whether by accident, Kindred error or simple mortal moxie, these ordinary men and women take up the struggle to beat back the darkness to which their minds have been exposed. For whatever reason, they're onto the Kindred and they mean business.

These individuals, often known simply as "hunters," are often more dangerous to the undead than anything else. As mortals in a mortal world, they're under no compunction to remain hidden themselves (except from the eyes of certain authorities who might not understand their calling). Unlike werewolves or other supernatural creatures, hunters need be concerned only with the hunt, and that gives them a distinct advantage in a shadow conflict such as this. In addition, hunters can move by day, and they aren't nearly so restricted in their activity cycles as are the creatures they hunt.

As might be expected, the Kindred don't take too kindly to finding themselves on the reverse end of the predator-prey scenario. Most are taken by surprise, as they have grown accustomed to being the ones to startle mortal prey with savage revelations before the moment of consummation. Indeed, some vampires are so taken aback that they never have a chance to recover from the shock — all it takes is one well-aimed strike, even against a vampire. Those who survive their initial encounter with a hunter (or group of hunters) often descend into panic, unless they've experienced such a situation before. The first thought to race into a vampire's head is, "Do they know the location of my haven?" Until there is a satisfactory answer, that question continues to occupy his mind, while awake and asleep.

The other danger that hunters pose is that they can organize, often in a disturbingly short amount of time. A single hunter created after one encounter with the Damned might lead an entire cell of well-informed, well-equipped vampire-hunters after six months. To the Kindred mind, which remains static and patient as the years wear on, this nearly ant-like level of cooperation and efficiency is startling.

Kindred in a World of Darkness

Despite the fervent wish of some to the contrary, the Kindred have more with which to be concerned than their fellow Damned. The World of Darkness might be the consummate nesting ground for the Kindred, but it is hardly a private paradise. The world contains much that would trouble a vampire, including the likes of other supernatural creatures, mortal witch-hunters and even time itself. If the World of Darkness is a home to the Kindred, then it is a home they must share grudgingly and cautiously with horrors both internal and external.

Cellmates in the Gilded Cage

The fact of the matter is, most Kindred with more than a few years behind them are aware that the undead are not alone in the world. An equal fact is that most of them care only as much as they absolutely have to. Vampires are damned creatures, most of whom have an eternity's worth of problems to sort out, on top of the night-to-night struggle of continued existence. As any Prince can attest, maintaining the Masquerade is a full-time job, and any activity that unduly jeopardizes the success of that endeavor is either a waste of time, far too great a risk to Kindred society, or both.

As a result, even the most erudite Ordo Dracul scholar knows better than to preoccupy himself with the affairs of other supernatural beings. Study? Yes, where possible. But prying into the activities of creatures who are known for their savagery is considered unwise by all but the most powerful of Kindred. Given this mindset (on both sides, as best the Kindred can figure), a sort of détente has been reached over time, a tenuous understanding that amounts to a universal wariness of the other supernatural denizens of the World of Darkness. By and large, the Kindred know that there are angry, shapeshifting beasts out there. They've even given them a name — Lupines. But they don't really want to know a whole lot more than that, because once they open that door, the next step is to go inside.

The same applies to the wonder-makers, the ones the scholars call mages. What little the Kindred have seen of these enigmatic beings has scared them enough to recognize that discretion is the better part of valor. No one knows the full extent of these beings' powers, motivations or capabilities, and finding out the hard way is just, well… reckless. Sure, rumors of mortals calling down sunshine at midnight are probably just that, but what if they're not? What if some Kindred actually saw one of these mages ignite a member of his coterie like a piece of kindling? In that case, would a vampire actually want to pursue the matter further? If mages don't actively come after the Kindred (and most of them probably don't), then the Kindred are bound — by common sense, if nothing else — to return the favor. By and large, Kindred know very little about such creatures, and until something gives them reason to worry, they're content to leave well enough alone.

Exceptions exist, of course. Every now and then, a vampire sets up shop in the wrong part of town and irritates existing occupants, with predictably unpleasant results. Likewise, a werewolf or mage might decide to dip his toe into a domain that a particular Kindred has claimed as his own private sphere of influence. In these cases, conflict is likely inevitable, but more often than not, both sides know better than to let a true blood feud ensue. What usually happens is that once the initial matter has been settled (whether by peaceable means or by someone's demise), the case is closed. Those most likely to violate this arrangement are the Lupines, whose pack mentality demands restitution on occasion, but even they tend to stop short of all-out war against the entire race to which the offender belonged. No, the supernatural denizens of the World of Darkness are significantly (and perhaps surprisingly) more realistic about the nature of conflict than are the mortals who surround them.

Learned Kindred also know that werewolves and wizards are not the only creatures with whom the undead share the night. Certain Kindred are known for trafficking with the spirits of the restless dead, though they remain tight-lipped about the hows and wherefores of it. These beings (ghosts, if they must be given a title) surely know of the Kindred, but only the mediums themselves can say with any surety what feelings, if any, the dead have toward the undead. Upon learning of the existence of the restless, some concerned Kindred grow obsessed with them, eager to discover just what makes one soul pass on to its final reward but forces another to stay behind. (Surely no earthly crime deserves such punishment, so some Kindred say.) Alas, the curiosity of such individuals is rarely if ever satisfied, as few necromancers are known for their open discourse.

And then come rumors of even stranger cohabitants amid the Kindred's strange land. Sorcerous vampires tell of eldritch beings from the hoary host of Hell itself — demons, with whom no sane Kindred would ever knowingly interact. Most believe such tales to be nothing more than the Order of the Dragon's macabre sense of humor, an attempt on the part of one damned race to terrify its kin by means of an even more damned race. If so, the irony is lost on most Kindred, who would just as soon prefer the Dragons stopped talking about it. All the same, stories surface with just enough regularity to be generally disconcerting about entities to whom Kindred can go for assistance, if the conviction is strong enough. Creatures who carry the promise of power, prestige and anything else one desires.

Although all of these entities (and more) are known to vampires, it is important to note that the Kindred don't truly understood any of them. Vampires are an insular, self-absorbed lot, and most are too preoccupied with their own schemes, fears and apprehensions to even be put in a position where they might glean some true understanding of these other creatures. No, most undead are content to adhere to their ordained role as participants in the Danse Macabre, moving to the somber sounds of their own private Requiems.

The secret world of the Damned commands its own entire subculture, and this subculture includes language. In addition to the various proper names and titles that exist only among the undead, a complete lingual set of vampire-specific words and phrases has arisen over time, resulting in a sort of Kindred "dialect." Like all language, this dialect grew and expanded, resulting in the eventual break-off of another, more modern style of speech. These two vampire dialects are referred to as "old form" and "common parlance." A third vocabulary, the language of the Kindred "street," is new to most everyone and is considered vulgar by all but the most brash of neonates. Being creatures of stasis, the Kindred loathe unnecessary change, and one can often tell the age if not the vampiric origins of a speaker by the way in which he uses the terms of his kind.

The following terms are used freely and frequently by both neonates and those elder Kindred familiar with vernacular (or who wish to disguise their true age). Some of the newer words have come into circulation only in the last few years, but due to their utility or style, they are not considered vulgar argot. The common parlance lexicon includes a pronunciation guide for its uncommon vocabulary.

Acolytes: A common nickname for members of the Circle of the Crone.

Ancilla (an • SILL • uh): Kindred too old to be considered neonates, but not yet elders, whose Requiem has lasted roughly 50 to 150 years. (The plural term is ancillae (an • SILL • ae).)

ancient: The rare vampire who has existed for over a millennium.

Avus (AY • vuss): A character's "grandfather" or patron in a bloodline from which she is not truly descended. (See p. 256.)

Barrens: Portions of the city unfit even for hunting.

Beast: The inchoate urges that drive vampires away from the *Man*.

Belial's Brood: A raucous, reckless covenant of vampiric Satanists.

blood hunt: A citywide hunt for a particular Kindred fugitive, in which most if not all local Kindred are expected to participate.

bloodline: A group of vampires that splits off from a parent clan to form a distinct lineage of its own. Some bloodlines do not differ from the parent clan in significant ways, while others claim different powers or weaknesses.

Carthian (KAR • thee • enn): A vampiric idealist, one who believes in reconciling the Requiem with the politics and society of modern mortals.

childe (CHILD): Kindred "offspring"; also used to refer to particularly young neonates, or as a minor insult (akin to calling someone a "child" in mortal circles). The plural is childer (CHILL • der).

clan: One of five families of Kindred whose lineage links back to times beyond Kindred memory.

Circle of the Crone: A covenant of ritualistic Kindred that reveres pagan gods, spirits, pantheons and/or progenitors.

Coils of the Dragon: A mystic way of learning that allows vampires to ignore certain aspects of their curse, as practiced by the Ordo Dracul.

coterie: A group of allied Kindred.

covenant: A faction of Kindred who share certain political and theological beliefs. The covenants exist worldwide, though details often differ from domain to domain.

Crúac (KREW • ack): The bloody, witchcraft-like magic practiced by the Circle of the Crone.

Daeva (DAY • vuh) : A clan of vampires known for being emotional, sensual and desirable.

Damned, the: The race of Kindred; vampires.

Danse Macabre: The state of eternal infighting between and among the Kindred of different clans, covenants and age distinctions.

diablerie (dee • AHB • ler • ee): Kindred "cannibalism"; draining another vampire of not only his blood but his soul.

Disciplines: The preternatural abilities and edges the Kindred possess, allowing them to vanish, turn into bats and perform myriad other inhuman feats.

domain: A region ruled (ostensibly) by a single Kindred authority. The largest domains correspond to cities and often contain smaller domains within them.

Dragons: A common nickname for members of the Ordo Dracul.

elder: A vampire who has survived for over 150 years; also a term of respect.

Elysium (ell • ISS • ee • um): A location used for Kindred gatherings and declared a neutral, "no violence" sanctuary by the Prince.

Embrace: The act of turning a mortal into a vampire.

Final Death: A Kindred's real, true, ultimate death; when her unlife ceases and she never again rises as a vampire.

First Estate: A common nickname for the Invictus.

frenzy: A berserk state in which the Beast takes total control over a vampire. Rage, fear and hunger can induce frenzies; when precision is needed, the term is qualified by cause (rage frenzy, fear frenzy or hunger frenzy) or by a special term (*Rötschreck* or *Wassail*). Unqualified, the term generally indicates rage frenzy.

Gangrel (GANG • grell): A clan of vampires known for being primal, hardy and savage.

ghoul: A mortal fed Kindred Vitae and possessed of various supernatural abilities, though far weaker than most vampires.

Harpy: A Kindred in a position prominent or estimable enough to raise up or put down others in vampire society.

haven: A vampire's residence; where one finds sanctuary from the sun.

Herald: A spokesman for the Prince.

herd: A collection of mortals from whom a vampire feeds regularly.

Hound: A personal agent of the Prince; assassin, leg-breaker, capo.

Invictus (in • VICK • tuss): One of the largest of the Kindred covenants, which believes in rule by a vampiric "elite" made up mostly of elders.

Kindred: The modern (and most frequent) term by which vampires refer to themselves and their race.

kine: A term for mortals; the phrase "Kindred and kine" refers to everyone.

Kiss: Both the act of biting and taking blood from a mortal, as well as the pleasure it provides both participants.

Lancea Sanctum (LAN • kay • uh SANK • toom): A covenant of vampires, made up of vampiric religious zealots who honor the Roman centurion Longinus, whom they have adopted as a form of "patron saint" for the act of testing Christ's divinity.

Lupine: A werewolf.

Man, the: The humanity a vampire maintains (or tries to); the spark of mortality that distinguishes him from the *Beast*.

Masquerade: The efforts and system of laws required by the Tradition of Secrecy to hide Kindred existence from the mortal world.

Master of Elysium: The Kindred responsible for places of Elysium, who also makes sure that everything is prepared, that nobody fights and that word gets out about events.

Mekhet (MEK • et): A clan of vampires known for being quick, discreet and wise.

neonate (NEE • oh • nate): A young vampire, engaged in his Requiem for less than 50 years.

Nosferatu (noss • fur • AH • too): A vampire clan known for being stealthy, strong and terrifying.

Ordo Dracul (OR • dough drah • KOOL): A covenant of vampires known for its mystic studies and desire to transcend the vampiric condition.

poacher: One who feeds in another Kindred's domain without permission.

Primogen (PRIM • oh • jen): An elder who advises the Prince of a domain (also plural).

Prince: The ruler of, or most powerful Kindred in, a domain.

Priscus (PRISS • kuss): The informal "head" of a specific clan within a domain. The plural is Prisci (PRISS • key).

Rack: The best parts of the city in which to feed, including nightclubs and other loud, crowded areas.

regnant: The Kindred who holds regency over a thrall; the dominant member of a Vinculum. Also "domitor."

Requiem: The Kindred condition; the whole miserable, cursed song of a vampire's unlife, whether singularly or metaphorically.

revenant: A vampire who has lost all Humanity and exists in perpetual frenzy.

Sanctified: A common nickname for members of the Lancea Sanctum, singular and plural.

Seneschal: The Prince's right hand and assistant.

Seven: A clan, covenant or other group of vampires that detests the Kindred race and seeks to destroy it, its own members excepted.

Sheriff: The Kindred responsible for enforcing the Prince's laws and dictates.

sire: A vampiric "parent," one who has Embraced a childe; alternatively, a verb, meaning "to Embrace."

Theban (THEE • ben) Sorcery: A mysterious form of blood magic practiced primarily by members of the Lancea Sanctum.

thrall: One who is bound to a regnant; the enslaved member of a Vinculum.

torpor: A death-like sleep into which Kindred fall if they are injured severely or starved for too long. Kindred can also enter torpor willingly to escape the world for a time.

Traditions: The three primary Kindred laws, passed down through the ages and observed inviolate due to the Kindred condition.

unbound: A vampire who refuses to accept the local rule of a Prince or other governing Kindred body. Also known as an unaligned or independent Kindred.

Ventrue (VENN • true): A clan of vampires known for being regal, commanding and aristocratic.

vessel: Any source of blood for the Kindred to feed on; usually but not always used to refer to a mortal.

Vitae (VIE • tay): Blood, particularly the blood of a vampire.

Vinculum (VIN • cue • lum): The artificial love and loyalty spawned by feeding from the same vampire three times. Also known less formally as a *blood bond*.

Whip: One who keeps his clanmates in line in order that they be taken seriously.

witch-hunter: A mortal who seeks out Kindred and destroys them.

Old Form

The following terms have been in circulation for as long as most elders can remember, and they are still considered the "proper" usage for the ideas they describe.

abactor: Literally, a "cattle thief;" a *poacher*.

Amaranth: Diablerie; the act of consuming another Kindred's blood and soul.

anarch: Historically, a Kindred rebel who opposed vampiric tyranny. Some anarchs sought to tear down the feudal systems of Kindred society in nights past, but many merely wished to be left to their own devices. Arguably the forerunners of the modern unbound.

blood oath: The *Vinculum*.

caitiff: A vampire of unknown clan. Usage: *Am I to understand that this caitiff is truly a Nosferatu of Wellington's brood? How could I not have guessed?*

Canaille: The masses of humanity, especially the uncultured or unsavory. Typically connotes a reference to sources of sustenance.

cauchemar: A vampire who feeds solely on sleeping victims.

cockalorum: A loud-mouthed iconoclast, or any weak vampire who acts the big shot.

comprador: A vampire who works for some other creature, such as a mage or even a mortal organization willing to uphold the Masquerade; also indicates the reverse (a supernaturally awakened creature in the service of a vampire).

consanguineous: Literally, "of the same blood," especially regarding lineage. Usage: *That vampire is consanguineous with the Ventrue Prince.*

co-sanguineous: Being brothers in the Blood; sharing the same sire. Usage: *We're rumored to be co-sanguineous but my sire is actually Maxwell, whereas his is not.*

cunctator: A Kindred who avoids killing whenever feeding from mortals.

draugr: The term for *revenants* in antiquity; still widely used by some Gangrel.

fief: A domain; still the favored term among many Ventrue, even numerous young ones.

footpad: One who feeds from vagrants, derelicts and other dregs of society.

fledgling: A neonate; a newly created vampire under his sire's protection.

gallant: A vampire who feeds from other vampires out of necessity or perversion.

gentry: The collective group of Kindred who prefer to prey at nightclubs, bars and other "red-light district" establishments.

Golconda: A fabled state of complete oneness with the vampiric condition; the true comprehension of both Beast and Man within a vampire's soul, wherein balance can be found. Rumored to be similar to mortal Nirvana, Golconda is only very rarely achieved.

inceptor: The founder of a new Discipline, a new bloodline or both. Such feats carry some measure of prestige among the Kindred.

Leech: A mortal who drinks vampire blood but acknowledges no regnant.

Lextalionis: The tradition of the blood hunt.

lineage: A vampire's bloodline; one's sire and the line of sires before him.

Osiris: A vampire who builds a mortal cult following around himself, as a means by which he can better feed or influence the mortal world.

Papillon: The red-light district; an area of a city that is punctuated by bars, whorehouses, gambling casinos and other places of debauchery. Also refers to a city's prime hunting grounds, where mortal disappearances go largely unnoticed.

praxis: The right of Princes to govern; one's claim to domain. Can also refer to a Prince's matter of policy or individual edicts.

retainer: Any individual who serves a vampiric master (whether under thrall or not). The term hails from a time when many vampires kept large estates with entire entourages of servants.

Rötschreck: The "Red Fear"; a fear frenzy, usually instigated by the presence of fire.

siren: A female vampire who seduces mortals in order to feed from but not kill them.

Suspire: The rumored moment of epiphany a vampire experiences just before attaining (or failing to attain) Golconda.

Wassail: Hunger frenzy, during which a vampire seeks to feed until sated.

whelp: Derogatory term for a young Kindred, originally used in reference to one's own progeny.

whig: Contemptuous term for a vampire who retains interest in mortal trends.

The newest of terms, those rising out of the grime and crime of the modern-gothic streets, reflect both the times and the attitudes of tonight's brash neonates.

alleycat: A vampire with no permanent haven, who sleeps in a different place each day. Also refers to one who feeds exclusively from the homeless.

banking: The practice of "withdrawing" blood from blood banks and hospital reserves. Such refrigerated blood has very little taste, but it provides some small nourishment nonetheless. Banking is frowned upon by older or more refined Kindred.

blister: A vampire "Typhoid Mary" who contracts a mortal disease and spreads it to the vessels upon whom she feeds.

blood doll: A mortal who freely gives blood to a vampire, gaining a perverse satisfaction from the Kiss and actively seeking out vampires to give it to them.

butterfly: A Kindred who mingles among mortal high society and prefers to feed from the rich and famous.

Casanova: A vampire who seduces mortals to feed but does not kill them. Most prefer to erase the memory of their presence from their vessels' minds, if possible.

Change: The moment a person ceases to be mortal and becomes a Kindred.

Cleaver: A vampire who tries to maintain the illusion of a human family life.

donor: Sarcastic term for a vessel, typically a mortal.

farmer: Derogatory term for vampires who prefer to feed from animals alone.

head: A vampire who feeds on drug or alcohol-laced blood. Those with a fondness for specific drugs have their preference added as a prefix (e.g., crackhead, pothead, smackhead).

headhunter: A Kindred who hunts and feeds on other vampires.

juice: Human blood, often modified by a descriptor, usually one indicating either the origin of the blood or some chemical within the blood (e.g., "cranberry juice" indicates Irish blood, while "happy juice" is mortal blood laced with stimulants).

juicebag: Contemptuous term for mortals.

Lick: A mortal, especially one from whom a vampire feeds.

lush: One who feeds regularly from drugged or drunk mortals to experience the euphoria or inebriation in the blood.

pedigree: A sarcastic term for *lineage*, typically used to make fun of another vampire's Kindred family tree (or the self-importance drawn therefrom).

rake: The newest euphemism for *gentry*; a habitual visitor to the *Rack*.

ripper: Modern term for a revenant, based upon the condition in which such creatures typically leave their victims.

sandman: A *cauchemar*.

slumming: The practice of feeding from derelicts and other dregs of society.

tease: A *siren*.

turf: Modern term used in reference to a domain; can also refer to the area under one gang or coterie's influence.

I shall sleep but not rest. I gird myself for battle, not of the body, but of the mind. As I lie in torpor I shall duel my weaker selves, I shall kill any memory that makes me less than I ought to be, less than I need to be, less than the greatest of my kind.
— Rites of the Dragon

Chapter Two: Character

Were I a pagan bard, I would invoke a muse of fire to fill me

with passion for the task ahead. I would beg a god

to put his words in me, to blow his wisdom through me

like a trumpet, to make me resound with truth for the people.

I am no pagan bard. My enemy is fire,

and I am more likely to rebuke my passions

than to bid them spill forth.

What am I? I have been a tyrant, a warrior

and one of the fallen on battle's field. I have been a Christian and

a wanderer and an enemy of God. I have begged and murdered,

tortured and rescued, pledged loyalty and given treachery.

I have died and returned and I drink hot blood.

My name is Vladislaus, onetime Prince of Wallachia,

onetime commander of armies. Called Tepes,

called Kazîglu Bey, called Dracula,

I am now much more than once I was. Perhaps much less, as well.

— Rites of the Dragon

Methoughts a legion of foul fiends
Environed me, and howled in mine ears

— William Shakespeare, *Richard III*

Now that you're familiar with the setting of the Kindred's World of Darkness, it's time to take a look at the traits and systems that bring vampires to vital unlife. This chapter details the systems by which you create your character to participate in stories and chronicles. It also includes information on the five clans from which all vampires claim descent. Finally, it thoroughly explains Disciplines, the supernatural powers upon which vampires can call to aid them in their Requiems.

Character Creation

The character-creation system is intended to offer a set of tools with which players can craft fictive personas rather than a mechanical device that churns out generic, assembly-line stereotypes. The development of a vibrant back story and a true depth of character takes precedence over dots on a page, but some framework must be established so that players' characters can interact in a meaningful way with regard to the game.

Try not to look simply at a character's traits in black and white, gauging how higher scores in certain areas afford her greater success in the coming chronicle. Instead, make an effort to understand the character's history and persona, then choose those dots that most accurately represent her personality and abilities. Storytellers should work closely with their players during character creation, making sure that choices made involving game mechanics have justification and rationale in terms of a character's developed persona.

CHARACTER-CREATION PROCESS

Use the character-creation rules from the **World of Darkness Rulebook**, and add the following template to Kindred characters during Step Five.

Choose a clan (see p. 91)

For beginning Disciplines, allocate three dots, two of which must be spent on clan Disciplines.

Vampires can have additional Merits from a special list (see p. 100).

Morality is now called Humanity in **Vampire** (see p. 92).

Roll a die to determine how much Vitae your character has at the beginning of the story.

Step One: Character Concept

Concept is the stone from which well-developed characters are sculpted. Before thoughts of game mechanics focus a player's attention on microcosmic details of his character's personality, it is important to hammer out a rough-hewn form, seeing the whole before concentrating on the parts.

Concept needs only to be a general idea — renowned socialite, musical prodigy, heroic savior — but it should be enough to spawn ever more complex ideas about the character's motives, environment and relationships. Of course, a concept can be far more complex: "My character was a staunch defender of New York's homeless, fighting for their rights and tending to their needs. His Embrace into the Mekhet clan frightened him into hiding among the downtrodden, who have now come to see him as a predator of the alleys."

As shown in that example, some players might want to include clan and covenant at this time. Information regarding clan and covenant is detailed in Step Five. Players creating prelude characters would forgo the selection of clan and covenant entirely, instead arriving at those choices through play.

Step Two: Select Attributes

After the more qualitative aspects of a character have been solidified, players must assign numbers that support their decisions. The first step in determining a character's numeric traits is to prioritize his Attributes. Attributes represent raw, natural ability. How strong is the character? How smart? How agile? What impression does he make as he enters a room? Attributes take these questions and more into account, ultimately providing the foundation upon which a character is built. Characters have nine Attributes, divided into three categories: Mental (Intelligence, Wits, Resolve), Physical (Strength, Dexterity, Stamina) and Social (Presence, Manipulation, Composure).

First, you must decide in which of these categories your character excels the most (primary). You then select the group of Attributes in which your character is average (secondary). Finally, the remaining category is designated as the character's weakest area of natural talent (tertiary). Is your character a scrawny intellectual, or possibly a brute lacking in social graces? Your character concept should provide insight into where to

assign your priorities, but you may decide to break with that mold — say, by creating a short, sinewy mob enforcer whose intensity and rage more than make up for his lack of size.

All characters begin with one dot in each Attribute, reflecting the basic capabilities of all human beings. The priorities established in the preceding paragraph determine how many dots are allocated for each Attribute cluster. Five additional dots are added to the primary group, four additional dots to the secondary group and three dots to the tertiary group. For example, the scrawny intellectual mentioned previously would have five dots in his Mental category, four in his Social and three in his Physical category, while the tactless brute would have five dots in his Physical category, four in his Mental and only three in his Social category.

The fifth dot in any Attribute costs two dots to purchase. So, a player who wants his character to have a Dexterity of 5 needs to spend five dots. (He starts with one free dot, spends three more to achieve a score of 4, and then spends two more for the fifth dot.)

Step Three: Select Skills

Skills are divided into the same three subcategories as Attributes: Mental, Physical and Social. Mental Skills tend to rely on knowledge of the world and are improved through study and practical application. Physical Skills rely on training, improved mainly through practice and repetition. Finally, Social Skills rely heavily on interpersonal experience and improve through interaction with others or through trial and error.

Like Attributes, Skill groups must be prioritized during character creation. Players should select primary, secondary and tertiary categories for their Skills. The primary group receives 11 dots, the secondary group gets seven, and the tertiary group receives four. Note that, unlike Attributes, characters do not begin the game with an automatic dot in any Skill, as Skills dots are obtained through dedication to a field, not natural talent alone. As before, the fifth dot in any Skill costs two dots to purchase.

Step Four: Select Skill Specialties

While characters might have considerable training in Firearms or expertise in Medicine, they excel in certain aspects of these Skills more so than in others. For instance, Officer Grimes might have a special proficiency with his particular sidearm but not with rifles, shotguns or chain guns. He might understand the basic principles of using these firearms, but the bulk of his training has been with his pistol. Represented in game terms, such a character may have three dots in Firearms, with a Specialty in 9mm automatic pistols.

Players choose three Skill Specialties during character creation. These should be very specific, though players may choose more than one Specialty for any given Skill. So, using the previous example, Officer Grimes might have Specialties in both 9mm automatic pistols and 12-gauge shotguns.

Step Five: Add Vampire Template

Here is where your character sloughs off her mortal coil and truly becomes a creature of the night. The Embrace changes a character into something no longer mortal, endowing her with special abilities and unique advantages unimagined in her previous existence. Aside from entering a new world based on clan and covenant, supernatural changes affect her Attributes and allow her access to the powers of the Blood.

Clan

A character's clan serves as a sort of extended family of the night, bound by lineage and responsible for certain similarities among its members. Vampires are always of the same clan as the sires that Embrace them, though it is possible to later start a new bloodline that deviates slightly from other close blood relations. Examine the five clan descriptions presented (see pp. 104-113), and determine which clan to which you want your character to belong. Your Storyteller may place restrictions on your choice at the start, depending on the limitations of her planned chronicle. Preludes concerning the Embrace might take this decision out of your hands entirely, basing it solely on the Storyteller's discretion.

When choosing a clan, you might wish to choose a specific bloodline that deviates slightly from the norm, a subset of your vampiric family that holds to different ideals and behavioral standards. Be sure to confer with your Storyteller before making such a decision, as certain bloodlines might not be allowed in her chronicle, or might not exist at all. Alternatively, it is possible to create an entirely new bloodline, provided your Storyteller approves.

Covenant

A covenant is more social than familial, concerned with a character's worldview and relationship to other Kindred rather than the advantages and bonds of the Blood. Each of these societies seeks different goals using (sometimes dramatically) diverse methods, all sure in the knowledge that their way is "right," or at least more right than all the others. Covenant is not governed by clan or sire, though childer often begin their Requiems in the covenants of their sires, either out of familiarity or promise of status.

If a covenant is chosen during character creation, there is no reason why it can't be changed as a character comes to more fully understand her place in the world. While a character's covenant is not set in stone, those who change allegiances are often viewed with suspicion and might have difficulty gaining trust or status within the new social hierarchy. Your character's covenant need not be decided upon at character creation, though your concept should give some clue as to which covenants are most or least comfortable. Storytellers may disallow this choice at the start of a chronicle, intending characters to handle this decision during play.

Covenants grant certain benefits to their members. A character must have at least a single dot worth of the Status Merit in a covenant (see p. 102) to avail himself of its benefits. Covenant advantages are as follows.

• **The Carthians:** Members of the Carthians may purchase the Allies, Contacts, Haven and Herd Merits at half the normal experience-point costs (rounding up). This cost break does not apply to purchases of these Merits during character creation.

• **The Circle of the Crone:** Members of the Circle of the Crone may learn the Discipline of Crúac.

- **The Invictus:** Members of the Invictus may purchase the Herd, Mentor, Resources and Retainer Merits at half the normal experience-point costs (rounding up). This cost break does not apply to purchases of these Merits during character creation.

- **The Lancea Sanctum:** Members of the Lancea Sanctum may learn the Discipline of Theban Sorcery.

- **The Ordo Dracul:** Members of the Ordo Dracul may learn the Coils of the Dragon.

Favored Attributes

The Embrace forces drastic changes upon the human body, altering its aspects to that of a vampiric predator. While all vampires possess the same vulnerability to fire and the need to consume blood, their bodies adapt more subtly based on the blood of their sires. Each clan has adjusted somewhat differently to the rigors of the Embrace, choosing a divergent path of development toward becoming a more successful predator breed. These adaptations are carried through the blood of the clan, altering the natural abilities of newly Embraced childer.

Each clan has a pair of favored Attributes, enjoying a more acute development of certain natural aspects of the body. Once a clan is chosen, choose one Attribute from a clan's favored pair and add one dot to it.

Clan	Favored Attributes (choose one)
Daeva	Dexterity or Manipulation
Gangrel	Composure or Stamina
Mekhet	Intelligence or Wits
Nosferatu	Composure or Strength
Ventrue	Presence or Resolve

Disciplines

When vampires are Embraced, their sires teach them certain blood-based mystical powers known as Disciplines. Disciplines are those mysterious and often terrifying capabilities that the Kindred can manifest at will. Taking the shape of an animal, running at superhuman speeds or bending a victim's will to one's own are examples of Disciplines in use.

Each character begins with three dots of Disciplines, which can be allocated as the player chooses. At least two dots must be devoted to a character's clan Disciplines, however, before any thought is given to an out-of-clan or bloodline Discipline. (That is, you may choose to spend two dots on clan Disciplines and a single dot on an out-of-clan or bloodline Discipline, but not two dots on out-of-clan or bloodline Disciplines and only one on a clan Discipline.) Each clan description that appears later in this chapter lists the Disciplines practiced by that lineage, along with some of the more prevalent bloodline variations.

Blood Potency

A character's Blood Potency represents how much innate, mystical power has concentrated within her dead veins. Characters with high Blood Potency possess both great mastery over their Vitae and much inherent potential in that Vitae. Characters with low Blood Potency are either unpracticed or their Blood is so young or inert as to have little connate potential.

All vampire characters receive the Blood Potency advantage at one dot for free. Blood Potency can be increased with Merit-point expenditure at a rate of three to one at character

creation. That is, a player may spend three of his character's seven Merit points for Blood Potency 2, or spend six of his character's seven Merit points for Blood Potency 3. Blood Potency is described on p. 99.

Step Six: Select Merits

A beginning character has seven dots worth of Merits, which may be distributed at the player's discretion. These traits should fit the character concept — a Daeva socialite isn't likely to have the Stunt Driver Merit, for example, unless her background involves it somehow. A Storyteller may encourage or disallow certain Merits, or even provide a dot for free (perhaps representing a political contact crucial to the chronicle). The fifth dot in any Merit costs two dots to purchase.

Step Seven: Determine Advantages

Rules regarding advantages can be found on pages 90-105 of the **World of Darkness Rulebook**. What follows concerns itself less with game mechanics and more with the importance of certain advantages to vampire characters.

Willpower

Vampires lead unlives of constant struggle, fighting against their base, predatory natures to retain control of their slipping connections to humanity. Fighting the Beast within them calls for a measure of self-reliance often lacking in ordinary mortals, making large amounts of Willpower a great value. Vampires' dangerous emotional situations can lead to violent, mindless frenzy (p. 178), and they hold their bestial tendencies in check through sheer force of will.

Vampires' experience points can be spent to recoup lost Willpower dots. See p. 93 ot 230 for more information on spending experience.

A player may spend Vitae in the same turn in which he spends a point of Willpower. For more on spending Vitae, see pp. 156-157.

I WASN'T EMBRACED YESTERDAY

Storytellers may choose to allow players a certain number of experience points to spend before play begins to represent the portion of the Requiem between the Embrace and the start of the chronicle.

Rank neonates	0 experience points
Up-and-comers	35 experience points
Established Kindred	75 experience points
Movers and shakers	120 experience points
Elders and other linchpins of undead society	180-300+ experience points

Humanity

After the Embrace, a vampire begins to lose touch with those elements of her nature that make her human. These qualities erode over time as the vampire becomes more jaded and the world evolves without her. For this reason, the concept of Morality as outlined in the **World of Darkness Rulebook** is replaced with Humanity here.

As an optional rule, Storytellers may allow those players applying the vampire template during character creation to trade dots of Humanity for experience points. This trade-in reflects some heinous past behavior the vampire engaged in and learned from (accounting for the added experience points), but which also scarred her deeply (explaining the loss in Humanity). Players may sacrifice one dot of Humanity for five experience points, dropping their characters' Humanity scores to as low as five (for a maximum of 10 extra experience points).

Virtues and Vices

The Virtues and Vices available to mortal characters are the same as those available to vampires, though they manifest in different ways. For instance, a character who suffers the Vice of Wrath might be prone to frenzy, while one indulging in Gluttony might

---

Vampire Template Quick Reference

This sidebar summarizes the changes that apply to vampire characters. Use it in conjunction with the summary of character creation on p. 34-35 of the **World of Darkness Rulebook**.

Clan

Choose a clan to which your character belongs. There are five clans from which to select.

Daeva: Emotional, sensual and desirable.

Gangrel: Primal, hardy and savage.

Mekhet: Quick, discreet and wise.

Nosferatu: Stealthy, strong and terrifying.

Ventrue: Regal, commanding and aristocratic.

Covenant

Choose a covenant in which your character claims membership. There are five covenants from which to select. If you wish to choose no covenant, record "unbound," "unaligned" or "independent" on your character sheet.

The Carthians seek to reconcile Kindred society with modern governmental structures and social systems.

The Circle of the Crone venerates a variety of female figures as an amalgamated creator of vampires, the Mother of all Monsters.

The Invictus is the aristocracy of the night.

The Lancea Sanctum seeks to influence Kindred society with the strictures of Longinus, who is believe to have been turned into one of the Damned by the very blood of Christ.

The Ordo Dracul commands rituals and mystical knowledge that allows the Kindred to transcend their vampiric states.

Favored Attributes

Based on your choice of clan, select one of the clan's two favored Attributes and give your character an additional dot in that trait.

Clan	Favored Attributes
Daeva	Dexterity or Manipulation
Gangrel	Composure or Stamina
Mekhet	Intelligence or Wits
Nosferatu	Composure or Strength
Ventrue	Presence or Resolve

Disciplines

Choose three dots of Disciplines, at least two dots of which must come from the clan's favored powers.

Animalism: Power over animals and even the Beast of Kindred.

Auspex: Preternatural senses and perception.

Celerity: Superhuman speed.

Coils of the Dragon*: The Ordo Dracul's secrets of transcendence.

Crúac*: Blood magic practiced by the witches of the Circle of the Crone.

Dominate: The ability to overwhelm the mind.

Majesty: Tremendous force of personality.

Nightmare: Manipulating fear itself.

Obfuscate: Hiding aspects of one's self, even one's body.

Protean: Shapechanging and adjustments of the vampiric form.

Resilience: Legendary toughness.

Theban Sorcery*: The Biblical "dark miracles" of the Lancea Sanctum.

Vigor: The epic strength of many men.

* Available to covenant members only.

Blood Potency

A character's Blood Potency begins at 1, but Merit points may be spent to increase it.

Merits

New vampiric Merits include Haven (• to •••••), Herd (• to •••••) and Status (• to •••••)

Experience Point Costs

Trait	Cost
Attribute	New dots x 5
Skill	New dots x 3
Skill Specialty	3
Clan or Bloodline Discipline	New dots x 5
Other Discipline*	New dots x 7
Theban Sorcery or Crúac Ritual	Ritual level x 2
Merit	New dots x 2
Blood Potency	New dots x 8
Humanity	New dots x 3
Willpower	8 experience points

* Includes Coils of the Dragon. See p. 149 for more information on increasing Coils of the Dragon.

leave a trail of exsanguinated bodies in her wake, finding it difficult to stop feeding before victims' hearts stop. On the other hand, a character with the Virtue of Hope might dedicate his nights to achieving Golconda, while a character with the Virtue of Justice might carefully choose his victims from among those deserving punishment (such as rapists or murderers), becoming a crusader of the night.

Step Eight: Spark of Unlife

At this point you should have a character, at least in a purely mechanical sense. You have all you need to use your character as a playing piece in your Storyteller's chronicle, combining Attributes with Skills and rolling dice as necessary.

Roleplaying, however, is not simply pitting dice against dice, or using spiffy powers left and right. The previous steps have created a basic framework, a rough sculpture of a character hammered out in the most simplistic of terms. Now is the time to break out the fine tools, refining the crude figure with details and nuance. Examine the dots on your character sheet and figure out why they're there. What in your character's life made him pick up his first firearm and begin training? How did he learn so much about the ways of the street or the methods of intimidation? When did he pick up his rudimentary medical skills? How will this background come across in the story? What parts *don't* you know yet about your character? Just like working a fine sculpture, shape and polish your character's physical, psychological and background details to make him one of a kind, even among the undead.

Just what exactly does having a Presence of 3 mean? Does your character possess the chiseled features of a runway model, causing all eyes to turn his way as he enters a room? Or does he have the hardened look of a dockyard worker who isn't to be trifled with? Perhaps he exudes an air of old money and confidence from behind his tailored suits and fine jewelry. What features cause others to react to him with such intensity? What color are his eyes, his hair, his skin? Does he have a clean cut, refined look or perhaps a nasty scar running from his scalp down between his eyes to his neck? Is his voice harsh and raspy, silky smooth or does he stutter, relying wholly on his looks to carry him?

While these final touches might seem the least necessary, they are the most important. Otherwise, your Ventrue with Presence 3, Manipulation 4 and Composure 3 will be just like every other Ventrue with Presence 3, Manipulation 4 and Composure 3. You want to avoid such two-dimensional characters and strive for something unique, fascinating and memorable.

Finally, the unlife of a vampire is certainly a place for ironies and fate. You've done all the work so far, choosing which traits you want your character to possess and arranging dots on the character sheet. As the final step of character creation, throw a single die. This is how much Vitae your vampire has in her system when the chronicle begins.

The Prelude

Personality and character are built on the experiences and decisions of the past. It is impossible to get any real sense of a person without having at least some knowledge of the path she has taken through life. Similarly, it is impossible to have any real sense of your character without first understanding where she comes from, what elements of her past have driven her headlong into the events of the chronicle. The prelude helps you fine-tune the personality of your character, hammering out less quantitative things such as mannerisms and speech patterns. It's something of a one-on-one mini-story in which you and the Storyteller sit down and roleplay some of the key events in your character's life before the actual start of the chronicle.

You roleplay a prelude in much the same way as a normal game session, only your character's entire history is condensed into a single night of decisions. It's as though you participate in a highlight reel where the key moments are played out but the bulk is glossed over. Romantic relationships, work, family, friends, enemies — any and all of these might need to be addressed during the course of a prelude, each rounding out your character in different ways and potentially foreshadowing her existence as a vampire.

More importantly, a prelude allows you to get inside your character's skin, to take her out for a test drive. It provides a frame of reference, letting you decide how she reacts to certain stimuli and in what ways she employs her capabilities. Preludes are often handled quickly, without the careful planning and downtime afforded during normal game play. While they are essential to character development, they simply provide background and needn't drag on and on.

A Storyteller's Guide to the Prelude

You meet your girlfriend at the restaurant where you had your first date, and you're running late as usual. It seems as though nothing has changed. Your heart races with nerves, but this time you have an engagement ring in your pocket. You're not sure what to say, even after endless practice. You worry about how you look and again realize just how beautiful she is. Waiting until the end of the meal to ask the question that has been burning in the back of your mind, you reach for the ring… and find that it's gone. What do you do?

The Storyteller spends the prelude with each player in a one-on-one setting, helping that player focus on his relationship with his character and enforcing the idea that the prelude is very personal; the character's past is his alone. It is possible for two players to share parts of a prelude, but they should do so only if their characters have some relationship that exists before the Embrace, and even then there should be only partial overlap. As Storyteller, don't be concerned about ignoring the other players while you focus on each prelude. While you should be as inclusive as possible once the chronicle begins in earnest, a little anticipation can help focus the group's mindset.

It's okay to be forceful in presenting a prelude, calling upon a player to make snap decisions, and jumping forward through time before events can fully be resolved. You're trying to get at the most basic, gut instincts about the player's character. In-depth analysis and reaction to certain decisions can be done on the player's own time, possibly as he waits for others to complete their preludes. Unless you plan to spend an entire

session on each character's prelude, you should condense things as much as possible, giving a concentrated dose of what a character's life is like. Doing so adds to the potency and impact, as the player has a barrage of past images in the forefront of his mind at the start of the chronicle — almost as though his life has passed before his eyes.

Checking your cell phone, you see your fiancée's number but have no time to talk. The strange woman ducked down an alley when you saw her last. You're sure she's the one you've been looking for. If you could only talk to her, ask her some questions; her story would affect millions. Running down the alleyway after her, you see that she seems to have disappeared — the only sign of life is your own panting breath condensing before your face. You stop to pull out your cell phone and call your fiancée back, only to drop it clattering to the ground when you realize the woman is standing right behind you. How do you respond?

You want the player to explore both the setting and the rules during the prelude. Have him try out a few rolls and even swap a few Merits or other traits around if they just don't seem to fit the character. Be wary of the player who uses this opportunity to create an invulnerable character by tweaking his traits. Any changes made should be for the benefit of the character's history and personality, not so dice rolls have greater success. You may even allow him to begin the prelude without having spent any of his Merit points, instead choosing and filling them in as the story progresses. Introduce allies and contacts, visit his job to explore where he gets his rent and food money, and explore the details of the character's environment. It's best to avoid

direct combat during the prelude. No one wants his character to die before the chronicle even begins. If absolutely necessary, describe the fight and determine the results without using dice rolls, therefore avoiding any unfortunate mishaps.

While it might seem strange to roleplay such mundane events in the course of everyday life, it builds a sense of comfortable normalcy that can be shattered by the Embrace. Juxtaposed against the usual trials and tribulations of the ordinary, the suddenly horrific attack and rebirth as a vampire should jar a player's consciousness, tearing him from his former world and driving home exactly what his character loses.

As you describe things, allow the player to interject his own ideas and details regarding his character's background. Remember that you're telling this story together; view the player as your partner. You can also throw in details to provoke the player's emotions. ("Your sister's voice is exultant as she tells you you're a bone marrow match for her infant son.") Obviously, once a character becomes a vampire, there's no way for him to offer his bone marrow or to donate his blood. **Vampire** is a game of personal horror, and a character must experience great loss before he can truly understand what it's like to exist as one of the Damned.

The woman grasps you by the throat and pulls you close, staring into your eyes. Every muscle in your body screams to fight, to resist, but something about her holds you back. A sheer and utter terror grips you. Her eyes seem to weigh every ounce of your soul before she smiles slightly and sinks her teeth into your neck. Your breath catches in your throat and your blood pounds in your head as your hands finally attempt to push her away. You faintly hear your cell phone ringing and think of your fiancée as the world fades away.

A character's Embrace should be a pivotal moment in his development and, as such, it should be roleplayed to the utmost. This moment is supremely important, defining just how he is changed by existence as a vampire. Play up the sensation of subtle anxiety, of a growing paranoia that he is being watched. Build the tension of being stalked by some unseen predator who's always just out of sight. Although the player knows what's coming, he doesn't know exactly how. It's your responsibility to make the event as visceral and frightening as possible, describing each moment in vivid detail. Play through the transformation, allowing the player to feel the physical and emotional trauma of the change. You might still want to play out some details of the character's existence before the opening of the chronicle, but the Embrace should stand out in a player's mind, lingering in his thoughts for a long time to come.

Questions, Questions...

The questions that follow can be used to flesh out a character's background, providing insight into areas a player might gloss over during character creation. Even if there is no time for a sufficiently detailed prelude, you should answer as many of these as you can, either by writing out a brief back story and description or talking about these issues with the Storyteller. The devil is in the details, as they say, and these specifics help make your character far more real once the story begins.

• **How old are you?**

When were you born? How old were you when you were Embraced? How long have you existed as a vampire? How old do you look to others? Are you more or less mature than you seem?

• **What was unique about your childhood?**

What do you remember about your early years? What forged your basic motivations and attitudes? Where did you go to school? Were you a good student? Who were your immediate family members? What is your clearest childhood memory? Did you go to high school. College? Did you have a hometown, or did your family move often? Did you run away from home? Did you play sports? Did any of your childhood friendships last until adulthood?

• **What kind of person were you?**

Were you a kind and gentle person or an arrogant bastard? Were you popular or a social outcast? Did you have a family? How did you earn a living? Did you have any real friends, or just acquaintances? What kept you going from day to day? Will anyone miss you?

• **What was your first brush with the supernatural?**

When did you first realize you were being stalked? Had you dabbled in the occult at all before your Embrace? When did you first meet a vampire? Were you afraid? Disbelieving? Curious? Angry?

• **How did the Embrace change you?**

How did your sire catch you? Was the Embrace painful? Did you get perverse pleasure from it? Did the Hunger tear at you? Were you frightened? Did it somehow feel right? Are you grateful to your sire? Do you want to kill her for what she did to you?

• **Who was your sire, and how did she treat you?**

What do you know of your sire? Was she seductive, forceful, abusive, cryptic or open? Why do you think she chose you? Did you even know your sire? How long did you stay with your sire? Did she teach you anything at all? How long was it until your sire released you? Where did you stay? Where did you go? Did you meet any other vampires during that time? Did your sire Embrace another? Do you judge other vampires by your opinion of your sire?

• **Were you presented to Kindred society?**

Did the Prince welcome you? Was he reluctant to accept you? Did prominent Kindred need to be bribed or threatened before accepting you? Did your sire have permission to create you? Are you on the run from Kindred authorities? What do you suppose your domain's preeminent Kindred think about you?

• **How did you meet the others in your coterie?**

Were you brought together by chance or design? Are you all of one covenant or clan? Are you united in purpose, working toward the same goal? How long have you been together? Did you know any of the others before your Embrace? Do your sires cooperate, or are they rivals? Do any of you share the same sire? What holds your coterie together when the situation is at its worst?

• **Where is your haven?**

Where do you sleep during the day? Do you have any permanent home, or do you migrate from place to place? Do you stay in or near the place you inhabited in your mortal life? Do you hide in an abandoned building? Is your haven above or below ground? Do you have anyone to protect you during the day?

• **Do you retain any connections to your mortal life?**

Have you been presumed dead? Do you still watch over old friends and relatives from afar? Do you pretend to still be alive? Have you abandoned your mortal existence entirely?

• **What are your habitual feeding grounds?**

Do you frequent a particular place to feed? Do you consider this territory yours alone, or do others use it? Do you compete with others to feed? What is your preferred prey? Will you risk hunger to find this type of prey? Do you ever kill when you feed? Do you have a specific herd? Do you seduce your prey? Kidnap them? Intimidate or beat them? Do they come to you?

• **What motivates you?**

Are you bent on revenge? Do you long for your mortal life, or to again look upon the sun? Do you have ambitions within Kindred society? Do you wish to Embrace any childer? Are you involved with inter-covenant conflict? If you could have any one thing in the world, what would it be?

A Final Note

Those without motivation are likely not to have survived the Embrace at all, or to struggle for survival in subsequent nights. Although a vampire's values often differ greatly from those of a human, stemming from his experience with death and rebirth, he must still have something worth existing for, or he would likely watch the next sunrise and be done with it. Give thought to where your character has been and where he's headed. Is there some overarching, ultimate goal or possibly several small ones? While **Vampire** is a Modern Gothic Storytelling game, these beings do not sit around each night lamenting their sad existence and wishing it would all just end. Once you have an idea of what it is that your character wants to achieve, you have come one step closer to making him a complete, realistic personality.

Example of Character Creation

Christopher plans to participate in Diane's **Vampire** chronicle. Diane tells Christopher that the chronicle focuses on a struggle between the covenants for supremacy in Chicago, each attempting to buck the power structure tenuously emplaced by Prince Maxwell and his flunkies. She informs him that vampires from all the covenants are shifting allegiances after the Prince has made a particularly unpopular decree, and that each covenant struggles to gain the influence it needs to claim praxis. She has designed her chronicle such that the covenants call in favors and gather the support of unaligned vampires, and that Christopher's character should be either unaligned or otherwise "up for grabs" — possibly openly dissatisfied with the leadership of his current covenant.

Diane hands Christopher a copy of the character sheet, and Christopher spends a few minutes brainstorming some ideas before turning them into a fully formed character.

Step One: Concept

Christopher's first responsibility is to come up with a concept for his character. He decides that he wants to play a politically active journalist who was Embraced while spending time in the back alleys of Chicago, trying to improve the conditions of the city's homeless population. Christopher decides that the Embrace was sudden and unwelcome, his abrupt loss of life forcing him to abandon his previous ways and become a predator of the street. Preying upon the homeless, Christopher's character turns his back on a fiancée and family he knows can never understand his cursed existence. Christopher toys with the idea of choosing Clan Nosferatu, tying in with the downtrodden, back-alley theme, but instead settles on Clan Mekhet, deciding to focus more on his character's newfound unlife hiding among the forgotten denizens of the streets.

Not wanting to name his character after himself, Christopher decides that his character's name is James Cesar, freelance journalist and former political activist of mixed Latino descent.

Step Two: Attributes

Christopher must now prioritize and assign James' Attributes. Based on his concept, Christopher decides that Social Attributes would be James' strong suit, so he sets them as primary. Of course, Christopher wants there to be meaning and truth behind James' words instead of just flash and show, so he sets Mental Attributes as the secondary category. That leaves Physical Attributes as tertiary, which Christopher ties into his concept with the decision that James is more likely to talk his way out of trouble than anything else.

Christopher now has five dots to allocate among Social Attributes. He decides that James has an engaging way with words, whether he's writing them in an article or addressing the city council. With that in mind, he assigns two of his available dots to Manipulation, raising the total to 3. Next, he feels that James would have considerable grace under pressure, even in the face of threatening street thugs in the alleys where he would spend much of his time. He uses two of his remaining dots on Composure, raising it to a total of 3. His final dot would raise his Presence to 2, making him unremarkable at best and nothing special to look at. Christopher feels that this allocation makes sense for a character who would put so much stock in words instead of looks.

With four dots to assign to Mental Attributes, Christopher decides that Wits are most important to James, as life on the street would have required him to think on his feet. He places two of his four dots in Wits for a total of 3, then places one dot each in Intelligence and Resolve to bring James up to average in each area.

Finally, Christopher turns his attention to the Physical category to finish off his Attributes. He sees James as slim and somewhat scrawny, having spent most of his nights either behind a desk or living off fast food, so he adds nothing to Strength. Christopher assigns two dots to Dexterity, reflecting James' tendency to run rather than fight, and places his final dot in Stamina.

Step Three: Skills

Like Attributes, Skills must also be prioritized and chosen. Christopher decides to stay with the same prioritization as he used for Attributes, placing Social as primary, Mental as secondary and Physical as tertiary. James has spent his life developing those Skills that come most easily to him and neglecting those with which he has little natural aptitude.

With 11 dots to assign in Social Skills, Christopher tries to imagine what would be most important to James while working in the alleys and streets of Chicago. Streetwise is an obvious choice, and Christopher assigns three dots. Two dots each go to Expression, Persuasion and Subterfuge, owing to James' mortal experience subtly plying the homeless for information about their living conditions, writing articles bringing their stories to the public, and arguing with city councilmen on their behalf. One dot goes to Socialize, reflecting his ability to establish camaraderie with his many contacts, and the last is assigned to Empathy, as he knows that his words go only so far without a basic understanding of the human condition.

Looking at the list of Mental Skills, Christopher decides how to spend his seven dots. Given James' experience as a journalist and political lobbyist, he chooses to assign two dots each to Investigation and Politics to represent political acumen. A single dot goes toward Academics as Christopher decides that James spent two years in journalism school before dropping out to become a freelancer. Another dot goes to Medicine, representing a first-aid course James has made great use of during his time on the streets. The final dot goes to Occult, as time in the more remote alleys of the city has exposed him to far stranger sights than the average person has seen.

Finally, Christopher needs to assign four dots to the Physical group. Knowing James has no physical prowess or strength to speak of, Christopher feels that he would spend some time training with firearms to protect himself during his long nights on the street, and places two dots in that Skill. His next dot goes to Survival, owing to James' occasional need to find food in dumpsters or gutters while spending time among the homeless, and the last dot is placed in Athletics, again owing to James' tendency to run from trouble rather than confronting it head on.

Step Four: Skill Specialties

Now that Christopher has assigned James' Skill dots, he needs to decide where to place his three Skill specialties. Glancing over the Skills he has chosen, he tries to imagine which would be the most refined and singles out Streetwise, Politics and Subterfuge. Focusing on Streetwise first, Christopher decides that James would have an added advantage when dealing with the homeless, rather than the various gangs, dealers or other criminal elements of the street. James' political ability would rest primarily with the Chicago city council and government, rather than on the state or federal level, and his Subterfuge would be concerned mostly with body language, keeping in line with his focus on his Social Skills.

(If he wanted to, Christopher could have assigned two or even three of his character's Specialties to the same Skill. Say, "Homeless," "Street Gangs" and "Drug Dealers" to Streetwise.)

Step Five: Vampire Template

Christopher decided upon James' clan when he developed his character concept, and Diane has limited his options regarding covenant. Rather than resentfully connecting James to a covenant he's unhappy with, Christopher chooses to make him more of a dabbler, only recently Embraced and not yet sworn wholeheartedly to any faction. James' sire is of a similar disposition, once of the Carthians before she became jaded and adopted a reclusive and mysterious lifestyle in the alleyways. Christopher has decided that James' sire Embraced him shortly after she rose from a long torpor, hoping to rekindle some of her own passion and to reconnect with the world, but she quickly lost interest and has only a sparse relationship with him. Christopher makes James a Carthian out of his sire's legacy, but knows that things might change as Chicago politics heat up.

The Mekhet's favored Attributes are Wits and Intelligence, and Christopher feels that James' personality would more naturally lend itself to an increased Wits, especially on the streets. His Embrace adds an edge to his demeanor, manifesting primarily in a collection of habits he's acquired — never sitting with his back to a door, always noting a room's exits.

Christopher has three dots to spend on Disciplines, which he may spend in any way he chooses, provided at least two of his dots go to Mekhet clan Disciplines. He decides that James' sire taught him the Discipline of Auspex to further bolster his already impressive command of his senses, and he assigns two dots thus. Christopher isn't drawn to any of the out-of-clan Disciplines because James has had little to no experience with vampires other than his sire. Looking at the Mekhet's other clan Disciplines, he feels that James would be more interested in learning Celerity than Obfuscate, continuing with the theme of avoiding direct physical confrontation, and assigns his last Discipline dot thus.

Step Six: Merits

Christopher must next spend seven dots on Merits. Looking over the list of suggested Merits in the **World of Darkness Rulebook**, he tries to find those that might reflect James' political life before his Embrace. Christopher leaves Blood Potency at 1, as James is still relatively new to the rigors of the Requiem. Time spent lobbying the city council and dealing with political activists not only gives him capabilities in those areas, but other tangible assets. Christopher spends three dots on Contacts, selecting City Hall, Media and the Police, all groups with which he had some dealings in life. Christopher also purchases the Status Merit at one dot, represented by an old press pass, allowing him to play on his connections to gain a measure of acceptance at city political functions. It's not quite as good as full journalistic credentials, but Christopher thinks that James probably hadn't "paid his dues" to that degree, anyway. Diane approves of the one-dot press pass and Christopher moves on.

Thinking next about James' unlife after the Embrace, Christopher chooses to put two dots in Haven Security, reflecting the efforts James has made to conceal himself and establish a new home. He would much rather stay hidden and ignored by the world than have a large haven or an obvious one close to a major population center. He discovers a long-neglected, underground public service maintenance room accessed through an unused manhole. Finally, he places a single dot in Herd, representing a small, deranged group of beggars who view him as a powerful defender of the alleys, rather than the predator that he is.

Step Seven: Advantages

Once the numerical statistics have been decided upon, Christopher must determine his character's advantages. Adding his Resolve and Composure, he records a Willpower score of 5 on his character sheet. His Humanity score starts at the standard 7, and Christopher chooses Charity as James' Virtue (given his former desire to help the helpless, as mortal habits die hard) and Pride as his Vice (he has a tendency to use his political leverage to get back at those who cross him).

Adding his Size factor of 5 to his Stamina, Christopher determines that James has seven dots of Health, and draws a dark vertical line to the right of the seventh box on the Health Chart. Combining his Dexterity with his Composure, he determines his Initiative to be 6, and notes his Defense of 3, as his Dexterity is lower than his Wits after the Embrace. Finally, he adds his Strength + Dexterity + 5 to find his Speed, which he records as 9.

Step Eight: Spark of Unlife

Christopher has a pretty good grasp of his character at this point, at least conceptually, but the specific details of appearance and relationships are still a bit hazy. He looks over the questions on p. 96 to further round out some of the specifics regarding James' background.

He decides that James came from an upper-middle-class family and grew up in a New Jersey suburb, eventually being accepted by a decent journalism college. After two years of study, he had a falling out with his family, dropped out of school and ran off to Chicago, where he nearly died of starvation living on the street for several months.

His first freelance story detailing his experiences on the street was picked up by a major newspaper and syndicated across the country, putting his name on the map, and he landed a job writing articles, giving him enough money for a tiny, rundown apartment near the elevated train. Seeking to intensify the loss James felt after his Embrace, Christopher decides that James developed a relationship with another writer at the newspaper and got up the nerve to propose marriage, which she accepted. In the weeks before his Embrace, he had received a raise, was planning his wedding and had started to patch things up with his parents.

As the chronicle starts, James has abandoned his previous life entirely, struggling to accept the realities of his new condition. Unable to face the world, he hides in the alleys, preying upon the homeless he had spent his career trying to defend. He becomes jaded with the world and his previous work, realizing that hunger and cold are hardly any threat when creatures who feed on human blood lurk in the darkness. His hair is disheveled; his clothes are ragged and dirty; he spends his nights stalking unwary beggars, talked about in hushed words as though he were nightmare made flesh. Christopher leaves James' three contacts, his sire and the state of his family in Diane's hands to detail during the course of the chronicle.

And that's it. Christopher takes a final look over his character sheet to make sure everything is exactly the way he wants it and informs Diane of his decisions. James is ready to be thrust into the chaotic World of Darkness.

Traits

After the Embrace, vampires gain unique traits that separate them from their mortal lives. While many of them represent internal, physical changes that mark the loss of life and the start of the Requiem, social conditions after the Embrace also cause changes in behavior and lifestyle, marking more external adaptations to the night.

New Advantage: Blood Potency

Although the Kindred each call upon the Blood in different ways, not all wield the same levels of power. Blood Potency determines the degree of power the Blood bestows upon a vampire. Having more dots of Blood Potency allows characters to learn more advanced Disciplines and to develop their traits to superhuman levels. Further, vampires with more dots in this advantage can hold more Vitae within their bodies, as it is more potent and therefore more concentrated. In short, the higher a character's Blood Potency, the greater her potential.

All newly Embraced vampires start at Blood Potency 1, regardless of their sire's potency, with nowhere to go but up. Blood Potency can be purchased during character creation as a Merit (at three Merit-equivalent points per dot), but after play begins, it can be increased only by experience, diablerie or age. The purchase of additional Blood Potency at character creation needs to be rationalized before play begins. Perhaps the character engaged in diablerie or had already spent many years as a vampire before the start of the chronicle. Players who want their characters to start with more dots of Blood Potency must thoroughly explain what in their character's history justifies the additional dots and have it approved by the Storyteller before play begins.

As Blood Potency increases, feeding requirements become more stringent. Only blood of potency a certain degree lower than a character's can provide sustenance (see the accompanying chart). In fact, some elders' blood is so potent that they can't feed on mortals at all, requiring the Vitae of other vampires to nourish them. Only those with the fewest dots of Blood Potency can feed from animals.

Eventually, a vampire's blood becomes so potent that he is unable to find regular prey and falls into torpor, the duration of which is based on his current Blood Potency and Humanity (see p. 175). While in torpor, a thinning of the blood occurs. Torpor also causes fever dreams and a general distortion of the mind.

A vampire's Blood Potency increases by one every 50 years. In torpor, however, it decreases by one every 25 years. As Blood Potency is rated on a 1-to-10 scale, a vampire will more than likely fall into torpor in about 500 years — as blood requirements grow ever more refined and hard to fulfill — sooner for those who engage in diablerie. Characters who diablerize several vampires in a short span of years can remain active through seven to nine diableries before the potency of their blood causes them to succumb to torpor. Such Kindred tend to have short but violent bouts of activity between long periods of torpid idleness.

When Blood Potency decreases (through torpor, for example), any traits that exceed the character's new capacity

EFFECTS OF BLOOD POTENCY

Blood Potency	Attribute/Skill/Discipline Maximum	Max Vitae/Max Vitae per Turn	Vampires can feed from...
1	5	10/1	Animals +
2	5	11/1	Animals +
3	5	12/1	Humans
4	5	13/2	Humans
5	5	14/2	Humans
6	6	15/3	Humans
7	7	20/5	Vampires
8	8	30/7	Vampires
9	9	50/10	Vampires
10	10	100/15	Vampires

disappear. If Blood Potency increases again during the chronicle so that a character could once again gain access to them, the player must spend experience points a second time to "re-learn" what was lost.

Example: *Stephanie of Clan Daeva has achieved a Blood Potency of 8 after repeated success at diablerie and has subsequently raised her Presence to 7. Unable to find any vampires of sufficient Blood Potency to feed upon, she slips into torpor for a period of 80 years. In this time, Stephanie's Blood Potency drops three dots (one for every 25 years) to 5.*

When she wakes, her Presence is reduced to 5, the trait maximum for a Blood Potency of 5. Over time, especially if Stephanie continues her practice of diablerie, she will have the opportunity to increase her Presence again. Her player, however, needs to spend the experience points to raise these dots as though Stephanie had never possessed them.

Rumors persist of truly ancient vampires who have found a way to stave off torpor, seemingly defying the effects of Blood Potency. Some swear that such a thing is possible through intensive study of blood magic with such faith akin to the belief in Golconda, creating a sort of religious fervor in those seeking to attain transcendence.

Merits

Merits represent advantages a character may have due to circumstance and opportunity. They include material possessions and social networks, elements external to the physical changes brought on by the Embrace. While the **World of Darkness Rulebook** describes Merits in greater detail and provides lists of examples, vampires are removed somewhat from mortal society and often require unique or specialized Merits.

What follows are traits designed solely for vampires, allowing players to further distinguish their characters from ordinary mortals and other nonhuman beings. These Merits are available at character creation and during the course of the chronicle. The first instance assumes that your vampire character is already Embraced at the beginning of play or is Embraced very soon afterward. (It's not possible for a strictly mortal character to have the following traits as presented here.)

Haven (• to •••••; special)

Effect: A haven is a place where a vampire sleeps, protected from the sun during the deadly daylight hours. Legends tell of vampires in dark, twisted citadels on high mountain peaks, complete with labyrinthine catacombs, but the reality is far less grandiose. In truth, a haven can be as simple as a sewer or an abandoned warehouse or a crate in a forgotten storage closet, as long as it is undisturbed between dawn and dusk.

All havens are not created equal. A warehouse might have plenty of space and proximity to a significant amount of prey, but it might not be secure against unwanted visitors. An abandoned subway car in a long-forgotten tunnel has space and adequate security, but it might be so far out of the way that finding prey is difficult. Great time and effort is spent finding suitable havens, and their value is represented by three factors — location, size and security. Players who

choose this Merit must also choose how to allocate these three factors when spending points. For instance, two points may be spent on Haven Location, with a third spent on Haven Security.

A good Haven Location makes it easier for a vampire to feed, situated near a meeting place for large numbers of humans. A haven with many dots in this category might be close to several nightclubs or bars that do considerable nighttime business, while one with few dots might simply be close to a bus or train station that brings travelers on a regular basis. Each dot of Haven Location grants a +1 die bonus on hunting checks for the character who controls it and any whom she allows in. Havens without any dots in Location are sufficiently secluded so as to not provide any bonus.

Haven Size is important to characters who need a place to safely store their possessions and valuables. A haven with no dots in Haven Size is just large enough for its owner and perhaps a single companion, with minimal if any storage capacity — the aforementioned crate in the forgotten storage closet, or a cramped apartment. By spending points to increase a haven's size, a player allows for accoutrements and personal effects. Larger havens can be anything from mansions to mountain hideaways to vast subterranean catacombs. Note, however, that havens of considerable size are not necessarily easy to maintain.

•	A small apartment or underground chamber; 1-2 rooms
••	A large apartment or small family home; 3-4 rooms
•••	A warehouse, church or large home; 5-8 rooms, or large enclosure
••••	A abandoned mansion or network of subway tunnels; equivalent of 9-15 rooms or chambers
•••••	A sprawling estate or vast network of tunnels; countless rooms or chambers

Of course, Haven Location and Haven Size do not prevent rival vampires from attempting to find and steal choice havens, nor do they prevent intrusion by mortals (police, criminal organizations, social workers). Players of characters who wish to ensure privacy and safety may choose to spend points on Haven Security, thus making it difficult for others to gain entrance. Havens with no dots in Haven Security can be found by those intent enough to look, and offer little protection once they have been breached. Each dot of Haven Security subtracts one die from efforts to intrude into the haven by anyone a character doesn't specifically allow in. This increased difficulty may be because the entrance is so difficult to locate (behind a bookcase, under a carpet) or simply difficult to penetrate (behind a vault door). Also, each dot of Haven Security offers a +1 bonus on Initiative for those inside against anyone attempting to gain entrance (good sight lines, video surveillance).

Characters whose players spend no points at all on Haven might have their own small, humble havens, or perhaps they share the haven of a sire or Prince. In any event, they simply do not gain the mechanical benefits of those who have spent Merit points improving the quality of their homes.

Each aspect of the Haven Merit has a limit of 5. In other words, Haven Location, Haven Size and Haven Security may not rise above 5 (to a maximum of 15 points spent on this Merit).

Special: It's possible for the Haven Merit to be shared among characters in a close-knit group. They might simply be devoted to one another and willing to pool what they have, or perhaps their mutual reliance on an individual or trust could bring them together to share what they have in common.

To share this Merit, two or more characters simply have to be willing to pool their dots for greater capability. A shared rating in the Haven Merit cannot rise higher than five dots in any of the three aspects of the trait. That is, characters cannot pool more than five points to be devoted to, say, Haven Size. If they wish to devote extra points to the Merit, they must allocate those dots to a different aspect of the Merit, such as Location or Security.

Shared Haven dots can be lost. Coterie members or associates might be abused or mistreated, ending relationships. Group members might perform actions that cast themselves (and the group) in a bad light. Money might be spent or lost. If any group member does something to diminish the haven, its dots decrease for all group members. That's the weakness of sharing dots in this Merit. The chain is only as strong as its weakest link. The Storyteller dictates when character actions or events in a story compromise shared Haven dots.

Characters can also leave a shared haven. A rift might form between close Kindred. A character might meet Final Death. Or one could be kicked out of the haven by the others. When a character leaves a shared-Haven relationship, the dots he contributed are removed from the pool. If the individual still survives, he doesn't get all his dots back for his own purposes. He gets one less than he originally contributed. So, if a character breaks a relationship with his coterie, his two Haven dots are lost by the group, but he gets only one dot back for his own purposes. The lost dot represents the cost or bad image that comes from the breakup. If all members agree to part ways, they all lose one dot from what they originally contributed.

The Storyteller decides what reduced dots mean in the story when a character leaves a shared haven. Perhaps no one else picks up the character's attention to Haven Security, leaving that to drop. The haven might not be tended as fastidiously, causing a drop in the Haven Location value. Maybe a portion of the haven falls into disuse or even collapses, causing an effective drop in Haven Size. Whatever the case, a plausible explanation must be determined.

A character need not devote all of her Haven dots to the shared Haven Merit, of course. A Kindred might maintain a separate haven of her own outside the communal one represented by the shared trait. Any leftover dots that a character has (or is unwilling to share) signify what she has to draw upon as an individual, separate from her partners. For example, three characters share a haven and expend a group total of five dots. One character chooses to use two other dots on a private haven for herself. Those remaining two dots represent a haven entirely separate from what she and her partners have established together.

To record a shared Haven Merit on your character sheet, put an asterisk next to the name of the Haven Merit and fill in the total dots that your character has access to thanks to his partnership. In order to record his original contribution, write it in parentheses along with the Merit's name. It is not important to note which aspect of the Haven Merit on which those points are spent, as this allows greater flexibility should a character ever decide to withdraw from the community arrangement. The result looks like this:

In this example, the character shares a Haven Merit dedicated to the coterie's communal shelter. He contributes two dots to the relationship, and the group has a total of four dots that are made available to each member. The character also has his own private Haven Merit rated ● ● ●, which he maintains by himself. And, the character has Retainer rated ● ● that is also his own Merit.

Herd (● to ●●●●●)

Some vampires tire of the hunt and seek to develop a small group of mortals upon whom they can feed without fear. Such a herd may take many forms, from a brothel of prostitutes to a blood cult worshiping a vampiric god. These mortals provide nourishment without the difficulties of the hunt. Typically, herds are not very controllable or closely connected to the vampires who use them, nor do they possess great skill in any one area. (For effective agents, the Allies or Retainers Merit is more suitable.) Each dot of Herd adds one die to feeding rolls (p. 164).

Status (● to ●●●●●; special)

While certain Merits detailed in the **World of Darkness Rulebook** focus on recognition in mortal society, certain Status concerns itself with the social orders of the night and represents recognition among other vampires. Status is divided into three areas — City, Clan and Covenant. Players must choose one of these three areas for each Merit point spent. (Enterprising Storytellers may come up with additional types of Status, and clever players might have unique applications as well. Status is designed as a sort of "umbrella" Merit, under which new types can be created.)

City Status represents a vested responsibility and according acknowledgement in the affairs of a domain. Regardless of clan and covenant, certain individuals rise to the top of the social or feudal strata, exemplary because of their efforts in the name of the domain as a whole. Princes, Regents, Primogen, Harpies and other "officers" of a given domain fit this description.

Additionally, City Status represents those Kindred who aren't part of the prevailing social structure, but who nonetheless have significant esteem, sway or reputation among the Kindred. Examples include bosses of powerful gangs, Kindred who have considerable influence in specialized areas

(prominent businessmen, city government, health care and hospitals, religious communities), or even just those who are powerful in their own right but largely apolitical, as with a potent elder who abstains from city responsibilities but whose territory is respected by all other local Kindred.

In some cases, City Status is very much a chicken-and-egg situation — does Prince Maxwell have City Status 5 because he's Prince, or did his accumulated City Status result in his claiming praxis? In other cases, City Status obviously reflects accomplishment, as with a political activist who has many mortal supporters — but those supporters obviously didn't join his cause because they knew he was a vampire. Harpies, in particular, make much of these distinctions, but some speculate that that's because their own Status falls under the definition of City Status.

- ● Hound or "rising star"
- ● ● Sheriff or "accomplished individual"
- ● ● ● Harpy, Seneschal, Master of Elysium or "much-deserved reputation"
- ● ● ● ● Regent, Primogen, Herald or "cornerstone of Kindred society"
- ● ● ● ● ● Prince or "true paragon"

Clan Status is concerned with lineage and the Blood. At the outset of a chronicle, a Kindred's standing often reflects the prestige her sire has gained and passed along, such as with regard to the Ventrue. Many assume that childer who were Embraced by powerful and influential members of the clan have already shown some special quality or excellence, otherwise they would not have been chosen by so great a sire. This kind of recognition is short lived, however. A neonate might enjoy prestige by association under the purview of her sire, but such a favored childe is expected to make a name for herself.

Vampires who truly embody the ideals of their clan and who establish themselves in positions of power and influence (often as Prisci) gain the respect of others in their clan, being perceived as models for success. While the Daeva tell tales of particularly vicious Harpies of distant cities, the Gangrel speak of brooding hulks who confidently brave the Lupine-infested wilds alone. Those who diverge from the expected behavior of the clan in remarkable ways gain renown (or notoriety), as well, perhaps founding bloodlines that become known to vampire society as a whole.

Clan Status is not so rigidly defined as City Status. While individual clan titles might arise, the notion of esteem is more general in this context.

Covenant Status represents rank, achievement and responsibility, less concerned with clan ideals and more with covenant actions, philosophies and accomplishments. The various covenants are not bound by any supernatural means or governed by clan lineage. They find a commonality of goals and ideologies, instead. It is not enough to be powerful or exemplary of clan ideals; a covenant is concerned with what its members have done to benefit its cause and combat its rivals.

Those Kindred who enjoy the greatest covenant-based esteem are often the core members of their factions in a given city, those around whom others rally. These Kindred instigate or mediate conflict with other covenants, generally looking to further certain idealistic goals and establish themselves or other members in positions of influence in the local hierarchy. A Mekhet in command of a massive spy network might have status within his clan, but the lowliest of his spies might risk her unlife to gather a specific piece of information that helps oust the Invictus Prince, subsequently enjoying far more status with, say, the Ordo Dracul than her master.

A character must have at least a single dot of Covenant Status in order to gain the benefits of any special abilities of that covenant. In other words, a character must have at least one dot of Covenant Status (Lancea Sanctum) in order to learn Theban Sorcery. Or a character must have at least one dot of Covenant Status (Invictus) to take advantage of the experience-point break on the Herd, Mentor, Resources and Retainer Merits. If a character leaves a covenant after learning some of its secrets, he does not lose any of those traits for which he paid experience points, but he may not learn additional dots of those traits (or additional dots at that particular price break, as with the Invictus and the Carthians). See p. 91-92 for the complete list of which covenants grant which benefits.

Like Clan Status, Covenant Status is not so specifically tied to certain titles. It is more a notion of an individual's accomplishments. A Lancea Sanctum Priest, for example, has a greater title than, say, a noted ethicist of the covenant, but that ethicist might have written numerous treatises on the state of undeath and the soul, according her more esteem among her peers than the Priest who rides solely on the weight of her title.

- The character is known to a select subset of the clan/covenant — a spy network, perhaps.
- • The majority of the clan/covenant in the city recognizes the character's face and can recall her exploits.
- • • The character's deeds are known to all in the local covenant, even in other nearby cities; many members of other covenants recognize her face.
- • • • Word of the character's exploits has traveled far, and her name is known in cities around the country.
- • • • • The character's name and face are synonymous with her clan/covenant; her exploits are taught to new members of the clan/covenant.

Status can serve as a mixed blessing, however. Those who enjoy the most might be able to use it to their advantage, but they are also visible targets for their enemies. High levels of Status make it almost impossible to pass unnoticed, even while they open doors that would otherwise remain closed.

Status works like a "social tool" in that it adds to dice pools for social interactions between members of the sub-group in question. That is, Covenant Status adds to dice pools for interactions with members of the same covenant, Clan Status enhances interactions with members of the same Clan, and City Status affects those who are recognized residents of the given domain. City Status, however, may be ignored by those who are among the unbound.

Example: *Loki wants access to the Mekhet Priscus, but the Priscus is already occupied with an envoy from Clan Daeva. He instead finds himself dealing with one of her aides, another Mekhet. Loki, a Mekhet himself, tries to convince the aide that he has important business to discuss with the Priscus. His player adds Clan Status to a Manipulation + Persuasion dice pool. Loki has Manipulation 2, Persuasion 3 and Clan Status (Mekhet) 2, creating a pool of seven dice for the task.*

Status does not add to dice pools predicated on supernatural powers. For example, a Prince's City Status is not added to a dice pool for use of his Dread Gaze power.

Dealing with Status can be a mire of responsibility, though clever characters can turn it to their advantage. They may actually have a variety of Status — it is not unheard of for a character to have City Status, Clan Status and Covenant Status.

A character may have Clan Status only as a member of his own clan. For instance, a Nosferatu never gains Clan Status (Gangrel) no matter how much aid he provides the Savages. His aid of the Gangrel may certainly earn him esteem, but such concern is better handled on a case-by-case basis by the Storyteller, not in the form of Clan Status.

Covenant Status is unique in that a character may, on occasion, have more than one form of it. This occurs almost exclusively at low levels, where a character is often beneath the notice of most other members of his covenants. A character may never have more than three dots total in Covenant Status among multiple covenants. A double-agent, for example, might take two dots worth of Covenant Status (Carthians) and a single dot of Covenant Status (Lancea Sanctum), representing the character's true allegiance to the Carthians as well as the fact that he's in on the ground floor of the Lancea Sanctum so that he can feed information back to his Carthian fellows. A character may even have a single dot of Covenant Status in three different covenants — perhaps he's somewhat accomplished in each, but has yet to determine where his true loyalties lie. Naturally, a character with Status in only one Covenant is not beholden to the three-dot limit.

A character with dots in Covenant Status through multiple factions does indeed gain access to those covenants' special benefits. Covenants expect certain contributions of their members, however, and if other Kindred find out that the vampire in question plays multiple sides against the middle, he might see that Status vanish in a single night in which he's called upon to account for his treacheries. Such is also the reason that cumulative Covenant Status is limited to three dots. By the time a character gains a certain degree of Status in a single covenant, he sticks out like a sore thumb if he turns up among another covenant's members. (An exception to this might occur if a character is truly some sort of deep-cover agent or other mole, but that circumstance is best handled at the Storyteller's discretion).

Other Kindred envy their beauty and grace, their ability to incite passion in mortals, the ease with which they glide through the masses — and that envy is almost as potent a draught to the Daeva as blood itself. These Kindred are consummate predators, and they would seem to be the perfect vampires. Alas, most are too dead inside to enjoy it.

Called Succubi by other clans, the Daeva are experts at making their prey come to them, practically offering themselves not merely as food but as playthings. No self-respecting Daeva resorts to attacking transients in alleyways. Rather, these are the Kindred who accompany a smitten young mortal back to her place, leaving her languid and sexually spent by morning (if she's fortunate) or an exsanguinated husk (if she's not). Seducers and sensualists, the Daeva could practically charm the unease off a Nosferatu. When the fancy strikes them, they play politics like a finely tuned instrument. Even allies and coconspirators who know they cannot trust a Succubus find themselves lulled into doing just that, caught up in the Daeva's personal magnetism. Daeva become Harpies more than Kindred of any other clan, and they wield that power mercilessly. A stinging rebuke from a Daeva Harpy can shred a vampire's reputation faster than a denunciation by the Prince himself.

Most Succubi are overtly sensual beings, drawn by beauty and blood in equal measure, but it's an artificial passion. Their ability to feel true attachment to other people atrophies over years of manipulating the love of mortals and the respect of their fellow Kindred, until the Daeva can no longer understand those emotions as anything other than tools to be exploited and motions to imitate. For all their apparent fervor, most Succubi are as dead spiritually as they are physically. They claim to understand desire, but all they truly know is need, and it is this deadening of emotions that causes so many jaded Daeva to become depraved in their efforts to feel again.

Daeva move through the circles of society in which their lustful natures best serve them, whether among high society or low culture. Drawn to beauty and congregations of mortals, they often frequent theaters, galleries, trendy clubs, whiskey dives, drug dens, brothels and everything in between. Personal preferences aside, the Succubi are found through all strata of society. Their seductive natures allow these vampires to find willing vessels no matter where they go, and this ability has enabled them to thrive, to become arguably one of the most numerous clans. No single social class has room for them all, so newcomers and losers of political and social games often find themselves dwelling among the poor and unwashed — or at least the middle classes, which, since their blood is as red as any other, means basically the same thing to most Succubi. Few Kindred are as desperate as a Daeva trying to claw his way into his own niche. Wise Kindred know better than to take advantage of a Daeva in such a position, for fear he'll one night achieve the position and privilege he seeks. The Succubi never forget a slight.

Nickname: Succubi (male Daeva are sometimes called Incubi, but the clan itself is referred to by the more common female sobriquet)

Covenant: The majority of these Kindred are found within the Invictus. They are well suited to the political game, and here they can surround themselves with lessers, becoming ever more jaded and inhuman as they grow older. Most Daeva are too self-centered to feel the religious calling of the Lancea Sanctum, but those few exceptions who are able to channel their sensual drive into matters of faith often obtain positions of prominence, making the clan seem more numerous in the Lancea Sanctum than it really is. Few Daeva bother with the Carthians. Why fight for an egalitarian society when the current system favors the Daeva? The Ordo Dracul covenant is home to a small number of devoted Daeva, and it would have more if the rigors of the covenant's policies didn't make being a hedonist among its ranks less than rewarding. The Circle of the Crone has few Daeva for much the same reasons as the Lancea Sanctum, and those who do join often do so more out of a debased and jaded sense of rebellion against societal mores than any real belief in the Pagans' teachings. A surprising number of Succubi fall in among the unaligned, convinced, in their own self-perceived superiority, that they have no need for the laws and restrictions of society.

Appearance: Daeva often Embrace out of infatuation — or at least going through the motions of passion — and they rarely choose to involve themselves with unattractive mortals. Thus, most Daeva are surpassingly beautiful. The clan is also highly in tune with trends and fashion, the better to prowl among and attract prey.

Havens: Daeva havens vary, but they're almost universally comforting… in a subtly alarming way that suggests an artificial appeal to whatever vessels a Kindred favors. Most are convenient to social or political centers. The specific aesthetics vary, but most are intended to impress any compatriots, allies or victims who might be invited in. Penthouses and condominiums are particularly popular. Many Daeva don't bother to keep up appearances if they don't think they'll bring prey home, meaning that some havens are sloppy or cluttered with unsettling reminders of previous vessels' presence.

Background: With a growing number of exceptions, Daeva are Embraced from the ranks of society's elite. Succubus sires look for some combination of charm, culture, seductiveness, desire to achieve, passion and physical beauty. Many Daeva Embrace mortals to whom they have become attached, but this attachment almost invariably proves false, a mixture of lust and simple hunger. Few relationships are as euphoric as those between a Daeva and a newly Embraced childe, and few grow cold as swiftly.

Character Creation: Social Attributes and Skills are of primary concern, particularly those that aid in making good first impressions, in persuading and in seducing. Social Merits are equally common, representing the character's connections to both mortal and Kindred society. Given that most Daeva feed almost exclusively through manipulation and betrayal, a high starting Humanity score is a good idea, since it's likely to fall precipitously.

Favored Attributes: Dexterity or Manipulation

Clan Disciplines: Celerity, *Majesty*, Vigor

Weakness: Perhaps out of some deep longing for the true passions they lost after the Embrace, the Daeva have difficulty steeling themselves against the hedonism they allow themselves as members of the Damned. Any time a Daeva has an opportunity to indulge her Vice but does not do so, she loses two points of Willpower (as opposed to gaining one by partaking in its pleasures).

Organization: Status among the Daeva is entirely a social issue, and many young ones resemble squabbling cliques more so than undying creatures of the night. Not even elder Daeva are strangers to petty vendettas and long-nursed grudges. While a Succubus is likely to join with one of her own in the face of an outside threat, they compete with one another as much as they do with other Kindred, if not more so. The Daeva therefore have no true formal structure. Those who are dominant in the Danse Macabre's social and political scene are dominant among the clan as well.

Bloodlines: Duchagne (an aristocratic but degenerate European bloodline that seems to have the ability to directly manipulate the senses and sensations of others), Toreador (a branch of the clan that has recognized its loss of passion and tries to re-create it by inspiring mortals either to creative pursuits or extreme emotions; they invariably grow bored and move on, leaving their former wards desolate), Xiao.

Concepts: Bored socialite, club hopper, club owner, cult leader, cultured serial killer, full-time Harpy, jaded vampire who gets off on being a creature of the night (a fairly melodramatic attitude found only among the very young before the weight of the Requiem fully settles on them), Kindred politico, local covenant spokesman, patron of the arts, professional "escort"

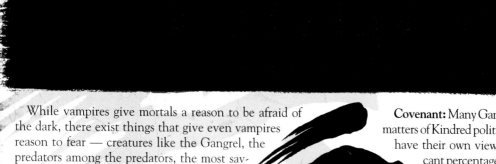

While vampires give mortals a reason to be afraid of the dark, there exist things that give even vampires reason to fear — creatures like the Gangrel, the predators among the predators, the most savage of beasts. Perhaps the only clan whose mere mention almost always elicits a chilled shudder or a reverent nod, the Gangrel are, in many ways, the "noble savages" of the vampiric race. Upon their Embrace (and sometimes before), the Gangrel seek to sever their ties with everything pertaining to their mortal lives. Many prefer the counsel of animals and other beasts, and some eschew contact with the mortal world entirely. While many retain and even value their humanity, they do so within the bounds and context of their newfound existence, and not as an attempt to hold onto what's been lost, for no other option is practical to a clan whose very soul is so intimately intertwined with its Beast. While others delude themselves about what the Embrace "truly means," the Gangrel know what they've become, so they strive to make peace with it. On the whole, they spend more time in communion with their bestial side than other vampires do, and though such activity more than accounts for their nickname and reputation, few would disagree that the Gangrel truly benefit from their introspection.

Their special bond with the Beast seems to give many Gangrel a unique insight into the Kindred condition, and some of the wisest vampires to be found in all the world hail from this clan. Whereas other Kindred try to become scholars or philosophers, collecting endless data and positing on the theoretical, the Gangrel are its yogis and medicine men, its bodhisattvas and whirling dervishes. The unequivocal and irreplaceable benefit of first-hand experience flows through them, supplanting the theoretical with the practical, and making the Gangrel widely respected among those who recognize the primeval nature of the Kindred soul. This insight makes the clan invaluable, but also makes it dangerous, and some would just as soon silence the Gangrel as hear their frank wisdom.

Nickname: Savages

Covenant: Many Gangrel are largely unconcerned with matters of Kindred politics, but that's not to say they don't have their own views. Perhaps surprisingly, a significant percentage of the clan is active in the Circle of the Crone, which provides spiritually minded Gangrel with a ready-made forum for their rituals and beliefs, and a great many of the Circle's leaders hail from the clan's ranks. Some of the more proactive Gangrel find the Carthian mindset appealing, and a number of highly motivated Savages have taken up the cause in recent years. A few Gangrel fall in with the Lancea Sanctum and Invictus, due to the nature of each covenant's beliefs. Those who are active in the latter group usually work for important elders or are elders themselves, while the few Gangrel of the Lancea Sanctum are among the most frightening and relentless Kindred anyone would ever (not) want to meet. Likewise, the Ordo Dracul sees few Gangrel, though some who join do so not to learn the blood magic of the covenant but to pursue mysteries of their origin without the hauteur of the Lancea Sanctum. A great many Gangrel also find their place among the independent and unaligned Kindred, whose lack of structure and love of freedom are attractive to Savages who prefer that elders of other clans keep their politics to themselves.

Appearance: The archetypal Savage is rarely concerned with his appearance, though most recognize the need to both blend in and put potential prey at ease. As a rule, Gangrel prefer function over form, and are rarely caught clad in anything that restricts movement to any great degree. Due to their clan weakness, they must always be wary of just how bestial they appear to others, and some especially old (or angry) Gangrel typically learn some amount of Obfuscate to avoid potentially disastrous situations.

Havens: One of the clan's greatest strengths is its deft maneuverability, a good portion of which stems from its Discipline of Protean, which allows the Gangrel to take rest in any natural soil. Sleeping in the ground does, of course, have its drawbacks, and even the most feral of Savages comes to appreciate

> ## Stereotypes
>
> **Daeva:** Primp and preen all you want, but you're more like us than you imagine.
>
> **Mekhet:** Fine. Stay hidden.
>
> **Nosferatu:** Proof that not all Kindred are created equal; some are way more fucking scary than others.
>
> **Ventrue:** I'll piss blood on their boots and wear their skins as a trophy.
>
> ***
>
> **Lupines:** Next time you think you're the shit, I'll show you one of these and we'll settle the matter for good.
>
> **Mages:** Under that mask of power lies a human face, warm and flush with blood.
>
> **Mortals:** They move in flocks, so never forget what they are to us wolves.

having an actual place to hang his hat after a while. A number of the more urbane (or at least urban) Gangrel therefore elect to take traditional havens, though their restless spirits and mistrust of other Kindred tends to keep them moving.

Background: Potential Gangrel can come from nearly any former life, but few Savages would choose a mortal who did not possess a strong survival instinct. Beyond this, most are quite particular about those they sire. Gangrel loathe personal weakness and those who are soft of body or mind (especially given their weakness), particularly those with a paper-thin or disconnected sense of being. Clan members most admire those whose greatest strengths are the strengths of the self — self-awareness, self-confidence and self-reliance. While it is not unheard of for a Gangrel to Embrace someone who lacks these qualities (usually as a cruel test to see whether the Embrace will sufficiently toughen the person up), most Gangrel hold to their standards, as not doing so is often more effort than it's worth.

Character Creation: Gangrel are very honest with themselves about what is and is not their forte, and they seek to improve those things to which they are especially or innately suited. Many Gangrel come off seeming hyper-specialized, their players having devoted significant dots to those Attributes and Skills in which they are focused. This rule is a very general one, however, and numerous exceptions apply. Due to temperament, the aptly named Savages are rarely very strong in the Social department (though entire bloodlines of sociable Gangrel probably exist somewhere), preferring instead to hone body and reinforce the mind. An even mix of Physical and Mental Skills is always good, erring toward the Physical side.

Favored Attributes: Composure or Stamina

Clan Disciplines: Animalism, *Protean*, Resilience

Weakness: As befits their sobriquet, the Gangrel are more closely tied to their Beasts than are other Kindred. The more they feel the call of the Beast, the more bestial they become, and the more their minds become those of less principled animals. With regard to dice pools based on Intelligence and Wits Attributes, the 10-again rule does not apply. Additionally, any 1's that come up on a roll subtract from successes. (The latter part of the weakness does not affect dramatic-failure rules.) This weakness does not apply to dice pools involving perception or reaction to surprise (see p. 151 of the **World of Darkness Rulebook**), or to the Resolve Attribute.

Example: *The Gangrel Unholy is chasing Loki, who manages to elude her, but not before he drops a mystic artifact he stole from one of her other old enemies in the Ordo Dracul. The Unholy has a chance to figure out what the artifact is, her player rolling a dice pool of Intelligence + Occult (seven dice). The dice come up 10, 8, 7, 7, 6, 3 and 1. Normally, the player would roll the 10 again, but not in this case, as this dice pool involves the Unholy's Intelligence Attribute. Furthermore, the 1 rolled cancels out one of the player's two successes, leaving only one. The Unholy knows that this is an item of mystic significance, but she has no inkling as to what it does or what might activate it.*

Organization: The Gangrel are perhaps the least organized of the clans. They have no hierarchy per se and are largely disinterested in either clan structure or intra-clan activity for its own sake. The only nod they give to such matters comes in the form of an event called a Gather. These meetings serve a twofold purpose. First, as an opportunity for Gangrel to unite and update one another on the events of the intervening time. Second, as a forum for official intra-clan dispute resolution. Before this practice began, ferocious Savages visited their rage upon one another at will and without process, and the clan as a whole suffered. Thus began the practice of settling disputes at gatherings of the clan before a Priscus or Primogen, where any conflict (or combat, if necessary) could be moderated and monitored by the peers of both Savages. As a result of this practice, the clan has grown more cooperative over time, leading to markedly fewer intra-clan kills. The majority of such disputes now stop short of Final Death.

Bloodlines: Anavashra (mysterious ritualists who claim domains in India and Bangladesh); Anubi (Egyptian cultists who have feuded long with the Lancea Sanctum); Bruja (a rogue biker gang that slakes its thirsts at will and terrorizes Baja Mexico and Southern California); Matasuntha (a bloodline of warriors descended from an ancient warlord of the Huns); Taifa (sociable and sophisticated, these Middle Eastern Gangrel are known for their political savvy and social aptitude).

Concepts: Archeologist, bodyguard, bumpkin, circuit rider, guru, mercenary, nomad, shaman, survivalist, urban predator, zookeeper

Vampires have always been creatures of the night by design, but none more so than the dwellers in darkness who compose Clan Mekhet. Darkness is the hallmark of this lineage, and its members surround themselves with it like a corpse wears a shroud. The hallmarks of the clan are stealth and wisdom, so it is entirely fitting that they are associated with darkness — the better to hide them and the source of the knowledge they exhume.

Clan Mekhet comprises one of the most cosmopolitan memberships among the great families of the Kindred. Although they compose a clan born of darkness, these Shadows, as they are known, interpret that darkness in many ways. Some of the clan's members are masters of the night, using their gifts and undead powers to make a place for themselves within the aristocracy of the Damned. Others are literal skulkers in the shadows, ready to plant a stake in a rival's heart or steal the wealth from a rival's haven. Still others are poets or painters, heirs to darkness of a more personal nature. Yet more Mekhet are diviners of secrets, questing after information itself forgotten and thus relegated to the darkness of memory. Clan Mekhet runs the gamut from filth-streaked murderers to enlightened philosopher-Princes and everything in between.

While the clan certainly has coarse members, the Mekhet are, by and large, marked by a certain degree of finesse with whatever aspect of tenebrous unlife they choose to pursue. A Mekhet bodyguard, for example, is unlikely to be a brawling brute, but more likely to know an ornate fighting style. A Mekhet infiltrator is gracious or invisible, not a sloppy vandal. A sage or scholar might have such supernatural acumen that his abilities are downright oracular instead of merely archival. Mekhet Kindred very much consider themselves paragons of the vampiric state, so whatever they do, they devote themselves to it and refine their capacity almost to the point of second nature.

Nickname: Shadows

Covenant: A great many Mekhet fall in with the Carthians or the Lancea Sanctum, both of which have strong traditions of politics and secrecy to which the Shadows can lend their talents. The same can be said of the Circle of the Crone, which typically draws Mekhet by virtue of its underlying message of redemption and meaning in the unlives of the Damned. Less philosophical and more viscerally impassioned Shadows are often drawn to the ranks of the unaligned, whose ideology of freedom (or anonymity…) is an easy fit for the wild at heart. This is not to say that the clan is weak within the Invictus, though. Invictus Shadows are simply quieter about their covenant affiliation than their boastful brothers, or are at least more reserved about the reasons for their affiliation, which typically coincide with those of the Carthians or Lancea Sanctum. More than a few Mekhet find themselves among the Ordo Dracul, as the study of its esoteric principles often coincides with artifact-finding expeditions or secrets to be gleaned from other Dragons.

Appearance: Of all the clans, the Mekhet are perhaps the least uniform in the way they appear to others. Some play the clan archetype to the hilt, dressing in black clothing and adopting styles that allow them to blend into the scenery. Others choose from popular mortal styles and fashions, attempting to blend in with the crowd by evading individual notice. This practice is particularly common among Mekhet who associate with one particular subculture, thereby becoming an iconic, though rarely outstanding, example of that group's tastes.

Havens: Of all the clans, the Mekhet are typically the most polarized by their preferences and proximity to the mortal world. Some Mekhet prefer to keep close to where the action is. In large cities, where their numbers are strong, many take flats in the downtown core, or at least within short distance of various urban hot spots or the Rack. Older or more withdrawn Shadows are often preoccupied with security, and many elect to dwell in

STEREOTYPES

Daeva: They thoughtlessly despoil what they once were, and shamelessly mock what they've become.

Gangrel: Noble in their own way, but sadly disconnected from their roots.

Nosferatu: Brothers in darkness — but beware sibling rivalries.

Ventrue: Great company until events conspire to put one of you in an elevated position, at which point they quickly grow intolerable.

***

Lupines: I suspect there is more to them than the savagery we witness from afar.

Mages: Some secrets the Kindred should not know, yet the mages wield them with such grace.

Mortals: See them for what they are: the source of our sustenance and the bane of our existence.

large homes on the outskirts of populated areas. Such Kindred often keep dogs and other servitors, made strong by the cursed Vitae of their masters. A few paranoid Shadows even take havens underground, where they cohabitate (or compete) with Nosferatu for shelter from the sun.

Background: Prospective Mekhet can come from just about any walk of mortal life. The only common thread linking potential candidates is an affinity for the night itself or some metaphorical darkness, such as a pained soul or a thirst for knowledge. Many Mekhet are tutored heavily by their sires post-Embrace, in order that they understand the nature of the clan and its duties. A Mekhet sire who leaves a new childe to the misinformation of other Kindred is a rarity indeed. Some prefer to let their progeny discover the Kindred world on their own, but not even these sires stray so far that they can't watch a protégés' progress.

Character Creation: Most Shadows prize those traits that best assist them in furthering their passion or their cause. Violent or politically motivated Mekhet typically favor Physical and Social Attributes and Skills, to improve their dealings with others and to allow them to strike from their namesake. Scholarly or philosophical clan members tend to acquire as many dots worth of Mental traits as they can. For many Shadow players, the process of assigning new traits is like being a kid in a candy store — just about everything looks good, but you don't have a whole lot to spend. The best solution is to keep your character's personality in mind when deciding what to take.

Favored Attributes: Intelligence or Wits

Clan Disciplines: *Auspex*, Celerity, Obfuscate

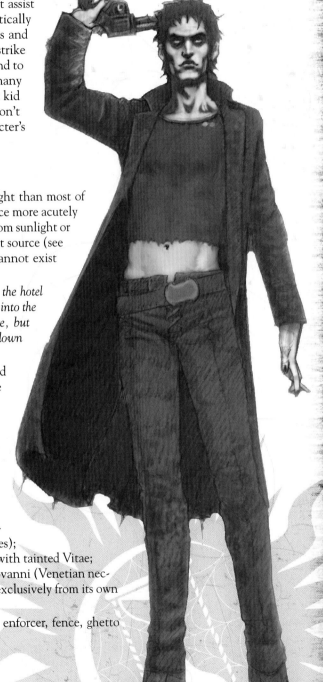

Weakness: As creatures of darkness even more sensitive to light than most of the Damned, the Mekhet suffer certain banes of vampiric existence more acutely than do their fellow Kindred. Whenever Mekhet suffer damage from sunlight or fire, they take an additional point of aggravated damage from that source (see p. 172 for more on sunlight and fire damage). Just as shadow cannot exist without light, so too does light banish shadow.

Example: *Loki catches the telltale smell of smoke and realizes that the hotel where he's visiting the Mekhet Priscus is on fire. He dashes out the door into the burning hallway. Normally, this would cause three points of damage, but Loki's Mekhet susceptibility to flame increases it to four. Loki sprints down the hall, hoping the whole building isn't an inferno….*

Organization: While Mekhet is not the most tightly organized of clans, it does have some structure. The majority of it falls in line with the clan's various bloodlines, which are generally more independent than those of other clans. Nonetheless, some clanwide structure does exist. In addition to the Primogen in any Mekhet-heavy city, the Shadows often give more deference to a Priscus in clan affairs than do members of other clans, particularly if a Priscus has earned a reputation for wisdom.

Bloodlines: Agonistes (Mediterranean historians and philosophers who seek to record and retain the knowledge Kindred lose over time and in torpor); Mnemosyne (fervent vampires who possess the ability to share memories and experiences through blood ties); the Morbus lineage of European origin that suffers the Requiem with tainted Vitae; Norvegi (an inbred, degenerate cult of spies and thieves); Sangiovanni (Venetian necromancers who maintain a tight family structure that Embraces exclusively from its own mortal stock).

Concepts: Antiquities scholar, assassin, Casanova, diplomat, enforcer, fence, ghetto Harpy, pilgrim, policeman, power behind the praxis, seer

Not all curses are created equal, and even the Damned have outcasts. These are the Nosferatu, the most overtly disturbing of the undead. Only sometimes able to pass as human, the Haunts are horribly warped by the Embrace, either physically or… otherwise. They dwell in shadows that other vampires would not dare. Even other undead fear the Nosferatu, for their unsettling seemings are constant reminders that those Kindred who look mortal are not. They grudgingly respect the Nosferatu as well. These blighted creatures have incredible powers of stealth, terrifying strength, and they embody the monstrous destructive force that every one of the Damned can muster if pushed too far. If they had their druthers, most other clans would prefer never to associate with the Nosferatu at all, yet the Haunts' inarguable talents and brute force make them too dangerous to ignore. So other Kindred offer them a tense hospitality, hide their unease behind wary diplomacies and pray that the Nosferatu leave as soon as possible.

Many Nosferatu conceal their loneliness and resentment behind masks of indifference. They scoff in turn at those who recoil from them, belittling pretty vampires with soirées and silly political games, all the while seething at their exclusion. This isolation has fostered strong familial bonds among the Nosferatu. To those outside their ranks, they put on a unified front, creating the impression of a single extended network. The truth, of course, is that Nosferatu squabble and compete with one another as much as members of any other clan — but when faced with an outside threat, they close ranks.

The Nosferatu's inability to blend in with society forces them to dwell apart, often congregating in places others shun. Some find sanctuary in the sewers, using influence with mortal government and construction, as well as their own substantial strength, to expand simple maintenance tunnels and sluiceways into vast underground warrens. Others lurk in cemeteries, sharing aboveground crypts with sedentary occupants. Still others prefer abandoned homes, often giving rise to neighborhood urban legends of haunted houses, or exist in the basements or boiler rooms of modern office buildings. Tradition holds that any Nosferatu is welcome in any warren until she provides her brethren reason to expel her. The Haunts might not all get along, but they recognize their common bond — not that they have any choice, since it follows their aspect like a miasma.

Feared by and therefore ostracized from society, many Nosferatu become as alien as their demeanor. Others choose the opposite path, becoming surprisingly cultured, well mannered and well spoken to compensate for their unnerving seeming. The latter are the Haunts most frequently found playing politics with other Kindred. The Nosferatu are also known as purveyors of information. Not only do their supernatural powers make them foes to be reckoned with, but many elder Nosferatu are keepers of ancient lore, rivaling anything preserved by the Ventrue or Mekhet. Sophisticated Haunts trade knowledge the way other Kindred trade favors, and if a Nosferatu doesn't know something, he can probably scare someone who does into telling him. It is this trade in terror, more than anything else, that makes the Nosferatu too valuable — and too dangerous — to ignore. After all, one never knows what the horrid Haunts tell one's enemies, or how many of them wait in ambush.

Nickname: Haunts

Covenant: The Nosferatu are everywhere. The Invictus nervously welcomes them as enforcers, informants and soldiers. Those Nosferatu who obtain power in the First Estate tend to extremes; becoming relatively benevolent rulers, remembering what it was like to be downtrodden, or attempting to make up for the anguish they suffered by heaping it upon others. Haunts who seek to understand why God has done this to them, and those penitents who feel that they must atone for whatever sins drew the curse upon them, find solace in the ranks of the Lancea Sanctum. Haunts often find a place among the Ordo Dracul, where

STEREOTYPES

Daeva: Got themselves fooled into thinking they can fuck the pain away.

Gangrel: Just pat 'em on the head, pretend you're grateful, and whatever you do, don't call 'em on their idiocy. You may be a creep, but your face looks better on the front of your head than hanging from some animal's claws.

Mekhet: Moths are drawn to flame just like shadows. Do shadows burn, too?

Ventrue: They want to play king of the mountain? Fine. Haven't seen one yet willing to come over here and enforce his "rule."

***

Lupines: Scarier than *this*? I sure fucking hope not.

Mages: They know something… I'm just not sure I want to know what it is.

Mortals: Yeah, it sucks having to hide from your food. Yeah, you could take any mortal out without thinking about it. When you can take out a few thousand of 'em, then come talk to me. Until then, keep your fucking head down.

their disturbing bearing has little immediate effect on their achievements in the covenant (and might even aid them, as it discourages casual social calls). The Carthians appeal to those who are concerned with constructing a society in which everyone, no matter how unsettling, has a voice. Those Nosferatu who truly suffer beneath the weight of their curse often find the redemptive teachings of the Circle of the Crone far too tempting to resist. Even the unbound attract those who accept their terrifying nature and who want to tear down the system that quakes at their passing — or those who just want to get away.

Appearance: No two Nosferatu have exactly the same air, though troubling characteristics often follow patterns within "families." Discolored leathery skin, gaping maws, rubbery skin, misshapen heads, odors like grave earth, bulging eyes, queasy stares and personal habits, gnarled hands, ineffable feelings of dread, sagging flesh — all these and more are the hallmarks of the clan. Not every Haunt is physically deformed. Indeed, many are not, instead discomfiting those who look upon them with indescribable unease. The darkness and filth in which many Nosferatu dwell make their foul miens (and fouler odors) even worse.

Havens: Most Nosferatu dwell in places far from mortals, such as abandoned warehouses, graveyards, basements and of course the ever-popular sewers and subway tunnels. That said, some few Nosferatu choose to flout tradition and take their havens in penthouses, fantastic manors — anyplace where they can enjoy the luxuries of wealth yet still count on substantial privacy.

Background: Nosferatu normally choose progeny from among society's castoffs, such as the homeless, the mentally ill and criminals. Many Nosferatu Embrace out of spite, using the curse to punish vanity, cruelty or other such "sins." Assuming a sire wants a childe to survive — which isn't always the case — Haunts tend to choose self-reliant individuals who might actually be able to manage their new condition. Few Nosferatu Embrace out of love or affection, though even this is not unheard of. Rare but heartbreaking are the tales of a Nosferatu determined to "gift" his love with the Requiem, only to find himself the object of his beloved's loathing when she learns what's been done to her.

Character Creation: Physical and Mental Attributes are more useful to most Haunts than Social. Nosferatu frequently make use of Skills such as Stealth and Survival. It's unwise to begin with too high a Blood Potency; until a Nosferatu has obtained some experience in the Requiem, he might be forced to rely on animal blood. Although Nosferatu aren't social creatures, certain Social Merits such as Contacts can be useful for gaining information from inaccessible areas.

Favored Attributes: Composure or Strength

Clan Disciplines: *Nightmare*, Obfuscate, Vigor

Weakness: All Nosferatu are repulsive or at the very least uncomfortable to be around. The cause need not be a physical deformity. A palpable aura of menace, a charnel odor or the undeniable manner of a predator is just as compelling as a twisted body. With regard to dice pools based on Presence or Manipulation Attributes in social situations, the 10-again rule does not apply. Additionally, any 1's that come up on a roll are subtracted from successes. (This latter part of the weakness does not affect dramatic-failure rules.) This weakness does not apply to dice pools that involve the Intimidation Skill, or to the Composure Attribute.

Example: *The Nosferatu Scratch attempts to smooth-talk his way past a ghoul standing guard at a nightclub door. Scratch has a Presence of 4 and a Persuasion of 2 — his player rolls six dice and comes up with 1, 5, 6, 8, 9 and 10. The net result is two successes: The 1 cancels the 8, the 9 counts as normal, and the 10 isn't rolled again.*

Organization: The Nosferatu have little formal organization, but as stated previously they do tend to band together in the face of outside threats. The clan is almost tribal, with differing "families" of Nosferatu often sticking together or warring against one another. Clan hierarchy, such as it is, is usually determined by a combination of seniority and actual merit.

Bloodlines: Acteius; Baddacelli; Noctuku (violent cannibals who dwell near rural areas and who prefer to feed on other Kindred); Yagnatia (a Russian family that claims unbroken lineage from both ancient nobility and witches); Burakumin (an Asian lineage that might possess necromantic powers, but information on Asian vampires is regrettably scarce even by Kindred standards).

Concepts: Bogeyman, circus freak, crude sadist, guardian angel, leg-breaker, parvenu, petty thief, rat king, reclusive eccentric, snitch, sycophantic servant

The Ventrue offer a very simple boast: They win. They *always* win.

Other Kindred often despise the Lords, but they seldom dispute the clan's boast. All too often, a Kindred works and schemes to win some prize, only to find that a Ventrue owned it all along. The officers who lead a city's Kindred almost always include several highly placed Ventrue. The Lords acknowledge no defeats, only setbacks. The clan shares a ruthless will to power and the power to enforce its will.

Their favored Disciplines account for some of their success. The Ventrue learn to command the thoughts of other beings almost by instinct. Their mastery of lesser animals harks back to nights of domains in which the Lord was a master of beasts as well as men. Although they do not especially cultivate the arts of combat, they often prove remarkably hard to kill. Ventrue regard their supernatural gifts, however, as merely a tool to begin the acquisition of real power — the power of money, property, corporate stock, political contacts, rank in Kindred society and large numbers of mortals, at every level of society, begging to lick their boots and fulfill their commands.

The Ventrue take the feudal nature of Kindred society very seriously. Every sire tells her childe that some people rule, and some are ruled. As Lords, they should strive to place themselves among the rulers. Most Ventrue neonates already believed this before their Embrace. Throughout the clan's history, the Ventrue have sought power in whatever forms mortals offered. Kindred historians say that in ancient Rome the clan Embraced senators and patricians. In the Middle Ages, they brought knights and churchmen into the fold. As commerce became an avenue to power, they cultivated merchant princes, bankers and magnates. When states grew more bureaucratic, the Lords Embraced high-ranking civil servants. The rise of organized crime brought mob bosses and drug kingpins into the clan. At the start of the 21st century, Ventrue elders ponder the merits of Embracing scientists, engineers and computer wizards. No matter where in society the power lies, the Ventrue vow to exploit it before other Kindred even know it exists.

Nickname: Lords

Covenant: Many Kindred see the Ventrue as almost synonymous with the Invictus. Indeed, Ventrue tend to rise to leadership positions within that covenant. Almost as many find a place in the Ordo Dracul, acquiring immediate power of a different stripe, which the Lords ultimately turn toward the same ends. They also rise to leadership among the Sanctified, however, and some Ventrue find the power they crave within the Carthians, the Circle of the Crone or even amid the ranks of the unbound. Some Ventrue neonates hardly bother to hide their intent to use a gang of unaligned Kindred as a stepping-stone to power within another covenant.

Appearance: Ventrue often adopt a conservative, low-key appearance that expresses high status without being flashy. Young Lords sometimes favor a "preppy" look, the timeless suit-and-tie uniform of business, or (for female Lords) elegant gowns or business skirt-suits, with unobtrusive jewelry. Ventrue elders might keep the styles of long ago, at least in their own havens, and in public they still tend to look decades out of date. Even rebellious young Ventrue wear their metal-studded jackets like a uniform, asserting their dominance. A Lord surrounds himself with other trappings of wealth and status, too, from the big, fancy car in the garage to the wine cellar full of vintages he will never again have the opportunity to enjoy.

Havens: If a Ventrue did not possess great wealth before the Embrace, she often becomes rich afterward. Ventrue select their havens to reflect their wealth and power. Many Lords dwell in mansions or actual walled estates. Few would settle for anything less than a classic townhouse or penthouse apartment (with secure curtains, of course).

Clan tradition holds that any Ventrue may claim sanctuary from the sun at any other Lord's haven and

Stereotypes

Daeva: Our only serious rivals. Watch them as you would a deadly viper.

Gangrel: Stray dogs with sharp teeth. Train them when you can.

Mekhet: Acknowledge their wisdom, but be sure they know they have their place.

Nosferatu: What was it Machiavelli said about love and fear?

***

Lupines: You can no more rule their kingdoms than you can rule a wildfire. Treat them with care — or avoid them if you want to see another night.

Mages: Do not try to understand their powers. You cannot. Do not use your powers upon them. Their revenge, should you fail, will be terrible. Their fears and desires, however, remain human — and so you can bend them to your will.

Mortals: Rule them, use them, feed upon them without pity. They are born to serve and suffer and never know why.

not be refused, but few Lords ever invoke this right. Not only do proud Lords hate to beg another Kindred's aid, a supplicant henceforth owes a debt of honor to the Ventrue who provided refuge. Great shame would befall any Lord who denied a clanmate or who could not provide a comfortable rest, however, so a prudent Ventrue makes sure his haven can accommodate a Kindred guest or two.

Background: The Ventrue most often seek childer among the ranks of professionals or the cream of high society. Some Lords prefer childer from "old money" families or political dynasties, as the closest the modern world comes to feudal nobility. Other Lords prefer self-made leaders such as millionaire entrepreneurs, politicians, military officers or even crime bosses. As new professions and new forms of power arise, the Ventrue bring them into the clan. The rise of the computer industry, for instance, has prompted a wave of tech-sector childer.

Character Creation: Ventrue favor Social Attributes and Skills — the traits needed for leadership — though they also value Mental Attributes and Skills such as Politics and Academics. The clan excels at Social Merits such as Resources, Contacts and Status. Most Lords possessed great social influence in life, and they acquire more in undeath.

Favored Attributes: Presence or Resolve

Clan Disciplines: Animalism, *Dominate*, Resilience

Weakness: Power corrupts, and among the Ventrue, even the thirst for power can corrode an ambitious Kindred's moral bearings. Over time, some Ventrue grow paranoid, ever more wary of rivals' desires (real or imagined) for their own holdings. Others become willing to do whatever it takes to acquire the smallest iota of additional power. Still others turn inward, delude themselves as to their ability and importance, or trouble their minds with other maladies. Ventrue Kindred suffer a -2 penalty to Humanity rolls to avoid acquiring derangements after a failed degeneration roll.

Organization: The Lords track their ties of blood and obligation through an old-boy network that extends across generations, bloodlines and continents. A respectable Ventrue knows his fellow Lords' ancestors, their broodmates, allies, enemies and Kindred owed and owing favors (though the information might be a century out of date). Two Ventrue often compare lineages and acquaintances when they first meet. Thus do they establish their relationships and status within the clan.

The Ventrue also take clan offices very seriously. Ventrue Whips, Prisci and other clan leaders often try to hold monthly meetings of all clanmates, regardless of covenant. The Lords use these meetings as opportunities to brag, size up the competition, cut deals and chide clanmates who seem to show insufficient ambition. After all, the Ventrue have a reputation for steel-fisted power to uphold. One does not want other Kindred thinking that any Lord might go soft.

Bloodlines: Much of the clan consists of lineages that claim descent from famous Ventrue of the distant past, such as the great Cassius. These "bloodlines" merely express pride in ancestry: A Cassian Ventrue, for instance, does not differ greatly from other Lords. Other prestigious lineages include the Licinii, the Beni Murrahim and the Rötgrafen. The comparatively new Malkovian lineage suffers even more debilitating madness than the parent clan.

Concepts: Corporate CEO, crooked cop, gang chief, military officer, old-time ward boss, patron of the arts, political consultant, rave promoter, realtor, society matron, technical wizard

Disciplines

Much debate occurs over the nature of Disciplines among the Kindred community. Many young vampires, as yet unfamiliar with the price that the Embrace demands of their souls, see only the upside of Disciplines, thinking of them as powers they can wield over lesser creatures such as mortals. Penitent vampires, as well as those of traditional or theological bent, often see Disciplines as edges granted by whoever created vampires so that the terrible race of the Damned can more effectively fulfill that individual's plan. Still others consider Disciplines their own ends, as with the Ordo Dracul and its proscribed but powerful Coils of the Dragon.

The truth, of course, remains as unknown as any of the answers to the Kindred condition. What leaves no doubt, however, is the terrible efficacy of vampires' powers.

Using Disciplines

You'll note from character creation and the clan write-ups, presented previously in this chapter, that among each clan's three "Clan Disciplines" is one that is listed for no other clan. These individual powers are presented in italics in the five clan descriptions. For example, the Daeva is the only group with Majesty listed as a clan Discipline. Meanwhile, Ventrue is the only one with Dominate listed as a clan Discipline. Such special Disciplines allow members of each clan immediate access to a particular vampiric power. That Discipline is one of the things that makes each clan unique. These capabilities are not wholly exclusive to their respective clans, however. Characters of other clans can learn them through the expenditure of experience points, but these specialized Disciplines are considered "out of clan" and are expensive to acquire (as explained on p. 230-231). Adopting a bloodline may allow access to another clan's signature capability, as explained on p. 259. And of course, there's the option of acquiring the capabilities of another clan's Disciplines by committing diablerie on vampires of that lineage. Gaining these powers by such horrific means is explained on p. 159.

The basic system for using a Discipline is a bit different from the standard dice-pool mechanic. The Attribute that governs a certain power's use is included in the system subsection of the capability's description. In conjunction with that Attribute is a specific Skill that lends finesse or emphasis to the power. Remember that characters who have no dots in required Skills will suffer penalties to their dice pools to activate certain Desciplines. Additionally, the character's mastery of the Discipline as a whole adds dice to the pool. The result is a dice pool composed of three traits instead of the usual two for mundane Skill or Attribute tasks. For example, the first Discipline power in this chapter is Feral Whispers, under Animalism. The power lists Manipulation as its requisite Attribute and Animal Ken as its requisite Skill. If a character has Manipulation 2, Animal Ken 3 and Animalism 4, his player rolls nine dice to determine the margin of success of using Feral Whispers. The fact that Feral Whispers is a level-one power isn't important; the character's ultimate potential with Animalism as a whole is what's key.

Other information contained in the system subsection includes the following:

- Trait costs, if any, such as Vitae or Willpower expenditures.
- Bonuses or penalties to dice pools based on circumstance. These lists are not exhaustive, just a few commonly encountered situations that a character using the Discipline might experience. As always, the Storyteller is free to modify these circumstances in any additional ways he sees fit.
- Other specific details that need to be described in game terms.

A character may use only those Discipline powers that are available at her level of mastery of a given Discipline, and below. Thus, a character with Dominate 3 can use the Discipline's level-one, -two and -three powers.

Elders speak of mighty powers becoming available once a Kindred's Blood Potency reaches a certain degree. Levels one through five of a given Discipline always produce the listed effects, but some elders insist that once a vampire's potential with a Discipline reaches a certain point, she may break from the static incarnations of a given Discipline and manifest powers with her own personality invested in them. That is, mystic wisdom suggests that there is no hard-and-fast level-six power for Auspex, for example, and that a Kindred who masters Auspex at such a high level creates her own unique application. Tales of such powers are unreliable, though. The nature of Blood Potency is fluid enough that what a Kindred masters one night might vanish if he sinks into torpor and forgets what he once knew.

SUPERNATURAL CONFLICT

It's inevitable that the undead come in contact with the other terrifying and bizarre denizens of the World of Darkness. Vampires might clash with werewolves, mages or stranger *things*. When such contact can't be resolved peacefully, supernatural powers and capabilities can be brought to bear to decide which creature prevails.

In this book, Disciplines are applied against mortal human beings and other vampires. In those cases, the rules operate as written. There's little question as to what protection a target might have. A mortal probably has little protection other than his relevant Resistance Attribute, and another vampire has the protection described for the power in question. For example, a vampire who's made the target of Dominate has a contested dice pool composed of Resolve + Blood Potency. Meanwhile, a mortal target of Dominate has only his Resolve to apply in a contested roll against a vampire's Intelligence + Intimidation + Dominate. (After all, a mortal has no Blood Potency.)

So what happens when a vampire encounters a supernatural being and is subjected to the powers that creature wields? How do the vampire's inherent nature or capabilities protect him? In cases where a contested roll is made to determine the power's effects, the vampire's relevant Resistance Attribute + Blood Potency is rolled. The Resistance Attribute is any one of the vampire's

Stamina, Resolve or Composure. Stamina is used against powers that have a physical effect, Resolve is used against powers that have a mental effect, and Composure is used against powers that have an emotional effect.

For example, if a mortal mage seeks to transform your vampire's body, roll Stamina + Blood Potency in a contested action to resist. If a werewolf tries to use spirit magic to alter your character's mind, roll Resolve + Blood Potency to resist. If a mysterious creature seeks to strike terror into your vampire, roll Composure + Blood Potency to resist.

Otherwise, follow all the other rules that apply to the power used. The main difference here is that vampires benefit from their Blood Potency in resisting supernatural phenomena.

The Storyteller can invoke this general rule whenever he confronts your character with monsters of his own creation — weird beings that might have never been seen before. Or he can allow you this kind of contested roll when your **Vampire** chronicle overlaps with **Werewolf: The Forsaken, Mage: The Awakening** or any other Storytelling game. When the Gifts, spells or other powers from those games are turned upon your character, you know that his inherent potency as a creature of the night may afford him some protection.

Note, however, that such protection doesn't apply when no contested roll is allowed against the power in question. Say the Storyteller rolls a dice pool to determine the effects of a witch's spell cast on your vampire, and the rules say your character's Resolve is simply subtracted from that pool. In that case, your vampire's Blood Potency is not subtracted from the pool. Since no contested roll is involved to fight off the power, your character's Resistance Attribute alone applies as a dice-pool penalty.

Be prepared! Just as vampires get special defenses against the powers of other supernatural entities, so too do those beings get extra benefits against vampire Disciplines. When Disciplines are combated with contested rolls, creatures such as werewolves and mages get special dice pools based on their own otherworldly nature. Their extra protection is addressed in **Werewolf: The Forsaken, Mage: The Awakening** and other Storytelling games.

Animalism

Although most look human, all the Kindred conceal within them a feral predator, a Beast that divides all others into only two categories: threat or prey. Some Kindred feel their affinity with the animals of the world, and their connection with their own animalistic nature to a greater degree than others. These Kindred often develop the Discipline of Animalism, which allows them to bond with the beasts — and the Beasts — around them. They can not only commune with lower creatures, but project their will upon them, forcing them to obey. As the Kindred gain power, some develop the ability to join with animals, or to influence the Beast lurking with their own souls or the souls of other vampires.

Most Kindred are repellent to animals. Lesser creatures grow agitated in the presence of the undead and normally flee the scene (or, in some cases, attack the vampire in question). Kindred who possess Animalism are a very different story. Animals are often attracted to such Kindred, and their presence is soothing even to restless beasts.

Other sentient, supernatural beings such as shapechangers who have animal form or who can assume animal form are not affected by Animalism. Their intelligence makes them the purview of the Dominate Discipline. Therefore, a Ventrue can try to ply his will on a werewolf — even a werewolf in wolf form — by using Dominate. Similarly, Animalism is useless on another vampire who assumes wolf or another bestial form. Animalism is of no avail to the vampire in regard to such intelligent beings.

Note that any Animalism power that requires eye contact is made more difficult if the subject does not stand still or is not otherwise immobilized. If the animal in question moves about, the roll to initiate the relevant power suffers a -1 penalty in addition to all others listed.

Feral Whispers

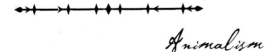

The Kindred with this ability has learned to understand the lesser creatures that surround her, and to speak with them and make herself understood. It is the foundation upon which all other Animalism abilities are built, for without understanding there can be no obedience. The vampire must initiate eye contact with the animal in question; doing so forges a strong empathic bond between Kindred and beast, allowing communication. This contact is at least partially mental. The vampire may either whisper to the animal in her own language (or any language she knows), or she may hiss, bark, chirp or make whatever sounds the animal might use to express itself. (Some Kindred prefer the latter, feeling that it joins them more closely with the animal in question, though many others deride them for it and consider the practice vulgar.) The animal, in turn, might make some sort of noise while responding. It might be a growl, a low chirp or anything else. The precise nature of the sound is irrelevant, as the meaning is conveyed mostly via the empathic link. Most animals instinctively respond quietly when answering Feral Whispers, unless the situation is a tense or violent one. The Kindred must maintain either eye contact or a constant dialogue with the animal. If she fails to do so for even a single turn, the link is broken and she must reinitiate contact if she wishes to speak further.

Because Feral Whispers requires initial eye contact, animals that cannot see cannot be affected. Additionally, the simpler or less intelligent the animal is, the more difficult it is to link with its Beast or its emotions. Mammals, raptors and certain large reptiles are relatively easy to communicate with; insects, invertebrates and most fish are very nearly impossible.

Note that while Feral Whispers makes sure that the animal communicates with the vampire, it does not compel the creature to obey commands or perform tasks. Further, the nature of the information conveyed by the animal depends largely on its intelligence and awareness. A cat might be able to explain that a large number of humans scared it out of a nearby building, but it's unlikely to understand questions such as, "Was one of them wearing a green baseball cap?" or to have any real concept of numbers.

Cost: —

Dice Pool: Manipulation + Animal Ken + Animalism

Action: Instant

Roll Results

Dramatic Failure: A dramatic failure indicates that the character misreads the animal, gaining false information. Additionally, the animal is immune to any further uses of Animalism by that character until the next sunset.

Failure: Failure indicates that the character cannot communicate with the animal.

Success: Success indicates that the character can fully communicate with the animal, to whatever degree it is capable.

Exceptional Success: Exceptional success indicates that the animal is not only communicative but actively helpful, even volunteering information unasked if it considers that information important (so far as its intelligence allows).

Suggested Modifiers

Modifier	Situation
+1	The animal is a predatory mammal (wolf, cat, insectivorous bat).
+1	The character is able to assume the same animal form via the Protean Discipline as the creature with which he tries to communicate (though he need not actually make the transformation).
+1	The character attempts to communicate with an animal in its "native tongue" by hissing, squeaking or what have you (assuming the player is willing to attempt to roleplay such actions).
—	The animal is another sort of mammal, a predatory bird or a large reptile (rat, owl, alligator).
-1	The animal is another sort of bird or a small reptile (pigeon, snake).
-3	The animal is an insect or fish.

•• Obedience

Having mastered the ability to commune with beasts, the Kindred's connection with his own feral nature now allows him to command them as well. No longer need he beg, threaten or cajole animals into doing his will. He demands, and they obey as best they can.

The vampire must make eye contact, as with Feral Whispers, and convey to an animal precisely what he wants it to do. The animal obeys to the best of its ability, but its nature and intelligence might cause it to interpret its orders in unusual ways. Once it has received an order, the animal carries it out, assuming it can be completed before the following sunrise. At dawn, the compulsion ceases, regardless of whether the task is complete or not.

It is extremely difficult to order an animal to do anything blatantly against its nature (such as ordering a sparrow to attack someone) or obviously self-destructive (such as forcing a guard dog to lie down in front of a moving truck).

A vampire can give single orders to only one animal at a time, but he may have as many animals currently under his control as circumstances allow, as long as he can give each one its orders individually.

Cost: —

Dice Pool: Presence + Animal Ken + Animalism – animal's Composure

Action: Instant

Obedience also requires a contested roll if the animal is already under the control of another Kindred with this power (in which case Obedience successes achieved must exceed those rolled for the original vampire).

Roll Results

Dramatic Failure: Dramatic failure indicates that the animal either attacks the character or does the exact opposite of what he commands it to do. In addition, that animal is immune to any further use of Animalism by that character until the next sunset.

Failure: Failure indicates that the character cannot command or communicate with the animal.

Success: Success indicates that the animal obeys the character's orders to the best of its abilities.

Exceptional Success: Exceptional success indicates that the animal develops a strong, if temporary, affection for the character. It attempts to please and to anticipate orders, even when not actively following a specific command.

Suggested Modifiers

Modifier	Situation
+1	The animal is a predatory mammal (wolf, cat, insectivorous bat).
+1	The character has already successfully used Feral Whispers on the animal he now attempts to command with Obedience.
—	The animal is another sort of mammal, a predatory bird or a large reptile (rat, owl, alligator).
-1	The animal is another sort of bird or a small reptile (pigeon, snake).
-1	The order is contradictory to the animal's nature or set of inherent abilities.
-1	The animal is a ghoul.
-3	The animal is an insect or fish.
-3	The order is blatantly suicidal.

••• Call of the Wild

The Kindred is so fully in tune with her own Beast that she can call out in a feral voice — howling, hissing, cawing or the like — that beckons all creatures of a specific type. Any animal of that sort within a given area is compelled to respond, immediately moving toward the Kindred at its fastest possible speed, via the most direct route it can find. Only animals that can hear the call are summoned, so creatures that have been deafened or that are insulated from the sound by thick walls or other barriers do not respond. Additionally, only natural animals respond to this call — no hell hounds or gargoyles (see p. 225-256), for example, answer it.

Animals that respond to the Kindred's call are not automatically under her control, but they are more easily subjected to other Animalism powers.

Cost: 1 Vitae

Dice Pool: Presence + Animal Ken + Animalism

Action: Instant

Roll Results

Dramatic Failure: All animals of the type called within 100 yards immediately turn hostile toward the character and are immune to any further uses of Animalism by that character until the next sunset.

Failure: On a failure, no animals appear.

Success: The area of the call is 100 yards for every success rolled. That is, a single success when summoning rats calls all rats within 100 yards. The Storyteller determines how many animals respond based on the environment. Hundreds or thousands of rats might appear in an inner city, while no hawks or coyotes would.

Exceptional Success: As per a normal success. In the previous example of the rat summoner, if the player achieved seven successes, all rats within 700 yards would heed the call.

Suggested Modifiers

The Storyteller may impose bonuses or penalties to the call based on weather, barriers or other ambient noise, as he feels is appropriate. A heavy wind might cut down the distance the sound can travel, for instance, imposing a -2 penalty.

Animals responding to Call of the Wild are easier for the beckoning character to influence with other uses of Animalism. Any further use of Animalism on these specific creatures receives a bonus equal to the number of successes on the roll to invoke this power. This bonus lasts for the remainder of the scene.

Sample animal traits are provided in the **World of Darkness Rulebook**, p. 202-203.

•••• Subsume the Lesser Spirit

By locking eyes with an animal, a vampire may psychically enter the creature's body and possess it as though it were his own. Some Kindred believe that doing so actually transfers the vampire's soul into the beast, though other, less mystically minded Kindred disagree. Regardless, the animal's own mind and instincts are completely subsumed, allowing the Kindred free reign to take whatever actions he chooses in the creature's body. The vampire's own body falls into a torpor-like state and appears for all intents and purposes to be a corpse. Until the character returns, his body cannot be awakened by any means (though Kindred urban legends tell of ghosts possessing such bodies and wreaking havoc). Also, it is whispered among certain circles that some vampires, addicted to the sensations of life they experience while riding an animal, remain too long in that form and forget their true nature.

Cost: 1 Vitae

Dice Pool: Manipulation + Animal Ken + Animalism versus animal's Composure

Action: Contested

Roll Results

Dramatic Failure: The character fails to bond with the animal; the animal grows hostile and is immune to any further uses of Animalism by that character until the next sunset.

Failure: The character loses or ties the contested action and fails to bond with the animal.

Success: The character wins the contested action and occupies the animal's body. He can use Animalism but no other Disciplines while doing so.

Exceptional Success: The character wins the contested action with five or more successes and occupies the animal's body, and can also use Auspex and Majesty while doing so.

If the roll made for the character wins the contested roll *and* gets successes in excess of the animal's Composure dots, the character is in total control and his mind remains clear. If his roll succeeds but garners a number of successes equal to or lower than the animal's Composure dots, a Willpower point must be spent for the character to take any actions contrary to the animal's instincts. Otherwise, bestial urges and impulses cloud the vampire's mind.

Additionally, if the player wins the contested roll but gets a number of successes equal to or lower than the animal's Composure, his character's consciousness is so closely intertwined with the beast's that he maintains some bestial behaviors even after returning to his own form. Until the player spends a total of three Willpower points specifically to overcome this effect — the points can't, say, be spent to gain three extra dice in unrelated rolls — the character continues to think and feel in an animalistic manner. (This effect has no "hard" mechanical applications, but it should be roleplayed. If the character doesn't indulge in animalistic activity, the Storyteller should feel free to either dock the character future experience points or spend Willpower automatically for the character when a particularly bestial response is appropriate but not displayed.)

While possessing an animal, a character can travel as far from his own body as he wishes and is unharmed by daylight, but he must still force himself to stay awake during the day (see Humanity on p. 184). The vampire may choose to end the possession and return to his body at any time, regardless of distance. This occurs automatically if the vampire fails to remain awake. Any injuries inflicted on the animal also affect the vampire's body. If the animal dies while the vampire is still present, the Kindred falls into torpor immediately. (Some believe that the soul attempts to find its way back to its own body during this time.) If the Kindred's physical form is destroyed, his psyche remains trapped in the animal until he finally fails to remain awake, at which point his spirit is lost to oblivion and is unrecoverable.

It is possible, though uncommon, for a vampire to neglect his physical body long enough for it to starve into torpor while he's "out." If a vampire's dormant body slips or is forced into torpor, the vampire's spirit automatically returns to its body.

Suggested Modifiers

Modifier	Situation
+1	The animal is a predatory mammal (wolf, cat, insectivorous bat).
+1	The character has already successfully used Feral Whispers on the animal he now attempts to possess.
+1	The character is able to assume the same animal form via the Protean Discipline as the creature he tries to possess.
	The animal is another sort of mammal, a predatory bird or a large reptile (rat, owl, alligator).
-1	The animal is another sort of bird or a small reptile (pigeon, snake).
-1	The animal is a ghoul.
-3	The animal is an insect or fish.

••••• Leashing the Beast

The vampire's connection with the Beast is so powerful that she can manipulate not only the lesser creatures around her, but her own Beast and that of other Kindred.

This is not overt control, as with Obedience or the Dominate Discipline. Rather, the Kindred learns to rouse the Beast's instincts, inspiring it — and thus the vampire within whom it lurks — to behave in a certain manner. Of course, communing with the Beast is dangerous even under the best of circumstances, and a few unfortunate Kindred have been destroyed by their own failed attempts to manipulate others' Beasts.

The subject must be a vampire and must be within the character's line of sight. (If the character makes herself the subject, she need not be able to see, so she can do so even in complete darkness or when otherwise blinded.) The player must decide to invoke a rage frenzy or Rötschreck, or to alleviate either of them.

Cost: 1 Vitae

Dice Pool: Manipulation + Empathy + Animalism versus Composure + Blood Potency (to affect another); Manipulation + Empathy + Animalism (to affect oneself)

Action: Instant (to affect oneself) or Contested; resistance is reflexive (to affect another)

Roll Results

Dramatic Failure: Used on another, the character's power rebounds and a Willpower point must be spent or she enters either frenzy or Rötschreck, whichever she attempted to influence. Additionally, the subject is immune to any further Leashing the Beast attempts by the character until the next sunset. When the power is used on the character's self, the opposite kind of frenzy sought is invoked (Rötschreck when rage frenzy was intended).

Failure: The character fails the instant action, or loses or ties the contested action and the power fails.

Success: The instant action inspires or calms rage frenzy or Rötschreck in the character herself. Or, the character gets the most successes and manipulates another's Beast. Frenzy or Rötschreck rules apply as normal for the remainder of the scene if either is induced.

Exceptional Success: The character fulfills the instant action or wins the contested roll with five or more successes, and the subject is immediately forced into (or out of) frenzy or Rötschreck. If the subject is forced into frenzy or Rötschreck, he or she remains in that state for the remainder of the scene, regardless of surrounding events or circumstances. Additionally, Willpower cannot be spent to end the frenzy prematurely. If the subject is brought out of frenzy or Rötschreck, he or she is not subject to frenzy or Rötschreck for the remainder of the scene, regardless of surrounding events or circumstances.

Suggested Modifiers

If the character knows another's Virtue and/or Vice, such knowledge grants a +1 bonus, though she must cajole the Beast by specifically focusing on those aspects of the subject's personality. These bonuses are not cumulative. Knowing a character's Virtue *and* Vice nets only a +1 bonus, not a +2.

If this power is turned on a vampire with whom the user has a blood tie (see p. 162), a +2 bonus is gained.

If the character is already in frenzy and uses this power to calm herself, a -2 penalty applies.

Auspex

This potent Discipline grants a character superlative sensory capabilities. At the lowest levels, it sharpens a Kindred's mundane senses. As one progresses in mastery, entirely new avenues of insight open up before the user. Ultimately, this is the Discipline of gleaning information, whether that data comes from sights and smells, from auras and patterns of energy or directly from the mind of another creature. In addition, Auspex can be used to pierce the veil of powers that cloud, dissemble and deceive (see the "Clash of Wills" sidebar). Indeed, precious little can be kept secret from a true master of Auspex.

Once in a while, this uncanny Discipline provides extrasensory and even precognitive visitations. Such premonitions might come as quick flashes of imagery, overwhelming feelings of empathy or even as an ominous sense of foreboding. The Kindred has absolutely no control over these insights, but he can learn to interpret their significance given time and experience.

Such potent sensitivity can have its drawbacks, however. When a vampire actively uses any level of Auspex save the fifth (Twilight Projection), he runs the risk of his delicate senses being overwhelmed by excessive stimuli. Sudden or severe occurrences such as a gun report or flash bulb in the eyes can distract the character unless the player succeeds on a Resolve roll. Failure disorients the character, making him effectively unaware of his surroundings until the end of the following turn.

CLASH OF WILLS

Although Auspex is a potent Discipline, especially at high levels of mastery, a given Kindred's execution of it is not always flawless. Other supernatural powers and abilities can cloud or contest the power of Auspex, the most common of these being Obfuscate — the direct opposite of Auspex, in many ways.

The heart of any Auspex-versus-Obfuscate contest is a clash of mighty wills, for both powers stem from and rely upon the power of the Kindred mind. When a character with Auspex uses his acute senses to see through another's Obfuscate, make a contested roll of Wits + Investigation + Auspex versus Resolve + Stealth + Obfuscate. Whoever accumulates the most successes wins the battle of wills. Ties go to the defender. Most of the time, ties result in the Obfuscated character remaining hidden (as the Auspex-user is the initiator), but not always. In the event that a vampire uses Obfuscate right in front of a Kindred with Auspex, the hiding character is the challenger, as it is he who tries to hide in plain sight.

Obfuscate is not the only supernatural ability with the potential to foil the clarity of Auspex. For example, a character using the Twilight Projection power might be seen by a character using the Heightened Senses power. The general rule of thumb is to apply the same system, but in regard to whatever mechanic is used: Wits + Investigation + Auspex is still rolled for the perceiving character, and Resolve + an appropriate Skill + the Discipline in question is rolled for the defender.

• Heightened Senses

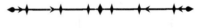

When this power is activated, all of the vampire's senses sharpen to a razor's edge, effectively doubling both the range and clarity of all stimuli received. Heightened eyesight allows the vampire to perceive the most minute details of objects at great distances, while a heightened sense of smell might alert a character to the presence of trace amounts of alcohol on a mortal's breath. Kindred with this power also have the option of magnifying a single sense, as opposed to all five, in order to better block out unwanted stimuli from other sources. Note, however, that the risk of sudden distraction remains, regardless of how many or how few senses are currently heightened. (Note that vampires do not breathe. As such, the Kindred do not smell unless they actively will themselves to do so, and thus cannot be overwhelmed suddenly by smells unless they are actively smelling at the time.)

Cost: —

Dice Pool: This power typically involves no roll. The player simply activates the power and explains to the Storyteller what his character is doing and with which sense(s). The Storyteller responds by relating whatever information can be gleaned. The only time a roll comes into play for Heightened

Senses is when the Storyteller wishes to permit the character a chance to perceive an imminent threat. In this case, the Storyteller may allow the player to add her character's Auspex dots to a surprise roll (Wits + Composure — see the **World of Darkness Rulebook**, p. 151).

This power allows a vampire to see in pitch-black darkness.

Action: Instant

Aura Perception

With this mystic power, a vampire can open his perceptions to the psychic auras that surround all sentient creatures. Numerous and often-shifting hues and patterns compose these auras, and it can take many years before a vampire becomes truly proficient at reading them correctly with any degree of regularity. Although the strongest emotions predominate, almost every individual has more than one color to his aura at any given time, and an observer can see any number of streaks or flashes of these other colors.

"Psychic colors" change with the subject's mental or emotional state, creating an ever-moving pattern that is as unique to each person as a fingerprint. As a rule, the more powerful the emotions, the more intense the colors, but even this guideline is betrayed by any number of mitigating factors, depending on circumstance. All the same, practice makes perfect; a true master aura-perceiver learns to understand the significance of each whorl and eddy.

Due to the peculiar nature of such creatures' auras, this power can be used as a means of detecting other supernatural entities. Vampire auras, for example, tend to be extremely pale, regardless of the colors. Werewolf auras are quite the contrary, nearly frantic in their intensity. Mage auras sparkle with power. Ghostly auras flicker like guttering candles.

Cost: —

Dice Pool: Intelligence + Empathy + Auspex – subject's Composure

Action: Instant (Note that though this is an instant action, it takes more than just a fleeting glance to see the detail in an aura. A character must scrutinize her subject's aura for two full turns to glean information from it, though only the single, immediate roll is necessary to determine if she can read it successfully.)

Roll Results

Dramatic Failure: The character gleans utterly misleading and wholly inaccurate information.

Failure: The character can distinguish no information at all.

Success: The character perceives a number of colors in the subject's aura equal to the number of successes obtained on the roll.

Exceptional Success: As per a normal success, with one additional color or degree of emotional intensity discernible to the character.

Note that a failure indicates that no useful information is perceived, while a dramatic failure indicates a false or misleading reading. The Storyteller may therefore wish to make the roll for the player, to keep the true results secret.

An Auspex user who observes someone in the act of lying may recognize that the subject speaks falsely. Intelligence + Empathy + Auspex is rolled versus the subject's Composure in a contested action. The Auspex user recognizes the lie if the most successes are rolled for him.

Applied toward reading the mood of potential combatants, this power also grants its user a bonus to Initiative equal to the number of successes rolled in activating the effect. Doing so requires that the vampire speaks to or is in the proximity of intended combatants for at least one turn before a fight breaks out. That period of interaction allows the reading vampire to recognize that events are about to turn violent, so he can react with advanced knowledge.

Aura Signifiers

Condition	Color
Afraid	Orange
Aggressive	Purple
Angry	Bright Red
Bitter	Brown
Calm	Light Blue
Compassionate	Pink
Conservative	Lavender
Depressed	Gray
Desirous/Lustful	Deep Red
Distrustful	Light Green
Envious	Dark Green
Excited	Violet
Generous	Rose
Happy	Vermilion
Hateful	Black
Idealistic	Yellow
Innocent	White
Lovestruck	Bright Blue
Obsessed	Bright Green
Sad	Silver
Spiritual	Gold
Suspicious	Dark Blue
Confused	Mottled, shifting colors
Daydreaming	Sharp, flickering colors
Diablerist	Black veins in aura
Dominated/Controlled	Weak, muted aura
Frenzied	Rapidly rippling colors
Psychotic	Hypnotic, swirling colors
Vampire	Aura colors are pale
Shapeshifter	Intensely vibrant aura
Ghost	Splotchy, intermittent aura
Magic Use	Myriad sparkles in aura

Suggested Modifiers

The number of dice added to or removed from the dice pool is determined by the amount of information the character wishes to discern.

Modifier	Situation
+2	Power is turned on a vampire with whom the user has a blood tie (see p. 162)
—	The shade (such as pale, bright or weak), but not the color of the aura.
-1	The primary shade and color.
-2	Color patterns, including information revealing the nature of the creature.
-3	Subtle shifts in the mixtures of color and pattern.

Thus, if a reader wants to study the subtle shifts in the mixtures of color and pattern in a subject's aura, the player suffers a -3 penalty. Each success rolled thereafter offers one piece of information in that regard. Two successes might indicate that a ghoul swings from love to hate toward his mistress (bright blue to black), and is envious of a fellow ghoul (dark green).

••• The Spirit's Touch

The Kindred's powers of perception have progressed to the point that he can pick up psychic impressions from objects simply by handling them for a moment or two. Such impressions can tell the vampire who last held the object, when it was last held and even what was done with it in the past.

These psychic impressions typically come in the form of quick and cryptic images, and as with other Auspex powers, learning how to decipher the information gleaned can be a task all its own. Most impressions (and therefore, most visuals stemming from them) pertain to the last person who handled the object in question, but two circumstances usually preclude such a reading. First, a long-time owner or handler of the object leaves stronger impressions than someone who handled it briefly, if more recently. Second, experiences associated with great emotion — be it hate, passion or fear — often linger in the form of intense psychic impressions on objects. It is these impressions that likely come to the fore over anything more recent or, in all likelihood, far less emotionally significant.

All that is required in order to glean information from an object by using this power is that the vampire turn the item over in his hands (or otherwise handle it) for a few moments, during which he enters a shallow trance. This trance is the gateway through which psychic snapshots arrive, and anything that prematurely disrupts the trance likely prevents any useful information from being received.

Cost: —

Dice Pool: Wits + Occult + Auspex

Action: Instant

Roll Results

Dramatic Failure: A dramatic failure indicates the psychic equivalent of a "mixed message" or a very believable but entirely false impression.

Failure: Failure indicates that no impressions come through.

Success: Success yields a sense of the previous handler or owner's identity, as well as a reliable vision or sense of the memory in question.

Exceptional Success: An exceptional success provides a comprehensive or extended chronological understanding of the event and its participants, such as an entire slideshow of images pertaining to the object and its past.

This power can also be used to glimpse the past of another. The subject must be touched, which could require a roll if the subject is resistant (see the **World of Darkness Rulebook**, p. 157). A contested roll of Wits + Occult + Auspex versus the subject's Resolve + Blood Potency is made. The subject's roll is reflexive, and he does not know that past events in his existence are perceived. If the reader gets the most successes, a vision is received of the subject's past, all from the subject's perspective. With no timeframe or criteria for the event witness, the last dramatic, tense or passionate act performed or experienced by the subject is glimpsed. If a specific timeframe or event is focused on, the Auspex user's roll suffers a -1 penalty for each night that has passed since the event. Therefore, witnessing a feeding that the subject performed three nights before imposes a -3 penalty to the contested roll made for the reading vampire.

Roll Results

Dramatic Failure: Events witnessed from the subject's eyes are misinterpreted. He seems to have been attacked rather than to have initiated an attack, for example.

Failure: The contested roll is lost or tied. No impressions come through.

Success: The most successes are rolled for the reading character. A distorted and blurred glimpse of the event or situation in question passes through his mind. He is left with an intuitive, general understanding of what transpired.

Exceptional Success: The reading character wins the contested roll with five or more successes. An instantaneous glimpse of the event or situation in question passes through his mind. He implicitly understands every aspect of what happened, essentially as if he were there in the subject's stead. The reader doesn't acquire any new traits or capabilities — say, if the subject committed diablerie. The reader simply knows what transpired.

Suggested Modifiers

Modifier	Situation
+2	Power is turned on a vampire with whom the user has a blood tie (see p. 162)
+1	The character has drawn a psychic impression from the object or person before.
—	Recent and intense (a murder weapon used four hours ago, or a murder was committed).
-1	Recent but mild, or old and intense (a dusty family heirloom in a chest).
-2	Emotionally shallow or long forgotten (a leisure suit found at a secondhand clothing store).
-3	Disconnected or spiritually muted (a set of keys found several weeks ago).
-3	Object or person read amid a fight or other stressful circumstance.

At this level of advancement of one's extrasensory perceptions, a vampire may project his consciousness into a nearby individual's mind. Doing so creates a mental link whereby the Kindred can communicate silently or even scan the surface of the target's subconscious. The user senses any thought picked up as a voice inside his own mind, and the data can hardly be considered unobtrusive. Nevertheless, this power has the potential to be one of the most potent of the abilities in any vampire's mystical arsenal. With enough practice, a vampiric telepath can uncover nearly any secret from any sentient being around him.

Telepathy is most effective on the mortal mind. When used on ordinary people, the character can maintain a link as long as he keeps concentrating, and as long as the mortal target does not leave his line of sight for more than moment or two. Trying to breach the supernatural mind, however, is a more difficult prospect. A given link is good only for the moment and must be reestablished each time the character wishes to send or dig for thoughts.

Cost: None for a mortal; 1 Willpower for a supernatural subject unless the supernatural subject is willing.

Dice Pool: Intelligence + Socialize + Auspex – subject's Resolve

Action: Instant

Roll Results

Dramatic Failure: Dramatic failure on a Telepathy attempt can be disastrous, as the user instantly adopts any derangements present in the target for the rest of the night.

Failure: Failure results in no link being established, and the character cannot try again for the remainder of the scene.

Success: Success allows a character to read from or add a thought to the subject's mind. See the suggested modifiers list that follows for specific applications of the Telepathy power.

Exceptional Success: Exceptional success at Telepathy allows the character to gain an additional piece of information (or an additional aspect to the original insight).

Note that the player of any subject who is aware that he is being probed or "ridden" may spend a Willpower point to eject the telepath. Each time the telepath sends a message, the subject instantly becomes aware that the thought didn't originate from his own mind. Each time the telepath digs out a piece of data, Intelligence + Composure is rolled for the subject to detect the intruder.

Suggested Modifiers

Modifier	Situation
+2	Power is turned on a vampire with whom the user has a blood tie (see p. 162)
—	Attempting to project a single thought/message into the subject's mind.
-1	Trying to probe the subject's surface thoughts for whatever idea is there at the time.
-1	Each derangement the subject possesses.

| -2 | Digging for one piece of data about which the subject isn't currently thinking. |
| -3 | Searching for a specific memory or event buried deep in the subconscious. |

Twilight Projection

Commonly seen as the pinnacle of Auspex achievement, this power allows a vampire to project her perceptions out of her physical body. Her senses take on an existence their own, traveling the material world like a spectre. Such a form, called a "ghost body," is immune to fatigue and physical harm, and it can fly at great speeds. Ghost bodies can even go underground at will — anywhere within and below the limit of the lunar sphere.

Cost: 1 Willpower

Dice Pool: Intelligence + Occult + Auspex

Action: Instant

Roll Results

Dramatic Failure: Dramatic failures can be disastrous. They usually result in the character projecting successfully but being flung to an undesired destination (around the world or deep into an unknown place, for example).

Failure: The character cannot separate her consciousness from her body, but may try again at her next opportunity.

Success: The Kindred separates her ghost body from her physical body and may venture throughout the world.

Exceptional Success: As with a normal success, but the separation occurs with ease and the character regains the Willpower point spent.

Interacting with the physical world or sprit world while using Twilight Projection is impossible. The character has no substance at all, not even spiritual substance — she is merely a projected consciousness. This state can be both a benefit and a drawback, in that the character is unimpeded by obstacles, but is also unable to affect any threats she encounters. It might come to pass that two vampires' ghost bodies or a projected vampire and a genuine ghost encounter one another. They can communicate as if they were in the real world, but no sorts of physical or mystical exchanges can occur between them.

A projected vampire's psyche is invisible to most physical beings. A child or animal might intuitively sense the vampire's presence, or even see him. Another Kindred using Heightened Senses or Aura Perception might spot the projected being by getting the most successes in a Wits + Investigation + Auspex (spotter) versus Resolve + Occult + Auspex (projector) contested roll. Both rolls are made reflexively.

A projecting vampire's other Disciplines do not work. Her spirit can certainly observe things, but its temporal connection to the body that serves as the conduit for the Kindred's mystic curse is too tenuous for other mystical powers to manifest.

While her consciousness roams, a vampire's body lies in a torpor-like state on the spot where she left it. As long as her ghost body is active, the character remains ignorant of what goes on around her physical body. If the body is subjected to either torpor or Final Death, the projected psyche is pulled back immediately.

A vampire's body continues to expend Vitae nightly for the purposes of sustaining itself. The player must succeed on a standard Humanity roll for the ghost body to remain awake during the daytime (see p. 184). The consciousness of a vampire who falls asleep returns to her body and she rises the nex night as normal, entirely within the physical world.

A ghost body appears naked and with no possessions. Artifacts that are composed entirely of spirit matter *might* be employed in this form, but no physical objects transfer over. Likewise, any objects found during the wraithly endeavor cannot be manipulated or return with the character when she finally rejoins her physical body.

A projecting vampire can potentially be barred mystically from returning to her body, or she might become lost and incapable of finding her body again. Rumors also speak of other spirits that can enter a vampire's vacant body, stranding the Kindred as a ghost body. Denied her own body (or perhaps another one to possess), each night that passes for the ghost body removes a dot of Blood Potency from its essence. When those dots are reduced to zero, the ghost-Kindred suffers Final Death and fades into oblivion.

Suggested Modifiers

Typically, no modifiers are necessary, but the Storyteller may penalize the activation roll up to two dice in the event of a hastened projection, such as when a vampire abandons her body at the moment of Final Death (after all, a ghost body is better than no body at all).

Celerity

Tales and legends of vampires ascribe to them inhuman speed, the ability to move faster than the eye can see, and even to appear in two places at once. While some of those accounts are exaggerated, Kindred with the Discipline of Celerity can indeed move far faster than any mortal. They appear to blur into nothingness, all others moving as if in slow motion in comparison.

Note that Celerity is obviously superhuman in use. Few Princes smile upon uses of Celerity that leave too many curious mortal witnesses unaccounted for.

Cost: 1 Vitae per turn

Dice Pool: Celerity is unlike many other Disciplines in that it is not actively rolled. Rather, it provides a group of benefits, many of which affect other rolls.

Celerity cannot be invoked more than once per turn. That is, you may not spend a second Vitae and double the benefits of Celerity in a given turn, though you may spend Vitae across multiple turns to enjoy the benefits over those turns.

In turns when a character activates her Celerity, her dots in the Discipline are subtracted from *any and all* attacking characters' dice pools, as the vampire moves much more quickly than normal and is harder to hit. This penalty to attackers' pools applies in addition to any armor the Celerity-using character may have, as well as to Defense (though note, like armor, Celerity's benefits do not diminish based on how many attacks the character faces). Celerity's protection even applies against firearms. For example, if a character has Celerity 3 and activates the Discipline, three dice are subtracted from any assailants' dice pools.

Celerity also adds to a character's Initiative during the turn in which it is active. The aforementioned character with Celerity 3 and Initiative 5 would have a basic Initiative modifier of 8 during turns in which his Celerity is active.

Finally, Celerity acts as a modifier to a character's Speed while it is active. His Speed increases by itself again for each dot of Celerity he possesses. (Simply add one to the value of the character's Celerity and multiply that number by his Speed.) Characters running while Celerity is active double this figure, as well. Assuming the sample character with Celerity 3 has a Speed of 12, he has an effective Speed of 48 — [(1+3) x 12] — during turns in which he activates Celerity. If he runs while his Celerity is active, his Speed is 96 — almost 65 miles per hour!

Action: Reflexive. A character may "pre-empt" her own action in a turn to activate Celerity if an opponent acts before her and the vampire wishes to call upon Celerity before the rival's action is performed. The vampire therefore gets Celerity's protection bonus early in the turn. Celerity's Initiative bonus is also added immediately in the turn, potentially moving the vampire's action before her attacker's in the Initiative roster. The vampire also gains the benefit of additional Speed for the turn. If one Vitae is spent to keep Celerity active into the next turn, all of these benefits carry over.

Example: *Virginia's Initiative total for a fight is 10. Her opponent's is 13. Virginia wants to activate Celerity in order to avoid her opponent's attacks and react more quickly. The Discipline can be activated on 13 in the Initiative roster as a reflexive action. Virginia has Celerity 2, so attacks staged against her automatically suffer a -2 penalty throughout the turn, in addition to penalties from her Defense and any armor she wears. Her Initiative for the turn also increases by two, to 12. That doesn't allow her to act before her opponent, but she is right on his heels.*

If a vampire doesn't activate Celerity until his stage of the Initiative roster in a turn, previous actions taken by others that turn aren't invalidated. (They aren't re-done because the vampire suddenly has a higher standing in the roster.) By activating Celerity "late" in the turn, the vampire forfeits his Initiative bonus that turn. The vampire also gains Celerity's protection only against attacks that come after his place in the Initiative roster for the turn. If Celerity is kept active into the next turn, the vampire's Initiative bonus and full protection applies throughout.

Dominate

Some Kindred are capable of overwhelming the minds of others with their own force of will, influencing actions and even thoughts. Use of Dominate requires a character to capture a victim's gaze. The Discipline can therefore be used on only one subject at a time, and is useless if eye contact is not possible.

Dominate does not grant the ability to make oneself understood or to communicate mentally. Commands must be issued verbally, though certain simple commands (such as "Go over there!" indicated with a pointed finger and a forceful expression) may be conveyed by signs at the Storyteller's discretion. No matter how powerful a vampire is, she cannot force her victim to obey if she cannot make herself understood — if, for example, the victim doesn't speak the same language, she cannot hear or the orders simply make no sense.

Note that victims of Dominate might realize what's been done to them. That is, they do not automatically sense that they are being controlled, but they might subsequently wonder why they suddenly acted as they did. Wise Kindred, especially those familiar with Dominate, are likely to figure it out in the moment, and few vampires take kindly to being manipulated in such a fashion. Most Kindred who develop Dominate are forceful, controlling personalities, and they can make a reputation for themselves if they use this Discipline wantonly.

In all cases, a dramatic failure while attempting to Dominate a victim renders the would-be victim immune to the character's Dominate until the next sunset.

Dominate is far more effective against mortals than it is against other Kindred. Most Dominate abilities described here allow the victim to struggle against the effects; that is, a contested roll is made against the Dominator's player. As no mortal has Blood Potency, the vast majority of humans are at a disadvantage when dealing with the Discipline.

Dominate is also more effective against those whom the user has subjected to a Vinculum. A regnant may use Dominate powers (with the exception of Conditioning) on a thrall without the need for eye contact; the thrall merely has to hear the regnant's voice.

Other sentient, supernatural beings such as shapechangers who have animal form or who can assume animal form are affected by Dominate rather than by Animalism. A vampire can therefore try to ply his will on a werewolf — even a werewolf in wolf form — by using Dominate. Similarly, Animalism is useless against another vampire who assumes wolf or another bestial form. Animalism is of no avail to the vampire in regard to such intelligent beings.

Note that any Dominate power requiring eye contact is made more difficult if the subject is not standing still or otherwise immobilized. If the target moves about, the roll to initiate the relevant power suffers a -1 penalty in addition to all others listed.

• Command

Once he has established eye contact, the vampire issues a single, one-word command that must be obeyed instantly. The order must be clear and straightforward — freeze, jump, run, stop, fall, cough, blink and so forth. If the command is ambiguous or confusing, the subject might respond slowly or perform the task poorly. Further, commands are always interpreted (within reason) in the subject's best interests. For example, if the victim stands on the edge of a roof and the character commands "Jump!" the victim might jump up and down, rather than leap off the roof. Of course, the victim would probably not leap off the roof even if the character could find a way to

order it. Subjects of Command cannot be made to directly harm themselves, so an obviously suicidal order such as "Die!" is ineffective. "Sleep" and the like causes the subject to follow the order only if she does not believe herself to be in any mortal danger. A character seduced by a Kindred might sleep if so instructed, but one in the middle of a combat or interrogation certainly does not. In such situations, the character merely falls senseless, but only for a turn.

The vampire may include the command word in a sentence, in order to conceal her use of the power from others. The command itself must be stressed, and the character must make eye contact precisely when that word is spoken. Observers may notice the unusual emphasis, but only the most alert — and those familiar with the Discipline — are likely to realize what has occurred.

Cost: —

Dice Pool: Intelligence + Intimidation + Dominate versus Resolve + Blood Potency

Action: Contested; resistance is reflexive

Roll Results

Dramatic Failure: The subject does not obey and is immune to the character's Dominate until the next sunset.

Failure: The character loses or ties the contested roll and the subject does not obey.

Success: The character wins the contested roll by getting the most successes, and the victim obeys literally and with appreciable self-preservation.

Exceptional Success: The character wins the contested roll with five or more successes, and the victim not only obeys but rationalizes what she does as her own decision until and unless someone questions her about it in depth.

Assuming the commanded action is one that can carried out for some time, such as "wait" or "sleep," the subject obeys for a number of turns equal to the successes obtained on the Command roll.

If this power is turned on a vampire with whom the user has a blood tie (see p. 162), a +2 bonus applies to the user's roll.

Mesmerize

The source of many legends of the vampire's hypnotic gaze, Mesmerize allows the Kindred to implant a false thought or suggestion into the subject's subconscious mind. The power requires not only eye contact but intense concentration and precise wording, so both the character and the subject must be free from distraction. The Kindred may activate the imposed thought or command immediately — "Walk over here and open the door" — or he may establish a stimulus that activates the suggestion at a later date — "When you see a man in a blue suit with a red rose in his lapel, you will spill your drink on him." The victim must be able to understand the vampire. The Kindred must maintain eye contact only as long as it takes to implant the suggestion or idea.

Mesmerize can deliver truly complex and long-term commands, such as following someone, taking notes on her activities and reporting back on the first of the next month. A subject can have only one suggestion implanted at any given time.

Cost: —

Dice Pool: Intelligence + Expression + Dominate versus Resolve + Blood Potency

Action: Contested; resistance is reflexive

If this power is turned on a vampire with whom the user has a blood tie (see p. 162), a +2 bonus applies.

Roll Results

Dramatic Failure: The subject does not obey and is immune to the character's Dominate until the next sunset.

Failure: The character loses or ties the contested roll and the subject does not obey.

Success: The character wins the contested roll by getting the most successes, and the victim obeys to the best of his ability.

Exceptional Success: The character wins the contested roll with five or more successes. The victim not only obeys, but rationalizes what she does as her own decision until and unless someone questions her about it in depth.

This power lasts for as long as it takes the subject to carry out the required task, or until the character is destroyed or enters torpor. Impossible actions such as, "Count every grain of sand on this beach," automatically fail to take root in the subject's mind. If, during the course of carrying out the implanted suggestion, the victim realizes he puts himself in danger or acts completely contrary to his normal moral code, a Resolve roll may be made to shake off the compulsion. This is a contested roll. Successes rolled must exceed the number of successes obtained for the dominating character when the individual was first mesmerized.

Dramatic Failure: Not only must the subject continue to carry out the command, no more Resolve rolls may be made to shake the dominator's control, no matter what the subject is forced to do.

Failure: The victim must continue to carry out the command as ordered.

Success: The victim escapes the suggestion.

Exceptional Success: The victim defies the suggestion, and the dominator incurs a -1 penalty to future attempts to Dominate him until the next night.

No matter how strong the dominator's will is or how many successes he obtains, he cannot make a subject harm himself directly. Any command to commit suicide is therefore ignored, although commands that are likely to lead to harm — such as, "Walk into that crack house and shoot the man in the red shirt" — are enforceable, subject to the Resolve rolls discussed above.

If a vampire attempts to Mesmerize a subject who is already under the influence of a previously implanted directive, compare the successes rolled in the attempt against the successes gained during the implantation of the first suggestion. If the character obtains more successes than the previous Kindred, the new command may supplant the old one. If he does not, the original command remains active and the new one fails to take root. In case of a tie, the original command takes precedent over the new one. A vampire seeking to supplant an old suggestion with a new one must also acquire successes in excess of those rolled for the subject in his contested Resolve + Blood Potency roll.

... The Forgetful Mind

A vampire with this power can literally delve into a subject's mind, stealing or reshaping memories at whim. The power, as with all uses of Dominate, requires eye contact. The Forgetful Mind does not allow for telepathic contact. Instead, the vampire acts much like a hypnotist, asking direct questions to draw answers from the subject, and then describing in detail any new memories she wishes to impose on the victim. Simple alterations, such as blurring brief and recent memories, are easy enough (and very effective for eliminating evidence of feeding or other Masquerade breaches). More comprehensive alterations, up to and including a complete reconstruction of the victim's past and even identity, are possible albeit substantially more difficult.

The victim's subconscious struggles to resist false memories implanted from without, so the degree to which the vampire details new memories has direct bearing on how fully the subject assimilates them. An incomplete or simplistic false memory shatters much more swiftly and easily than does one with more attention to detail. For instance, "You drove home after work and had a very bad evening" is not likely to hold up. Far more effective would be an account such as, "You left work late, due to a last-minute change ordered by the client. You still managed to get stuck in rush hour for an extra 25 minutes, and you were seriously frustrated by the time you pulled off the freeway. There weren't even any good songs on the radio. Three blocks from home, a cop pulled you over for coasting through a stop sign. At least he only gave you a warning, but it was still just one more hassle. The frozen dinner you microwaved was awful, the TV movie starred some has-been you didn't like, and the news was depressing. You finally turned off the TV in disgust and went to bed."

Truly effective use of The Forgetful Mind, then, requires substantial finesse and patience, as well as the ability to carefully and thoroughly think things through ahead of time. It's fairly simple to sift through a victim's memories and strip out recent events without even knowing precisely what happened, but doing so leaves a gap in the memory that can lead to further problems. Most people aren't comfortable realizing they've lost a few hours or a night's worth of memories, and they're likely to try to find out what happened. Even new memories that the character imposes rarely have the same strength as the originals, and they can be broken or at least contradicted through investigation. For instance, a victim might not recall that she was attacked by a vampire, but she might remember being bitten, chalking it up to an animal attack or a spider. More vivid memories can return as snippets in dreams or be triggered by an unusual olfactory stimulus or spoken phrase. The process might take weeks or even years before the victim can begin to make

sense of these flashes, but even the most effective memory manipulation is far from perfect — or truly permanent.

A vampire may also use The Forgetful Mind to sense whether someone has had her memories altered in this fashion, and he can sometimes use his own power to draw forth and restore the original thoughts. No Kindred may use The Forgetful Mind to restore his own lost or altered memories, however.

Cost: —

Dice Pool: Wits + Persuasion + Dominate – Resolve

Action: Extended (1-100+ successes, based on the detail and complexity of memory; each roll represents five minutes of mental manipulation)

Roll Results

Dramatic Failure: The attempt fails, and the subject is immune to the character's Dominate until the next sunset. All accumulated successes are lost and the subject continues to remember what happened.

Failure: The attempt fails.

Success: The character makes headway toward altering a block of memories.

Exceptional Success: The character makes considerable headway toward altering a block of memories.

Even a single success pacifies the victim for the length of time it takes to complete the process. Both vampire and subject must be safe and relatively composed when this power is used; it cannot be used to calm someone already in combat, for example.

To restore stolen or false memories, or to sense when memories have been altered, a character must possess Dominate at a level equal to or greater than that of the vampire who first tampered with the subject's mind. If such is the case, the player then makes a contested roll in each stage of the extended action, to be compared against the initial user's attempt, and must score more successes than the predecessor did.

Suggested Modifiers

Modifier	Situation
+2	Power is turned on a vampire with whom the user has a blood tie (see p. 162).
-1 to -3	The character's description of the new memories is lacking in detail.

•••• Conditioning

Through constant veiled whispers, subtle hints and frequent sustained manipulation, a vampire can slowly render a particular victim substantially more suggestible. Conditioning is normally used only on favored or valuable servants and, over sufficient time, makes the character's efforts to Dominate a subject far easier while making it harder for any other Kindred to do so. Acquiring such complete control over even the weakest mind is no easy task, however, and it normally takes weeks or even months to accomplish.

While they are undeniably loyal, servants subject to Conditioning lose much of their ability to think for themselves, their own personalities blotted out by the will imposed on them. They follow their orders literally and to the letter, rarely showing any imagination or judgment, or taking the initiative to act on their own. Some Kindred have remarked that, after a sufficiently lengthy period of Conditioning, their servants actually resemble the walking dead more so than their masters.

Mortals, thralls, other vampires and other supernatural creatures are all subject to Conditioning, if it can be performed on them over the required period of time.

Cost: 1 Willpower per roll

Dice Pool: Wits + Subterfuge + Dominate versus Resolve + Blood Potency

Action: Contested and Extended (6-15+ successes; each roll represents one week of mental manipulation); resistance is reflexive

Roll Results

Dramatic Failure: All of the user's successes to date are negated and the subject is immune to the character's Dominate until the next sunset.

Failure: The character loses or ties a contested roll and the attempt fails.

Success: The character wins a contested roll and makes progress in his efforts to suborn the subject's will.

Exceptional Success: The character wins a contested roll with five or more successes and makes substantial progress in his efforts to suborn the subject's will.

Conditioning does not have any mechanical effect until five more successes are accumulated in excess of the victim's Willpower dots. (If the subject has Willpower 6, Conditioning begins to take effect once 11 successes are achieved.) Once this benchmark has been reached, all future attempts by the character to use any Dominate ability (including further uses of Conditioning) on the victim receive a +1 bonus, and all attempts by other Kindred to Dominate the subject suffer a -1 penalty. For every additional five successes that are accumulated, the bonus and penalty each increase by one, to a maximum of +5 and -5. The Storyteller, not the player, should keep track of the number of successes accumulated.

Once the character's bonus reaches +3, he no longer needs to make eye contact with the Conditioning subject to use any Dominate abilities, though giving orders through artificial or impersonal means (such as by phone) imposes a -5 penalty to that particular attempt.

Subjects of Conditioning are oblivious to the process being inflicted upon them unless they also possess the power. The Storyteller *may* allow a victim or someone close to him a Wits + Occult roll to recognize that something is wrong. If the roll fails, the process may continue unaffected. If the roll succeeds, an effort may be made to interrupt the process. If the Conditioning vampire is particularly careful about how suggestions and messages are conveyed, the Wits + Occult roll might suffer a -1 penalty. Interrupting the process could mean fleeing the vampire or restraining the subject from meeting the vampire before all the required successes are accumulated.

It is possible, albeit extremely difficult, to break a subject's Conditioning after the required successes are gathered. If the victim is isolated from her master for a number of weeks equal to twice the master's current Conditioning-granted bonus, the bonus drops by one. For example, a subject has been Conditioned for a long time, and her master has achieved a bonus of +4 to Dominate her. If she is kept completely isolated from her master for eight weeks, the bonus drops to +3. Six more weeks, and it drops to +2, and so forth. The subject's own personality and creativity slowly reawakens during this period, though she still experiences periods of listlessness, depression and desperation. For at least the first few weeks, the subject most likely makes every attempt to return to her master. Until the subject is completely free, it is horrifyingly easy for the vampire to reassert his dominance, as he likely has at least some bonus to Dominate the individual for a long while.

If the subject of Conditioning is also the thrall of the vampire, all successes on a Conditioning roll are doubled. So, if a vampire seeks to Condition his own ghoul, and he gets three successes to her two in one roll to program the subject, he actually accumulates six successes in that Conditioning session.

If this power is turned on a vampire with whom the user has a blood tie (see p. 162), a +2 bonus applies.

Possession

By this point, the Kindred need not rely on spoken commands and limited understanding. With the mere locking of the victim's gaze, the vampire can utterly supplant the subject's own psyche with her own, possessing the subject like a malevolent spirit.

Once the Kindred has crushed the victim's will, she literally takes over the body, inhabiting it and controlling it as easily as she does her own. The mortal enters something of a fugue state while possessed, and he is aware of events only in a dreamlike, distorted fashion. The Kindred suffers the opposite effect. Her mind now resides within the victim, and her own body falls into a torpor-like state, becoming indistinguishable from a true corpse. The vampire may choose to break the possession and return to her body at any time, over any distance, but until and unless she does so, her true physical form is utterly helpless.

Kindred cannot possess other Kindred in this fashion, regardless of force of will or differences in Blood Potency. Mortals alone are subject to possession, although whispers of possessed Lupines and mages sometimes circulate.

Cost: 1 Willpower

Dice Pool: Intelligence + Intimidation + Dominate versus Resolve

Action: Contested and Extended (see below); resistance is reflexive

Roll Results

The vampire locks eyes with the victim and begins the process of utterly stripping away the subject's Willpower. The vampire must obtain a number of successes in excess of the victim's

Willpower. The victim is held, trapped in this psychic struggle, as long as the vampire's player continues to win each contested roll. Each roll occupies a turn's time.

Dramatic Failure: The attempt is over and the victim is immune to that vampire's Dominate until the next sunset. All previously accumulated successes are lost.

Failure: In any turn in which the vampire loses or ties a contested roll, the victim may attempt to escape. If the vampire succeeds in restarting the process during the same scene, the contest picks up from where it left off.

Success: The character wins a contested roll and accumulates successes in her attempt to exert ultimate control over her subject.

Exceptional Success: The character wins a contested roll with five or more successes in her attempt to exert ultimate control over her subject.

Once the character has exceeded the victim's Willpower in number of successes, she may take control of his body. The character may take any actions she chooses, travel as far from her own body as she wishes, and is unharmed by daylight while possessing the subject, but she must still force herself to stay awake during the day (see Humanity on p. 184). The vampire may choose to end the possession and return to her body at any time, regardless of distance. This occurs automatically if the vampire fails to remain awake. Any injuries inflicted on the subject also affect the vampire's body. If the subject dies while the vampire is still present, the Kindred falls into torpor immediately. (Some believe the soul attempts to find its way back to its own body during this time.) If the Kindred's physical form is destroyed, she remains trapped in the mortal body until she finally fails to remain awake, at which point her psyche is lost to oblivion and is unrecoverable. Any attempt to "re-Embrace" a vampire's spirit trapped in a host body results only in Final Death.

When finally freed of vampiric possession, some mortals recover immediately, while others lie comatose or suffer trauma-induced psychoses for days or even weeks before recovering.

Because a vampire experiences everything her physical body does — tasting food, soaking up the sun — many become addicted to the sensations and spend more time possessing mortals than inhabiting their own bodies. It is possible, though uncommon, for a vampire to neglect her physical body long enough for it to starve into torpor while she's "out." If a vampire's dormant body slips or is forced into torpor, the vampire's spirit automatically returns to its body.

If this power is turned on a vampire with whom the user has a blood tie (see p. 162), a +2 bonus applies.

Majesty

One of the most legendary powers of the undead is the ability to attract, sway and control the emotions of others, especially those of mortals. Majesty is perhaps the most versatile of Disciplines, for its potential uses and applications are both varied and multitudinous. The more savvy the practitioner, the more use he can get out of each of the Discipline's levels.

Unlike some other Disciplines, Majesty can be used on entire crowds of targets simultaneously, making it even more potent — in the right hands. The only requirement for use of most Majesty powers is that any potential targets see the character. Eye contact is not required, nor is the ability to hear the character (though it certainly doesn't hurt).

The downside to Majesty, such as is it is, is that its subjects retain their free will. Unlike victims of Dominate, who follow the commands of the Kindred nearly mindlessly, those acting under Majesty are simply emotionally predisposed to do whatever the power (or its user) suggests. While retention of personality makes victims more useful in the long run, it also means they require more care in handling than targets of Dominate. An abused victim of Majesty certainly subverts or represses what his emotions suggest in order to behave in the most appropriate manner. Meanwhile, subjects treated well might be persuaded to act against even their own interests.

Any mortal can resist Majesty for one turn if a Willpower point is spent and a successful Composure roll is made (though the Willpower point does not add three dice to the roll). This roll is reflexive. If the roll fails, the Willpower point is lost and the target remains under the effects of the power(s). If the roll is successful, the mortal probably spends his turn of "freedom" fleeing the vampire's proximity, lest he continue to be affected. Refusing to pay attention to the vampire, rather than fleeing, can allow a mortal to resist the spell for a turn, but the power resumes effect if the mortal remains in the Kindred's vicinity. Vampires resist Majesty in much the same way (by spending a Willpower point), but Blood Potency is added to Composure rolls made for them. In addition, vampires of higher Blood Potency than the character invoking Majesty are able to resist his power for the entire scene with the expenditure of one Willpower point and a successful Composure + Blood Potency roll.

By and large, the Kindred who choose to develop their Majesty abilities are those who recognize that one achieves more with honey than with vinegar. Those who swear by Majesty often find Dominate, seen as "the flip side of Majesty," to be both boorish and crass, and they would swear to calling upon it only in times of dire need.

• Awe

This power makes the user seem exponentially more charismatic and magnetic than he normally is. The force of his personality issues forth in waves, drawing people to him like moths to a flame. Perhaps the greatest use for Awe is its ability to facilitate public speaking or debate. Whatever the vampire says, people are likely to lend serious credence to his position and views, and even the staunchest opponents gladly hear him out. Awe can often turn the tide in a tense negotiation, tipping the scales from "potentially" to "definitely."

As with other Majesty powers, Awe ceases to be useful when more pressing matters come to the fore. Personal safety always takes precedence, and any commotion pulls even the most rapt listener from his reverie of attention. Those subjected to the character's stature likely remember how good they felt around him, and tailor future reactions accordingly.

Cost: —

Dice Pool: Presence + Expression + Majesty

Action: Instant

Roll Results

Dramatic Failure: A dramatic failure indicates that the character actually makes himself more unappealing, and people actively seek to avoid him until he leaves.

Failure: Failure indicates that the power simply does not activate. The character knows this immediately and may try again next turn.

Success: The character succeeds in dazzling his intended audience with his overwhelming charisma.

Exceptional Success: An exceptional success indicates that the subjects' Composures are considered one less than normal for the purposes of determining who is affected.

The number of successes the player acquires is compared to the Composure of each intended subject. If the number of successes exceeds a given target's Composure, that subject is affected by the character's powerful personality. If a subject's Composure is equal to or higher than the number of successes earned, that subject goes unaffected. A character may Awe whomever is present (see the suggested modifiers below), and comparisons are made from lowest Composure to highest among potential subjects. Effectively, a character may not single out an individual subject in a crowd to Awe. He simply "turns on the charm" and lets it work its magic.

Those individuals affected by Awe raptly fawn over the user. Any social rolls he engages in with them gains a number of bonus dice equal to the number of successes rolled to activate the power. This effect lasts for one scene, and people may well expect to thrill to the character's presence the next time they see him.

Suggested Modifiers

Modifier	Situation
—	Character attempts to Awe one person
-1	Character attempts to Awe two people
-2	Character attempts to Awe six people
-3	Character attempts to Awe 20 people
-4	Character attempts to Awe a vast number of people in the vampire's immediate vicinity (an auditorium, a mob)

•• Revelation

The allure and reassurance of a Kindred with this power is enough to make others forego caution and share their innermost feelings and secrets. A few complimentary or compassionate words or a heartfelt look from the vampire can break down a person's prudence and fear, inspiring a desire to share deep feelings or dark secrets in an upwelling of affection or release.

Cost: 1 Vitae

Dice Pool: Manipulation + Persuasion + Majesty versus subject's Composure + Blood Potency

Action: Contested; resistance is reflexive

Roll Results

Dramatic Failure: The vampire's manipulative efforts are obvious for the intended subject to see. No more of the vampire's attempts at Revelation on the same subject work for the remainder of the night.

Failure: The character loses or ties the contested roll. He may try again.

Success: The vampire wins the contested roll by getting the most successes, and the subject bares his soul.

Exceptional Success: The vampire wins the contested roll with five or more successes. The subject bares his soul until every sin or crime he can think of is revealed. No Willpower can be spent to make a Composure roll to stop.

While a vampire can gain the information he seeks by use of this power, he must be prepared for a litany of confessions from a particularly guilty or tormented subject. A longtime criminal might have many sins to confess, for example, only one of which is important to the character using Revelation. A successful Manipulation + Socialize roll may be required for the vampire to steer the confession to a matter of interest. If the roll fails, the vampire must endure everything that the subject has to say. Should the confession go on for more than a single turn, and the subject turns to particularly deep, dark or dangerous secrets, a Willpower point may be spent and a Composure roll made for the subject to break the spell for a turn (see p. 129).

The subject remembers what he confessed after the effects of the power have passed. He undoubtedly can't explain his lack of discretion, and he might do anything in his power to compensate for his "error in judgment."

Suggested Modifiers

Modifier	Situation
+3	The subject is a thrall to the Kindred, under a full Vinculum to her.
+3	The subject is already under the influence of Entrancement.
+2	The subject is already under the influence of Awe.
+2	The subject is under the second stage of a partial Vinculum to the Kindred.
+2	Power is turned on a vampire with whom the user has a blood tie (see p. 162)
+1	The subject is affected by the first stage of a partial Vinculum to the Kindred.
-1	The subject is an enemy.
-2	The Revelation user has inflicted violence upon the subject in the scene.

••• Entrancement

This power is perhaps the closest thing that Majesty gets to serious command over the thoughts of another. Its power warps the emotional state of the subject, making him a willing servant of the vampire. Subjects retain their sense of identity and free will, believing that every instinct to serve and admire comes of their own volition.

When the duration of an Entrancement ends, however, confusion and displacement arise, often leading to mixed feelings. Similar to falling out of love, re-entrancing a former "lover" is difficult at best.

Cost: —

Dice Pool: Manipulation + Empathy + Majesty versus subject's Composure + Blood Potency

Action: Contested; resistance is reflexive

Roll Results

Dramatic Failure: A dramatic failure offends the subject, making him immune to the vampire's "advances" for the rest of the night.

Failure: The character loses or ties the contested roll. The Entrancement fails and the subject reacts to the vampire normally.

Success: The character wins the contested roll by getting the most successes, and brings the subject under his sway for an hour or so — long enough to complete a single task or set of tasks.

Exceptional Success: The character wins the contested roll with five or more successes. An exceptional success indentures the target for at least at least a week, and potentially a month or more.

When a period of effect wears off, the subject does not necessarily bear the vampire any ill will. After all, he has no idea that something unnatural has taken place. He merely comes to the conclusion that he no longer feels the way he once did for the character (even if "once" was an hour ago). At this time, he likely returns to going about his own life, content with never seeing the vampire again. Typically, a vampire who wishes to retain the attention of an affected subject calls upon more reliable (or stringent) methods of indenturing, such as the Vinculum.

Suggested Modifiers

Modifier	Situation
+2	Power is turned on a vampire with whom the user has a blood tie (see p. 162)
-3	The Kindred has already successfully Entranced the subject within a week.

••••• Summoning

This rather potent power allows the vampire to call any individual he knows personally to his side. In short, the vampire reaches out with the force of his personality and makes a colleague, acquaintance, rival or outright enemy *know* without doubt that he wishes that person to attend him at once. There is no limit on the distance or range of this power, but summoning someone halfway around the world takes time, even under the best of circumstances. The subject of Summoning takes the most direct possible routes to the vampire's location and intuitively knows when the vampire moves, though doesn't necessarily know the final destination until he gets there (it's like a sort of direction sense).

The summoned individual knows to whose presence he travels, and he may pause to make arrangements before

departure, if necessary. In other words, the compulsion is strong and the subject doesn't dilly-dally unnecessarily, but he is hardly a single-minded drone in his desire to reach the vampire. The subject does, however, use any resources at his disposal to see that he arrives both safely and punctually.

The call of a summoning fades with the first rays of the sun at dawn. Therefore, if a subject is truly far away or a sufficiently fast means of transportation is not available to him, he can deny the compulsion to attend the summoner at dawn. Indeed, he could return home and go about his business. If the subject is predisposed toward the summoner, however, he may continue the quest of his own accord. During the day, he is under his own power to find the vampire and loses his "direction sense." Another vampire is not compelled to seek the summoner to the very light of day, causing his Final Death. The seeker finds shelter beforehand. Unless the subject already knows where and how to reach the summoning vampire, the call must be repeated each night until the subject arrives. If, as in the preceding case with the resistant subject, the distance is too far or available transportation is too slow, the subject might never arrive. He falls into a cycle of being drawn to and fleeing from the summoner.

If a Willpower point is spent and a Composure + Blood Potency roll is made for a subject to resist this power, as explained on p. 129, any success defies a summons for a whole night, not just a turn or a scene.

Cost: 1 Vitae

Dice Pool: Manipulation + Persuasion + Majesty versus subject's Composure + Blood Potency

Action: Contested; restance is reflexive

Roll Results

Dramatic Failure: The target is aware that the vampire tried to summon him, and is immune to that vampire's Summoning attempts for the rest of the story.

Failure: The character loses or ties the contested roll. The subject remains unaware of the Summoning, and nothing happens.

Success: The character wins the contested roll by getting the most successes. Complete success brings the subject as quickly as possible within the space of one night, without questioning the motivations or origins of the summons.

Exceptional Success: The character wins the contested roll with five or more successes. An exceptional success draws the subject to the vampire with all deliberate haste, no matter how long the journey takes. The compulsion to arrive prevails even during daylight, and the subject's sense of the summoner's location persists throughout.

Suggested Modifiers

Modifier	Situation
+3	The subject is dedicated or loyal to the summoner.
+2	Power is turned on a vampire with whom the user has a blood tie (see p. 162).
+1	The subject is predisposed toward or friendly with the summoner.
+1	The summoner knows exactly where the subject is.
—	The summoner doesn't know specifically where the subject is, but knows that he is in the same domain.
-1	The summoner has no idea where the subject is.
-1	The subject resents being summoned or dislikes the summoner.
-3	The summoner has no idea where the subject is and he's more than 500 miles away.
-3	The subject has urgent business elsewhere or reviles the summoner.
-5	The summoner has no idea where the subject is and he's on the other side of the world.

••••• Sovereignty

One of the most potent of all Kindred abilities, Sovereignty augments the power of a vampire's personal deportment to incredible levels. The newly empowered mien inspires devotion, respect and fear in those who stand in the vampire's proximity. The weak-willed (and cunning) supplicate themselves for the chance to serve, and the stout of heart find themselves at a loss to do anything but acquiesce. Sovereignty's power influences decisions, breaks hearts, cripples confidence and shakes the ambitious to the foundations of their determination.

The vibe the vampire gives off makes others quick to surrender, and the thought of risking his displeasure quails even the heartiest souls. Raising one's voice to a sovereign Kindred seems unthinkable; aggressing upon him seems impossible. The power of this level of Majesty is a terrifying thing to behold, and a difficult thing to rein in once it's let loose. Elders are wise not to abuse it or use it too flippantly, as its power is most effective when used both sparingly and exactingly. Despite its mighty prowess, Sovereignty is a finely honed tool — a scalpel, rather than a sword.

Cost: 1 Willpower per scene

Dice Pool: Presence + Intimidation + Majesty versus subject's Composure + Blood Potency

Action: Instant; contested and reflexive

Sovereignty is considered "always active" during scenes in which it is invoked, though it may be turned off at the Kindred's discretion. Activating the power requires an instant action. Its capacity is tested whenever challenged. When the power is at its "normal" level, people can speak freely around the vampire as long as they don't try to defy or criticize him, though their demeanor is marked by an obvious obeisance to the Kindred invoking Sovereignty. Anyone wishing to attack the vampire, however, whether physically, mystically or socially, calls the user's Sovereignty into question. A reflexive and contested roll is made for presiding vampire and would-be attacker.

Note also that, unlike other uses of Majesty, Sovereignty may not be overcome with the expenditure of a Willpower point and success on a Composure + Blood Potency roll (see p. 129). The power is defensive and overwhelming, and it must be countered by a determined foe as described here.

Roll Results

Dramatic Failure: A dramatic failure is rolled for the sovereign vampire. The assailant may attack, use Disciplines or criticize for the rest of the scene without having to make challenges to the character's Sovereignty.

Failure: The sovereign character loses or ties the contested roll; attacks, Discipline uses or criticisms proceed without penalty, but the attacker feels the weight of his action in every movement.

Success: The sovereign character wins the contested roll by getting the most successes, and the assault cannot be carried out this turn. A subsequent attempt calls for another contested roll.

Exceptional Success: The sovereign character wins the contested roll with five or more successes, and the would-be assailant cannot attack or disparage the vampire for the duration of the night.

Note that a contested roll must be made every time someone wishes to make a new attack, use a Discipline or criticize the vampire who uses Sovereignty (with the obvious exception of dramatic failures and exceptional successes).

The power applies against physical attacks as well as intended uses of Disciplines that could harm or affect the reigning vampire negatively. Intentions to speak an ill word about or at the sovereign vampire invoke the same contested roll. If the effort fails, the would-be critic cannot bring himself to say what he wishes to.

If the presiding vampire responds to aggression by physically attacking back, he breaks his Sovereignty with respect to that subject alone. Use of a Discipline in a damaging or negative way against a would-be aggressor also breaks the spell against that individual alone. All other would-be combatants, Discipline users or naysayers must continue to overcome the reigning vampire's power if they wish to turn aggressor. The sovereign vampire does not break his spell over a subject by disparaging him publicly.

Suggested Modifiers

Modifier	Situation
+3	The challenger is a thrall to the sovereign Kindred, under a full Vinculum to her.
+2	Power affects a vampire with whom the user has a blood tie (see p. 162).
+2	The challenger is under the second stage of a partial Vinculum to the sovereign Kindred.
+1	The challenger is affected by the first stage of a partial Vinculum to the sovereign Kindred.

+1	The challenger has already attempted one attack in the scene, which was denied by the Discipline.
—	The challenger seeks to attack the sovereign Kindred.

Nightmare

There's no question that one of the foremost powers of legendary vampires is the ability to strike fear in the hearts of mortal men. Also born of mortal existence, other now-supernatural beings are susceptible. Fear is a fact of existence that transcends any origins.

Vampires who delve into the dark side of their being — often exploring the Beast or what it means to be monstrous — invest in the Discipline of Nightmare. They learn to bear that which is terrifying or unholy about their spirits, manifesting their inhumanity in their appearance or letting unfortunate onlookers peer deep into the creatures' depraved souls. The results can take a jaded individual aback or subject an unsuspecting victim to a fatal physiological reaction (to literally be frightened to death).

Practitioners of Nightmare explore this route to power for different reasons. One vampire might exult in his inhuman nature and enjoy lording over lessers. The Discipline offers immediate gratification, and these Kindred display what is hideous about themselves to everyone, hiding it only insofar as they must in order to observe the secrecy of the Traditions. Other undead recognize the wisdom or even benevolence that fear affords. What better way to deal with a problem or avoid a confrontation than by frightening away an opponent? How better to protect someone from harm than by scaring her off? And if one seeks solitude, striking fear is certainly more effective than issuing threats, trying to reason with would-be intruders or orchestrating ever more elaborate means by which to hide.

Note: All uses of Nightmare gain a +2 bonus if the individual power is turned on a vampire with whom the user has a blood tie (see p. 162). Naturally, this bonus does not apply to the subject's resistance.

• Monstrous Countenance

The true face of a vampire is a frightening thing, indeed — made all the more terrifying by the assistance of this entirely unsubtle Nightmare power. When a Kindred activates Monstrous Countenance, he does so in conjunction with a ferocious baring of fangs and a raspy, malevolent hiss. The result is a visage most foul, one that can make stalwart foes cower at the vampire's feet.

Cost: —

Dice Pool: Presence + Intimidation + Nightmare versus subject's Composure + Blood Potency (The Nosferatu clan weakness does not apply to the Discipline user's roll.)

Action: Contested

An activation roll is made for the vampire, and a reflexive and contested roll is made for anyone who looks upon him. For a group of observers, particularly mortals, the Storyteller may roll the highest Composure of the crowd as an indicator of the group's reaction. Any onlooker must see the vampire in person; the character's appearance is frightening on a television or video camera, but no more so than any special effect. The vampire may maintain his frightening countenance and manner for the remainder of the scene and terrify anyone whom he encounters. Record the successes achieved on the power's activation roll to compare to all comers' contested rolls.

Roll Results

Dramatic Failure: The vampire is incapable of Monstrous Countenance for the remainder of the scene.

Failure: The subject's successes exceed or tie those rolled for the vampire. The subject is a bit shaken, but otherwise unaffected.

Success: Successes rolled for the vampire exceed those rolled for the subject. The victim flees the vampire's presence entirely, using all available means at his disposal to do so. He continues fleeing for one turn per success rolled and will not come within sight of the vampire for the remainder of the scene.

Exceptional Success: An exceptional success reduces the subject to a cowering heap, unable to take any action of his own volition. If attacked, a terror-stricken foe can defend himself (he is allowed Defense but not a dodge action), and may attack anyone who attacks him. He cannot attack the Nightmare-user, even if she is also the source of an attack. The victim remains terrified as long as the vampire remains in the vicinity.

•• Dread

While an outward, physical manifestation can strike fear in onlookers, it is an overt, blunt means by which to prey upon the weak. More insidious and subtle is a general sense of unease, rising panic and paranoia that a vampire can engender with this power.

Cost: 1 Vitae

Dice Pool: Manipulation + Empathy + Nightmare versus subject's Composure + Blood Potency (The Nosferatu clan weakness does not apply to the Discipline user's roll.)

Action: Contested

Gloom, disquiet and uncertainty creeps into the hearts of people around the vampire. Anyone within three yards per Willpower dot that the vampire possesses can be affected. One contested roll may be made reflexively for a crowd of prospective victims — probably mortals — based on the highest Composure among them.

Roll Results

Dramatic Failure: The vampire is incapable of Dread for the remainder of the scene.

Failure: Successes rolled for the subject exceed or tie those rolled for the vampire. The subject feels no ill effects.

Success: The most successes are rolled for the vampire using Dread. See the following for results.

Exceptional Success: The roll made for the vampire wins the contested roll and gets five or more successes. See the following for results. Each victim also loses a Willpower point.

The atmosphere of fear persists either as long as the vampire concentrates on it or until the end of the scene, whichever comes first. If the vampire does anything else drastic such as attacking someone, performing a dodge maneuver or activating another Discipline, the effects of Dread cease. Record the number of successes rolled for the vampire when this power is activated, and compare it to any rolled for newcomers to the power's area of effect.

Those who lose the contested roll suffer a -2 penalty on all actions out of an inexplicable rising panic. Nor can they spend Willpower to gain three extra dice on any rolls, or +2 to any Resistance traits. (Willpower can be spent to activate capabilities or powers that require it, however.)

Dread cannot be used selectively on some people surrounding the user, and not on others. Its effects are all or nothing. Nor can it be used more than once on any subject in a single scene.

••• Eye of the Beast

The terrifying nature of the Beast is a horrific reminder of the fundamental predator-prey dichotomy of existence. Shown the Beast, another being is reduced to the most primal of instincts, foregoing all reason and cunning in the face of primeval horror. The vampire makes eye contact with a subject and reveals the inner core of the Kindred's being. The Beast looks hungrily upon the subject and invokes a reaction appropriate to that person's nature. Direct eye contact is required between vampire and target; looking at someone over a satellite transmission does not apply.

Cost: 1 Vitae

Dice Pool: Presence + Empathy + Nightmare versus subject's Composure + Blood Potency (The Nosferatu clan weakness does not apply to the Discipline user's roll.)

Action: Contested; resistance is reflexive

Roll Results

Dramatic Failure: The vampire is incapable of Eye of the Beast for the remainder of the scene.

Failure: Successes rolled for the subject exceed or tie those rolled for the vampire. The onlooker is taken aback, but no effect is triggered.

Success: The most successes are rolled for the vampire against a mortal. The victim is paralyzed with fear, incapable of moving or taking any action. If the victim is attacked, his Defense applies and he may act in the next turn and thereafter, but he must dedicate all his efforts to escaping the vampire's proximity. Therefore, he doesn't take time to attack anyone unless doing so is necessary to escaping. Unmolested, a mortal remains paralyzed as long as the vampire remains in his presence. If the spell is broken with an attack, the victim spends the remainder of the scene trying to flee the creature.

Alternatively, the most successes are rolled for the character against another vampire or another supernatural being that is capable of frenzy. The victim must flee the vampire for the remainder of the scene as per the Frenzy rules (see p. 178). Another vampire is subject to Rötschreck, for example. In this case, if successes rolled for the subject tie those rolled for

the character, the subject simply frenzies for the remainder of the turn without fleeing, attacking anyone near him. That might include the user of Eye of the Beast.

Exceptional Success: As a success, but the subject also loses a point of Willpower.

•••• Shatter the Mind

No description can be given to this level of Nightmare mastery other than inhumane brutality. And yet, the power is horribly insidious for affecting only a victim's mind, leaving the body untouched. The vampire confronts a subject with her greatest fear, driving her mad.

Cost: 1 Willpower

Dice Pool: Manipulation + Empathy + Nightmare versus subject's Composure + Blood Potency (The Nosferatu clan weakness does not apply to the Discipline user's roll.)

Action: Contested; resistance is reflexive

Roll Results

Dramatic Failure: The vampire is incapable of using Shatter the Mind for the remainder of the scene.

Failure: Successes rolled for the subject exceed or tie those rolled for the vampire. There is no effect.

Success: The most successes are rolled for the user of the power. The victim loses her next action as she reels from the vision with which she is confronted. Her Defense still applies, but she cannot perform a dodge maneuver. All other actions for the remainder of the scene are performed at -1, and she loses one Willpower point. The victim is subject to a mild derangement (see the **World of Darkness Rulebook**, p. 97) for a number of weeks equal to the successes rolled for the Discipline user. The Storyteller decides what the derangement is. If the victim already has a mild derangement, the Storyteller can upgrade it to a severe one for the duration.

Exceptional Success: The roll made for the vampire wins the contested roll and gets five or more successes. The victim falls unconscious and remains so until the end of the scene. Upon waking, she loses one Willpower dot and is subject to a severe derangement of the Storyteller's choosing. This ailment is permanent unless the victim can overcome it through treatment (addressed in the **World of Darkness Rulebook** on p. 96)

By use of this power, a vampire actually inflicts no physical harm upon the subject. He simply awakens her thoughts to the most horrific thing that she can imagine befalling her, and her subconscious mind proceeds from there. The victim imagines that a doomed fate befalls her, regardless of how implausible or nonsensical it might be under the circumstances — drowning while walking down a city street, for example. And yet, she imagines and is convinced that the situation occurs all the same.

Once used successfully on a victim, Shatter the Mind cannot be applied against her again in that scene by any vampire.

••••• Mortal Fear

At this point, the vampire is able to inspire fear as a weapon unto itself. A victim is so thoroughly and intensely frightened by the vampire that he suffers physical damage. He ages prematurely, his hair turns white and his heart stops temporarily — or permanently. Even other vampires can be affected. They're reminded of what fear meant back during their breathing days, no matter how long ago those days might have been. The subject must be able to see the vampire employing this power for it to take effect.

Cost: 1 Willpower

Dice Pool: Presence + Intimidation + Nightmare – Composure (The Nosferatu clan weakness does not apply to the Discipline user's roll.)

Action: Instant

Roll Results

Dramatic Failure: The vampire is incapable of inflicting Mortal Fear for the remainder of the scene.

Failure: No successes are achieved. While the subject is taken aback, he suffers no pain or other effects.

Success: Each success inflicts a point of lethal damage on a living being, whether mortal or supernatural in nature, including ghouls. Each success costs another vampire a Willpower point.

Exceptional Success: As a success, except the victim also loses a Willpower *dot*.

The power can be used on only one target at a time. A crowd of onlookers may see the activating vampire, but he wracks the body and soul of only one of those people. Other onlookers see nothing particularly frightening. Once used successfully on a victim, Mortal Fear cannot be applied against him again in that scene by any vampire.

Obfuscate

Night-dwellers, predators by nature and keepers of the Masquerade, vampires are inherently (and necessarily) creatures of secrecy and stealth. From hiding minute objects to the ability to appear as someone else to the power to fade from sight entirely, the Discipline of Obfuscate grants the Kindred uncanny powers of concealment, stealth and deception.

Obfuscate clouds the mind in practice. For example, a character hiding an object by using this Discipline doesn't actually make the object disappear, nor does someone using the Discipline to hide himself truly vanish. Rather, the mind sees "around" the Obfuscated object, refusing to acknowledge it, even if that requires a bit of filling in mental blanks. To continue the example, if a character Obfuscated a large sheet of plywood and tried to hide behind it herself, those looking at the plywood would, indeed, see the character lurking behind it but not see the plywood itself.

The shroud of Obfuscate is very difficult to penetrate. Few Kindred or other supernatural creatures can see through it, and only under the rarest of circumstances do mortals have any hope. Because they operate on a less conscious and mostly instinctual level, however, animals often perceive a vampire's presence — and react with appropriate fear or hostility — even if they cannot detect him with their normal senses. Similarly, children, the mentally ill and others who see the world

in ways not quite normal might pierce the deception at the Storyteller's discretion.

Some Kindred with Auspex are able to see through Obfuscate, or at least sense the presence of a supernatural deception. Refer to the "Clash of Wills" sidebar on p. 119 for details.

It's important to note that Obfuscate affects the viewer's mind, rather than making any true physical change to the vampire. Thus, the Discipline is not effective at cloaking a character from mechanical devices. Photographs, video cameras and the like record the normal blurred image that all vampires leave in such media, not the assumed appearance. Obfuscate *does* affect any individual currently using the recording device, however, so someone videotaping an Obfuscated vampire sees the illusion when looking through the lens, discovering the truth only later when he reviews the tape itself.

Unless stated otherwise, Obfuscate powers require very little concentration to maintain once invoked, and they last for the duration of a scene.

• Touch of Shadow

This first level of Obfuscate allows the vampire to conceal small items, either in her grasp or on her person. If she is skilled enough, even a thorough search fails to turn up a hidden object. Increasingly larger objects might be hidden if the Discipline user is particularly adept.

Cost: —

Dice Pool: Wits + Larceny + Obfuscate

Action: Instant

Roll Results

Dramatic Failure: The attempt fails and the user actually draws attention to the fact that she's trying to hide something. Further uses of Obfuscate against people present to witness the dramatic failure incur a -1 penalty for the remainder of the scene.

Failure: The attempt fails.

Success: The character can hide a single object from sight, unless someone actively searches for that specific item. Indeed, "specific" is very literal here — a character looking for "an Obfuscated book" does not find it, though she does if she's looking for "the Ordo Dracul Kogaion's handwritten and leather-bound copy of 17th-century rituals" and has seen it before.

Exceptional Success: The character hides the object even if a searcher knows exactly what she seeks.

The player must declare which specific item is concealed and the power must be invoked separately for each item.

If the roll succeeds, the item goes undetected. Perhaps a careful search such as a pat-down or close examination reveals it, along with a Wits + Composure roll, successes from which must exceed those rolled for the activation of the power. As with all Obfuscate abilities, a character with Auspex might be able to see through Touch of Shadow (though he would still have to find the object normally if it were inside a pocket or otherwise physically concealed from view). Once the character does anything to draw attention to the object — such as deliberately showing it to someone or using it to attack or threaten — Touch of Shadow ends. If someone successfully detects the item, he can point it out to others. A Wits + Composure roll is made for each such person, and successes achieved must exceed those acquired in the Wits + Larceny + Obfuscate roll made for the Discipline user. If an onlooker's successes aren't high enough, he still doesn't recognize the item, even when it's pointed out.

Note that this power affects only the item in question. A character could not, for example, conceal a mailbox and then hide behind it or conceal a computer and hide a stake beneath it. The mailbox or computer would indeed be concealed but the character or stake would not.

Once invoked, Touch of Shadow lasts for a scene or until ended prematurely.

Suggested Modifiers

Modifier	Situation
+2	A tiny item, one easily concealed in the palm of a hand.
+1	An item that can be hidden in a pants pocket.
—	An item that can be squeezed into a pants pocket or easily hidden in a jacket pocket.
-1	An item that can only barely be squeezed into a large jacket pocket.
-2	An item that can be concealed under a jacket without too obvious a bulge.
-3	An item too large to be naturally hidden, but still small enough to be carried easily.
-3	The "item" is actually an abstract ideal or negative space, such as a hallway or portal to another room. If a closed door seals the portal, this is not subject to the penalty, as all the Kindred needs to do is hide the door, not the portal itself.
-4	An item as large as the vampire herself, such as a motorcycle.
-5	An item bigger than the vampire herself, such as a car or large shipping crate, but smaller than five times the vampire's Size.

Apocryphal tales insist that sepulchers, tractor-trailers and even entire buildings have been hidden from the sight of others, but that's just not possible… is it?

•• Mask of Tranquility

The Kindred masters the art of hiding himself to such a degree that he may subvert some of the stains that undeath leaves upon his soul. A vampire who knows this power can mask his Kindred nature from onlookers, leaving them without the impression that the Predator's Taint inflicts.

Cost: —

Dice Pool: This power involves no roll, and is considered "always on." The character does not trigger the Predator's Taint (see p. 168). Therefore, the character doesn't even appear as a vampire to other Kindred who see him. Kindred who can discern auras fail to register the vampire as undead; his aura is no different from a

mortal's (the colors are not pale like a normal Kindred's). Note that this power doesn't render the user immune to the Predator's Taint himself, he merely doesn't cause the reaction in others.

The character may turn off this power if he wishes, but such is an all-or-nothing proposition. He may not turn off certain aspects of this power and keep others active. Note also that uses of Auspex may call this power into question — see the "Clash of Wills" sidebar on p. 119 for details.

Action: N/A

••• Cloak of Night

An essential expression of the Kindred's secretive nature, Cloak of Night allows a vampire to literally fade from sight, becoming completely invisible to observers. Though it's easiest to invoke the capability out of sight, Cloak of Night is so potent that it allows the vampire to vanish even under direct observation.

The actual process of fading away is subtle, but its effect on witnesses might not be. Mortals are likely to panic and flee the area, or to find some way to justify what they've witnessed, even if it means constructing new memories of the event. ("I glanced away for a moment, and when I looked back I *think* I saw him leave through that door.") Some especially weak-willed mortals might simply forget the vampire was ever present at all. Kindred, of course, tend to be less strongly impacted, though even an experienced and knowledgeable vampire might find the experience somewhat startling.

Cost: —

Dice Pool: Intelligence + Stealth + Obfuscate

Action: Instant

Roll Results

Dramatic Failure: The character believes he has vanished from sight, when in fact he has not.

Failure: The character does not vanish at all, and knows it.

Success: The character vanishes from sight. Mortal witnesses reconstruct the scene in their memory to justify the character's disappearance if successes achieved on the invocation roll exceed their Willpower dots.

Exceptional Success: Five or more successes are rolled for the Discipline user. The character vanishes from sight. See preceding text for the effect on mortals. Kindred witnesses reconstruct the scene in their memory to justify the character's disappearance if successes gained on the invocation roll exceed their Willpower dots.

Successful use of Cloak of Night renders the character invisible until and unless he does something to draw attention (launching an attack, smashing a window, shouting a warning), in which case the cloak drops.

Hiding oneself with this power even accounts for a character inadvertently revealing himself. A vampire doesn't accidentally bump into bystanders, as they subconsciously move out of his way. No one hears when he steps on a squeaky floorboard unless they have somehow already pierced his Obfuscate.

Suggested Modifiers

Modifier	Situation
+1	Character is by himself when he activates the power.
—	Character vanishes before a single witness.
-1	Each witness after the first present when a character invokes the power.

•••• The Familiar Stranger

This power allows the character to assume the image of whomever the subject most expects to see under the circumstances in which they meet. The character has no say in whom he "becomes." In fact, he is not even immediately aware of what aspect he is perceived to have, unless the target gives the identity away through verbal or behavioral clues. For this reason, The Familiar Stranger is best used under circumstances when contact between the character and the subject is likely to be brief. Otherwise, the character runs a substantial risk of giving the deception away through improper behavior.

Note that this power does not actually change the vampire's true appearance. It merely convinces an onlooker that the Kindred is someone other than who he truly is by clouding the subject's mind.

Cost: —

Dice Pool: Wits + Subterfuge + Obfuscate versus subject's Resolve + Blood Potency

Action: Contested; resistance is reflexive

Roll Results

Dramatic Failure: The character believes she is accepted differently, when in fact she is recognized as herself.

Failure: The vampire loses or ties the contested action. The character's recognition does not change, and the vampire is aware of the failed attempt. Onlookers see the vampire for who she is.

Success: The vampire wins the contested action and is recognized as someone else for the duration of the scene.

Exceptional Success: Five or more successes are rolled for the Discipline user. The vampire wins the contested action and is accepted as someone else for as long as she wishes, rather than for the scene.

If faced with more than one observer, the character must choose one and hope the others expect to see the same person. Success in the contested action indicates that the character assumes the aspect of whomever the chosen subject most expects to see, and the others see that person as well, even if they have no knowledge of him or her. The character himself does not gain any knowledge of the individual, and might prove unable to maintain the deception for long. A character with Auspex can potentially see through this disguise, as per the normal rules for Auspex versus Obfuscate (see p. 119). Note also that it's entirely possible that the next person the subject thought she would see is the vampire himself....

Example: *Scratch uses The Familiar Stranger to appear before a child at home, who is attended by a babysitter. Three*

successes are rolled for him and none are rolled for the child. The child sees Scratch and shrieks, "Daddy!" which alerts the babysitter — who sees a person who she assumes is the child's father.

Suggested Modifiers

Modifier	Situation
+2	Character knows for a fact who the subject expects to see.
+2	Power is turned on a vampire with whom the user has a blood tie (see p. 162).
—	Character has no idea who the subject expects.
-1	Character displays an emotion or undertakes an action not entirely appropriate to the circumstances.
-2	Character displays an emotion or undertakes action clearly out of place under the circumstances, or one largely foreign to the person whose appearance he mimics.

••••• Cloak the Gathering

A more powerful manifestation of Cloak of Night, Cloak the Gathering allows the vampire to extend her powers of vanishing from the mind's eye over others.

Cost: —

Dice Pool: Intelligence + Stealth + Obfuscate

Action: Instant

Roll Results

Dramatic failure: The character believes that he and his entourage vanishes from sight, when in fact they do not.

Failure: The characters do not vanish at all.

Success: The characters vanish from sight. Mortal witnesses reconstruct the scene in their memory to justify the characters' disappearance if successes achieved on the invocation roll exceed their Willpower dots.

Exceptional Success: Five or more successes are rolled and the characters vanish from sight. Check previous for the effect on mortals. Kindred witnesses reconstruct the scene in their memory to justify the characters' disappearance if successes gained on the invocation roll exceed their Willpower dots.

A vampire can hide one extra individual per dot of Obfuscate she possesses, not counting herself. She may attempt to hide more, but in doing so invokes a penalty to the player's roll.

While under the effects of this power, each individual must obey the rules of Cloak of Night. That is, anyone who draws attention through loud or brash actions likely becomes visible. If the Discipline user herself becomes visible, the effect fades away utterly, exposing everyone involved. Vampires under the effects of Cloak the Gathering can see each other, but if an individual ever leaves the sight of the vampire extending "invisibility," the power ceases for him. He becomes visible while the rest of the characters remain hidden.

Suggested Modifiers

Modifier	Situation
+1	Character is with only those to whom she extends this power when she activates it.
—	Characters vanish before a single witness.
-1	Each witness after the first present when a character invokes the power.
-1	Each person Obfuscated beyond the number equal to the character's level of Obfuscate, not counting the character herself.

Protean

Easily one of the most overtly spectacular of the gifts of the Damned, the Discipline of Protean is the study of physical metamorphosis and transformation. The nature of this power is hotly debated among the Kindred, for its abilities are so varied while simultaneously stemming from no obvious aspect of the Curse. Whatever its cause or origin, Protean allows its masters to assume virtually any form or shape.

Since the core of a vampire's self doesn't alter with his shape, a transformed Kindred can generally take any action or use any Discipline that his new form can reasonably allow. Gangrel in the form of a cloud of mist, for example, could read auras (as the sense of sight doesn't vanish), but couldn't Dominate someone effectively (as the prerequisite eye contact can no longer be established). A vampire's clothes and personal effects change shape with him, but he cannot normally transmute especially large objects or other creatures.

Unless stated otherwise, Protean powers — being permanent physical changes — last as long as the vampire wishes them to, or until he is forced into torpor. Any state that prevents the character from taking action (such as being staked) likewise prevents transformation; the vampire needs the freedom to invoke his will.

• Aspect of the Predator

The most basic ability of this Discipline allows a vampire to project a supernatural mien of savage predatory ferocity.

Cost: —

Dice Pool: This power involves no roll. A character is not subject to the usual relationships of Blood Potency upon meeting an unknown Kindred for the first time. If the character's Blood Potency is lower than that of the unknown Kindred, treat it as equal. If the character's Blood Potency is equal to or higher than the unknown Kindred, this power has no effect.

A character may choose to suspend this power if he so desires, but if he does, it ceases to function for an entire scene. He may not selectively apply it to individual vampires he meets within that scene.

Action: N/A

•• Haven of Soil

The vampire who has achieved this much-prized level of mastery over Protean has learned how to meld his form with that of any natural substance. One can blend his form only with simple soil at first, but with time and experience he can eventually learn how to conjoin with other elements. While so interred, the character is immune to threat of harm from the sun's rays, or to any physical attack as his corporeal form is actually merged with that of the substance itself. Some Gangrel rely on this ability while traveling from domain to domain, as its power gives them the ultimate freedom to do so.

This style of rest is the method of choice for many Kindred who must enter torpor. Whiling away the decades in a largely protected state, free from risk of detection or Final Death, is an attractive prospect. While such a character cannot be dug up, any significant disturbance to the area in which he resides alerts the vampire to the presence of intruders, though not necessarily to the details of their intrusion. If enough damage is done to the sleeping Kindred's resting place, he returns immediately to corporeal form (and full wakefulness) in a shower of whatever substance he had taken for his haven.

Cost: 1 Vitae

Dice Pool: No roll is necessary. Becoming one with a natural substance is automatic and takes a character's action in a turn to complete. While in this state, the character's consciousness hovers slightly above the torpor level (unless the vampire is both in torpor and in this state, in which case he is unaware), making perception of his surroundings distant at best. A player must succeed in a Humanity roll in order for his character to be aware of the presence of others in or around his place of rest (barring significant alteration to the vampire's haven, of course, in which case he becomes aware automatically).

Since the character is literally part of the earth, all attempts at locating him (via his scent, his aura or even through mystical methods of tracking) suffer a -3 penalty to their dice pools. Indeed, a searcher is likely to be confounded a bit even if he is successful. No attack can harm the interred vampire while he is in this state; a significant disruption of his surroundings can only cause him to resurface.

When this power is first acquired, the character can meld his form only with natural earth or soil. If any other substance — including asphalt, wood or concrete — lies in the way between the vampire and natural ground, he cannot activate this power. (He must dig his way to natural soil or else find a way to stand thereupon.) With the expenditure of an additional three experience points, however, the vampire can select another natural substance from the following list: wood, water, natural stone or processed stone. "Processed stone" includes varieties of prepared surfacing materials such as concrete and asphalt. He can now meld into soil and this extra substance with equal ease. Thus, if his player spends 12 experience points, a vampire can rest in all five materials — virtually anywhere. Note that there must still be enough of a substance to accommodate the vampire's form in roughly his natural Size. (A large tree trunk might suffice, but a small branch does not.) Those who meld with water leave a barely visible, humanoid-shaped outline just below the surface, but are otherwise just as protected and concealed as though they were inside soil.

Action: Instant

Claws of the Wild

Upon activation of this power, the vampire's nails grow into long, fearsome talons, capable of rending bone and flesh alike. This power makes many Gangrel truly fearsome combatants, and other Kindred tend to give them a wide berth. Note that not every vampire's claws look the same. Some seem to be modeled after real-world animals', such as wolves', tigers' or the talons of birds of prey, while other claws seem to have no natural correlative at all. As might be expected, when these last vampires unsheathe their claws, they tend to greatly unnerve those around them.

Cost: 1 Vitae

Dice Pool: This power involves no roll. The wicked claws grow by silent act of will on the part of the vampire, and they can be sprouted from both a vampire's hands and feet.

Imbued with the unholy power of Vitae, these ferocious weapons offer a +1 bonus to attack pools in unarmed close combat, and inflict aggravated damage. Of course, these bonuses require that the character actually attacks with his claws — one cannot invoke Claws of the Wild and then gain a +1 bonus and aggravated damage if attacking with an axe or pistol, for example. In addition to their combat potential, the claws add two dice to any climbing-related rolls as long as they remain invoked. The claws remain for the scene unless the vampire retracts them prematurely.

Action: Reflexive

Shape of the Beast

The canon of vampire legend is filled with stories of undead lords taking the semblance of the "children of the night." This power is the source of those legends. With it, a Kindred can take the shape of an ordinary animal, most commonly a bat or a wolf. While in this form, the vampire retains his mind and temperament, but he can call upon the physical qualities of his newfound body (increased speed and senses as a wolf, sonar sense and flight as a bat).

With time and experience, the character can learn to adopt the other form (bat or wolf) or others.

Cost: 1 Vitae

Dice Pool: This power requires no roll to activate. The transformation from human to animal or back again requires a character's action in a turn. All clothing and small possessions shift with the vampire, and he can remain in his animal state until he chooses to shift back. A vampire can even sleep the day away in animal form, but must still avoid sunlight, which always affects vampires regardless of form. In addition, sleeping in animal form is taxing on the vampiric state, requiring the expenditure of an additional Vitae upon awakening.

While in animal form, a vampire can use any Discipline in his repertoire except for Theban Sorcery, Crúac and Dominate (which becomes impossible when one tries to bark and yip commands). Each animal form conveys a separate host of benefits. As a wolf, the vampire's claws and teeth inflict lethal damage and add a +1 bonus to attack pools, Speed is doubled, and two bonus dice are added to any Wits + Composure rolls to be aware of events that happen in the wolf's environment. As a bat, the vampire's Strength becomes 1, but he can fly at a Speed of 20 (plus five more per dot of Vigor activated); three dice are added to all hearing-based rolls, and Defense increases by two.

(At the player's discretion, he may spend another Vitae and allow a character in wolf form or any other suitable form as described here to activate Claws of the Wild. As with normal uses of that power, these claws are obviously supernatural or otherwise remarkable, and even those unfamiliar with the world of the Damned will know that something is *not quite right* about the animal in question. A character who has assumed Shape of the Beast and also activates Claws of the Wild gains a +1 bonus to attack pools and inflicts aggravated damage instead of gaining a +1 bonus to attack pools and inflicting lethal damage with claw attacks.)

When this power is first acquired, only bat *or* wolf form is available. With Storyteller permission, every three experience points spent allows a character access to the other form, or to an altogether different predatory animal, usually a mammal, although it's rumored that Kindred in far-flung lands can assume the forms of predatory and scavenger birds. Storytellers are encouraged to use the models given here and on p. 202-203 of the **World of Darkness Rulebook** as examples of animal traits.

A vampire in animal form is not subject to the Animalism Discipline. Dominate may still be used on him in whatever form — human or animal — he assumes.

Action: Instant

••••• Body of Spirit

The pinnacle of most vampires' achievement in the transfiguring art, this power enables a Kindred to transform his entire body into a fine, chilling mist. As a small cloud of vapor, the character can float along above the ground at his normal Speed, slipping under doors and in between screens with ease. Although especially strong winds can divert him from his desired course for a time, not even gale-force winds can fully disperse his misty essence.

Cost: 1 Vitae

Dice Pool: This power involves no roll to invoke. The full change takes one action to complete.

If a strong enough wind picks up, the character's vaporous body could be subjected to unwanted direction change if he does not resist successfully. Roll Strength (plus any Vigor that the vampire activates). There's no modifier for a light wind. A strong one imposes a -1 penalty, and a gale-force wind imposes a -3 penalty. A success allows the vampire to travel in any direction desired for the turn, even against the wind. An exceptional success allows him to travel in any direction for the remainder of the scene. A failure indicates that the vampire is pushed by the wind for one turn at the speed it travels. And a dramatic failure causes the vampire to blow out of control (but still as a cohesive whole) for the entire scene.

While in mist form, the character is immune to all physical attacks, which merely pass through his gaseous body. Mystical attacks, however, still affect him normally, though mystical attacks that use mundane methods of delivery are similarly ineffective (such as claws or enchanted physical weapons). Even fire and sunlight inflict one less point of damage than normal. The trade-off, of course, is that a vampire in this state cannot physically attack anyone (not even another vampire using this power). Disciplines that do not require a body might still be effective, though. A vampire in gaseous form can use any Discipline he knows except for Theban Sorcery, Crúac and Dominate (which is useless when he has no eyes with which to make contact and no mouth with which to speak commands).

A vampire in mist form cannot be "bottled" or otherwise trapped in part by someone trying to contain or disrupt his form. Bottling a portion of a vampire's mist doesn't cause him to resume human form without an arm, for example. A vampire's entire mist form can be contained in a room or other large space that is airtight. Of course, the question arises of how one can lure a vampire in mist form into an airtight room, or how one even has access to an airtight room.

Action: Instant

Resilience

Legends abound of vampires who are able to withstand even the most brutal punishment to their unliving forms. While all Kindred possess a certain degree of the toughness of which these tales speak, those with the Discipline of Resilience are commensurately more stalwart. Vampires with several dots of Resilience are capable of walking through a hail of bullets, shrugging off even the most punishing blows, and even resisting the deadly claws and fangs of supernatural foes.

Cost: 1 Vitae per scene

Dice Pool: Resilience is unlike many other Disciplines in that it is not actively rolled. Rather, it provides an augmentation of physical potential that lasts for the scene in which it is activated, and which affects other rolls.

Each dot of Resilience increases the character's Stamina by one for the scene in which the Discipline is active. This bonus also increases the character's Health dots during the scene. Resilience may not be invoked more than once per scene. That is, you may not spend a second Vitae and double the benefits of the power.

Example: *Prince Maxwell is a Ventrue with Resilience 4 and Stamina 4. While returning to his haven, he encounters a resentful Kindred whom he snubbed at Elysium two nights before. Just to be sure, Maxwell activates his Resilience — his Stamina increases to 8 and his Health dots increase to 13 (Size 5 + Stamina 4 + Resilience 4).*

Additionally, Resilience "downgrades" a number of aggravated damage points per scene equal to Resilience dots. This damage becomes lethal instead. Aggravated wounds suffered in excess of the character's Resilience dots remain aggravated, however. This downgrade doesn't apply to any aggravated wounds that the vampire already possesses, just to newly acquired ones suffered while Resilience is active. (In the preceding example, Maxwell would be able to downgrade no more than four points in total.)

Example: *Maxwell is engaged in combat with a witch-hunter, who clubs him with a flaming torch. The torch inflicts five points of aggravated damage — but Maxwell's Resilience of 4 downgrades that to four points of lethal damage, with one point of aggravated damage remaining.*

Note that the extra Health dots a character gains in a scene while Resilience is active can have consequences later. If a vampire suffers more damage than he has his usual Health dots, those excess wounds upgrade existing wounds (bashing becomes lethal, lethal becomes aggravated) as per the damage rules on p. 171-172 of the **World of Darkness Rulebook**. In other words, once the character's Resilience "powers down" at the end of the scene and the extra Health dots that the power confers are lost, he might have to contend with more serious wounds than initially harmed him unless he heals them while Resilience is still active. See the "Temporary Health Dots" sidebar on p. 173 of the **World of Darkness Rulebook** to see what happens when extra Health is lost.

Also, if a character suffers damage that upgrades her Health chart, Resilience does not downgrade it. For example, if a character with seven Health dots and a single dot of Resilience suffers nine points of lethal damage, that ninth point stays aggravated. The other eight points are recorded normally as lethal (seven for the Health dots plus one for the Resilience), but the ninth stays aggravated as it upgrades the leftmost box on the character's Health chart. If that's all the damage the character suffers by the end of the scene, another of those points of lethal damage upgrades to an aggravated wound once Resilience ceases and the character's Health dots drop to seven again. Kindred with Resilience are advised to be wise in combat, though they might feel invulnerable while invoking the Discipline.

Action: Instant

Vigor

Nearly every vampire legend across the globe expresses the preternatural strength possessed by the undead. In truth, not all Kindred possess such inhuman might, but the Discipline of Vigor makes those who do far more powerful than any mortal could ever hope to be. Vigor allows Kindred to strike opponents with the force of a falling boulder or speeding car; to lift enormous weights as though they were paper; to shatter concrete like glass; to leap distances so great that those elders with obscenely high levels of Vigor may, in fact, be responsible for legends of vampiric flight.

Cost: 1 Vitae per scene

Dice Pool: Vigor is unlike many other Disciplines in that it is not actively rolled. Rather, it provides an increase of physical strength that lasts the duration of the scene in which it is activated, affecting other rolls.

Each dot of Vigor increases the character's Strength by one while the Discipline is active. Vigor cannot be invoked more than once per scene. That is, you may not spend a second Vitae and double the benefits of the power. Note also that certain derived traits (such as Speed) might also be affected by the use of Vigor.

Example: *Solomon has Vigor 3 and Strength 4. He is surprised to find a ghoul creeping about his haven after he returns from a meeting with the Prince. Solomon decides to teach this ghoul a lesson and activates his Vigor — his Strength increases to 7 for the duration of the scene. The ghoul's eyes widen in fear, anticipating the brutal beating she's no doubt about to receive.*

Additionally, a character's Vigor affects his ability to jump. The dice pool to jump, as per p. 66 of the **World of Darkness Rulebook**, is Strength + Athletics + any relevant equipment. When using Vigor to augment a jump, the character's Vigor dots are added to the number of feet leapt per success. On a vertical leap, a character jumps (Vigor + one foot per success rolled). For a standing broad jump, the character jumps (Vigor + 2 feet per success rolled). On a running jump, the distance jumped is Size + (Vigor + 4 feet per success rolled). For example, say a character has Strength 3, Athletics 3, Size 5 and Vigor 2 and makes a vertical leap. Six dice are rolled and three successes are achieved. The character leaps nine feet upward (2 Vigor + 1 foot, multiplied by the three successes rolled). Now say the character makes a running jump. The character crosses a base of 5 feet + another 6 (2+4) per success rolled. If he gets three successes, that's 23 feet (6 more feet then he would have achieved without Vigor).

Action: Instant

Crúac

Crúac is the common name for the pagan blood sorcery practiced by the Circle of the Crone. A type of ritual magic, Crúac, meaning "crescent," is a mixture of pre-Christian and pagan magic from across the globe whose only common element is a reliance on blood sacrifice. Crúac is denounced by many traditional Kindred as "black magic" or "witchcraft," and in areas where the Lancea Sanctum holds sway, Crúac's known practitioners are occasionally persecuted as heretics. Of course, it is such very derision and fear of Crúac that leads many to the Circle of the Crone and, by extension, to this Discipline's study. The Circle of the Crone's message of empowerment speaks to many a neonate, and for some there is no greater expression of that empowerment than this Discipline.

Crúac is one of the central mysteries of the Circle of the Crone's belief structure, as well as a potent weapon in the covenant's arsenal. As might be expected, knowledge of the Discipline is a closely guarded secret. New initiates are not usually trusted with its secrets. As a new member in a quasi-religious Kindred faction, a vampire might well have to prove his loyalty to the Circle through tests and ordeals before its adherents are willing to share their knowledge. Though vampires who leave the Circle of the Crone for other covenants invariably take their knowledge with them, many find it all but impossible to increase their knowledge of Crúac outside the Circle's structure. A character must have at least one dot of Covenant Status (Circle of the Crone) in order to learn Crúac. A player who buys at least one dot worth of that Merit at character creation may spend one of his character's three Discipline dots on Crúac if he wishes. Any time a player wants to increase his character's Crúac score, the character must

still have at least one dot of Covenant Status (Circle of the Crone) to do so.

Because of myriad cultural differences within the Circle of the Crone, many rituals exist that approximate the following ones in effect if not in name. Thus, the level-one ritual Pangs of Proserpina may be known as the Appetite of Limba in New Orleans or the Curse of Tawrich in Tehran. Other **Vampire** books offer new Crúac rituals, and players and Storytellers are encouraged to create their own using those presented here as models.

Cost: Uses of Crúac always cost at least one Vitae. Unless the text for a specific power (known as a ritual) specifies otherwise, assume that the cost is one Vitae. Vitae plays a very important role in the use of Crúac — it literally calls upon the power inherent in the Blood to fuel supernatural effects. Use of Crúac requires that the Vitae be "spent" in a visible or otherwise significant manner. For example, when a Vitae is spent for a character to activate a ritual, he likely has to cut himself with a dagger and bleed on the ground, activating the magic with the spilled Vitae (or through some other direct appeal to the power of the Blood).

Crúac does not have the same linear progression that other Disciplines do. A character's mastery dictates the highest level of rituals that he may learn. Rituals are bought with experience points. For example, a character with two dots of Crúac can know an unlimited number of level-one and level-two rituals (provided the experience points to learn each of them are paid). He may not learn any level-three Crúac rituals until his Crúac dots increase to 3. Each time a character acquires a dot of Crúac (including at character creation), he gains a ritual of that level at no additional cost.

Crúac is insidious. It demands a certain degree of subservience and even cruelty from its practitioners, possibly in deference to the dire old gods from whence the Discipline is rumored to come. For some power-hungry sorcerers, Crúac indulges the will instead of enlightened use of the Discipline. A character's dots in this Discipline, subtracted from 10, is the maximum to which his Humanity may rise. For example, the Gangrel Roland Gentry possesses Crúac at level three. His maximum Humanity is therefore 7. If a character increases his Crúac score higher than his Humanity would normally allow, his Humanity immediately drops to the appropriate level and the player makes a Humanity roll to see if the character acquires a derangement in the process of heightening his occult knowledge. (See pp. 182-188 for more on Humanity rolls and derangements.)

Dice Pool: Manipulation + Occult + Crúac. Because of its sanguinary nature, Crúac doubles any bonuses that a vampire's blood ties might apply, such as in a ritual performed on a sire, grandsire, childe or grandchilde. Also, the Nosferatu clan weakness does not apply to the Discipline user's roll.

Action: Extended. The number of successes required to activate a ritual is equal to the level of the ritual (so a level-three ritual requires three successes to enact). Each roll represents one turn of ritual casting. Note also that each point of damage suffered in a turn is a penalty to the next casting roll made for the character, in addition to any wound penalties that a caster might suffer.

Costs to activate Crúac rituals must be paid before the roll can be made. Normally this isn't an issue, as a ritual that costs one Vitae can have its activation roll made in the same turn (as spending Vitae is a reflexive action). In some cases, though, a ritual costs more Vitae than the caster can spend in a single turn. In cases like these, the caster's player makes the roll on the turn he (reflexively) spends the last Vitae necessary to invoke the ritual.

If a character fails to complete the ritual in time (such as by being killed before accumulating enough successes) or decides to cancel the ritual before garnering enough successes to activate it, the effect simply fails. Any Vitae expenditures made are not recovered, however.

Roll Results

Dramatic Failure: The ritual fails spectacularly, inflicting some aspect of itself as a detrimental effect upon the caster. A ritual intended to damage a subject inflicts its damage upon the caster, for example, while a ritual designed to plague its victim with pangs of hunger visits its effects upon the caster.

Failure: The ritual fails entirely, but not dangerously. Vitae is consumed as normal, but the ritual has no effect.

Success: The ritual takes place as described.

Exceptional Success: The ritual takes place as described. In many cases, extra successes are their own reward, causing additional damage or conferring extra duration, capacity or similar benefits.

Unless specified otherwise, rituals last for the duration of a scene or until the next sunrise, whichever comes first.

Suggested Modifiers

Modifier	Situation
+4	Power is turned on or applies to a vampire with whom the user has a blood tie (see p. 162).
—	The character is unaffected by threats or distractions.
-1 to -3	The character is rushed or distracted, such as by invoking a ritual in combat or while being harried by pursuers. This penalty is cumulative with multiple distractions (such as by casting a ritual in combat during a hurricane). Successes gained on a meditation roll for the night (see p. 51 of the **World of Darkness Rulebook**) offset interruption penalties on a one-for-one basis.

Pangs of Proserpina
(Level-One Crúac Ritual)

The sorcerer causes feelings of intense hunger in a subject, who must be within sight. The afflicted subject feels the desire to eat or feed. Activation involves a contested roll against the subject's Composure + Blood Potency, and resistance is reflexive. If the performer gets the most successes, the victim avails himself of any sustenance available. A mortal even eats raw meat, though he doesn't resort to such dire acts as cannibalism or drinking blood. Kindred might attack nearby vessels or even fellow vampires if their hunger is severe enough

to make them frenzy. Even after he eats or feeds, a subject's rapacity does not subside until the effects of the ritual pass. (Vampires affected by this ritual are considered "starving" for the purposes of resisting frenzy; see p. 179.)

Rigor Mortis
(Level-One Crúac Ritual)

With the power of this ritual, a vampire may temporarily interrupt the reanimating effect of vampiric Vitae, rendering a Kindred immobile as the stiffening of muscles common to dead bodies takes hold. The number of successes garnered on the Crúac roll determines the number of dice by which the victim's next Physical dice pool is penalized. This applies only to dice pools for actions, and does not affect Physical resistances. Rigor Mortis is useless against mortals, ghouls, Lupines and mages, since they don't depend on the power of vampiric Vitae to animate their bodies.

The roll to activate this power is penalized by the subject's Composure.

Cheval
(Level-Two Crúac Ritual)

This ritual allows the performer to "ride the senses" of his subject. The subject must be within direct sight when the ritual is performed, but the subject can stray from the caster to any distance thereafter. At any time he wishes for the duration of the effect, the performer may see or hear through the eyes or ears of his subject. No other senses can be substituted — if the subject is blind or deaf or both, all "riding" yields is blackness and/or silence. A subject so "ridden" is unaware that his senses also report to another.

While riding another's senses, the ritualist is only dimly aware of her own body, which falls into on a trance-like state. She is unaware of minor environmental stimuli affecting her own body (such as an insect crawling across her skin or drops of water falling on her head), but more aggressive actions perpetrated against her body draw her consciousness back to it.

This ritual remains in effect for one night per success on the invocation roll, though the caster may end the ritual at any time. The performer can therefore indulge in a subject's senses and return to her own body as often as she likes throughout the rite's duration.

The roll to activate this power is penalized by the subject's Composure.

The Hydra's Vitae
(Level-Two Crúac Ritual)

By invoking this ritual, the performer protects himself from would-be diablerists and from those who would otherwise feast upon his blood. This ritual transforms the sorcerer's Vitae into a kind of poison. Kindred who drink it suffer one point of lethal damage for every Vitae consumed; mortals who imbibe suffer two points of lethal damage for each Vitae. When a Kindred consumes a quantity of venomous Vitae, she gains no nourishment from it.

Vitae altered by this ritual is poisonous only so long as it's in the performer's body (or until the next sunrise). If the Vitae leaves, it becomes as any other Vitae spilled from a Kindred's body. Thus, it cannot be used to create poisoned weapons, and if one consumes the Vitae from a container after it leaves the body, it is simply normal, non-poisonous Vitae.

Deflection of Wooden Doom
(Level-Three Crúac Ritual)

The performer invokes a mystic protection against attempts to impale her heart with a stake. If the ritual succeeds, any attempt to stake the vampire fails for the duration of the spell. Stakes used in this manner rot or disintegrate as wielders attempt to use them against the performer. An attempt to stake the Kindred in question must be made for this ritual to take effect. (It does not simply rot all stakes and would-be stakes in her presence.) This power cannot be invoked to protect others; it works only on the sorcerer herself. This ritual fades at sundown of the subsequent night, though it may be invoked again immediately thereafter.

Touch of the Morrigan
(Level-Three Crúac Ritual)

The caster performs this ritual (Manipulation + Occult + Crúac is rolled) and channels his righteous ire into a tangible force. If the performance roll is successful, the user's mere touch becomes deadly. The sorcerer must then touch a subject with his open palm. (See "Touching an Opponent," p. 157 of the **World of Darkness Rulebook**.) Contact inflicts an amount of lethal damage equal to the number of successes gained on the activation roll. (The power cannot be delivered through a punch or other unarmed close-combat attack.) This harm can be delivered only once per performance of the ritual, and the user's touch has the potential to inflict harm for one hour for every success gained on the activation roll. If that period of time passes without a touch being made, the power fades.

The mark made by contact is physically manifest in accordance with its severity. A Touch of the Morrigan that inflicts one point of damage looks like a minor scar or livid bruise, while one that delivers five points of damage leaves the subject almost entirely blackened and charred looking. The visible injury fades as the damage is healed. This power affects only vampires, ghouls and other supernatural creatures. It seems that Kindred cannot inflict their viciousness on mortals in this manner.

Blood Price
(Level-Four Crúac Ritual)

The sorcerer mystically claims one third of the Vitae that a subject imbibes. The subject must be within sight when this ritual is performed. Every time the subject feeds, a third

of the Vitae he consumes is denied him and transfers invisibly to the sorcerer, regardless of either vampire's location. This Vitae is "neutral," which is to say that the feeding Kindred does not subject the sorcerer to a Vinculum in this manner, and neither does feeding from a third-party vampire apply any blood bonds to the sorcerer (though it certainly does to the feeding vampire). The effects of this ritual expire after one feeding or the next sunrise, whichever comes first.

A contested roll is made to activate this power, pitting the sorcerer's Manipulation + Occult + Crúac versus the subject's Composure + Blood Potency, and this resistance is reflexive. If the most successes are rolled for the caster, the subject has no idea where some of the Vitae he consumes disappears to, yet he knows that he goes undernourished.

Willful Vitae

(Level-Four Crúac Ritual)

The performer makes herself immune to the Vinculum and blood addiction when another Kindred's Vitae is consumed. After this ritual is performed, if another vampire's blood is taken in the same night, no step is taken toward a Vinculum with the provider of the blood, and no addiction to blood forms for the character. Of course, the blood donor has no idea that the recipient is immune. The ritual cannot be performed on another vampire, only on the caster's self. The ritual does not countermand or alleviate any existing Vinculum to which the caster is already subject.

Blood Blight

(Level-Five Crúac Ritual)

This potent ritual taints the blood of its target, whether mortal or vampire. Roll Manipulation + Occult + Crúac in a contested action against the target's Stamina + Blood Potency (resistance is reflexive). If the roll for the caster gets the most successes, that number of successes is inflicted as lethal damage to a mortal target. A vampire target immediately loses the equivalent of Vitae in his system and could be subject to frenzy as a result. Indeed, a vampiric victim might be forced into torpor. The caster must be able to see the intended victim when the ritual is performed.

Feeding the Crone

(Level-Five Crúac Ritual)

When the performer calls upon the power of the Crone herself (by whatever name is used), and a Vitae is spent, the vampire's mouth transforms into a maw of wicked, gnashing teeth. The vampire need not perform a grapple attack in order to bite a victim; the attack is made directly. The number of successes achieved on the ritual's activation roll is added as bonus dice to attack rolls, and aggravated damage is inflicted. Note that these teeth are so vicious that feeding cannot occur when they are borne; too much blood is wasted in the gory slaughter to get nourishment. Feeding the Crone remains in effect until another Vitae is spent to revoke the change, or until sunrise.

Theban Sorcery

Theban Sorcery is the miraculous magic practiced by members of the Lancea Sanctum. According to the covenant, it is a tradition of magic taught (or stolen, depending on to whom one listens) by an "avatar of God." The practice is said to have been received when early members visited Thebias in northern Egypt with a contingent of Christian soldiers during the reign of Diocletian, after Longinus had vanished from the world. The Discipline has decidedly judgmental overtones, combining a focus on Biblical elements (rains of blood, plagues of locusts, the vengeance of God) with a very overt and occult reliance on righteousness.

Theban Sorcery is as jealously guarded as anti-Sanctified factions widely believe, if not more so. While few Lancea Sanctum hit squads lurk in the shadows to whack non-Sanctified vampires who seem to be able to use the Discipline, few covenant members want to see their divinely inspired powers taken for granted. The Lancea Sanctum isn't foolish. It makes its mystical knowledge available "on loan" if the covenant has something to gain.

Vampires who leave the Lancea Sanctum for other covenants invariably take their knowledge with them, but find it all but impossible to increase it. A character must have at least one dot of Covenant Status (Lancea Sanctum) in order to learn Theban Sorcery. A players who takes at least one dot worth of that Merit at character creation may spend one of his character's three Discipline dots on Theban Sorcery if he wishes. Any time a player wants to increase his character's Theban Sorcery score, the vampire must still have at least one dot of Covenant Status (Lancea Sanctum) to do so.

Cost: Uses of Theban Sorcery always cost one Willpower point. Willpower is critical to use of the Discipline. It invokes the soul of the Kindred who performs a ritual. Willpower spent in this manner does not add three dice to activation rolls. Indeed, because one may spend only one Willpower point per turn, a Willpower point may *never* be spent to augment Theban Sorcery rolls unless specified otherwise. Willpower merely makes the magic possible.

Additionally, Theban Sorcery rituals require certain items to be used or consumed to activate the powers. These components are known as offerings. Practitioners believe these items are offered in sacrifice to God, Longinus or to whomever provides the actual manifestation of the power. Attempts to invoke Theban Sorcery without suitable offerings fail outright. Offerings are consumed upon the invocation of a ritual, leaving behind nothing but a handful of ash.

Like Crúac, Theban Sorcery does not have the same linear progression that other Disciplines do. A character's mastery dictates the highest level of rituals that he may learn. Rituals are bought with experience points. For example, a character with two dots of Theban Sorcery can know an unlimited number of level-one and level-two rituals (provided the experience points are paid to learn each), but he may not learn any level-three Theban Sorcery rituals until his base Theban Sorcery dots are increased to 3. Each time a character acquires a dot of Theban Sorcery (including at character creation), he gains a ritual of that level at no additional cost. More rituals may be acquired with experience points. Other **Vampire** books offer Theban Sorcery rituals, and players and Storytellers are encouraged to create their own using those presented here as models.

Dice Pool: Intelligence + Academics + Theban Sorcery. Unlike Crúac and its relationship to the Nosferatu, the Gangrel clan weakness *does* apply to the Discipline user's roll on attempts to invoke Theban Sorcery rituals.

Action: Extended. The number of successes required to activate a ritual is equal to the level of the ritual (so a level-three ritual requires three successes to enact). Each roll represents one turn of ritual casting. Note also that each point of damage incurred in a turn is a penalty to the next casting roll made for the character, in addition to any wound penalties suffered.

If a character fails to complete the ritual in time (such as by being sent into torpor before accumulating enough successes) or decides to cancel the ritual before garnering enough successes to activate it, the effect simply fails. Any Willpower expenditures made are not recovered, however, and offerings are still burned to ash.

Roll Results

Dramatic Failure: The ritual fails spectacularly, inflicting some aspect of itself as a detrimental effect upon the caster. A ritual intended to damage a subject inflicts its damage upon the caster, for example, while a ritual designed to store Vitae in an object depletes the caster of some amount of his own.

Failure: The ritual fails entirely, but not dangerously. Willpower and offerings are consumed as normal, but the ritual has no effect.

Success: The ritual takes place as described.

Exceptional Success: The ritual takes place as described. In many cases, extra successes are their own reward, causing additional damage or conferring extra duration or capacity.

Suggested Modifiers

Modifier	Situation
+2	Power is turned on or applies to a vampire with whom the user has a blood tie (see p. 162).
—	The character is unaffected by threats or distractions.
-1 to -3	The character is rushed or distracted, such as by invoking a ritual in combat or while trapped in a burning building. This penalty is cumulative with multiple distractions (such as by casting a ritual in combat during a hurricane). Successes gained on a meditation roll for the night (see p. 51 of the **World of Darkness Rulebook**) offset interruption penalties on a one-for-one basis.

Blood Scourge
(Level-One Theban Sorcery Ritual)

The vampire transforms a portion of his own blood into a wicked instrument of punishment. For each dot that the character possesses in Theban Sorcery, he may create a stinging whip of Vitae with which to scourge his foes. An attack with the weapon has a dice pool equal to the character's Strength + Weaponry + the number of lashes created, and inflicts lethal damage. The Blood Scourge lasts a number of turns equal to the player's success on the invocation roll. At the end of that time, the Vitae whips turn to dust.

A character can invoke Blood Scourge only once until its duration expires. He may thereafter invoke another whip, however. A character may voluntarily terminate a Blood Scourge if he does not want to keep it for the full duration of the power.

Offering: The Kindred's own blood is the offering. In enacting the ritual, the vampire must slice open his wrist with a sacrificial knife. The scourge created — regardless of its number of lashes — costs one Vitae.

Vitae Reliquary
(Level-One Theban Sorcery Ritual)

The character takes an ordinary object and stores an amount of Vitae in it that may be called upon later (whether as sustenance or for any other purpose that requires Vitae). Any Kindred or ghoul can call upon the stored Vitae, not just the caster, though the person using the Vitae must know that it's there. The amount of Vitae that can be stored in the object is equal to the amount of successes the player achieves on the invocation roll, although the caster may infuse the object with less if he wishes. The Vitae to be stored comes directly from the caster's own body. This ritual can be cast only once on the item in question. Any object can contain the Vitae, regardless of its size, though the item must be at least the size of a person's fist. The Vitae remains indefinitely until consumed. The act of consuming the blood might involve taking it to one's lips, or holding the item tight and willing the blood to pass from object to body. This Vitae is "neutral," which is to say that the feeding Kindred does not subject the sorcerer to a Vinculum in this manner, though blood addiction is still a risk.

Offering: The vessel of infusion itself is the offering, which is destroyed after the last Vitae is removed. The offering crumbles to dust. Prior to that point, the item functions as it normally would (a rapier may still be used to attack, a book may still be read).

Curse of Babel
(Level-Two Theban Sorcery Ritual)

This ritual leaves a victim speaking in tongues, unable to communicate. Even his written word is rendered nonsensical; both handwritten and typed messages come out as gibberish. Not only is the Curse of Babel an effective means of controlling the spread of blasphemy (and gossip), it proves an effective limit to a subject's use of the Dominate Discipline. The number of successes achieved on the invocation roll determines the duration of the ritual's function: one hour per success or until the next sunrise, whichever comes first. The subject must be within earshot when this ritual is performed.

The roll to activate this power is penalized by the subject's Resolve.

Offering: An animal's or person's tongue

Liar's Plague
(Level-Two Theban Sorcery Ritual)

The character curses her subject so that if he speaks any lies over the course of the scene, beetles swarm from his mouth.

The ritual involves a contested action, pitting the sorcerer's Intelligence + Academics + Theban Sorcery against the subject's Resolve + Blood Potency. Resisting this power is a reflexive action.

Offering: An insect's carapace, whole and uncrushed.

Blandishment of Sin
(Level-Three Theban Sorcery Ritual)

The subject of this power suffers increased damage the next time any harm is inflicted on him. That wound is upgraded one degree of damage. Thus, three bashing damage becomes three lethal, and three lethal damage becomes three aggravated. (Aggravated wounds do not increase to any other sort, and the effects of the ritual are wasted.) If, at the end of the night, the subject has not suffered any damage, the ritual ends, though it may be invoked against him on the following night.

If the subject activates Resilience, that Discipline offsets the benefits of this ritual for the next wound he suffers only if the damage upgrade would make the next wound aggravated. The injury in question inflicts its upgraded, aggravated damage, which Resilience downgrades again.

The action to activate this power is contested, pitting the sorcerer's Intelligence + Academics + Theban Sorcery against the subject's Resolve + Blood Potency (resistance is reflexive). The subject is unaware of the power applied to him and doesn't know why his next injury is so severe.

Offering: A scrap of paper, upon which the subject's name must be written. The paper is then burned in sight of the subject as the ritual is cast.

Malediction of Despair
(Level-Three Theban Sorcery Ritual)

The sorcerer curses his subject with regard to a specific action. The next time the subject engages in that action, her normal dice pool is not rolled. A chance roll is made, instead. The curse can be as general ("Your next attack in combat is doomed to failure!") or as specific ("When next you feed upon a blind Christian at midnight…") as the caster chooses. The curse remains until its conditions are met. If the subject suspects that she is cursed by this ritual, the player may spend a Willpower point and make a Composure + Resolve roll. If this roll yields more successes than were achieved to invoke the malediction, the curse ends without ever coming to pass.

The action to activate this power is contested, pitting the sorcerer's Intelligence + Academics + Theban Sorcery against the subject's Resolve + Blood Potency. Resisting in this manner is reflexive.

Offering: A lock of hair from the subject.

Gift of Lazarus
(Level-Four Theban Sorcery Ritual)

A successful invocation of this ritual brings the dead back to a semblance of life, though it is a pale echo at best. While the rite certainly reanimates the dead, it does not return a being's soul, nor does it halt the body's slow decline into rot and putrescence. The power effectively creates a painfully self-aware zombie, who most likely just wishes to be allowed to rest in peace. Initially, all of the former person's faculties may be intact (it still has access to its former Skills, but has no Willpower). The pathetic wretch can neither heal damage nor feel physical sensations in any true sense, however, so it suffers no wound penalties. The length of time in nights that the creature remains animate equals the number of successes on the Theban Sorcery roll made to create it. For every day that the creature was dead prior to the invocation, subtract one dot of the Storyteller's choosing from an Attribute in each of its Physical, Mental and Social categories, and also do the same for every day it is animated by this ritual. When any Attribute is reduced to zero, assume that any rolls involving that trait fail automatically. Multiple animations of the same corpse are possible but sequentially more disturbing and less useful. A walking corpse of this sort that loses all of its Health dots to lethal damage is too wounded to move, but still aware and possibly even capable of communication (depending on the type of damage sustained and to what portions of its body).

The vampire who enacts this ritual is the only one who can command the zombie. That vampire may, however, instruct the corpse to accept direction from other individuals. A corpse-creature left to its own devices takes no actions of its own volition; it must be given direction, and undoubtedly laments being forced to carry them out.

A corpse suffers damage — lethal, bashing and aggravated — as it did in life. It remains active until its rightmost Health box is occupied with aggravated damage. A zombie does not bleed to death upon suffering lethal damage in its rightmost Health box, and must be attacked repeatedly until utterly destroyed.

Offering: A Communion wafer placed under the dead person's tongue.

Stigmata
(Level-Four Theban Sorcery Ritual)

Although the majority of Theban Sorcery's rites have a decidedly Old Testament flavor, Stigmata takes the very suffering of the New Testament's Prince of Peace and turns it into a weapon of divine punishment. The victim of this ritual must be within sight when it is cast. He bleeds from the wrists, feet and side, the traditional five wounds of Christ. Mortals suffer one point of lethal damage per turn from blood loss, while Kindred lose one Vitae each turn. If a vampire runs out of Vitae during the course of the ritual, she proceeds to suffer lethal damage and is likely to frenzy (see p. 178). A vampire whose rightmost Health box is filled with lethal damage by this means falls into torpor (see p. 175).

The roll to activate this power is penalized by the subject's Stamina.

The number of turns the subject suffers from Stigmata equals the number of successes achieved on the Theban Sorcery roll.

Offering: A crucifix, which crumbles to ash as the ritual is enacted.

Transubstantiation
(Level-Five Theban Sorcery Ritual)

The character transforms one substance or object into another. It can be water into blood, for example, or a tree branch into a snake, or a person into a pillar of salt. The object or substance transformed becomes a perfectly normal, mundane version of whatever it is. Transubstantiation does not turn a frog into a Lupine, for example, though it could change a frog into a wolf. The only limits on the transformation are that it works only on objects smaller than the caster, and that the product cannot simulate human (or vampiric…) intelligence. That is, the same frog could be transformed into a child, but the child wouldn't be able to have any intelligent discourse or even perform many complicated activities since it's just a frog turned into the simulacrum of a child. The substance or object reverts to its original form when the sun next rises (though a person transformed into, say, ice and whose arm is broken off has both portions of herself turn back to normal in different locations, and swiftly bleeds to death).

If this power is used to affect another creature, the invocation is contested, pitting the sorcerer's Intelligence + Academics + Theban Sorcery against the subject's Stamina + Blood Potency (resistance is reflexive). The sorcerer must be within arm's length of the subject changed.

Offering: A drop of liquid gold

Wrathful Judgment
(Level-Five Theban Sorcery Ritual)

This ritual metes out divine punishment by turning a Kindred's own Vitae to fire in his veins. The ritual is unlike other Theban Sorcery practices in that the sorcerer "charges" the ritual before the player makes the final roll, and that charge can consist of multiple points of Willpower. (Remember, though, that a player may spend only a single point of Willpower in a single turn, so invoking this power can take multiple turns.) Each point of Willpower invested in this ritual deals one point of aggravated damage to the subject and consumes one Vitae from her as the victim's blood burns away in a conflagration of divine fire. For more on fire damage, see p. 172. If the sorcerer has some personal object of the subject's, he may invoke this ritual from anywhere in the world. Otherwise, the vampire must be able to see his subject. The object must be of some importance to the intended victim — a picture of his dead wife works, while his car keys or cell phone might not. Objects taken from the subject's body itself (hair, a fingernail) are more than satisfactory.

This ritual has no effect on mortals or other supernatural beings. It does affect ghouls, however.

The roll to activate this ritual is penalized by the subject's Stamina. If no successes are rolled for the ritualist, all Willpower invested into the rite is lost.

Offering: One of the casting vampire's eyes or hands, either plucked out or cut off. The Kindred suffers two points of lethal damage in the process.

The Coils of the Dragon

The Requiem presents Kindred with a number of advantages that no mortal can attain, but the curse of vampirism far overshadows these petty powers. The vampires of the Ordo Dracul, however, believe that such doesn't have to be the case. Through the Coils of the Dragon, this covenant strives to cheat the curse levied upon its founder, stripping away the limitations and requirements of undeath until members achieve purity.

The Coils of the Dragon include three distinct philosophies, each of which has three tiers. The Coils of the Dragon, like Crúac and Theban Sorcery, truly belong to no one clan. Members of the covenant can study any or all of the coils, but they recognize that no vampire has ever truly achieved mastery — at least, not to the order's knowledge. A character must have at least one dot of Covenant Status (Ordo Dracul) in order to learn any Coils of the Dragon. A player who takes at least one dot worth of that Merit at character creation may spend one of his character's three Discipline dots on the Coils of the Dragon if he wishes. Any time a player wants to increase his character's Coils of the Dragon score, the character must still have at least one dot of Covenant Status (Ordo Dracul) to do so.

Activating a tier of the coils requires no roll or asset expenditure in and of itself (though some tiers augment rolls or permit certain abilities when they might not otherwise be allowed). A character always has the option of using a tier available to him, and the benefits of the tier may be "turned off" at the Kindred's discretion.

New dots of the Coils of the Dragon are purchased like a Discipline, with the number of tiers the character already commands serving as the current level and the "new level" being the next to be achieved. For example, a character knows five tiers of the Coils of the Dragon. For him to learn a sixth, his player has to spend 42 experience points (6 [the new level in the coil] times 7 [the experience-point multiplier for out-of-clan Disciplines]). Tiers must be learned in order in each coil, though a character need not advance one coil to completion before he can advance another. That is, a character with two tiers of Coil of Blood could learn the first tier of Coil of the Beast without learning the third tier of Coil of Blood. Because the Coils of the Dragon do not constitute a true Discipline, they are not limited by Blood Potency trait maximums. A character need not have a Blood Potency of 6 to learn six different tiers of coils, for example. Yet, increasingly more dots in a coil are always bought as if they're out-of-clan Disciplines.

The Coil of Blood

Vampires must feed on living blood to survive, and only the weakest of the Kindred can draw sustenance from the blood of animals. The Coil of Blood seeks to lift this requirement, allowing the Kindred to feed on their own terms, rather than forever be slaves to their hunger.

First Tier: Blood Seeps Slowly

The Dragon's undead body doesn't demand as much Vitae to animate itself as do those of other, less enlightened Kindred. The player need spend only one Vitae for his character to wake for a number of nights equal to the vampire's Resolve. So, a Kindred with a Resolve of 2 loses a Vitae every other night for rising.

Second Tier: Blood of Beasts

No matter what the vampire's Blood Potency is, she can take sustenance from animals and humans.

Third Tier: Perspicacious Blood

The character gains three Vitae for every two Vitae she takes from a human, and receives double the Vitae consumed from Kindred or other supernatural vessels.

The Coil of Banes

The two major banes of the Requiem are fire and sunlight. Any attempt to conquer the curse of vampirism must overcome these two obstacles. While no vampire has yet managed to truly surmount them, the Coil of Banes provides a place to start.

First Tier: Conquer the Red Fear

The character gains a +2 bonus to resist fear frenzy triggered by fire or sunlight. Fear frenzies triggered by other stimuli occur as normal.

Second Tier: Surmounting the Daysleep

The player can spend a Willpower point for the character to remain awake for an entire day without penalty (though the character must still take precautions to remain out of the sunlight and "waking" the next night still costs a Vitae). Dice pools during the day are still limited by Humanity (see p. 184). If the character does sleep and is disturbed, add three dice to the player's wake-up roll.

Third Tier: Sun's Forgotten Kiss

Sunlight at twilight and dawn causes only bashing damage to the Dragon, rather than aggravated. After the sun has fully risen, however, its rays cause aggravated damage as usual. At sea or on a mountaintop, the sun might fully rise within a mere five minutes and take some time to set (10 minutes). In a dense forest or deep in a city, the sun might rise slowly (10 minutes) and set quickly (five minutes).

The Coil of the Beast

The Beast seeks always to subsume the Man, which is probably the most serious impairment on the Coils of the Dragon. If legends are true, the order's founder struggled with his Beast even before his Embrace, and so it only makes sense that he would have pioneered a means to control it.

First Tier: Chastise the Beast

The player spends a Willpower point for his character to resist a frenzy of any kind automatically. The player may choose to roll Resolve + Composure as usual for his character to resist frenzy, spending the Willpower only if the roll fails.

Second Tier: Lure the Beast

"Riding the wave" does not cost a Willpower point, and it requires a base of only three successes, not five. All other rules still apply (see p. 181).

Third Tier: Exhaust the Beast

The character may spend an hour per night in frenzy (usually doing so under controlled conditions such as in a locked room or far from mortals). For the rest of the night, the character does not enter frenzy unless she wishes to do so, no matter how strong the trigger is.

Devotions

The rote Disciplines that are common to all Kindred are not the only supernatural capabilities at their disposal. Every so often, an entirely new Discipline "technique," formed by a curious combination of two or more standard powers, emerges from the ranks of the undead. Like standard Disciplines, these techniques — called Devotions — can be learned from or taught to other Kindred in much the same time frame and manner as the broader powers from which they originate. Any vampire with the appropriate prerequisite Discipline dots can, in theory, develop the Devotions for which he qualifies. It's simply a matter of time and effort.

Some claim to have truly secret Devotions, however, and the claim does have some basis in truth. Kindred may find themselves incapable of developing some of the more esoteric techniques without a learned mentor at their side. Indeed, not all Kindred have even heard of Devotions. By their nature, they are far rarer than the common Disciplines are, and knowledge of them is a bit more fleeting than the understanding of the unique Disciplines that sometimes accompany the creation of new bloodlines. Only a relative handful of Kindred possess Devotions, and fewer still have been wise enough to create their own. Kindred may learn of them through a "secret knowledge" a sire wishes to pass on to them, the confidences of a mentor, stolen wisdom in the hands of rebellious vampires, or by any other manner in which they come up in a story.

Although any Kindred can potentially learn any Devotion as long as she has the Discipline prerequisites, some measure of "creator's pride" exists pertaining to each, depending upon who claims to have developed the power first. Most of the Devotions stemming from and involving the Protean Discipline are known as Gangrel Devotions, for example, while those involving Theban Sorcery are referred to as Lancea Sanctum Devotions.

The following are sample Devotions that vampires might encounter and learn. Remember that if a Devotion is turned against or applied to a vampire with whom the user has a blood tie (see p. 162), a +2 bonus is gained on the power's activation roll. For information on creating one's own Devotions, see p. 265.

Knowing the Stranger
(Auspex ••••, Obfuscate ••••)

The Familiar Stranger is a versatile and useful ability, but its use becomes perilous when the vampire has no idea who he should be impersonating. Knowing the Stranger serves as a short-term fix to that problem. It allows the character to discern in advance who the target most expects to see under the circumstances, before The Familiar Stranger is activated (so the Devotion and Discipline power are applied separately). The character does not have any choice over who he "becomes," but he does know exactly who he's supposed to be, even if he has never met that person before. The character gains the knowledge mystically and may act accordingly. The information drawn from the subject's mind even allows the Kindred to custom-tailor certain aspects of the power to her. For example, the Kindred learns that the man the subject sees is her father, that he is gruff but caring, and that the last time he and the subject parted ways, they did so on bad terms and the subject feels remorse for that interaction.

The vampire must be able to see the person whom he plans to dupe when this Devotion is activated.

Cost: 1 Vitae

Dice Pool: Intelligence + Empathy + Obfuscate versus Resolve + Blood Potency

Action: Contested; resistance is reflexive

If the contested roll is won, the vampire knows in advance for whom he will be mistaken. If the contested roll is tied or lost, the vampire gets no impression of who he might be mistaken for. He can try to use the Devotion again or may forge ahead with The Familiar Stranger and hope for the best. If the vampire suffers a dramatic failure, he assumes that he appears as one person when the subject actually interprets him as another.

This power costs 21 experience points to learn.

Arcane Sight
(Auspex ••, Crúac •)

Those who know this Devotion have learned how to expand their mystical sight by incorporating rudiments of blood magic. Kindred with this power can use their Auspex to scrutinize the auras of objects, as well as people, and may glean information from the eddies of power that whorl through the world.

Cost: 1 Vitae per scene

Dice Pool: Wits + Occult + Auspex

Action: Instant

Rather than sensing patterns of emotions as with Aura Perception, the user sees the ebb and flow of magical power. A Kindred possessing this Devotion can learn a variety of information, including the following: whether an object (or person) has any magic of its own or is currently under enchantment; whether the magic comes from the object or creature directly or from an external source; the nature of the magic (beneficial, harmful, illusory);

even detailed information as to the type and level of magic employed. Scrutinized individuals who are capable of any sort of magic (vampiric or otherwise) always glow with sparkling crackles of energy. Although this Devotion does identify sources of magic or items possessed of enchantments, it does not reveal magic effects in action (such as a magical fireball or an illusion). Each success on the activation roll yields one piece of information about the magic in question.

This power costs 10 experience points to learn.

Body of Will

(Resilience ••• , Vigor •)

Truly tough Kindred can call upon personal reserves of will to shore up their toughness in the face of adversity. By means of this Devotion, a vampire learns how to funnel his strength of will through his supernaturally altered form, allowing him to shrug off the deleterious effects of his wounds — for a time.

Cost: 1 Vitae

Dice Pool: Composure + Athletics + Resilience

Action: Reflexive

Each success gained on the activation roll allows the character to ignore any current wound penalties, as well as any penalties he acquires from new wounds, for one turn. Therefore, if three successes are rolled, the character is wound-penalty-free for the duration of the existing turn and for two turns thereafter. A new Vitae expenditure and roll is required each time the vampire wishes to reactivate the Devotion.

This power costs 15 experience points to learn.

Instantaneous Transformation

(Celerity •• , Protean ••••)

Sometimes the shift into animal (or otherwise inhuman) form simply takes too long. Developed by the Gangrel, Instantaneous Transformation allows such a shift to take place, not over the span of seconds, but literally in the blink of an eye.

Cost: 1 Vitae (in addition to other costs required by the transformation)

Dice Pool: Stamina + Survival + Protean

Action: Reflexive

Success on the activation roll indicates that the character transforms into an alternate shape instantly — so fast, in fact, that he may still take a normal action in that turn. If the roll fails, the character still transforms normally for the Protean Discipline used (in the space of one turn). He simply loses the one Vitae for this Devotion, and any other points must still be spent for the change itself. If a dramatic failure occurs, the character cannot change at all this turn, and he loses one Vitae to the wasted Devotion.

Note that this Devotion is most useful to those vampires who can exhaust multiple Vitae in a single turn.

This power costs 18 experience points to learn.

Iron Façade

(Obfuscate •• , Resilience ••)

Sometimes intimidation is a vampire's best weapon, particularly when facing an opponent who is unaware of the Kindred's true ability. Through the use of this power, the vampire appears to shrug off even the mightiest of blows, to ignore wounds that should cripple even one of the undead. Kindred with this power have been known to rout far more capable foes, for the enemy truly believed that such vampires were invulnerable.

Cost: 1 Vitae

Dice Pool: Intelligence + Survival + Obfuscate

Action: Instant

With a successful invocation roll, the character can hide the full extent of his injuries. Wounds are invisible and he does not appear to slow down, limp or grow weary. He seems to function at full capability, regardless of how badly injured he actually is. Iron Façade does not actually heal wounds or reduce dice-pool penalties. It simply *appears* to do so, making it impossible for any observers to determine the character's true condition. Once activated, Iron Façade lasts for a scene or until the character is sent into torpor by his wounds. A vampire with Auspex might be able to see through this power, as per the standard Auspex-versus-Obfuscate rules (see p. 119).

This power costs 10 experience points to learn.

Lessons in the Steel

(Auspex • , Resilience •••)

Some rather intrepid Kindred develop the ability to gain insight into a foe's combat prowess by willingly subjecting themselves to opponents' attacks. Knowledge is power, after all, and any vampire wounded in this way is gifted with power that can then be used against the enemy.

Cost: 1 Vitae

Dice Pool: Resolve + Investigation + Resilience − opponent's Resolve

Action: Instant

In order to activate this Devotion, the vampire must first suffer an attack from an opponent that successfully inflicts at least one point of damage of any type in close combat. Upon suffering this wound, the vampire's player makes the requisite roll. His dice pool is reduced by one die for each piece of information sought about the attacker (up to a maximum of five) beyond the first. The information the character seeks must be related to combat or other martial prowess. For example, Joe's character wishes to learn two bits of relevant information about the Kindred who just hit him, so Joe rolls Resolve 3 + Investigation 2 + Resilience 3, minus one die for the second piece of information sought. One success is achieved and the Storyteller reveals that the attacker has great prowess with a blade (Weaponry 4), but rather poor follow-through (Strength 1). This power has no effect on ranged attacks, nor on attacks that are themselves manifestations of other Disciplines. Theban

Sorcery's Blood Scourge, for example, provides no information, but an opponent invoking Vigor for a pummeling attack does.

This power costs 12 experience points to learn.

Partial Transformation
(Protean •••, Resilience •)

With this power, any vampire who is capable of assuming a bestial or inhuman shape may choose to stop the process partway through, granting herself a single aspect or trait of the animal. The nose of a wolf allows for tracking prey, and the wings of a bat or bird — while unable to provide true flight, as the Kindred simply aren't built for soaring — are useful for breaking falls or gliding short distances. Technically, this power can also be used for sprouting claws, but as the Protean Discipline already allows for that effect such a use would be somewhat redundant.

Cost: 1 Vitae

Dice Pool: This power involves no roll to invoke.

Action: Instant

Once the transformation begins, the character halts it, granting herself only those animalistic features that she chooses. Obviously, the character may take on only the qualities or features of an animal she can already become through use of Protean. Thus, a character with two alternate forms — a wolf and a bat — could assume wings or a wolf's nose, but not the tail of a scorpion or the eyes of a hawk. Partial transformations of this sort last for the duration of the scene or until the character chooses to remove them.

Use of this power provides a bonus of one or two dice to the circumstances in question, as determined by the Storyteller. A character using a wolf's nose might gain two dice to attempts to track something by scent. Combat applications of this power add one die to attack rolls and inflict lethal damage.

This power costs 15 experience points to learn.

Quicken Sight
(Auspex •, Celerity •)

With this power, the Kindred is able to combine her Heightened Senses and superhuman reaction time to see fast-moving objects in detail that neither Discipline alone can reveal. She can follow a specific card in a deck as it's shuffled, track the loaded chamber in a game of Russian Roulette, pick out subliminal messages in a film or on television, and even read the headline on a newspaper as she drives past the newsstand at 60 miles per hour.

Cost: 1 Vitae

Dice Pool: This power involves no roll to invoke.

Action: Reflexive

Any time the character wishes to observe, follow or examine something that moves too quickly to follow with normal

sight, the player may add five dice to a Wits + Composure roll while this Devotion is active. (Especially fast-moving or small items might impose a penalty of -1 to -3 on the roll, at the Storyteller's discretion, for a net +2 to +4 bonus.) Quicken Sight lasts for the duration of a scene.

This power costs five experience points to learn.

Touch of Deprivation

(Auspex ••••, Dominate ••)

With a simple touch, the Kindred can temporarily shut down one of a victim's five senses. This Devotion is most frequently used as a combat or interrogative tool to blind or deafen a subject, but it can just as easily be used to negate one of the other senses. In fact, a vampire who is immune to pain does not suffer wound penalties, so some Kindred have been known to use this power on their allies in a crisis.

Cost: 1 Vitae

Dice Pool: Intelligence + Medicine + Auspex versus Resolve + Blood Potency (if the subject is unwilling)

Action: Contested; instant if the subject is willing

The character must touch the subject (see "Touching an Opponent" in the **World of Darkness Rulebook**, p. 157) or an unarmed attack might be made. Once contact is established, the contested roll is made if the subject is resistant. If the player gets the most successes, the vampire chooses which of the five senses is negated. The victim goes blind, deaf or is otherwise impaired. If an equal number of successes is rolled or the subject gets more, the power

has no effect. On a dramatic failure, the vampire using the Devotion loses one of her own senses for the scene. If an exceptional success is rolled for the vampire, a second sense can be shut down in the victim. This effects of this power last for a scene. (See "Fighting Blind" in the **World of Darkness Rulebook**, p. 166.)

If the vampire possesses a higher Auspex than the subject, she may negate a supernatural sense (such as The Spirit's Touch), rather than one of the mundane five.

This power costs 21 experience points to learn.

Veridical Tongue

(Dominate ••, Majesty ••)

With this power, a character is able to sift through the tide of Kindred lies by rendering one subject unable to speak anything but the truth as he knows it. Lies cannot escape his mouth, nor is his tongue able to utter them. Targets may choose to remain silent, of course, but when they speak, they simply can't lie. The subject must be in the Discipline's user's presence when this power is invoked.

Cost: 1 Vitae

Dice Pool: Presence + Subterfuge + Majesty – Composure

Action: Instant

If the roll is successful, the target must speak the truth for a number of turns equal to the successes gained. He may choose not to speak at all, but in many cases silence equates to guilt among the Kindred.

This power costs 12 experience points to learn.

To overwhelm my first, fiercest and most enduring flaw, the thirst that makes me murder, the hunger which makes me unclean... this is the challenge, to coil upon the blood and squeeze that need into submission. What allies can I find in the fight against this need?
— Rites of the Dragon

Chapter Three: Special Rules and Systems

You have sent men to deal with me, priest.

You have had me cut with knives, pierced with arrows

and beaten with clubs. You have had your men burn me with fire;

you have left me to die in the sun.

All of these I have bested; every time I have eluded you.

You will not stop me, priest.

You will not stop me until I have taken the life's blood

from your body and left you on the altar of your absent savior.

—A letter from "the Vampire of Montcalme"

to a foreign priest, dated 1643

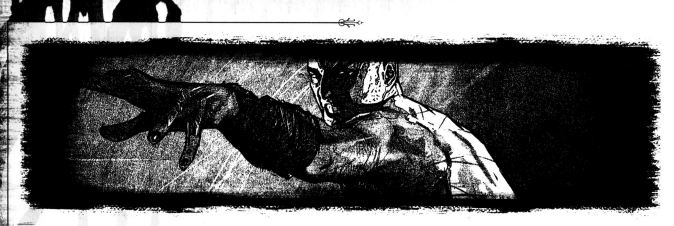

I had not thought death had undone so many.

— T. S. Eliot, *The Waste Land*

In addition to the powers and advantages provided by such aspects of the Requiem as Blood Potency and Disciplines, vampires are subject to certain physical, mental and emotional states outside those of the mortals through whose world they secretly move. This chapter describes and explains a number of special rules and conditions that apply to Kindred characters alone, or that affect the undead differently than they affect mortals.

Topics covered in this chapter include the following.

• Properties of the Blood: How the Kindred acquire and use Vitae, in addition to the unique effects it has on vampires.

• The Predator's Taint: How vampires instinctively react to one another.

• The Traditions: How the physiological laws of being affect the undead, as well as the restrictions (and protections) it places on them.

• Damage, Wounds and Healing: Suffering harm is inevitable when one becomes a vampire, and recovering from it is paramount. Torpor is handled herein as well.

• Frenzy: From fear frenzies to hunger frenzies to berserk rampages, the Kindred are given to fits of uncontrollable passion.

• Humanity: How the Kindred stave off the wiles of the Beast Within, and the toll its actions take upon their sense of morality.

• Derangements: When a Kindred's mental or moral state erodes, she sometimes exhibits dangerous psychological quirks.

• Golconda and Other Means of Transcendence: Some Kindred believe that vampirism itself can be overcome, its curse overturned by good works or a greater understanding of the Kindred condition.

Properties of the Blood

More than anything else, blood defines the Kindred. Within seconds after a vampire consumes blood, the vital fluid changes into something quite different that the Kindred call Vitae. Vampire Vitae looks like mortal blood, but it doesn't flow like mortal blood. A vampire's Vitae moves through her body at the behest of the character's will, not because of a beating heart. Kindred don't bleed when they are wounded; Vitae might pool slightly in the wound, but it does not flow forth unless the vampire wills it to do so.

Vitae retains its supernatural properties for a few minutes after it leaves a vampire's body and is exposed to air, and then reverts to ordinary blood. A scientist who examines a sample of former Vitae would find a mixture of blood from many sources, with some of the cells broken down. Some Theban Sorcery practitioners know procedures to preserve the supernatural power of Vitae outside a vampire's body, and blood that came from a vampire always retains a mystical connection that ritualists can exploit.

Kindred employ their Vitae for many purposes. As a vampire calls upon the occult power in her stolen blood, the actual mass and volume of Vitae in her body decreases. As a character uses up her Vitae, her skin tightens and blanches and her body shrinks slightly. She looks less alive. Feeding enables her to restore her lifelike appearance — as lifelike as the character can manage, anyway.

A player may spend Vitae in the same turn in which he spends a point of Willpower. Spending a Vitae is *always* a reflexive action. Even if the actions that doing so enable might not always be reflexive themselves (such as with certain Disciplines), the act of spending the Vitae is.

Waking Up

A vampire expends one Vitae in the course of his daily slumber. If a Kindred falls asleep without any Vitae in his body (an unlikely event, but it could happen), he enters a longer torpor for a duration set by his Humanity and Blood Potency, just as if he had lost all his Health points to lethal damage. See the rules for torpor that follow.

For accounting on the character sheet, mark off the Vitae when the character awakens. Usually, the Vitae is counted as being spent at nightfall, the normal time for vampires to rise. If a Kindred forces herself to wake up during the day, the character must expend a Vitae. If the vampire lets herself sleep again before night falls, she expends another Vitae when she rises again that evening.

Counterfeiting Life

Although vampires are dead, they can imitate some of the things that living people do. The Damned know this process as "the blush of life." A Kindred can force Vitae into his outer tissues to give his skin a lifelike flush, or to force his heart to beat and his lungs to inhale and exhale in a normal rhythm. Kindred who want to engage in sexual intercourse — perhaps to feed upon a suitably distracted mortal vessel, or perhaps for simple pleasure — can force blood to the appropriate section of anatomy as well.

Normally vampires vomit up any food or drink they consume immediately. If a Kindred wishes to consume food or drink, her player must spend a Vitae. This is in addition to the "blush of life" a character may have already paid during the course of the scene, though a character need not invoke the blush of life to be able to consume food. At the end of the scene, the character noisily, messily and bloodily eliminates the consumed matter by way of regurgitation, so it's best to make sure that no one's around to see the Kindred afterward.

Imitating the appearance and functions of life or the ability to consume food for one scene costs a character one Vitae, and both expenditures are reflexive.

Physical Augmentation

A vampire can call upon his Vitae to enhance his muscular power, speed and agility, or ability to withstand harm. In rules terms, for each Vitae the player expends, he adds two dice to one Physical dice pool — one based on Strength, Dexterity or Stamina. This boost lasts for one turn and is a reflexive action.

Example: *Prince Maxwell is beset by three foolish street thugs who think they can mug him. Maxwell feels reluctant to endanger the Masquerade by using Disciplines, so he resolves to give the thugs a thorough but mundane thrashing. Hefting his stout walking stick as the young toughs advance (and wishing he had his saber instead), Maxwell calls on the Blood.*

Thanks to his Blood Potency of 6, Maxwell can expend three Vitae in each turn. He fed earlier in the night, so he has a full 15 Vitae. Maxwell sees that all three punks carry guns, so he decides that his first priority is to not get shot. Three Vitae are pumped into his Strength, raising his dice pool by six dice, which is used to deal a drubbing to one of the thugs. (Maxwell's player marks off the Vitae expended on the character sheet.) On the next turn, Maxwell's player spends two more Vitae to raise Maxwell's base Strength pool by four, pounding another one of the hooligans senseless. The Prince doesn't mind expending so much Vitae on the fight. After he batters the punks unconscious, he plans to restore his losses from their veins.

Healing Wounds

A vampire can also use Vitae to heal wounds. See p. 173 for details, as the subjects of wounds and healing are significantly different for Kindred than they are for mortals. Spending Vitae to heal wounds is a reflexive action.

Discipline Use

Most Disciplines do not cost Vitae to use. Some of the most formidable powers do, however, as do the rituals of Crúac, Devotions and the rare, exotic Disciplines known to some bloodlines. See each power or ritual to see how much they cost.

Blood Addiction

Even mortals can taste the stolen life that charges them with power and turns them into ghouls (see p. 166). That power makes Vitae the most delicious taste in the world. What could satisfy more than life itself? Stolen fruit is always sweetest. Anyone — mortal, animal, vampire or other — who drinks a vampire's blood risks becoming addicted to it. They want to taste that power again. A character might know perfectly well that this bloodthirst could enslave him, maybe even destroy him, but knowing doesn't make the thirst easier to resist. Just like an alcoholic offered a shot of whiskey, it's all too easy to swear that you'll quit — after this one.

In rules terms, any time a character who has imbibed Vitae receives a chance to do so again, the player rolls Resolve + Composure. A single success allows the character to resist the temptation.

The more one gives in, the harder it is to exercise self-control. Each time a character gives in to the thirst for Vitae, subsequent attempts to resist temptation suffer a cumulative -1 die penalty on the Resolve + Composure roll. Eventually, the character's Resolve + Composure dice pool drops to zero and a chance roll is all that's left. At that point, the character is completely addicted. Not only does he have very little chance to resist the thirst, he doesn't want to. A derangement (see p. 186) is imposed instantly if the player makes a dramatic failure on a Resolve + Composure roll to resist the temptation of the Blood.

Addicted mortals and animals often become obsessed with drinking mundane blood, thinking that they might gain some power by doing so. They also frequently grow obsessively dependent on any vampire who supplies their Vitae, becoming willing to do anything — anything! — for another fix. The Kindred exploit such addiction, but doing so carries its own risks. Obsession can take many strange forms. Ghouls might preemptively punish themselves for imaginary infractions, to show "the master" the depth of their loyalty. Two ghouls might become insanely jealous of each other. A ghoul might think that his master speaks in his mind, telling him to do things. Others suffer even stranger varieties of insanity.

Addicted Kindred have been known to wound themselves to lap at their own blood. Vitae addicts also often turn to diablerie in their search for an even greater rush. The connection between Vitae addiction and diablerie is so strong that many Kindred simply assume that a known Vitae addict is also a diablerist and blame him for any unexplained disappearances of local Kindred. If no one has disappeared, the Prince and Primogen might still order the Vitae addict to be chained and driven into torpor. Twenty-five years of torpor — long enough for a vampire's Blood Potency to drop by one — cures Vitae addiction… or at least the physical craving. The memory of pleasure can start the cycle all over again, but at least the character's dice pool to resist Vitae is reset to the standard.

If a mortal or Kindred character can resist the lure of Vitae, +1 die bonus is gained to subsequent attempts to deny the thirst. The character can beat her nascent addiction if the player ever scores an exceptional success on a Resolve + Composure roll.

It's as if the character never tasted Vitae at all. If she drinks vampire blood again, however, she feels the thirst once more.

When a character falls short of complete addiction, the thirst for Vitae can fade with time, as long as the character avoids temptation. For each year in which a character stays away from any exposure to Kindred blood, one die is added to Resolve + Composure pools to avoid temptation. A character never really beats the thirst, however, until the player scores an exceptional success on the Resolve + Composure roll.

SPECIAL EXCEPTIONS

In certain special cases, Kindred can drink another vampire's blood without risking Vitae addiction. Most importantly, the Vitae consumed during the Embrace does not provoke a further thirst for vampire blood. Compared to the shattering power of the Embrace itself, the addictive qualities of Vitae are as a light breeze compared to a hurricane.

Some rituals also require one vampire to drink another's blood. Such blood rites do not addict participants. In such cases, however, the Kindred use small quantities of Vitae, and the ritual channels the blood's power to a specific goal. The ordinary Vitae-junkie just lets the power roll over him. It's the difference between a doctor prescribing an opiate and a fiend shooting up. The drug is the same, but the application, the effects and the dangers are very different.

Elders, Addiction and Diablerie

Vitae addiction does not seem to become a problem for vampires who are so old and potent that mortal blood no longer sustains them. They must feed on other Kindred, but they do not seem to suffer the derangements and lack of control of Vitae addicts… unless they commit diablerie. In that case, the elder risks diablerie addiction. (Indeed, merely drinking vampire blood is different from the act of diablerie — described momentarily.) Diablerie addiction works just like Vitae addiction, but a player must roll her character's Resolve + Composure for her to resist the urge to diablerize another vampire, even if the character knows her crime could be discovered in a short time and bring her destruction. Few threats inspire as much terror among the Kindred as the possibility of such a diablerie-crazed elder.

Diablerie

The act of diablerie, sometimes known by the poetic name of Amaranth after a flower that never fades, is the process of drinking not only a Kindred's Vitae, but her very soul. Needless to say, diablerie is a heinous crime, much feared and punished by elders, and much misunderstood and mystifying to young Kindred. If drinking Kindred Vitae is looked down upon by other Kindred, the act of diablerie is held as an ultimate sin against both the Damned as a whole and their society proper.

To call it a crime doesn't do it justice, as diablerie provides a host of benefits along with its detriments and social stigmas. This is why the elders fear it — it is potentially an equalizer for young Kindred looking to cheat their way toward power, instead of letting time and experience hone the power of the Blood.

Committing Diablerie

Diablerie itself is a fairly straightforward act. Most importantly, the potential victim must be in torpor, when the soul is sluggish enough to be caught off guard, and the body is placid. Most would-be diablerists attempt their crimes on Kindred who are already staked or already in torpor, and little ignites the passions of power-hungry neonates like the rumor of a torpid elder. It is not unknown, however, for particularly violent Kindred to beat their victims into torpor themselves.

The diablerist must drink all of the Vitae the subject has in his system. Thereafter, the diablerist must keep drinking, sucking at the blasphemous essence that animates the Damned. Diablerie can benefit only one vampire; it is not possible for a coterie of diablerists to consume the soul of a single Kindred and spread it among themselves.

Consuming the soul requires a Resolve + Stamina roll on the part of the diablerist's player. This is an extended action. A number of successes must be accumulated equal to the Willpower dots of the Kindred being diablerized. Each roll represents one turn of effort. It is advised that the Storyteller does the record keeping, so the player doesn't know exactly what happens to his character, at least immediately. Circumstance penalties (such as those associated with wounds and supernatural curses) apply to Resolve + Stamina rolls. Furthermore, if the attacking character is in frenzy or "rides the wave" (see p. 181) when attempting diablerie, rolls suffer an additional -3 penalty. Attempting diablerie has a limit of rolls equal to the diablerist's Willpower dots. If the required successes haven't been accumulated in that many rolls, the victim's soul is just too potent or resistant and cannot be consumed. The victim is consigned to Final Death, instead.

A player may not spend a Willpower point on a diablerie roll, nor do any augmentations of his character's Attributes (through blood expenditure, Disciplines or mystic artifacts) apply. Only the character's natural Resolve and Stamina are relevant.

Dramatic Failure: The victim's soul wrenches free at the moment of its consumption, inflicting horrific trauma on the mind of the diablerist. The diablerist suffers the normal Humanity loss (see below) and gains an appropriate derangement of the Storyteller's choice. The victim succumbs to Final Death and cannot be diablerized.

Failure: The character makes no further progress in consuming the soul of the victim, as the soul fights to elude consumption.

Success: The character continues to draw the soul of the fallen Kindred into his own.

Exceptional Success: The Kindred makes significant headway in consuming the soul of his victim.

After all of a victim's Vitae have been taken, but before all successes are achieved in consuming the subject's soul, a diablerist can cease to feed and allow the victim to reach Final Death in (relative) peace.

Upon diablerie's completion, the Humanity of the diablerist drops by one automatically. He also gains the benefits and drawbacks described below. A diablerized Kindred crumbles to ash immediately, regardless of how old her body actually was upon the Amaranth.

Benefits of Diablerie

If the diablerized vampire had a higher Blood Potency than the Kindred committing the Amaranth, the diablerist's Blood Potency immediately increases by one. Blood Potency increases by only one, regardless of the difference between the vampires' Blood Potencies. This increase need not be paid for with experience points.

In consuming the fallen Kindred's soul, the diablerist actually consumes some of her knowledge as well. The diablerist acquires a single dot of either a Skill or a Discipline that the diablerized vampire possessed *at a higher level than the diablerist does*. This adds to the diablerist's dots in that Skill or Discipline, even if he didn't have any dots at all in the Skill or Discipline before. For example, if a neonate with Obfuscate 3 diablerizes an elder who has Obfuscate 2, the neonate may not take an additional dot of Obfuscate; he already knows more than the elder with regard to that Discipline. The diablerist may not take a dot in a bloodline's unique Discipline unless he is a member of the bloodline that practices that Discipline (see p. 260). Also, a diablerist may not exceed the trait maximum imposed by his Blood Potency (although if that Blood Potency now increases to a level that allows a higher level of those traits, he enjoys the benefit of that newly raised Blood Potency when deciding which dot of what to acquire). This increase need not be paid for with experience points.

It should be noted that the only benefit to diablerizing a vampire of lower Blood Potency is acquiring an extra dot in a Discipline or Skill. All of the detriments still apply, however.

Drawbacks of Diablerie

As noted prior, when a vampire commits diablerie, his Humanity decreases by one automatically. The Humanity roll that follows this loss to check for a derangement occurs normally; see p. 182.

A vampire committing the Amaranth risks blood addiction as normal when he consumes his fallen foe's Vitae and soul. See p. 158 for more information on blood addiction. This risk isn't redundant — the vampire need not check for addiction right as he tastes his victim's Vitae and then again as it turns into diablerie.

Finally, the act of Amaranth stains the diablerist's own soul upon its commission. The character's aura acquires black veins that reveal her crime to those who can scrutinize such things (see p. 120). These black veins remain in the diablerist's aura for one year per dot of Blood Potency the victim possessed. This time is cumulative; a vampire who diablerizes two Kindred of

Blood Potency 6 has veins in his aura for 12 years. If a character diablerizes his victims years apart, the additional years add on to the end of last. For example, if a Kindred diablerizes a vampire of Blood Potency 4 and two year later diablerizes a vampire of Blood Potency 5, the black veins appear in her aura for seven years following the second diablerie — or longer, if she keeps to her wicked ways and diablerizes again.

Limitations

Only vampires can commit diablerie. Ghouls, werewolves, mortals and the like aren't Kindred, so they lack the ability to consume the souls of the Damned. Furthermore, only vampires can be diablerized. Those selfsame ghouls, werewolves or mortals do not have the same spark of undeath animating them, so their souls cannot be consumed in this manner.

A vampire in Golconda cannot be diablerized. A would-be diablerist can certainly *try*, but the Kindred's soul eludes the consumption. In a situation like this, make the rolls as normal (in this case, it is certainly better for the Storyteller to roll for the player), but tell the player that the character feels that something isn't quite right as she commits the baneful act.

A diablerized vampire never leaves behind a ghost, as the diablerist consumes the soul that might become one of the lingering dead.

An Example of Diablerie

Vanian the Gangrel is supposed to deliver a message to his sire's Mekhet confidant. When he arrives at the meeting place, he finds nothing but a trail of blood and a torpid Nosferatu in bad shape. Vanian figures that he has a golden opportunity before him — he'll diablerize the Nosferatu and if anyone raises a fuss, he can implicate the missing Mekhet.

The torpid Nosferatu has only one Vitae remaining, which Vanian quickly devours. Thereafter, the process of diablerie begins, and Vanian has seven turns in which to succeed, as his Willpower is 7. The Storyteller rolls six dice (for Vanian's Resolve + Stamina), gaining two successes. The Nosferatu also has a Willpower of 7, so Vanian needs five more successes to complete the deed, but he doesn't know this. Vanian chooses to continue, so the Storyteller rolls again, this time acquiring three more successes. Vanian presses on, determined to complete the deed in spite of this tough old Haunt's tenacity. The Storyteller yields two more successes in the third turn, signifying that the diablerie is complete.

Vanian's Humanity automatically drops from 5 to 4 to pay for his base treachery, so his player rolls four dice to determine whether or not Vanian gains a derangement. Sure enough, he fails, and the Storyteller decides that Vanian acquires the derangement of sanguinary animism. That Nosferatu's voice shrieks acrimony inside his head every now and again. On the other hand, the Gangrel feels a rush of power. The Nosferatu had a Blood Potency of 4 and Vanian's was only 2, so it now rises to 3. In addition, he chooses to acquire a dot of Obfuscate, which he didn't know at all before.

Now all Vanian has to do is hope that no one studies his aura for the next four years, as the black veins therein will remain for that long. With any luck and his new knowledge of Obfuscate, he'll be able to lay low long enough to allay any undue attention.

Helping him in that aim will be Kindred suspicion of the Mekhet contact, who has fled the domain for some reason.

The Vinculum

The addictive power of Vitae takes a special twist if a mortal or Kindred repeatedly tastes the blood of a single Kindred. In this case, an emotional dependence on that specific vampire adds to the general thirst for Vitae. The Kindred call this dependence the Vinculum, the blood bond or the blood oath. The vampire who created the bond is called the regnant; the bound Kindred or mortal is the thrall.

Some Kindred say that the Vinculum is the closest the Damned come to true love. If such is accurate, it is a terrible letdown, as the Vinculum is artificial and empty. It is not true love; it is simply a supernatural approximation. For many Kindred, it is a painful reminder of what they once had available to them as mortals, while the emotions they experience in the Requiem are little more than echoes of those lost feelings. The victim of a blood bond feels utterly devoted to his regnant and does nearly anything she asks. Dominate cannot overpower the thrall's feelings for his regnant. Majesty imposes feelings for other Kindred, but it cannot negate the Vinculum's hold.

The Kindred most often apply the Vinculum to mortals. A ghoul is, necessarily, blood bound after a period of days, weeks or even months. Kindred can also bond other Kindred. No one, however, can be thrall to more than one regnant. A Vinculum to one Kindred precludes the character becoming bound to another vampire, as long as the regnant still exists.

Attitudes Toward the Vinculum

Most Kindred feel a healthy fear of the Vinculum. They know how their kind treats its slaves, and they shudder at the thought of becoming the pawns of one of their fellow monsters. In most cities, the Prince or other dignitaries threaten to apply the Vinculum only as a punishment for misbehavior. A Prince who too often orders other Kindred to submit to his regnancy might provoke a rebellion. Kindred who believe that love can be eternal (if not entirely natural) might drink each other's blood to form a mutual bond. They also recognize that their mutual bond protects them from ever becoming bound to anyone else.

The Invictus tolerates the Vinculum more than any other covenant does. Its elders see the blood oath as another tool by which they can rule over their juniors. In some cities, elders routinely blood bond their childer and all of their line. In most cities, however, a sire may not subject her childe to the Vinculum without special permission from the Prince. Princes do not like Kindred who love their sires more than they fear their rulers. Invictus elders accept such prohibitions because opposing them would turn too many Kindred against the covenant and would too blatantly contradict the covenant's pretense of meritocracy.

The other covenants generally disapprove of Vinculums, or at least their members say they do. The Order of the Dragon sees Vinculums as distractions, emotional baggage that diverts attention best focused elsewhere. The Lancea Sanctum holds that Kindred should serve only God and Longinus. The

Carthians see Vinculums as the acme of antidemocratic elder tyranny, while the unbound simply loathe submitting to anyone else. The Circle of the Crone merely notes that while Kindred should accept the Vinculum as one more aspect of their existence, forcing a Kindred into a blood oath serves no spiritual purpose. Political or spiritual dogma seldom prevents members of these covenants from blood bonding other Kindred when it suits their purposes, though.

Game Mechanics

Each time a character drinks another Kindred's blood, the character's emotional bond to her grows stronger. A character may have several partial Vinculums to any number of Kindred. Once an actual third-stage Vinculum forms, however, all other partial Vinculums vanish.

The first taste generates a mild interest, but the delicious power in the Vitae outweighs any personal interest. The character knows that the other vampire tastes good. The donor of the blood gains no particular hold over the character.

The second drink generates a stronger connection between the two Kindred, quite apart from potential Vitae addiction. The imbibing character considers the blood's donor an important figure in his unlife, though he is hardly enslaved. The character's interest might take the form of affection, trust, admiration or protectiveness, depending on the character's personality. The Storyteller might ask the character's player to attempt a Resolve + Composure roll if the character tries to attack the nascent regnant, or seriously harm her interests. The other vampire's player, meanwhile, receives a +1 dice bonus to all Social rolls directed at the nascent thrall.

The third drink *probably* creates the complete Vinculum. Usually it does, so most Kindred believe "three drinks, you're bound." Strong-willed or strong-blooded Kindred sometimes resist the third drink, though. The third time a character drinks a potential regnant's blood, ask the player for a Stamina + Resolve roll. Adjust the roll by the difference between the two Kindred's Blood Potency dots. If the potential thrall has the higher Blood Potency, add the difference. If the potential regnant has the higher Blood Potency, subtract the difference. If the adjusted Stamina + Resolve roll generates an exceptional success, the Vinculum doesn't "take," though the potential thrall still feels great affection for the would-be regnant. If the character drinks the other vampire's blood a fourth time, call for another adjusted Stamina + Resolve roll to see if the bond forms this time. Eventually, any vampire must succumb.

In the case of multiple Kindred's blood being consumed simultaneously (such as through commingled blood in a group ritual, for example), if the potential exists for multiple third-stage Vinculums being formed, the most potent Blood takes precedence. If that Vinculum fails to form, move down to the next most potent blood, and so on. If multiple vampires' blood is equally potent, determine randomly which of those equally potent Vitae takes precedence. For example, Vanian the Gangrel is two steps toward a Vinculum to the other two members of his coterie. They all share blood in a chalice passed around before a night of raising hell. Since this is Vanian's third taste of both of his coterie-mates' Vitae, he might become subject to a Vinculum to either of them. He makes his

first check for a Vinculum toward the coterie-mate with the highest Blood Potency. If that Vinculum doesn't form, he checks for a Vinculum with the other coterie-mate.

A character whose Blood Potency is higher than that of the blood donor has a chance to resist the formation of that blood bond. Once at each stage of the Vinculum, the player may spend a Willpower point for the opportunity to make a Stamina + Composure roll (the Willpower point does not add three dice to this roll). If the roll succeeds, the Vinculum doesn't take root at that stage. This does not, however, cancel any previous partial Vinculums. For example, a player who succeeds on the second roll doesn't negate the presence of the first stage of the Vinculum. If the character drinks again from the same vampire, his player might choose to roll again (with the expenditure of another Willpower point) to see if the second stage does occur. Vampires who have the same Blood Potency still threaten Vinculums as normal. No Stamina + Composure rolls are allowed to resist the steps toward a blood bond.

Subjecting a thrall to the Vinculum certainly offers some benefit to the regnant. The regnant can use certain applications of Dominate on a thrall without the need for eye contact (see p. 124). The thrall merely has to hear the regnant's voice.

Regnants are the objects of their thralls' love, artificial and unwilling though it may be. A regnant gains a +2 dice bonus on all Social rolls affecting her thrall. Further, thralls are subject to a Resolve + Composure roll at a -3 penalty any time they want to take an action (or engage in inaction) that might result in indirect harm to their regnants. For example, a ghoul thrall who tries not to run to her regnant when she sees obviously hostile Kindred breaking into his haven would be subject to this die roll. A thrall who directly tries to act against her regnant — say, the same ghoul trying to stake her regnant as he slept — is subject to the Resolve + Composure roll at a -5 penalty. Failing either of these rolls means the thrall cannot act against the regnant (or allow engage in the dangerous inaction). Dramatically failing either of these rolls means that the thrall isn't even allowed to make such a roll again for the next month, meaning she's unable to even consider allowing harm to befall her master.

Breaking Vinculums

The Kindred know of a few ways to break a Vinculum. The most certain consists of the regnant's Final Death. Torpor does not suffice. Some Kindred tell how they felt their blood oath break like a chain snapping and knew their regnant was no more. In other cases, Kindred have continued to work their regnant's will for years after their thralldom should have ended. In such cases, the thrall had an unusually dependent personality or an unusually kindly regnant, so the former thrall genuinely wanted to complete his master's last commands… or what he thought his master might command.

Simple time can erode a Vinculum. A mortal loses her blood oath if she goes for a full year without tasting her regnant's Vitae. One taste a year can preserve a mortal's thralldom indefinitely.

For the Kindred, a Vinculum takes much longer to fade. Some Kindred have remained blood bound through decades of their regnants' torpor. More dubious tales speak of regnancies lasting through centuries of separation, after everyone else had forgotten that one elder labored beneath a Vinculum to another — until the regnant reappeared and invoked the blood oath once more.

Generally, a successful Resolve + Composure roll can free a character who goes 50 years without tasting her regnant's Vitae. The character's player attempts another roll for every 50 years of separation thereafter. This guideline becomes important in a century-spanning "chronicle of ages."

Mistreatment can also weaken a Vinculum. If a regnant gives his thrall reason to hate him, that hatred can prove stronger than forced devotion. When love, hate and terror roil within a thrall's heart, the conflict might resolve itself with a murderous assault on the regnant. Succeed or fail, the thrall probably goes mad as well. We cannot provide a system for such hatred or madness, though. Too much depends on the details of how the regnant treats the thrall, the thrall's personality and the specific events that cause his mind to snap.

Blood Ties

Vampires call themselves "Kindred," but some are closer kin than others. The connection between sire and childe carries supernatural power. Kindred can affect their immediate, linear "family" with their Disciplines more easily than they affect other vampires.

For this purpose, all Kindred within two Embrace "steps" away from each other count as immediate family and are subject to this effect. Therefore, a character receives the blood-tie bonus to affect her sire, her sire's sire, her childer and her childer's childer.

The character receives a +2 bonus when she tries to affect these close "relatives" with certain Disciplines. These Disciplines include Auspex, Dominate, Nightmare and Majesty. Others state when such bonuses apply in their write-ups in Chapter 2. Certain bloodline Disciplines may apply as well (and Storytellers should consider this when allowing a player to create a new Discipline; see Appendix I for more details). A character must try to affect a "relative" directly with the Discipline in question. The bonus is not gained by a character for using a Discipline on herself and then doing something to another Kindred. For example, a character does not receive a bonus to hit a relative while using Vigor. Likewise, indirect powers don't enjoy the bonus. A character employing the Auspex power The Spirit's Touch does not receive the bonus. That Discipline affects the character herself, and what she does with the capability is incidental. Powers that affect targets automatically without the need for a player to make a dice roll do not gain any bonus. Further, the blood-tie bonus does not apply to any resistance to which a subject is entitled (logically, if the user gained a bonus and the subject gained the same bonus, that bonus would be effectively negated). The bonus is awarded only to the proactive user of a given power.

Example: *Prince Maxwell decides he doesn't want to continue an argument with his childe, Persephone Moore, so he orders her to forget about it — and backs up his command with Dominate. Maxwell's player would normally roll 12 dice for this effort. Because Persephone is Maxwell's childe, however, Maxwell's player rolls 14 dice instead.*

trabbold

The Taste of Family

Kindred can tell how closely they're related to another vampire by tasting their blood (with all the hazards of addiction that entails). The blood of one clan tastes a little different than the blood of another; a discriminating undead palate can tell the blood of a Kindred "relative" from that of a more distantly related clan member.

When a Kindred tastes Vitae, the player can roll Intelligence + Occult. Having active Heightened Senses (Auspex) grants a +2 dice bonus to the roll. One success is enough to tell whether the blood comes from the character's own clan, or to recognize the blood as coming from his immediate Kindred "family" — that is, in the taster's own line of sires and childer (see "Blood Ties," above). Two successes enable the character to recognize the clan (assuming the character has tasted Vitae from several clans). Or two successes tell the character if the subject is within two generations of him in the line (that is, if the subject is a grandsire or grandchilde).

The character can also mystically recognize blood from his mortal relations, if he should happen to drink it without his knowledge, with one success on the Intelligence + Occult roll.

Example: *The Nosferatu Gregor tastes the Vitae of a Kindred whom he plans to diablerize. Gregor's player obtains four successes on the Intelligence + Occult roll to determine if Gregor has any insight into the blood's origins. With four successes, Gregor determines that the individual he's about to diablerize is, in fact, his sire's sire! If Gregor's player had obtained only one success, Gregor would know*

only that this Kindred was closely related to him in the sequence of Embrace. If no such connection existed, one success would have confirmed that the other vampire was in fact a Nosferatu.

Blood Sympathy

On some occasions, Kindred can feel the proximity of their Kindred "relatives" (as specified by the blood-ties rules) or know what's happening to them. This normally happens spontaneously, when a "relative" feels some strong emotion or sensation such as frenzy, a grave wound or the pleasure of diablerie.

On such occasions, the Storyteller can ask a player to roll the character's Wits + Occult. The number of successes tells how much information the character gains from this flash of sensation. Active Heightened Senses (Auspex) adds two dice to this roll.

Dramatic Failure: Players cannot dramatically fail a roll for blood sympathy.

Failure: Nothing happens.

Success: The character has a strong feeling of what the other Kindred experiences and has a general notion of the direction and distance to his relative.

Exceptional Success: For a moment, the character perceives himself to be the other Kindred. He knows exactly what's happening and the exact location of the other Kindred.

A character can also try to force this psychic awareness of a relative and so learn the other Kindred's activities. Doing so costs a point of Willpower, which may not be used to add dice to the Wits + Occult roll. A character can also expend a point of Willpower to try to make a relative know what the character herself feels. The other character's player rolls Wits + Occult, but the first character has no way of knowing whether the attempt to "transmit" succeeds. The blood sympathy does not seem to extend further than about 50 miles, or beyond a metropolitan area. This 50-mile limit applies to affecting relatives with Disciplines, too. For example, if a character uses a far-flung Theban Sorcery ritual on a blood relation who's 500 miles away, she loses the bonus.

The Kindred bless and curse this blood sympathy. If a Kindred sends another vampire to Final Death or diablerizes him, his sire, childer or other "relations" might feel it. The chances are small that any of them will know exactly what happened and who did it, but would-be murderers (and diablerists…) must consider the possibility. Kindred also sometimes fret that their relatives might spy on their moments of strong emotion, be they benign, criminal or merely shameful. A proud Prince who holds court at the opera might not want his childe knowing that he breaks down weeping when he hears songs about lost love.

Feeding

It is the undeniable, dreadful truth of the Kindred condition: Vampires must hunt, and vampires must feed. In many cases, Storytellers will detail individual hunts themselves. In other cases, the details of the hunt are less important than the larger story. The Storyteller must strike a fine balance. Too little attention to hunting makes the story little more than a "dark superheroes" game, in which vampires simply need to recharge their "blood batteries," forsaking horror for displays of supernatural power. Too much attention to feeding, however, can slow the story's pace to a crawl, derailing it from its plot direction and making it a series of feeding vignettes in between which other things happen.

Unfortunately, we can offer no perfect solution. Storytellers must find the perfect balance that suits their troupes' tastes. To that end, we offer an abstract method by which vampiric feeding may take place. The system is relatively simple. Have a player describe the method in which his character wishes to feed, determine which dice pool applies, and make the roll.

Example: *Loki seeks to feed by seducing a vessel at a nightclub, going back to her place and slaking his thirst during a feigned act of passion. The Storyteller decides that the appropriate dice pool in this situation is Presence + Persuasion. The Storyteller decides on Presence over Manipulation because Loki's not being too terribly subtle — he wants his prey to know that he wants her to take him home.*

Example: *Solomon Birch is ravenous after a physical conflict in which his enemies escaped. He barges out of the warehouse on the dock where he was assaulted and grabs the first derelict he can find, intending to drink him dry. The Storyteller decides that Strength + Subterfuge is the appropriate dice pool. Strength represents the fact that Solomon's plan is to simply trap his prey in his clutches, but Subterfuge is necessary to keep potential victims from discerning his malign intent and fleeing him immediately.*

Roll Results

Dramatic Failure: The character has chosen to feed from a particularly dangerous or troublesome vessel. The would-be prey might escape having seen the character's face. She might not be such an easy mark after all, putting up a fight or screaming for help when the police happen to be nearby. Alternatively, the character might feed and lose control of himself, taking too much Vitae and leaving the vessel in a dangerous condition. Dramatic failure during the hunt has an almost limitless number of possibilities — Storytellers are encouraged to be creative and even a little malicious.

Failure: The character is unable to find a suitable vessel, or the vessel proves somehow elusive.

Success: The character obtains a vessel and may take as much Vitae as he wishes (though wise Kindred don't take too much, as the risk of harming the vessel increases with the blood consumed — see "Blood Supply").

Exceptional Success: The character feeds successfully until satiated. Furthermore, events coincide to either protect the character's identity or give him an alibi if he needs it. For example, the vessel genuinely might not remember the details of the event, or onlookers might mistake someone else for the person who waylaid the vessel.

Suggested Modifiers

Modifier	Situation
+2	The character seeks an animal vessel or some other source of Vitae that poses less risk than living prey (such as a blood bank.)
+2	The character hunts in the Rack or some other place where vessels are both plentiful and comparatively willing.
—	Vessels are neither especially numerous nor reckless with whom they share their company.
-2	The character takes efforts to hide his identity from other Kindred (whether present or through secondhand accounts).
-2	The character hunts in the Barrens or some other place where vessels are scarce or particularly suspicious of others.
-3 to -5	The character seeks a very specific vessel, such as "brunette women less than 40 years old" or "children of Eastern European descent."

Blood Supply

When a vampire takes blood from a vessel, he may take one Vitae per turn. A vampire need only lick the wound when he's done to hide the marks left by feeding. (This effect applies to only bite marks made for the purposes of feeding from prey, not to aggressive bites intended to cause damage. Further only the vampire's own bite marks are affected thus — a Kindred may not lick a wound left by another vampire and heal it.)

A vessel has a number of Vitae equal to its Health dots. In game terms, an average adult human contains seven points worth of Vitae. When a vampire feeds from a vessel, each Vitae taken inflicts one point of lethal damage on that vessel.

(Special effects that augment a character's Stamina or add temporary Health dots do not add to the quantity of Vitae in a character's body. A character always has a number or Vitae equal to her unmodified Health dots.)

In most cases the vessel doesn't resist, as the ecstasy of the Kiss overwhelms the shock the Kindred places on the mortal's system. Players of mortals and other living victims who wish to resist the Kiss must gain three or more successes on a Resolve + Composure roll. This depends on the environment, however. A vessel seduced or even surprised and subjected to the Kiss may lose herself in it, while a foe bitten in combat (or even one who feels threatened or otherwise at risk) does not yield to pleasure just because the Kiss feels good. Note that vampires are immune to the Kiss of other Kindred, know exactly what's going on and can fight back.

THE VAMPIRE'S BITE

According to p. 157 of the **World of Darkness Rulebook**, a character attempting to bite as a combat action first has to achieve a grapple hold on a target. On the following turn, the attacker can try to inflict damage by biting. If the victim has an action between the attacker's grab and bite, he can try to break free. The system uses Strength + Brawl – the victim's Defense to attack, but then Strength + Brawl – the victim's Strength to bite for damage. If the attack comes by surprise, the victim's Defense does not apply in the initial grab.

If the vampire wishes to feed from a foe in combat, he goes about the procedure as normal. Instead of biting to inflict damage, however, the vampire may choose to consume Vitae that turn. In this case, the vampire inflicts harm caused by blood loss: one point of lethal damage.

A vampire can take a few Vitae without harming a mortal unduly. Taking all the blood (inflicting points of lethal damage equal to the victim's Health dots), of course, risks killing the vessel. Remember that a mortal character reduced to zero Health points goes into a coma when her last Health box is crossed off. She isn't actually "bleeding to death," as the vampire has already taken all her blood, but the state represents her remaining will to survive. (Note that this progression affects the Embrace, too. If a vampire waits too long to give some of his own Vitae to his freshly exsanguinated childe-to-be, that potential fledgling might die before the sire is able to curse him with undeath. A Kindred cannot just place Vitae on the lips of any old corpse and cause it to rise as a vampire. The potential childe must have had all his blood removed, but be given a taste of Vitae before he's truly dead and gone.) For more information on bleeding to death, see p. 173-174 of the **World of Darkness Rulebook**.

Note that it takes two days for a mortal character to recover from a single point of lethal damage. A vampire expends a single Vitae to rise each night. Assuming the vampire does nothing other than rise — that is, his player spends no Vitae to power Disciplines, augment physical Attributes — a vampire still depletes a

single vessel of Vitae faster than she can recuperate from him slaking his thirst on her. In other words, even if the vampire takes only one Health point worth of blood from her each night, the victim recovers from that feeding completely only after *two* days. This is the reason why many Kindred vary their vessels (to avoid killing them, ultimately), and also the source of tales that involve vessels feeling woozy, sickly and exhausted when a vampire feeds from them.

Animals provide less Vitae. An animal that's smaller than an adult human often contains less blood to begin with. Animal blood also carries less vital force than human blood does, or at least it isn't as useful to the Kindred. An animal whose blood the Kindred consumes still suffers one point of lethal damage for each quantity of blood taken, it simply doesn't nourish the Kindred as much. Most animal blood is worth only half as much Vitae as an equivalent amount taken from a human being. Kindred who feed on mammals other than people receive only half the value in Vitae that they actually take from the vessel, rounded down. For example, a dog has 7 Health dots. Even if a Kindred drank all of the dog's blood, he would gain only three Vitae (the dog's 7 Health divided in two and rounded down). Lesser beasts such as vermin (including rats and bats), fish and other aquatic creatures yield only one-quarter Vitae per Health point of blood taken, again rounded down.

Kindred can also drink stored blood such as plasma reserves or the contents of a blood bank, but this, too, contains less vital force than the hot blood of a living person. Kindred find it much less satisfying. Stored blood yields only one-eighth the Vitae of a similar quantity taken from a live source. For example, a Kindred would have to consume an amount equal to 80 percent of the blood in a human body to glean a single point of Vitae if the blood in question was stored.

Vampires feeding from other Kindred do not inflict damage on those Kindred, they simply drain a direct quantity of Vitae. (Vampires may, however, choose to aggressively bite another vampire with the express purpose of causing damage; see the sidebar on this page.) Note that feeding from other vampires comes with its own host of other problems in the form of possible Vinculums and blood addiction.

Kindred rumor holds that Lupine blood is far more potent than mortal blood. Werewolf Vitae yields two-and-a-half times the equivalent amount taken from a human source, rounded down; two Health points of blood taken from a werewolf equal to five Vitae. The tales also say, however, that Kindred who drink werewolf blood become prone to frenzy for several nights afterward. Vampires who drink Lupine blood suffer -2 penalties to their rolls to resist frenzy for two nights per Health point (not the multiplied Vitae) so consumed. Thus, taking two Health points worth of blood from a werewolf causes a vampire to suffer a -2 frenzy penalty for four nights. Mortal mages, meanwhile, contain no more blood than any other human, but legend says their Vitae can induce strange hallucinations in Kindred who drink it. At least, they'd better be hallucinations. If these Kindred actually see aspects of reality known only to mages… well, most Kindred would not like to think that they know so little about the World of Darkness. Still, few Kindred feel much desire to test the truth of such stories. Kindred who take at least one point of Vitae from a mage suffer a derangement as chosen by the Storyteller for one night per Vitae so consumed. Storytellers are advised to take mages' mystical abilities into account when deciding what derangement is most appropriate.

Ghouls

A ghoul is a creature somewhere between the deathless state of the Kindred and the normal state of most mortals. In fact, ghouls are mortals, with the added condition that they have been fed Kindred Vitae and invested with some aspect of the curse of undeath. Not every mortal who simply tastes vampiric Vitae becomes a ghoul, though. It takes a specific devotion on the part of the Kindred to create ghouls, but once they do, those creatures can become as independent or reliant as their masters wish.

Creating a ghoul is an endeavor laden with risk. Ghouls are, by their nature, threats to the Masquerade, as they are mortals who have knowledge of the existence of vampires. Kindred who use ghouls argue that this knowledge also protects the secret, since a ghoul depends on vampiric Vitae to sustain that very state. Ghouls (and other mortals) suffer the same potential for blood addiction that the Kindred do, and since a single ghoul is rarely a match for any given vampire, most willingly suffer whatever eccentricities or cruelties their masters inflict on them as long as the promise of that precious Vitae is delivered.

Of those Kindred who create ghouls, most use them as agents for their agendas during the daytime, or as extra aides, muscle or specialists during their own active hours. Ghouls can and do come from all walks of life, from menservants of high-class Kindred to gangsters under a vampiric crime lord's sway to crooked cops or valued informants. In most cases, ghouls are utterly dependent on their Kindred masters. Many of them are codependent, addicted to blood or their masters' attention, or otherwise trapped in abusive, horrible relationships with their lords. And yet, stories travel through Kindred networks now and again concerning ghouls who go rogue, beholden to no particular master. They creep into sleeping Kindred havens to steal valuable Vitae.

Not every mortal who is a vampire's thrall is a ghoul. At the same time, not every ghoul labors under a Vinculum to a single vampiric regnant. It takes an act of will to create a ghoul, but a ghoul must drink from the same vampire three times to be subject to the Vinculum, just like everyone else.

Ghoul Creation and Support

A vampire who wishes to create a ghoul must feed a mortal at least a single Vitae. In addition, the vampire's player must spend a point of Willpower to invest the ghoul with some degree of the mystic state with which she is cursed. If a vampire simply gives a mortal Vitae but no Willpower point is expended, the mortal does not become a ghoul (though he is potentially subject to the Vinculum and blood addiction). This Willpower expenditure represents the creation of an artificial state, inflicting some of the benefits and detriments of undeath on the ghoul.

Upon becoming a ghoul, a mortal stops aging. Although time still passes normally, the ghoul's body doesn't become any more decrepit with age, nor does a ghoul child continue to grow. (Pregnant ghouls almost universally miscarry after

166   special rules and systems

the change.) So long as the ghoul obtains regular feedings of Vitae, this state of static age continues.

A ghoul requires at least one Vitae per month to sustain the state of ghouldom. When receiving this monthly "upkeep," either the vampire *or* the ghoul player must spend a point of Willpower. The Vitae need not come from the Kindred who initially created the ghoul. For the Kindred, this is a gamble. If the vampire player spends the Willpower point and/or Vitae herself, and the vampire never lets the ghoul know he can spend his own Willpower, the ghoul acquires a sense of expense associated with using that Willpower and Vitae. On the other hand, if the Kindred lets her ghoul know that he can spend the Willpower himself, she sets herself up for possible betrayal. If a vampiric master relies upon other Kindred to supply her ghouls' Vitae, those ghouls may eventually become subject to a Vinculum to another Kindred, which isn't always in the first Kindred's best interests.

A ghoul who does not receive his monthly infusion of blood slowly returns to his previous mortal state. The erstwhile ghoul ages one year per day that he is overdue for his monthly draught. If the ghoul does manage to procure more Vitae, he does not revert to his original age of ghouldom, but rather, suspends his aging from the point at which it has caught up with him. A ghoul deprived of Vitae who has outlived a normal mortal lifetime rapidly ages and dies as time catches up with him after having been cheated for so long.

Storyteller's Option: Ghoul Derangement

At the Storyteller's option a ghoul who falls behind on his monthly Vitae requirement might gain a temporary derangement. This derangement should be mild. Alternatively, if the character already has a mild derangement, the Storyteller may upgrade it temporarily to the severe form. This temporary derangement or temporary exacerbation of an existing derangement ends goes away when the ghoul procures his necessary Vitae.

We include this as an option because the ghoul might already be functioning under the mind-altering effects of a Vinculum and possibly blood addiction as well. If you as Storyteller choose to make the debilitating effects of blood withdrawal even more horrifying for ghouls, use this system.

If a ghoul doesn't have any Vitae in her system, she doesn't suddenly cease to be a ghoul. Rather, the transition back to the mortal state begins only when the mortal comes due for her monthly sustenance. In other words, if a ghoul misses her monthly feeding and has no vampiric Vitae in her system, she's no longer a ghoul. She loses all powers associated with being a ghoul and begins aging. If she later acquires more Kindred Vitae, she resumes being a ghoul, but not before any aging effects might have occurred in the interim. Ghouls who go through this "wayward" state do not forget any Disciplines they might have known. Without Vitae to employ them, however, those powers are useless — even those Disciplines that have no Vitae

costs associated with them. Once the ghoul loses that state, supernatural powers are no longer available to her.

Abilities and Powers

Once the ghoul imbibes Vitae, he may use it in several ways similar to a vampire. One primary difference, however, is that the ghoul does not eliminate any quantity of his own blood when he expends a Vitae. Similarly, when a ghoul consumes Vitae, that Vitae does not add to or replace his own blood. "Vitae" in a ghoul is merely the lingering cursed power transferred from the vampire. A ghoul with seven Health dots still has seven dots after taking one Kindred Vitae — the Vitae does not add Health dots to him, nor does it add any volume to the ghoul's own quantity of blood. A ghoul is still a mortal, and Vitae he consumes goes into his stomach as does anything else he drinks. A ghoul calling upon Vitae uses the power inherent in it, not the mass of liquid itself (which is eventually digested and otherwise eliminated). When using Vitae, a ghoul's player may only spend one per turn. A ghoul may have a total number of Vitae in his system equal to his Stamina. If the ghoul's Stamina drops for any reason and would leave a surplus, that extra Vitae is lost immediately. Examples of such situations include becoming sick or ending a scene in which the ghoul had activated Resilience.

Upon becoming a ghoul, the individual immediately gains a single dot in a physical Discipline (Celerity, Resilience or Vigor). Which Discipline manifests depends on the clan or bloodline of the vampire who creates the ghoul. If that clan or bloodline has two physical Disciplines, the sire — not the ghoul — chooses which Discipline to impart. For example, a Ventrue ghoul gains a single dot of Resilience, while the ghoul of a Daeva obtains either Celerity or Vigor as decided by his master.

Ghouls may use Disciplines, if they have them. A ghoul may learn Disciplines by spending experience points, which costs twice as much as it does for a vampire (10 times the new level in experience points for a clan or bloodline Discipline, 14 times the new level in experience points for an out-of-clan or -bloodline Discipline). In most cases, a ghoul must have a teacher to learn a Discipline or advance in level, with the exception of physical Disciplines. As long as the ghoul knows the first level of one of the physical Disciplines, he may learn other levels without a teacher (although he must be taught the first level). A ghoul may learn a unique bloodline Discipline if his master hails from the bloodline in question.

A ghoul may expend Vitae to augment physical Attributes, just like a vampire (see p. 157). A ghoul may also use Vitae to heal wounds, again like a vampire. If a ghoul doesn't use Vitae to heal wounds, he recovers in the same amount of time that a mortal does, as described on p. 175 of the **World of Darkness Rulebook**.

Ghouls do not use Humanity to measure their morality. Instead, they use Morality as described on pp. 91–94 of the **World of Darkness** rules.

Ghouls may spend one Vitae per turn. They have no Blood Potency.

Embraced ghouls keep all of the Disciplines they learned as ghouls when they make the transition to the ranks of the

Kindred. Vinculums and blood addictions the character has survive into undeath as well.

Animal Ghouls

Animals may be made into ghouls, but no animal is intelligent or aware enough to fully know what changes Vitae imposes upon its body. Animal ghouls suffer all of the detriments of being a ghoul (such as blood addiction, Vinculums, dependency on Vitae for survival) but gain few of the benefits. Ghouls animals may learn only Celerity, Vigor and Resilience by way of Disciplines. Further, they can use Vitae only to fuel these powers; they may not use Vitae to heal themselves or augment Physical Attributes. An animal ghoul may never spend its own Willpower during its sustenance feedings; it relies on the vampiric master to do so. Indeed, ghoul animals are relatively rare, and most Kindred with animal companions merely subject them to Vinculums to ensure loyalty rather than to make ghouls of them.

THE BLOOD AND OTHER SUPERNATURAL CREATURES

Kindred Vitae, while potent, does have its limits. When the other supernatural creatures with whom the Damned occasionally cross paths come into play, certain realities of the World of Darkness supersede the mystic strength of the Blood.

Werewolves and mages are immune to the Embrace. If a vampire is somehow able to extract all the blood from a werewolf or mage and attempt the Embrace, that Embrace fails automatically. Likewise with Vinculums and attempts at creating ghouls — they simply do not work with regard to Lupines and mages. Other supernatural creatures are subject to blood addiction, however, the absence of other supernatural effects notwithstanding.

Naturally, this physiological situation doesn't deter rumors of such things from spreading. Savvy Kindred who hear of such things, however, wisely dismiss them as the efforts of inexperienced vampires trying to codify something they don't understand.

The Predator's Taint

Despite the predilection some Kindred have for describing each other as parasites, the truth of the matter is that vampires are finely suited to the roles of predators. Their supernatural abilities allow them to hunt with great efficacy. Their mesmeric personalities draw people to them. Even their hideous or off-putting weaknesses can reduce their prey to impotent wretches from whom blood can be taken at will. The Kindred are consummate solitary predators, keenly able to procure their own sustenance without the aid of others of their kind.

It is no surprise, then, that when such perfect predators meet each other, the Beast inside each attempts to determine whether the other is a threat or an encroaching lesser. Indeed, when

Kindred meet for the first time, the Beast rages within, wishing to flee in terror of a greater predator or to conquer a less able creature in hopes of protecting one's own territory.

System

When a vampire sees another vampire for the first time (and only for the first time), compare the characters' Blood Potency dots.

The player of the character with the lower Blood Potency must immediately check for Rötschreck (see p. 179).

The player of the character with the higher Blood Potency must immediately check for frenzy (see p. 178).

If the characters have the same Blood Potency, both players check for frenzy.

Characters risk frenzy and Rötschreck only when they are aware of the presence of the other Kindred. It is entirely possible, say, for a vampire to see another, unknown vampire feeding in an alley and thereby cause her own frenzy check as her Beast senses the rival Beast. While the other vampire is preoccupied with feeding he remains oblivious; only when he becomes aware of the other Kindred does his Beast respond to the presence of the first.

One minor benefit of the Predator's Taint is that, due to the presence of the Beast, vampires instinctively know other vampires upon seeing them. Even if a vampire has met another Kindred before, the initial "surge" of the Beast takes place every time the two make contact, though it is far more manageable than the initial contact of the unknown. This also, unfortunately, explains the tense and mercurial nature of relations between vampires.

Suggested Modifiers

Modifier	Situation
+3	The character is at Elysium or some other social event that would invoke grave consequences for succumbing to frenzy.
+2	The character expects to meet another vampire, such as through a planned meeting suggested by a common acquaintance.
+1	The character frequents an establishment known to have common Kindred presence, such as a blood cult's temple or the Rack.
—	The character witnesses another vampire in a potentially threatening capacity for the first time.
-2	The character perceives the other vampire as an intruder or unexpected threat, such as by coming back to her haven and finding an unknown vampire there.

Storytelling the Predator's Taint

Important: *Use of the Predator's Taint should be based on the dramatic potential of the situation. Storytellers need not employ it every time a new vampire enters the narrative. They should not feel that they have to incorporate the Predator's Taint into every interaction between Kindred.*

This rule exists to highlight the xenophobic world of the Kindred, as well as to reinforce the local phenomenon of

Kindred domains. After all, even in a domain where one is on poor terms with the other local vampires, at least one knows them. In a new domain, the Predator's Taint threatens a would-be immigrant so as to make a "fresh start" in a new domain a very dangerous affair.

Don't use the Predator's Taint to be adversarial. Use it only to drive home the notion that a particular vampire is strange, threatening and, most important, unknown. Storytellers may assume that players' characters have met most of the other local Kindred in their domains during their period of indoctrination or protection under their sires. By the time the actual chronicle begins, characters are familiar, at least in the back story, with most Kindred of at least minor acknowledgement in their home domains. Characters have probably met the Prince. They are likely to have spoken with their Prisci and at least have been introduced to their Primogen.

Where the Predator's Taint comes into play most effectively is when a new Kindred shows up on the scene. Maybe this unknown vampire is a prophet of Golconda, but her unknown nature prompts a hostile, immediate response from the Beast. Perhaps a rabble-rouser drumming up support in the characters' domain spurs the Beast to a (arguably rightful) violent action. The envoy from a nearby domain might have the best of intentions, but the Beast instinctively causes the locals' hackles to rise. With high emotions charging the encounter, Kindred grow confused as to whether they can trust this interloper or must eliminate her as a possible cunning threat to their own well-being.

Most times, the result of a frenzy caused by the Predator's Taint is violent. In a few rare cases, however, other avenues may be pursued. Frenzied vampires may play a dangerous game of cat-and-mouse across a city's rooftops, for example, or they exert their dominance by engaging in some test of mettle such as running through a burning building, withstanding the impact of a speeding car or other gesture of power or endurance. As with other considerations regarding the Predator's Taint, let the drama of the situation dictate the results rather than rote adherence to the letter of the rules.

Note also, Storytellers, that the general guidelines need not always apply. In a plot development that should cause the characters to mistrust their Primogen, maybe they *haven't* yet made her acquaintance. A pretender-Prince or some similar archetype might not have met everyone in the domain, particularly at early stages of his rise to power. On the other hand, it might just bog everything down to check for frenzy with *every* new vampire a given character sees. For example, there's probably no reason to check for frenzy if a character walks down the street and a vampire passes by in a car. But if a character comes creeping home just before dawn and sees a foreign vampire hunched over the body of a bloodless vessel left lying in her doorway, a frenzy check is almost certainly in order. The situation should be taken into account as well. Two vampires catching each other's eye in a nightclub may not provoke outright frenzy, but it definitely sets both of their nerves on edge and makes them a bit more alert to their surroundings than they might otherwise be. A vampire seeing another vampire through binoculars, however, would almost never suffer a frenzy check.

Certain Storytellers might wish to adapt the Predator's Taint to other circumstances as well. A hungry Kindred might not see another vampire but might catch the scent of her on the wind as she prepares for the hunt (assuming her player states that the character searches for scents on the wind, as Kindred don't normally breathe), causing the Storyteller to call for a frenzy check. A Kindred might slide along a wall in utter darkness, touching a cold, clammy hand — and realize the hand belongs to another of the Damned, risking frenzy in the shock of the situation. These examples and environments are far less concrete, but might serve as good dramatic opportunities, anyway. Certainly the range of other senses doesn't apply as universally as vampires recognizing each other on sight, but given the proper story criteria, they can be just as valid.

The bottom line is that the Predator's Taint is certainly a downside to being a vampire, as well as one more thing that makes being a new vampire that much more difficult. Don't antagonize players' characters with the rules, though. Use them to heighten the drama of a situation when the aspect of the unknown comes to the fore.

The Traditions

According to numerous Kindred legends, three laws have governed the Damned since their first nights: that they should hide from mortals, that they should not sire any childer, and that they should not slay each other to consume the souls of the fallen. The Kindred break all three laws, but they find that the metaphysical limitations governing them are not easily flouted. Meanwhile, players learn that each Tradition has a tangible effect within the game.

The Tradition of Masquerade

The Tradition of Masquerade, sometimes known as the Tradition of Secrecy, commands the Kindred to not reveal their presence to mortals. Clearly, Kindred walk among mortals every night, but the Masquerade defends itself in a subtle way. Indeed, the Kindred discovered the full implications of this Tradition in recent nights. What they once took to be a self-defeating curse upon them now stands revealed as a blessing granted millennia in advance. Of course, any blessing on the Damned carries its own price.

The Kindred appear as blurry images in mirrors, photographs, video monitors and other media that capture or transmit visual images. This mystic distortion protects the identity of individual Kindred. As security cameras become more common, the odds increase that a camera will capture the image of a vampire feeding, committing some other crime, surviving a gunshot that would slay a mortal, or using a Discipline to perform some impossible feat. Anyone who looks at a photograph or camera image might tell that something strange, criminal or impossible has taken place, but they cannot identify the Kindred in question. Without a person to attach to the deed, the distorted image becomes just one more insoluble mystery in a mysterious world.

In some ways, this blurring endangers the Masquerade. Kindred need to stay away from large mirrors, lest mortals notice the one distorted reflection. Canny witch-hunters have identified vampires by glancing back and forth from the people around them to a small mirror hidden in hand. A security guard watching a monitor might be puzzled by why one person looks like a blur when everyone else shows up crisp and clear.

A Kindred can turn off this blurring effect for a scene by expending a Willpower point. With regard to lasting media, such as video tapes, photographs and digital film footage, spending a Willpower point allows a vampire's image to remain intact on that media for a number of days equal to 11 minus the Kindred's Blood Potency. A player may choose to spend a Willpower *dot* on behalf of the character when she is photographed (or filmed) to make that particular image permanent. As such, with an effort of will, a Kindred can have a photographic identification or "prove" to a vampire-hunter that of course she's not a vampire — she shows up in photographs just like anyone else!

The strange occlusion that occurs to vampire images does not apply to voice recordings. Kindred voices are recorded normally, without the expenditure of Willpower.

The Tradition of Progeny

The Tradition of Progeny commands the Kindred not to curse any other mortals with undeath. Here, surely, the Kindred have most egregiously disobeyed whatever unholy force has spawned them.

The act of creating a new Kindred exacts a steep price from those who break this law, requiring a supreme effort of will. Kindred who sire childer seem to pass part of their souls to their offspring. Their force of will weakens slightly, a debility that can remain for years. A Kindred who sires several childer in a short time could render himself so weak-willed that his enemies would surely ruin him — if his conniving get didn't get to him first.

In rules terms, a character must sacrifice a *dot* of Willpower in order to sire a childe. Nothing can restore the lost Willpower dot except increasing the trait with experience points.

The Tradition of Amaranth

As a sort of final commandment, the Damned find it difficult to commit diablerie upon each other. Any time the Kindred disobey their undead natures, they learn that their defiance carries a price.

Kindred rarely feel sorry when they kill each other. Or if they do, their regret seldom lasts long. Any Kindred, from the most ethical to the most jaded, finds herself a little more callous and ruthless after killing a fellow vampire and consuming his heartsblood. No contrition or atonement can avert this erosion of the Man and strengthening of the Beast. Vampires become less able to pass for human with mortals, they find that temptations to vice increase, and deeds that once repelled them no longer prick their conscience.

In rules terms, the Humanity dots of a character who commits diablerie decrease by one. The loss happens automatically, with no need for a degeneration roll (though the Humanity roll that follows to check for a derangement occurs normally; see p. 182). The circumstances don't matter, either. No matter how much another vampire deserves to die, none may be judged except by God, and the Tradition of Amaranth allows for no exceptions. A Kindred who diablerizes another Kindred can recover her lost Humanity

in time... but once again, doing so requires accumulating and spending experience points.

Damage, Wounds and Healing

The Kindred dwell in a dangerous world. Aside from the threats they face from each other, werewolves and other supernatural creatures, they can run afoul of muggers or thugs just like mortals do. Although the Kindred possess a few advantages over mortals in dealing with such dangers, they are not invulnerable. Kindred can also encounter disease, poison, electrocution and other hazards. Players and Storytellers therefore need to know how Kindred suffer damage, and how they can heal it back.

Taking Damage

Kindred encounter many of the same hazards that mortals do. They have less to fear, perhaps, from ordinary combat involving fists, broken bottles, guns and the like. On the other hand, as supernatural creatures, vampires suffer from anathemas — conditions benign to mortals but deadly to the undead, or that present special dangers and difficulties in healing. Kindred anathemas are fire and sunlight. In addition, sufficient damage of almost any kind can trap a vampire in a deathlike trance called torpor, or it can destroy him.

It is important to note that vampires are subject to the same wound penalties that mortals are when injuries are marked in one of their last three remaining Health boxes. See "Health" on p. 171 of the **World of Darkness Rulebook** for more information.

Bashing Damage

Fists, clubs and falls are all examples of bashing damage. Anything that inflicts bashing damage on mortals also inflicts bashing damage on Kindred.

Unlike mortals, vampires are never knocked unconscious by bashing damage. The vampiric body just doesn't have the same limitations that a living one does. A Kindred still feels the trauma and still suffers dice-pool penalties, though. When your character's rightmost Health box is filled with a slash for bashing damage, any further points of bashing damage inflicted on the character upgrade the least severe of his existing wounds, from left to right. Remember: Rolls for unconsciousness are not made for a vampire when his rightmost Health box is filled with a slash for bashing damage.

Lethal Damage

Knives, axes, chainsaws and other sorts of melee weapons that inflict lethal damage on mortals also inflict lethal damage on vampires. Chopping and slicing is almost as bad for the undead as for the living. Vampires can protect themselves from lethal damage by wearing body armor, just like mortals can.

Unlike mortals, however, the undead take bashing damage from firearms. A vampire has only two vital organs, the head and heart, and their importance is as much supernatural as physical. The other organs in a vampire's body don't actually do anything, so it doesn't matter if a bullet drills a hole through them. Thus, for Kindred, getting shot is no worse than getting hit by a club. This does not apply to archaic weapons, however. If an arrow from a bow (even though Firearms is rolled to make the attack), a thrown knife or anything of that sort impales a vampire, the weapon still inflicts lethal damage.

The exception for firearms has its own exceptions, though. If someone puts a high-caliber gun to a Kindred's head and blows most of his brains out, that's certainly lethal damage. Storytellers should exercise their own judgment in cases like this.

The undead do not bleed to death like mortals do when their rightmost Health boxes are filled with lethal damage. If a Kindred's last Health box has an "X" in it, he is in torpor. (See the chart on p. 175 to find the duration of this death-like state.) Any further points of lethal damage inflicted on the character are converted to aggravated damage.

To mortals, of course, an incapacitated or newly torpid Kindred seems dead. This appearance might save the vampire if the mortal did not mean to kill his foe. The mortal might run away, call an ambulance or do something else that gives the Kindred time to recover. If the mortal meant to kill the character but did not know he fought a vampire, he probably stops attacking, which can also give the character time to regain consciousness. If the mortal knows about the undead, though, the Kindred probably faces Final Death anyway, as an unconscious vampire is as easy to kill as an unconscious mortal. Prudent Kindred do not take lethal or even bashing damage lightly.

Aggravated Damage

Certain weapons such as magically enhanced werewolf claws or those that Kindred can grow using the Protean Discipline inflict aggravated damage to vampires. Various rare Discipline powers, rituals and other magical effects might deal aggravated damage as well. Such special cases are explained in the description of the relevant power or ritual. Attacks that deal large quantities of lethal damage can also be "upgraded" to aggravated damage if they would destroy large chunks of a character's body. For example, if a vampire throws himself on a hand grenade, the Storyteller has every right to declare that the character suffers aggravated damage from the explosion. For the most part, though, Kindred suffer aggravated damage because of the special anathemas to the undead: sunlight and fire.

Remember that aggravated damage is also inflicted when all other Health boxes are filled with lethal injuries, and more harm of any kind is incurred; lethal wounds are upgraded to aggravated from left to right.

If a Kindred's rightmost Health box is marked with aggravated damage — having suffered the harm either directly or by converting damage dealt to the torpid character — she suffers Final Death. Her body rots, dries and withers in minutes, and crumbles to dust within an hour. The longer a Kindred has spent undead, the more rapidly the final dissolution occurs.

Countering damage from sunlight and fire works differently than other sources of aggravated damage, in that fire and sunlight inflict automatic points of damage. The Resilience Discipline does offer some protection, allowing a character to downgrade this damage (see p. 140). Ultimately, though, even the oldest and toughest vampire has no chance to withstand

HOOP 04

extensive exposure to fire or sunlight. The Kindred have abundant reason to fear these phenomena more than anything else.

Fire

Fire presents an even greater danger to vampires than it does to mortals. Fire inflicts aggravated damage on Kindred. Only Resilience can shield a vampire from the flames, and that to a limited degree.

A fire's size and heat determines how much damage a character endures per turn. A small, very hot fire can deliver as much damage as a large but cooler fire. The Storyteller decides how much damage a particular fire can inflict, based on these guidelines:

Size of Fire	Damage
Small fire (example: torch)	1 point
Large fire (example: bonfire)	2 points
Inferno	3 or more points
(example: burning house, blast furnace)	

Heat of Fire	Damage
Feeble fire	No modifier
(example: red-hot coals, candle flame)	
Normal combustion	+1 point
(example: wood fire, red-hot stove)	
Hot fire	+2 points
(example: gasoline fire, Bunsen burner)	
Very hot fire	+3 points
(example: molten metal, welding torch)	

Remember that normal armor can protect Kindred for a few turns, but only specialized suits of heat-reflective fabric, such as those used by oil-well firefighters, can shield a vampire for longer. (See the rules for fire in the **World of Darkness Rulebook**, p. 180.) Meanwhile, the character must also withstand the supernatural terror called Rötschreck (see p. 178).

• **Clinging Fire:** Note that some burning substances stick to a character and continue burning for quite some time. Napalm is the most notorious example, but burning plastic is the most common source of clinging flames. Burning plastic inflicts damage at the same rate as a wood fire.

• **Disfigurement:** Characters who are damaged by fire but who still manage to survive (through first aid or mystical healing) might suffer a permanent impairment (reduced Physical Attribute), nerve damage (reduced Mental Attribute) or severe and disfiguring scars (reduced Presence), at the Storyteller's discretion. Such impairment can be defined as a Flaw (see p. 217 of the **World of Darkness Rulebook**) gained during play.

Sunlight

The Kindred fear sunlight even more than fire. After all, fire doesn't suffuse half the world, making half of each diurnal cycle deadly for vampires. Even the weakest sunlight presents danger. Sunlight filtered through a heavy curtain can still burn. Only the Resilience Discipline can protect a vampire from the daystar's rays, and then only against dim, faint exposure. Direct sunlight can sear even the mightiest Kindred to ash.

chapter three

The amount of damage a Kindred suffers automatically from sunlight per turn depends on the intensity of the light and how much of the vampire's body is exposed. The brighter and more direct the sunlight is, the more quickly a Kindred's undead flesh burns. The more of a vampire's body that is exposed to sunlight, the more extensive the damage is. For characters, little practical difference exists between an arm completely burned off in a second and losing most of one's skin from diffused exposure. Damage is damage.

Intensity or Exposure	Health Points/Turn
Faint, filtered sunlight (Example: light through heavy, closed drapes; cloud cover; twilight)	1 point
Filtered or weak sunlight (Example: light through thin drapes; outside on cloudy day; daylight through a window; reflection of sun in a mirror)	2 points
Direct sunlight	3 points
Exposure	**Damage**
Small part of body exposed (Example: one hand; part of the face; wearing heavy clothes, sunglasses, gloves and a broad-brimmed hat or balaklava)	+0 points
Large part of body exposed (Example: a leg; an arm; whole head)	+1 point
Much of body exposed (Example: whole torso; wearing thin clothing)	+2 points

Exposing specific body parts to sunlight can cause special, additional harm to a character. A Kindred who looks directly into sunlight is instantly blinded as the rays burn away her retinas and boil her eyes. A narrow beam of sunlight burns a Kindred's arm off, leaving him unable to do anything that requires two hands. Storytellers must judge such situations for themselves.

Moonlight consists of reflected sunlight. Fortunately, moonlight is faint enough that it cannot cause damage to the Kindred. At most, a few exceptionally sensitive Kindred might suffer a mild sunburn from exposure to the light of the full moon.

Recovering from Damage

Mortals heal wounds through time, rest and medical treatment. The undead heal supernaturally, using their stolen blood to repair their bodies. Ordinary medical treatment offers them no benefits whatsoever.

Kindred heal bashing damage quite easily. In one turn, a Kindred character can expend one Vitae to heal two Health points lost to bashing damage. Kindred who are able to spend more than one Vitae per turn may heal two points of bashing damage per Vitae spent per turn, up to their limit. For example, a character with Blood Potency 4 can spend two Vitae per turn (see p. 99), so he could spend two Vitae and heal up to four points of bashing damage in one turn.

Lethal damage heals less easily, since it requires building new tissue to replace and rejoin parts of the character's body. In one turn, a vampire can expend one Vitae to heal one Health point lost to lethal damage. As with bashing damage, vampires who are able to spend more than one Vitae per turn may heal one point of lethal damage per Vitae spent per turn, up to their limit. Both bashing and lethal damage could even be healed at the same time if you can spend all the Vitae required to do so.

A character can perform other actions while healing bashing or lethal damage, as this recovery is a reflexive action. An undead character can therefore take as much damage in a fight as a mortal does and heal the damage back while the fight continues. Of course, a Kindred carries a limited supply of blood, but she can replenish herself from a defeated foe. (Although bloodless corpses or the addictive taste of a fellow Kindred's Vitae pose their own problems.)

Aggravated damage presents much greater difficulties. Each Health point lost to aggravated damage costs *five* Vitae to heal, and the process takes two nights per Health point. Those five Vitae must be spent over the course of the two nights it takes for the character to heal the wound, though they need not be spent together. For example, a player might spend three Vitae after the character rises on the first night, and two Vitae after she rises on the second night to heal the wound.

Note that characters can never heal more Health points than their Health trait. For example, a character with 8 Health who has suffered five points of damage (of whatever type) can not heal six points of damage and raise her Health to 9.

When vampires heal themselves, the rightmost wound of the kind recovered is erased from your character sheet. So, if two bashing wounds are healed, the rightmost ones on your character's Health chart are erased. If a lethal wound is healed, the right most one is erased. The same applies for an aggravated wound. In the case of lethal and aggravated wounds, however, if any other wounds remain to the right of the healed one on your character's Health chart, those injuries shift left one square. No blanks are left in your character's chart.

Say your character's Health chart looks like this:

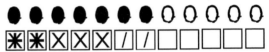

A Vitae is spent to heal one lethal wound. The rightmost one is erased, and all injuries to its right shift left one square to "close ranks." Your character's Health chart therefore looks like this:

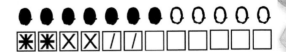

Now, let's say you spend five Vitae over the course of two nights for your character to recover from one aggravated wound. His rightmost aggravated injury is erased and all to the right of it shift to the left, like so:

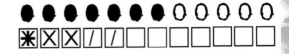

Other Sources of Damage

Now and then, characters encounter other things that can damage or debilitate them. The developed world abounds in toxic and corrosive chemicals, from industrial acids to household cleaners. Kindred might encounter electrical shock, either through lightning strikes, carelessness with machinery or electric fences. Characters might even deliberately introduce mind-altering drugs into their bodies. These hazards and others require special rules, chiefly to distinguish their effects on Kindred from their effects on mortals.

Chemicals, Drugs and Poisons

Most venoms and toxic chemicals do not harm the Kindred at all. Many snake venoms form a notable exception. Snake venoms often dissolve blood cells and body tissues. They not only inflict points of damage, they destroy Vitae, usually one Vitae per point of damage. Cobra venom also causes heart spasms. Storytellers can treat snake venom as inflicting lethal damage within several minutes of a bite. The amount of damage depends on the snake, but many cobras and African vipers routinely kill mortals with a single bite. Their blood-destroying venom should not inflict quite as much damage to Kindred (mortals are more fragile, what with their need for a metabolism), but enough to make a snakebite a bad experience. Kindred, like kine, seldom encounter deadly serpents in modern cities, but it might happen under various unusual circumstances. A tyrannical Prince might keep a terrarium of vipers for their sheer intimidation value.

Acids and other corrosive chemicals damage Kindred as easily as they damage kine. They typically inflict points of lethal damage. The amount of damage depends on the corrosiveness of the chemical and the quantity and length of exposure. Quicklime, for instance, burns away bodies rather slowly, but thoroughly, and it's available cheaply in large quantities. One lethal point every few turns adequately represents a large exposure to most corrosive industrial chemicals.

Drugs such as alcohol, marijuana and heroin affect Kindred just as they do mortals. A Kindred who wants to use a drug can either feed on an intoxicated mortal, or expend a Vitae to absorb the drug directly and suffuse it throughout his body. This capability puzzles some scientifically minded Kindred. How can a drug affect the undead when they don't have a metabolism? Especially when medications have no effect? The Lancea Sanctum and the Circle of the Crone supply the simple, rather obvious answer: It's magic.

Lancea Sanctum theologians explain in more detail. They say that God wants the Childer of Longinus to suffer the same temptations of gluttonous self-indulgence and addiction that mortals feel. The Kindred may therefore damn themselves by choice, as well as by the curse of undeath. Praise God for His terrible justice!

Electricity

By itself, electricity does little harm to the undead. Electrocution doesn't stop a Kindred's heart from beating, because it doesn't beat in the first place. Electricity doesn't interfere with brain function or nerve impulses, because vampire bodies work mystically. The heat generated by lightning or high-tension electric current can cause internal burns, however.

If a Kindred suffers some electric shock that could wound or kill a mortal, ask the player to roll the character's Stamina + Resilience. If the roll succeeds, the character suffers no damage at all unless the electricity is supernatural in origin. If the roll fails or if the electricity is supernatural, the electricity inflicts bashing damage. Assess the damage based on the strength of the current or at random. So many factors can influence the lethality of an electric shock, from the soles of a character's shoes to the humidity in the air, that any attempt to provide a "realistic" system is futile. Only in the rarest of circumstances, such as with certain magical attacks or overwhelming amounts of electricity, does a shock result in lethal or aggravated damage. These circumstances, when not detailed by specific rules, are determined by the Storyteller.

Kindred remain subject to the muscle-locking effect of electrocution, though, just like mortals. Use the system for pulling free from electrocution presented on p. 178 the **World of Darkness Rulebook**.

Extreme Pressures and Temperatures

Since vampires do not actually live, they suffer only minor discomfort from temperature and pressure extremes that would kill a mortal. For instance, Kindred cannot suffer from hypothermia or heat prostration. Being dead, they do not need to maintain a steady body temperature. Kindred can descend deep underwater and return to the surface quickly without worrying about decompression sickness ("the bends"). Gas bubbles in a Kindred's blood might cause a few aches and twinges, but they do not really harm his undead flesh. Altitude sickness means nothing to creatures that don't need to breathe.

In some of the most extreme cases, Storytellers might impose penalties of some sort for the most extreme conditions. Temperatures over 200°F might count as feeble fire (or at least set the panic of Rötschreck crawling in a character's mind). Then again, mortals routinely stick their hands into 400°F ovens without the hot air burning their skin. Prolonged exposure to freezing temperatures might force a character to expend a Vitae or two to avoid frostbite (-1 or more to Dexterity-based rolls). In the most extreme case, a Kindred could freeze solid and immobile — not harmful in itself, but eventually the character starves into torpor if she doesn't burn from exposure to daylight. The pressure at the bottom of a deep-sea trench (what sort of chronicle are you playing, anyway?) might crush an unfortunate vampire who lacks Resilience to endure it. Some fish live in those awful depths, but they have evolved to adapt to those conditions. Total vacuum (good *God*, what sort of chronicle is this?) could inflict bashing or, at most, a few points of lethal damage as blood vessels rupture. Since the undead don't need to breathe, a character could survive in a vacuum indefinitely once the pressure within his tissues drops.

DISEASE AND THE KINDRED

No mundane disease can affect the Kindred in any way. From cancer to the common cold, undeath "cures" them all and renders a character immune forever after. Kindred don't get allergies, infections or ulcers.

The Kindred do care about disease, though. A Kindred can still *spread* a disease from one mortal to another. A vampire drinks from an infected mortal, and like a mosquito carrying malaria or yellow fever, he injects the disease organism into anyone he feeds upon afterward. Diseases that are normally carried by contact between body fluids, such as HIV and other sexually transmitted diseases, prove especially likely to take permanent residence in a vampire's body. A few Kindred read about African outbreaks of ebola — a disease specifically and only spread by contact with an infected person's blood — and wonder if some African vampires have become careless.

In centuries past, the Kindred did not care much if one of their numbers became a plague-dog. Mortals got sick and died so often that no one noticed a few more victims every week. As more people went to doctors, however, the covenants all encouraged their members to avoid the diseased. Cases of doctors who became witch-hunters because of patients talking of strange people biting them convinced the Invictus and Lancea Sanctum, in particular, to declare plague-spreading a breach of the Masquerade. The rise of modern epidemiology and institutes such as the WHO and CDC increase the danger even more.

In a few cities, the Prince and Primogen execute Kindred found guilty of spreading diseases from vessel to vessel. More often, Kindred leaders settle for locking up a plague-dog until they can find a practitioner of Theban Sorcery who knows how to cleanse Kindred of disease (one of the rare occasions when Kindred deliberately seek to bring a foreign vampire to a city). Of course, they don't bother feeding the imprisoned Kindred. Let the pain of starvation be his punishment, they figure, and then let him wait in torpor until the sorcerer comes to set things right.

If one ever comes.

Reversion and Scarring

Normally, vampires revert to the state in which they were Embraced while they sleep during daylight hours. Hair cut during the course of the night grows back, a shaved five o'clock shadow returns if the Kindred was Embraced while scruffy, and minor wounds correct themselves. In some cases, however, this reversion is prevented. If a vampire suffers damage, those wounds persist until the vampire heals them.

In a few instances, a vampire might actively wish to change his appearance. Such is the case with tattoos or piercings that would normally expel the ink or push themselves out of the skin while the vampire slumbers. A few vampires even like to force their bodies to permanently exhibit a scar after a particularly significant battle or physical ordeal.

If a vampire wishes to keep a scar or other change to his body, the player must spend a Willpower point to do so. Truly severe modifications, such as permanently losing a limb or other heinous modifications cost a Willpower *dot*, and the Storyteller is the final arbiter of what constitutes the distinction.

Torpor

The ancients called sleep the brother of death. This is even more true for vampires than for mortals. Every day, the Kindred enter a sleep that mortal senses and science cannot distinguish from death. The Kindred experience it much as mortals experience sleep. The Kindred can also enter a deeper sleep, however, in which their souls come even closer to death. The Kindred call this state torpor. A vampire's daily sleep lasts a few hours, but torpor can last for centuries.

Wounding

Wounds sufficient to kill mortals send the Kindred into torpor, instead. If a vampire's rightmost Health box is occupied by a lethal wound, she enters torpor instead of dying. (Recall that sufficient bashing damage can convert to lethal damage, so a good beating with, say, baseball bats can send a Kindred into torpor.)

The duration of this torpor depends on the character's Humanity and her Blood Potency. A high Blood Potency extends the torpor's duration; so does having a low Humanity. High-Humanity vampires spend much less time in torpor than Kindred who have given most of themselves to the Beast.

To calculate the length of time a wounded Kindred spends in torpor, consult the following table. The character's Humanity score determines a base time spent in torpor. Multiply that span by the character's Blood Potency to find the total duration of the slumber.

Example: *Persephone Moore has a Blood Potency of 1 and a Humanity of 6. (She became one of the Damned quite recently, and has not had time to either increase the potency of her blood or to lose much of herself to the Beast.) A Nosferatu rival of her sire Prince Maxwell spitefully vents his frustration by clubbing Persephone into torpor. Humanity 6 gives a base duration of two weeks; multiplying this by Persephone's Blood Potency dots gives a total duration of just two weeks. At the end of that time, Persephone wakes up wondering what the hell happened.*

For contrast, the Unholy has a Blood Potency of 7 and has certainly earned her moniker with a Humanity of 2. For all her power, though, a pack of bold Lupines gives her a good thrashing. The Lupines think they kill her, but they actually leave her in torpor. Her Humanity of 2 gives a base time of 50 years. Multiplying this by her Blood Potency of 7 gives a total duration of 350 years, give or take a few. Given such long spans of time, we don't need to set an exact date for when she wakes. The point is, the Unholy stays out of circulation for a long, long time.

Zero-Humanity vampires form an important exception to this system. When they enter torpor from wounding, they sleep for an even millennium, regardless of their Blood Potency.

Humanity	Base time Spent in Torpor
10	One day
9	Two days
8	Three days
7	One week
6	Two weeks
5	One month
4	One year
3	One decade
2	Five decades
1	One century
0	One millennium

While in torpor, a wounded vampire can expend Vitae but can take no other action. His undead body still expends one Vitae per night as it tries to restore itself to its post-Embrace condition. The character can also expend Vitae to heal himself — a good idea, since otherwise the Vitae just trickles away without doing anything useful. Any damage that the vampire cannot heal remains on the character's withered body until he can rise and feed again.

If the vampire lacks sufficient reserves of Vitae to heal at least three points of the damage (whether lethal or aggravated) that sent her to torpor, that torpor lasts longer than usual. Calculate the torpor's duration as if the character's Blood Potency were one higher than it actually is.

If the character succumbs to torpor with no Vitae left and has lost all of her Health points to lethal or aggravated damage, she awakens having recovered one Health point as a result of the torpor, which she doesn't have to pay for with Vitae. In effect, the character recovers this Health point for free, as a result of the stabilizing sleep of torpor.

Example: *Duce Carter is beaten into torpor by a pack of Kindred enforcers under Solomon's command. When Duce sinks into torpor, he does so with only two Vitae in his system. Duce's Humanity is 6 and his Blood Potency is 3. Normally, this would result in a six-week torpor. Because he lacks the Vitae to properly heal himself, however, Duce's Blood Potency is treated as if it were one higher. This results in an eight-week torpor for Duce, and when he rises, the wounds from his right two Health boxes are erased — wounds recovered from the Vitae he had in his system and spent reflexively.*

Starvation

A Kindred who sleeps during the day and who has no Vitae — but who is not truly in torpor — fails to rise. All Vitae in him has been exhausted, so he has none to spend to rise the next night. For every night that passes under these circumstances, the character suffers a point of lethal damage in lieu of spending Vitae. In this state, the character is incapable of functioning at all, yet is not in torpor. This is important because this vampire does not need exceptionally potent Vitae to be roused yet — see p. 178. At this point, *any* Vitae given to him allows him to rise as normal (fed only a few Vitae, the character probably rises in a hunger frenzy). Denied any Vitae from an outside source, a starving character continues to suffer one lethal wound a night until he slips into torpor.

The character sleeps in torpor for a duration determined by the preceding chart: the base duration set by the character's Humanity, multiplied by a number one higher than the character's Blood Potency. At the torpor's end, the character awakens with only one Health point restored, as discussed previously.

Voluntary Torpor

Kindred can also enter torpor deliberately. Sometimes unlife just gets to be too much and a Kindred decides to sleep in hopes that some of her problems will be solved by the time she wakes again. Elder vampires also sometimes use torpor to reduce their Blood Potency when feeding becomes too inconvenient.

Vampires seldom enter voluntary torpor lightly. An extended torpor usually requires abandoning all responsibilities in the Kindred world and all the influence so painstakingly built in the mortal world. A Kindred might hope that his childer remain reasonably loyal and greet him with respect when he rises again. He might also hope that his centuries of experience bring him honor among other Kindred and win him at least a minor title in his covenant and city's undead community, but he cannot realistically hope to resume his old offices as if he'd never left.

Voluntary torpor lasts at least as long as the base duration set by the character's Humanity. At the end of that time, the character wakes if his player makes a successful Resolve + Composure roll. If the roll fails, the character remains in torpor for another increment of time, and so on, until the number of increments equals the Blood Potency the character had when the torpor began. At that point, he rises automatically.

Example: *Scratch finds himself on Prince Maxwell's shit list and decides to lay low for a while, seeking refuge in voluntary torpor. His Humanity is 4, so he spends at least one year in torpor. After that year, Scratch's player rolls Resolve + Composure but fails to achieve any successes. Scratch remains torpid for another year, at which point the player succeeds on the roll and Scratch is free to rise. If rolls to wake kept failing, and Scratch's Blood Potency were 5, he would rise automatically on what would be his player's fifth attempt.*

After the first increment passes, the character can also try to wake up if something disturbs his body. The character can recognize a disturbance if the player succeeds at a Wits + Auspex roll (if that Discipline is possessed) at a -2 penalty. If trouble is recognized, a Humanity roll is made for the vampire to rouse himself. If the disturbance is at night, a successful roll means the character wakes completely. During the day, the character can stay awake for one turn per success rolled. An exceptional success allows the character stay awake for the rest of the scene. The player can also make extended Humanity rolls to prolong the character's period of activity (see p. 184). The character achieves full wakefulness if the player accumulates five successes in the extended action, but the character falls asleep again if the player fails any of these rolls. (This is the same as the normal system for a character to wake up during the day, but under more challenging circumstances for rousing from voluntary torpor rather than from normal sleep.)

Note that no Vitae is spent upon waking from torpor, as it is upon waking from a day's sleep.

Staking

Finally, a vampire enters torpor when a wooden stake penetrates his heart. Only wood has this effect. Rods of metal, plastic or other substances can damage the vampire by piercing the heart, but only wood induces torpor. Kindred mystics offer a number of religious and occult theories for why wood has this power. Most Kindred simply accept it as a fact of unlife.

Driving a stake through a vampire's heart is extraordinarily difficult. The feat requires a melee or ranged attack with the stake. In combat, the attacker suffers a -4 dice penalty to strike so precisely. Then the attacker must inflict at least three points of lethal damage for the stake to actually thrust through the vampire's body and into the heart. The staked vampire immediately collapses into torpor, appearing stone dead for all that a mortal could tell.

A staked vampire remains in torpor indefinitely. The Kindred awakens only when someone or something removes the stake from his heart. An unwary mortal might remove the stake from what looks like a mummified corpse. A rat might gnaw at the stake enough to dislodge it, or termites might eat the stake away completely. Until something like this occurs, however, the vampire sleeps. Grim tales among the Kindred tell of vampires who work around Princely edicts forbidding murder and Humanity erosion by trapping their enemies with stakes through the heart and burying them in secure and secret crypts, there to sleep until the Day of Judgment.

Effects of Torpor

During torpor, a vampire's body seems utterly inert. Over the decades, it slowly shrivels in on itself until it seems like a mummified corpse. This happens more quickly if the character lacks the Vitae to heal all the damage he suffered when forced into torpor. A vampire starved into torpor looks withered already.

The vampire dreams slowly during torpor. These dreams tend to reflect the Kindred's state of mind when he entered torpor. If he slumbered willingly, his dreams remain largely peaceful, if not particularly sensible. If the Kindred entered torpor during a struggle (as is often the case), his dreams are full of wrath and terror. His mind can stay frozen on one thought or emotion for centuries. Kindred might awaken obsessed with Kindred or kine who became dust long ago.

Then there's the culture shock. Most of the world has changed more in the last century than it did in the previous thousand. Kindred who awaken from centuries of torpor often seem out of their minds, just because they are so out of touch with the modern world.

Decades or centuries of torpid dreaming scramble a Kindred's memory. Events from his past lose order. Fantasies and nightmares from dreams mix into real memories, so a vampire cannot tell which is which. Did he really hear two Primogen plotting against him — or was that just what he feared was happening? Did unbound Kindred really destroy his hated sire, or did he merely wish they had? Some Kindred write diaries and memoirs to refresh their memories in case they must endure a long torpor, but no memoir can capture everything. Some Kindred also wonder if open or hidden rivals might have found their diaries and rewritten them as part of subtle schemes to manipulate them. Other Kindred rise from torpor to find their memoirs gone, looted by savvy witch-hunters who used the notes to hunt down other Kindred — a Pyrrhic victory at best over one's enemies, and a considerable risk to one's progeny and allies. Such is the paranoia bred by the Danse Macabre.

No matter what causes torpor, a vampire still loses one Vitae per day. Any Vitae the Kindred uses to heal wounds does so in the normal order. After torpor of any length, therefore, a Kindred wakes up with no Vitae at all. Hunger frenzies are extremely likely after a vampire rises from torpor. The Storyteller may call for a Composure + Resolve roll to resist frenzy the first time the character encounters any creature upon whom she can feed.

Example: *When Solomon's bullies sent Duce to torpor, Duce had two Vitae left. Upon reaching torpor, he spent those two Vitae, thereby healing two of the lethal damage points he had suffered. That left him with no Vitae remaining in his system, so he begins shriveling at the end of the next day, when Duce would normally have spent the Vitae to sustain himself. When he rises, he is starving, but at least he has those two Health points back.*

Example: *Scratch voluntarily went into torpor to evade the Prince's wrath. As he had no wounds to heal when he did so, he had no need to immediately heal Health points, so all of his remaining Vitae went toward sustaining his body (at the normal expenditure of one point per day). Since Scratch's torpor was going to last at least a year (see the example on p. 176), he wouldn't have enough Vitae to tide him over for that complete length of time. If someone with more potent blood (see the "Forced Revival" sidebar) found him after only a few days of cold sleep and revived him, he might still have unused Vitae in his system.*

For every 25 years in torpor, a Kindred's Blood Potency drops by one dot, though never to less than 1. This decrease does not affect the length of torpor, though. The total duration of the slumber depends on the character's Blood Potency when torpor begins, no matter how the trait changes during the long sleep.

FORCED REVIVAL

Kindred can awaken early from torpor if someone feeds them sufficiently potent blood. One must force at least two Vitae into the torpid vampire's mouth. If the blood comes from a Kindred with a Blood Potency at least two dots higher than the torpid vampire's *current* Blood Potency (taking into account time already spent in torpor), the sleeping character awakens, no matter how much longer her torpor would have lasted on its own. If the vampire is fed Vitae that isn't potent enough, she remains in torpor, and the taste of blood likely permeates her dreams. In either case, blood fed to a vampire to revive her counts toward a Vinculum over her as well as potentially creating blood addition.

Blood fed to a torpid vampire that's not potent enough to rouse her can still be useful to the slumbering Kindred. The Vitae can be spent reflexively to heal wounds. Any Vitae that isn't spent to heal is exhausted at the normal rate of one for each night that follows.

Some Kindred believe that certain Theban Sorcery rituals can rouse a Kindred from torpor… or force one into the long sleep. Rumor has it that the potent blood of Lupines can also bring a vampire out of torpor early. As always, Storytellers must decide on the truth or falsehood of such legends.

Frenzy, Wassail and Rötschreck

Vampires work hard to hide the Beast Within. The politics of the Invictus and Carthians, the mysticism of the Ordo Dracul, Lancea Sanctum and the Circle of the Crone, even the bravado of the unbound — all are masks that vampires wear to hide the rage and bloodlust of the Beast, most of all from themselves. Hunger, wrath or fear, however, can weaken the Man enough that the Beast escapes restraint. Then a vampire becomes a monster and menace to every creature that crosses its path. The Kindred call this awful state frenzy.

The Nature of Frenzy

During frenzy, a vampire no longer acts according to any rational plan. The Beast doesn't think. It acts based on raw instinct, with no thought for the future or memory of the past. The Kindred no longer recognizes friends, foes or family. Any creature with blood in its veins is reduced to obstacle or prey. While in frenzy, hungry vampires try to feed without restraint from whoever is nearest. Angry vampires do anything possible to destroy the cause of their anger. Frightened vampires flee the source of their fear and kill anyone who gets in the way. They care nothing for the consequences of their actions, only for the immediate satisfaction of a primal drive.

When the Kindred refer to "frenzy," without any qualifier, they usually mean an outburst caused by anger. Kindred give special names to frenzies caused by hunger and fear. The former, they call Wassail; the latter, Rötschreck. Young Kindred who think it's pretentious to assign fancy names to ugly rampages simply speak of "hunger frenzy" and "fear frenzy."

All these forms of frenzy have certain aspects in common. A vampire who succumbs to the Beast no longer pays attention to wound penalties, except perhaps to rage even more fiercely. Injuries that would leave a sane vampire crawling on the ground don't bother a frenzying vampire a bit — the Kindred keeps fighting until he is forced into torpor or is destroyed. The vampire also becomes resistant to mental influences such as Dominate and Majesty. A frenzying Kindred routinely pushes his physical abilities to the limit, performing extraordinary feats of strength, agility and toughness. Kindred can employ their Disciplines while in frenzy, but only for the most rudimentary ends. For instance, a vampire can grow Claws of the Wild to attack prey, or use Majesty to drive people away who interfere with her flight, but she cannot command anyone using Dominate because that Discipline requires speech and a focused mind.

A vampire can slide from some kinds of frenzy to others. Yet, some forms of frenzy protect the vampire from others. Hunger frenzy is the weakest. A Wassailing vampire can be driven into a rage frenzy if he is kept from his prey, or a sufficient threat can drive him into Rötschreck. Self-preservation takes precedence over hunger, but sheer rage can overpower self-preservation if someone fights too hard to stop a fleeing vampire. While in a rage frenzy, a Kindred becomes immune to Rötschreck, but she can slide into a hunger frenzy as she guzzles the blood of a victim.

Systems for Frenzy

The Storyteller decides when a character runs the risk of frenzy. Anger can cause frenzy, but not every moment of irritation stirs the Beast. Hunger provokes the Beast, but most of the time characters can feed without going berserk and killing their vessels. Rötschreck — the "Red Fear" — usually occurs only when Kindred face the two forces most able to destroy them, fire and sunlight. Other sources of fear seldom provoke frenzy, though it can happen, as with meeting a new vampire of higher Blood Potency for the first time. These guidelines are vague because the relative strength of Man and Beast can fluctuate for many reasons. One time, a character might shrug off an extreme provocation. Another time, the Kindred might feel a weight of accumulated frustration or anxiety and lose control over a small matter. We offer examples of circumstances that can trigger frenzies, and how hard they might be to resist, but the Storyteller has final say.

In rules terms, frenzy has the following effects on a character:

• A frenzying vampire ignores wound penalties to dice pools, until wounds become severe enough to render the character torpid.

• All attempts to influence the frenzying character's mind, by Dominate, Majesty or other means, take place at a -2 dice penalty, while rolls for the character to resist or throw off mental influence receive a +2 dice bonus.

• Of course, a frenzying character cannot perform any action that requires much thought.

• The character receives one extra die for any Physical Attribute roll. The Beast goes all-out, all the time, and its blinding rage shuts out all distractions and doubts.

Resisting Frenzy

Resisting frenzy is an extended action. Whatever the cause of frenzy, Kindred may try to resist the Beast and maintain control. When a character is on the verge of frenzy, the player rolls Resolve + Composure. If any successes are achieved, the character resists the frenzy for one turn per success. At the end of those turns, the player rolls again in hopes of winning a few turns more of self-control for the character. If the player can accumulate a certain number of successes, the Beast subsides and the character completely avoids the frenzy. If any of the rolls fail, however, the character goes berserk and spends the rest of the scene in frenzy. If the player suffers a dramatic failure on a roll, the character stays in frenzy for as long as the Storyteller thinks is appropriate. The character also gains a derangement related to whatever caused the frenzy (see p. 186).

The greater the provocation to the character, the more successes the player must accumulate. Five successes suffice for most frenzies. Higher numbers represent the most extreme humiliation or peril to the vampire's unlife. The Storyteller may also impose bonuses or penalties to Resolve + Composure dice pools to reflect a trigger that's especially easy or hard to resist.

The rule doesn't change any, but it bears repeating: A Willpower point earns a character three extra dice on the roll to resist frenzy, as it does with most other rolls.

Anger Frenzies

Here are some typical events that can spark an anger frenzy, with sample numbers of successes needed to resist them, or modifiers to the Resolve + Composure dice pool.

Harassed by a panhandler	2 successes
Idiot scrapes your new car	2 successes
Insulted in public	3 successes
Hours of frustration and delay	3 successes
Reviled by someone you dislike	5 successes
Betrayed by a partner in a deal	5 successes
Shot by a mugger	5 successes
Loved one in danger	5 successes
Betrayed by someone you love	7 successes
Lose everything you own	7 successes
Loved one slain	10 successes
Reviled and humiliated by someone you love	10 successes
Provocation aligns with your Virtue or Vice	±2 dice
Provocation attacks your Virtue or Vice	±2 dice
Hungry	-1 die
Starving	-2 dice

Virtues and Vices can work either way. Someone who gains strength and purpose from Justice, for instance, might feel extra anger at some crime that she cannot correct, but she could resist the Beast more effectively when someone takes her to task and she knows that person is in the right. Someone beset by Pride might have extra trouble dealing with humiliation, but he could make an extra effort not to embarrass himself in other cases. The Storyteller decides when a Virtue or Vice can influence the difficulty of the Resolve + Composure roll.

Kindred also find it harder to resist the Beast when hunger adds to rage. A hungry character, defined as one who has no more than four Vitae in her system, suffers a -1 die penalty to Resolve + Composure rolls. A starving character, defined as having only one or no Vitae left, suffers a -2 penalty. These penalties are not cumulative with each other. You do not suffer a -3 dice penalty for being both starving and hungry.

Hunger Frenzies

Wassail can occur whenever a character feels hungry and encounters blood. Hunger frenzies are most dangerous when a character actually feeds. Kindred who care about their vessels adopt various strategies to reduce the danger to their loved ones, such as never letting themselves become too hungry, or having a favored vessel drain blood into a bowl instead of submitting to the Kiss. Few modifiers apply to hunger frenzies, and loss of control is less likely once a character has imbibed blood. See the foregoing for the definition of "hungry" and "starving" for vampires.

Sight or smell of blood (when hungry)	2 successes
First taste of blood (when hungry)	3 successes
Sight or smell of blood (when starving)	4 successes
First taste of blood (when starving)	5 successes
Has tasted vampire blood before	-1 die
Hungry	-1 die
Starving	-2 dice
Addicted to vampire blood	-2 dice

Fear Frenzies

In some ways, the undead have less to fear than mortals do. Vampires are hard to kill, and they can hope to make up for any minor loss, given time. Injuries are also more likely to anger a Kindred than frighten him.

Sunlight and fire, however, provoke a soul-deep terror among the Kindred. The Beast knows that these forces can cause its destruction. It instinctively flees sunlight and fire in a blind panic. While in Rötschreck, a vampire wants to do nothing but run away and hide, and she lashes out at anyone in her way. If a character cannot escape the cause of her fear frenzy, she might gain a derangement from excess terror.

Exposure to small amounts of sunlight or fire, at a safe distance or under the character's control, hardly ever provokes Rötschreck. A vampire might step away from a person lighting a cigarette, and she might prefer to stand well back from a screened-in fire in a fireplace, but she doesn't panic. Nor does a TV or movie image of a sunny day rouse her Beast… much. If someone jabs a lit cigarette at the character or a flashbulb goes off in her face, however, it might be a different matter.

Nothing about a character's personality has much effect on resisting Rötschreck. It's the quantity of fire or sunlight, or the degree of control, that makes resisting a fear frenzy more or less difficult.

Lighting a cigarette	1 success
Sight of a torch	2 successes
Flashbulb in the face	3 successes
Bonfire	4 successes
Burning building	5 successes
Obscured sunlight	7 successes
Direct sunlight	10 successes
Fire/sunlight at a safe distance	+2 dice
Surprised by fire/light	-1 die
Surrounded by fire/light, but not immediately harmed	-1 die
Burned by fire/sunlight	-3 dice

Roleplaying Frenzy

A frenzied character ignores all morals or loyalties in her blind compulsion to destroy her enemy, slake her thirst or escape sunlight or fire. She attacks friends, family members, lovers and even — most to the point — other players' characters if they get in her way. For instance, a vampire raging in anger frenzy prefers to attack the person who rouses her ire, but she just as readily tries to kill any friends if the enemy is not available as a target for some reason. The character probably feels utter horror when she emerges from her frenzy to find that she slaughtered her own mother, but the Beast does not know or care about such things. Atrocities committed during frenzy often lead to degeneration checks (p. 182) as a character tries to deal with remorse. Repeated frenzies can certainly grind down a vampire's Humanity.

Some players might not want to roleplay frenzy, but the Beast is part of being a vampire. Storytellers should encourage players to portray the frenzy in its full, brutal horror. If they cannot, the Storyteller should take control of a character and decide on her actions until the frenzy ends.

If a player wants, he can spend a Willpower point for a character in the throes of frenzy. Doing so permits the player to control one of the character's actions for one turn. In this way, a frenzying

vampire might manage to give her soon-to-be victim a chance to run away, or a person who gave offense a chance to make a hasty apology. This moment of control does not actually avert the frenzy, but the changing circumstances might redirect the focus of the character's rage. For instance, the frenzying character might throw the furniture around instead of ripping apart the mortal whose injudicious word uncorked several nights of building frustration. If a player ever has a character perform an action that the Storyteller thinks just isn't possible or appropriate for a frenzying character, the Storyteller can rule that the character expended a Willpower point to take that action.

The Storyteller decides how long a frenzy lasts. One scene is usually long enough, but keep in mind that a scene is a very flexible unit of time. A character trapped alone, or running wildly through empty streets, might not calm down for hours. A character who meant to take "just a sip" from her boyfriend and drank him dry instead might recover just in time to hear his death-rattle… and have a chance to Embrace him instead of letting him die a true death. Reducing a Kindred to torpor always ends frenzy.

Riding the Wave

Under some circumstances, characters might want to frenzy on purpose. For all the horror of what a character might do in frenzy, succumbing to the Beast carries power. The great difficulty lies in controlling one's actions so that the Beast achieves something useful. Young Kindred call such a temporary, negotiated surrender to the Beast riding the wave. Older Kindred call it damnable foolishness.

If a character wants to ride the wave, the player makes Resolve + Composure rolls and tries to accumulate successes as an extended action, just like fighting back frenzy. In this case, however, the vampire tries to goad the Beast while supplying it with a target of the Man's choice. The player also expends a Willpower point for trying to direct the frenzy in advance. Riding the wave always requires accumulating at least five successes. The Storyteller may ask for more, or modify the Resolve + Composure rolls depending on how well the desired task accords with the character's personality or existing emotions. For instance, a character probably has little trouble deliberately frenzying when he faces the Lupine that murdered two of his Kindred allies, his virtue is Justice, and his vice is Wrath. On the other hand, frenzying so he might have a better chance to climb up a building almost certainly doesn't work. If the player fails one of the Resolve + Composure rolls, the character falls into an undirected frenzy.

Riding the wave allows a character to end the frenzy at the point of his choice, rather than suffering its passions until the Beast rages itself to exhaustion. Note that if a character riding the wave faces other stimuli that might cause a frenzy, he must still deal with those stimuli as normal after ending the intended frenzy, quite possibly frenzying again.

A character who tries to ride the wave multiple times in a single night suffers a cumulative -1 penalty to Resolve + Composure dice pools for each time after the first time that he attempts to direct frenzy (regardless of whether or not he was successful at those attempts).

Example: *Loki faces two unbound Kindred who taunt him for being the Prince's lapdog. He feels the turmoil of frenzy deep inside him, but he knows that he can't lose himself completely to the Beast. Loki decides to ride the wave, teaching these punks a lesson but not wanting to relinquish control utterly. His player spends a Willpower point and makes a Resolve + Composure roll, gaining two successes. The next turn, Loki's player rolls again as the jeers of the unbound continue, this time accumulating three successes for a total of five. Loki directs his rage toward the unaligned Kindred, fighting like a Biblical terror and suffering no wound penalties for the damage they inflict on him and gaining an extra die to his attacks. After he sends them fleeing in bloody fear, he coaxes the Beast into calmness, rather than allowing it to continue unabated until it exhausts itself.*

Humanity

The change from life to undeath affects more than a person's body. It changes the soul. A Kindred shares his human consciousness with a force completely opposite to humanity — a thing devoid of reason, conscience or any emotions except hunger and rage. Kindred call it the Beast.

The presence of the Beast changes the very nature of morality for vampires. The Kindred can pretend to be human, but they are not. Even the most evil and monstrous mortal does not have a Beast. A vampire's existence is a constant struggle between the Man, the aspect of a Kindred that can make moral choices, and the Beast, which cannot.

The Beast follows a simple plan: Hunt. Kill. Feed. Sleep. Repeat. It feels no pity, only thirst for blood. It cannot even speak.

The Man consists of everything that resists the Beast: rational thought, a conscience, and most of all the ability to relate to other people. The Beast does not understand what other people think or feel, and it doesn't care. They are just food.

When a Kindred treats other people as prey or tools or inconvenient obstacles, the Man weakens. When Kindred make an effort to interact with mortals as fellow people, to care about their lives and happiness, the Beast… waits. The slide toward the Beast is easy. It comes naturally for creatures that must take blood from the living to survive. Strengthening the Man is very difficult. Most vampires slowly degenerate. Mentally, they become less and less human, more callous and brutal.

Most Kindred stabilize as monsters with some degree of self-control. They give the Beast some of what it wants and fight it just enough to preserve their existence. The Beast doesn't know how to hide the bodies; the Man does. These vampires hunt and feed and sometimes kill, but they try not to get caught.

Some Kindred cannot strike that balance. Each crime makes the next one easier. They no longer care if they kill their vessels. They show less discretion in who they feed upon, where or how. They might start… playing with their food. When the Beast nears total ascendance, the Man becomes little more than a psychological appendage, adding human perversity and cruelty to the Beast's predation. Even that remnant of mortality goes in time, and the vampire becomes a killing machine as mindless and ruthless as a shark that scents blood in the water. The vampire retains just enough self-preservation to hide from the sun, flee fire and fight back when attacked.

The Kindred call such creatures draugr, from an old Norse word for a reanimated corpse that viciously stalks and kills its living relations. A draugr leaves a trail of corpses and public attacks that attract mortal attention. Even bitter enemies put aside their struggles and cooperate to stop a draugr before it breaks the Masquerade beyond repair.

ISOLATION AND HUMANITY

The rules for degeneration checks take into account Kindred who actively encounter other individuals, and therefore have opportunities to transgress against them. Storytellers are certainly within their rights, however, to call for degeneration checks for Kindred who spend too much time in solitude, for their connection to humanity (and Humanity) can easily atrophy. No hard-and-fast system exists, but a good guideline can be obtained by subtracting the Kindred's Humanity from 11. Every time the resulting number of years passes in a game without the character making any significant human or Kindred contact, the player must make a degeneration check.

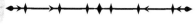

Humanity as Morality

In rules terms, a trait called Humanity represents the balance of power between the Man and the Beast. Humanity is the specific form that the general Morality trait takes for vampires. The trait measures the connection a Kindred feels to her leftover mortal feelings and to her capacity to empathize with other beings. The lower a character's Humanity goes, the less she cares and the more brutally she tends to act.

Humanity uses the same order of sins presented in the **World of Darkness Rulebook** (which is reproduced here for your

convenience). Just as with mortals, when an undead character performs an act that carries an equal or lower rating than his Humanity, the player rolls a certain number of dice to find out whether the character suffers moral degeneration. If the roll succeeds, the character manages to feel shame, regret or at least some human response. If the roll fails, the character feels nothing except satisfaction at getting what he wanted… and a little more of the Man slips away and the character has less with which to fight the Beast in the future. His Humanity drops by one. For what it's worth, the threshold for further moral crises drops too, so the player might not need to roll for degeneration as often — assuming the character can resist committing more heinous acts in the future.

As a character's Humanity degrades, he grows less concerned with the world, yielding ever more to the Beast. He becomes capable of virtually any depraved act against another person. When Humanity is lost because of a sin the character committed, roll the character's new Humanity as a dice pool. If the roll succeeds, the Kindred finds some kind of bulwark of sanity at his new level of Humanity. If the roll fails, a derangement manifests in the character's mind. Derangements are mental and emotional "scars," in this case brought on by the character's stress, grief or even remorselessness over acts performed. Derangements are detailed at length on p. 186.

Roll Results

When making a degeneration roll use only the dice pool associated with the sin committed. Likewise, when rolling Humanity to check for a derangement, do not add other Attributes or traits. You may *not* spend Willpower to gain a +3 modifier on either kind of roll, though other situational bonuses or penalties may apply (see below).

Dramatic Failure: Not possible on either kind of roll. At no point is a chance roll made.

Failure: On a degeneration roll, your character loses the struggle to maintain his standards of morality when faced with the reality of his sin. He loses one dot of Humanity. On a Humanity roll, he gains a derangement.

Success: Your character emerges from his crisis of conscience with his sense of right and wrong intact. His Humanity is unchanged, and he remains as sane as before.

Exceptional Success: Your character re-dedicates himself to his convictions in the wake of his sin, driven by remorse and horror at the deeds he has committed. Not only does his Humanity remain unchanged on a degeneration roll, he gains a point of Willpower (which cannot exceed his Willpower dots). No special bonuses are gained for an exceptional Humanity roll when testing for derangement.

Resisting Degeneration

Storytellers do not have to leave resisting degeneration as nothing but a straight dice roll. Ask the player to describe how the character feels about her sin, and what she intends to do about of it.

Short answers that don't suggest much thought, like, "My character feels real bad about doing that," receive an unmodified dice roll. So do defensive answers, such as, "Well, he was

HUMANITY AND SINS		
Humanity	Threshold Sin	Dice Rolled
10	Selfish thoughts (e.g., hurting someone's feelings)	Roll 5 dice
9	Minor selfish acts (e.g., cheating on taxes)	Roll 5 dice
8	Injury to another, accidental or otherwise (e.g., physical conflict)	Roll 4 dice
7	Petty theft (e.g., shoplifting)	Roll 4 dice
6	Grand theft (e.g., burglary)	Roll 3 dice
5	Intentional mass-property damage (e.g., arson)	Roll 3 dice
4	Impassioned crime (e.g., manslaughter)	Roll 3 dice
3	Planned crime (e.g., murder)	Roll 2 dice
2	Casual/callous crime (e.g., torture, serial murder)	Roll 2 dice
1	Utter perversion, heinous acts (e.g., combined rape, torture and murder; mass murder)	Roll 2 dice

asking for me to beat him up, mouthing off like that." At least the character tries to rationalize her actions. It isn't a great example of humanity at its *best*, but it's still very human.

Answers that show the character engages in extravagant but cost-free contrition, such as, "I return to my haven and scourge myself until dawn," don't quite pass muster. If you want to encourage that sort of melodrama, give the player a +1 bonus on the degeneration roll (but not the Humanity roll). If you think the character is lying to herself, don't give the bonus at all.

Serious answers that show the character engages in some soul-searching or an attempt to do better in the future could receive a +1 die bonus to the degeneration roll. For instance, one character might go to her sire and ask how she can better resist the Beast when she's angry, because she hates the results when she loses control. Another might pray for forgiveness. (Don't reward that, though, unless the player has established the character's religious feeling, or she does a good job of roleplaying the crisis that leads the character to a faith previously neglected or scorned.)

Attempts to find some good or at least necessity in the character's actions might be worth a +1 bonus to the degeneration roll. "Sure, killing that guy was wrong… but the way he beat his girlfriend? Eventually, he probably would have killed her, and she didn't deserve that. Better that he died than she did." Or: "I tried every other way to stop that journalist from running the story, but the bribes, threats, Dominate attempts and schemes to discredit him all failed. He had to die to protect the Masquerade. I feel horrible about it, but how many people would die if mortals found out about the Kindred? He would have started a war."

At most, a player should receive a +2 dice bonus to a degeneration roll, when his character shows deep regret and acts on it. Does the character try to make up for his sin? The character could apologize to someone he injured or secretly try to help the family of someone he killed in a Beast-driven rage. Anyone can "feel sorry," but acting on regret is something special. Of course, the very acts that bring him into contact with people he tries to help may endanger the Masquerade… or enemies might threaten those people to extort concessions from your character… or he might unintentionally hurt them himself. The Damned seldom find it easy to atone for what they've done.

At the other extreme, a player might say his character feels no remorse at all. She intended to commit the sin, enjoyed it and would do it again. In that case, you might assess a -1 penalty to the degeneration roll. Such a Kindred doesn't even try to resist the selfishness that's so characteristic of the Beast. Don't assess this penalty to a player rolling only one die for a degeneration check — the fact that the character's Humanity is so low that she has only one die available for the check already signifies that she's beyond caring and remorse.

Note that modifiers here apply to degeneration rolls alone, not to Humanity rolls to determine if derangements are gained.

Degeneration and Vices

The transformation from mortal to undead does not excuse a character from suffering his Vice as his Humanity drops. Characters who want to retain their Humanity need to resist their Vices as well as the Beast. Giving in to Vices can speed degeneration by eroding the self-control that a Kindred needs to fight the Beast. The lower a character's Humanity drops, the more often he feels tempted by his Vice.

At first glance, this would seem to put all Kindred on an accelerating death-spiral. Less Humanity means a more prominent Beast, which means more sins, which eventually means still less Humanity and an even more recalcitrant Beast.

That's not actually true, because a character can sink below the level of his Vice. A Vice drives a character to do something bad, but not the worst thing possible. A lecher might feel driven by lust to seduce, but he doesn't have to commit rape. An avaricious money-grubber might have trouble passing up a crooked business deal, but she doesn't have to rob banks. At low Humanity, the Kindred can find many ways to indulge his Vice without committing the most heinous acts. For instance, a Kindred who feels his pride insulted doesn't have to murder the offender. He might satisfy his pride by Dominating the offender into making a fool of himself, use Majesty to turn other people against him or simply spy on him under cover of Obfuscate to learn damaging secrets for blackmail or humiliation. These are all sleazy, selfish acts — but not as bad as murder (probably). Make no mistake, though: Kindred who stabilize at a low Humanity become deeply unpleasant characters.

Degeneration and Derangements

Derangements usually make it harder for characters to retain Humanity. Some derangements can cause characters to lash out in wild fury under certain circumstances, or make them believe they face deadly danger when they do not. Such outbursts can lead a Kindred to commit acts he later regrets — or not, resulting in Humanity loss.

On the other hand, some derangements can help preserve Humanity if a character genuinely cannot understand the significance of his acts. He might not realize what he actually did. For instance, the player of a paranoid vampire who believes that all banks are part of a Ventrue conspiracy might receive a bonus to any degeneration rolls that happen because of assaults on banks or bankers. The vampire thinks a greater good justifies his acts.

Players and Storytellers should remember, however, that derangements are expressly disadvantages that always cause more harm than good. Storytellers should allow a derangement-based bonus to Humanity checks only if a player has steadfastly roleplayed the disadvantages of madness — and then only in very specific cases where the character's delusions apply. At best, madness helps a character stabilize at a low Humanity, as a last-ditch attempt by the Man to protect itself from the Beast. Indeed, a character doesn't get "better," he simply mires himself ever deeper in insanity.

Regaining Humanity

Kindred who make a deep and prolonged effort can regain lost Humanity or even become more ethical creatures than they were in life. It isn't easy, though.

In rules terms, a player can spend experience points to buy dots of Humanity for her character. In story terms, the character must do something to show that he really tries to become a better person and more able to resist the Beast (see p. 92 of the **World of Darkness Rulebook**). If the player announces her intent to buy Humanity for her character, the Storyteller can examine the character's recent actions. Has he tried to atone for past crimes? Has he tried to avoid committing more sins? Has he resisted his Vice and upheld his Virtue, even when he cannot harvest Willpower? Has the character associated with mortals and cultivated relationships with them? If the character genuinely tries to act more human, the Storyteller should certainly permit the purchase.

Why demand an experience-point cost for an increased Humanity when characters lose the trait so easily? Shouldn't highly moral acts receive an immediate reward of restored Humanity?

Sorry, no. One moment of grace does not reverse the habits built through years, perhaps centuries, of abuse. Enduring gains against the Beast require a heroic struggle that never fully ends. Note that this contradicts statements made about regaining lost Morality for free in the **World of Darkness Rulebook**. This contradiction is intentional. Humanity is so central to the themes of **Vampire: The Requiem** that we want to reinforce characters' dangerous footing on the path of Humanity by being that much more stringent with the rules.

Example: *Persephone feeds from a vessel and is unable to stop herself, accidentally taking too much Vitae and killing her victim. Her Humanity is 7, so this bloody transgression causes her to test for degeneration. This amounts to "manslaughter," so Persephone's player rolls three dice, achieving no successes. Her Humanity drops to 6.*

*Persephone's player then rolls six dice (because her new Humanity is 6) for her Humanity roll, to see if she gains a derangement. Again, the player rolls no successes. The player and the Storyteller confer for a bit, deciding that the mild derangement narcissism (see the **World of Darkness Rulebook**, p. 97) is appropriate here. They come up with the rationale that Persephone just didn't care about the vessel and, indeed, that he did the world a good thing by dying so that Persephone might see her own desires through. Remember, this is what Persephone thinks, not the objective truth. That's why it's a derangement!*

The player writes "narcissism" on the character sheet next to Persephone's Humanity of 6. When and if the player buys Humanity back up to 7 with experience points, Persephone overcomes her narcissism derangement. Yet if her Humanity continues to drop, she might develop a more severe ailment, or even manifest some other type of derangement.

Game Effects of Humanity

Why struggle against the Beast? Why not compromise with the Beast and one's own desires and stabilize as a callous but self-controlled monster?

Many Kindred accept that logic. They sacrifice more than abstract ethics when they compromise with the Beast, though. Preserving Humanity offers tangible benefits. The more a vampire cultivates mortal feelings and ethics, the less tightly the curse of undeath binds him, at least in some ways.

Daytime Activity

The Kindred have trouble staying awake during the day. The lower a character's Humanity score, the harder it is to be active.

If a character wants to stay awake when the sun rises, the player rolls a dice pool of the character's Humanity. The character resists sleep for one turn per success rolled. Exceptional success helps the character stay awake for the rest of the scene. If a vampire tries to remain active for an entire day, the Storyteller can make the effort an extended action and require the player to accumulate five successes, though a failure at any point means the character falls asleep despite his intentions. A vampire might remain active during the day to undertake extensive research, to perform a lengthy ritual or to keep a vigil or to stand guard. Remaining active for a whole day doesn't preclude the normal Vitae cost for "waking" that night. In this case, the Vitae is spent for the vampire to continue functioning for the remainder of the night.

A Kindred can also try to wake up during the day if something disturbs her sleep. The player rolls Wits (+ Auspex, if the character has that Discipline) to determine if the sleeping vampire notices the disturbance. If the roll succeeds, the player makes the above Humanity roll to find out if the character can force herself awake. Rousing from sleep during the day also costs a Vitae, regardless of how long the character remains active thereafter. (Staying active during the day without ever having slept costs no Vitae.) If a vampire is roused from sleep during the day, a Vitae is spent for her to be active, and if she resumes sleep thereafter, another Vitae is spent that evening for her to rise for the whole night.

A Kindred has trouble putting forth her full effort when the Beast's instincts tell her to sleep. While a Kindred acts during the day — whether having remained active since the night before or having been awoken from slumber — dice pools for any task cannot exceed the character's Humanity dots. For example, Solomon stays up well into the day to puzzle out a few clues to a threat against his Requiem. Normally, Solomon's Intelligence + Investigation dice pool is seven, but since his Humanity is only 4, only four dice can be used in the Investigation roll.

Relating to Mortals

The more human a vampire feels, the more human he can act. Every second, mortals send and receive tiny cues that they pay attention to each other, that they care and respond — that they're alive. They look at each other's faces, mimic each other's flickers of expression, shift their weight when another person does so, nod slightly as another person talks. The Man does all that, the Beast doesn't. A Kindred with low Humanity can put great effort into acting like a living person. He can force himself to breathe and remind himself to blink now and then… but he can't fake that subtle, unconscious dance of nonverbal interaction. Mortals soon pick up on this. They cannot consciously spot the problem, but their instincts tell them that something is *very wrong* and they should *get away*. They sense the predator behind the human mask.

Kindred can suffuse their flesh with Vitae to look more alive. Vampires with high Humanity do so almost reflexively to preserve the illusion for themselves that they are still people, not monsters. Low-Humanity vampires do so less often and achieve less lifelike results. As the Man weakens, the Kindred tend to look paler and more corpselike.

When a Kindred interacts with people other than vampires, a player may use no more dice in Empathy, Persuasion or Socialize pools than his character has Humanity dots. For instance, if a character has a Humanity of 5, his player cannot roll more than five dice when attempting to use Wits + Empathy on a mortal, no matter how high the character's Wits and Empathy scores might be. This limitation does not apply to Discipline powers that call for Empathy, Persuasion or Socialize in their dice pools, as these powers are supernatural in effect and thus outside the normal realm of experience governed by Humanity.

If a situation imposes penalties on a dice pool, assess the penalties after the Humanity limit is applied. Continuing the example from above, if the character suffers a -2 dice penalty on his Wits + Empathy pool, the player rolls three dice. Bonuses cannot raise a player's dice pool over his character's Humanity limit, so add them before comparing a pool to a character's Humanity.

The subtle repulsion that mortals feel toward low-Humanity Kindred does not influence a character's actual Presence score. Kindred look different than they did when their Humanity was higher, but that change can be subtle. Mortals may perceive a low-Presence Kindred as bestial, while a high-Presence Kindred could have a deadly, frightening taint. The warmth that once attracted the eye chills to a reptilian fascination. Mortals who try to recount the look of a low-Humanity Kindred might describe an image quite different from the vampire's actual appearance, as unconscious fear shades their memory. Even someone captivated by a good-looking, low-Humanity Kindred might use phrases like "deadly beauty."

Summary: The Descent

Humanity tends to drop. All Kindred must face this stark, unavoidable truth. Their existence as predators forces them to commit abhorrent acts, if not deliberately, then when the Beast overpowers them. A Kindred might begin his unlife vowing that he shall never succumb to the Beast. Well, he shall never succumb to the Beast and not feel bad about it afterward. As the years and decades pass, Kindred find it hard to muster the same revulsion to a crime they have committed many times before. Humanity wears away from sheer weariness. High moral codes bend, then break, and are forgotten in time.

Kindred tend to live down to their Humanity. As the trait drops, less and less seems objectionable. What once caused horrified repentance seems expedient — maybe even thrilling. That way, however, leads to destruction.

So how can a Kindred survive the Requiem? How can he preserve some shred of human conscience when the Beast never tires? What limit can he set to his own monstrosity?

The characters must answer that question for themselves. That's what **Vampire: The Requiem** is all about.

Humanity 10-8

Kindred with Humanity scores this high can seem "more human than human." Neonates might recoil from their own monstrosity and take up ethical codes stricter than any they followed in life. They usually try to feed only from animals or seek other alternatives to victimizing mortals, and feed as little

as possible in any case. They don't have to act preachy or passively accept everything that unlife and their fellow Kindred throw at them, but they must work hard to avoid harming anyone else and to atone for any sin they commit. Interaction with mortals often matters a great deal to such Kindred, as interacting with the living helps them remember what life was like. They can also pass for mortal almost without effort.

Few mortals can maintain such high ethical standards, and even fewer Kindred succeed for long. A vampire eventually loses control and kills someone, and then kills again. Kindred harden themselves to this awful truth or destroy themselves to prevent further harm to others. Few Kindred find reason to both continue their existence and remain this moral.

Older, more jaded (or realistic) Kindred often find highly humane vampires insufferably naïve. They take dour satisfaction in the thought that the whelps will learn better, just as they did. Some elders are not above foisting "lessons" in callousness, selfishness or deceit on a neonate who thinks he can be a "good vampire."

Humanity 7-6

At this Humanity, Kindred have ethical standards like those of most mortals. They feel that killing, theft and cruelty are wrong, but they don't go all weepy if they shade the truth a little, hit someone who tried to hit them first, or take opportunities for a little fun that don't really hurt anyone else. Such a character has a Vice that she probably indulges in small ways with only minimal regrets. These Kindred can still easily pass for mortal, and they probably have mortal acquaintances.

Humanity 5

It's a tough world, and Kindred with this Humanity score accept that they need some toughness as well. Such characters can recognize and reject deliberate atrocities… but shit happens. If some happens to them, they throw it right back. Why should they act better than anyone else?

At this Humanity, a Kindred starts to show the eerie unpleasantness that puts mortals on their guard. A skilled dissembler can still persuade mortals to ignore their instincts, though.

Humanity 4

Most Kindred eventually stabilize at or around this Humanity. Characters with Humanity 4 become genuinely callous and selfish. Murder no longer shocks them. Violence, theft, treachery, lies — these are all just tools to help a Kindred get what he wants, to gain power and to protect his all-important self. Expedience becomes sufficient justification for nearly anything. A character suffers from his Vice and indulges it with little restraint. He can still recognize the practical, legal consequences if the mortal world discovers his crimes, however, so he takes care to hide his offenses.

Such a low-Humanity Kindred has a distinctly corpselike appearance, though makeup can compensate. Beauty carries a predatory taint or shows the bland, sterile attractiveness of a manikin. Only the inability to conceive of such a thing keeps mortals from recognizing the character as a walking, talking cadaver.

Humanity 3-2

A vampire does whatever he can get away with. Only the most remarkable sadism or perversion can bother Kindred with such a low Humanity… or at least seem too dangerous to justify the pleasure they would bring. All other creatures are tools, toys or food. Anyone who says otherwise has proved he is too stupid to deserve consideration. A character this inhumane feels the pull of such a potent Vice, on top of the Beast and his own ruthlessness, that he barely qualifies as sane.

No amount of dissembling can help such a character pass for human for long. Mortals know within minutes that they are in the presence of a monster, even if they don't realize what kind.

Humanity 1

Forget sanity — at this Humanity, a Kindred can barely function as a sentient being. Little except a deranged obsession or direct threat to existence can focus the vampire's mind against the hungers of the Beast and the drive of an overwhelming Vice. The character even has trouble mustering the cunning needed to hide her crimes and debauches from mortal authorities or other Kindred. Rotting corpses strewn about a gore-spattered haven is a perfectly typical setting for such degenerate vampire. Mortals instantly recognize the Kindred as a monster whom they should flee, or at least a psychopath in the last stages of mental disintegration.

Humanity 0

Hunt. Kill. Feed. Sleep. Repeat.

At Humanity 0, a character possesses no shred of free will and cannot be played any longer. From this final degeneration, there is no return.

Derangements

The human mind has its limits. People retreat into madness when they can no longer cope with extreme guilt, grief, terror or conflicting demands. A person might seek an illusion of self-control through elaborate private rituals, fantasies of power or emotional fixations. In more severe cases, the mind succumbs to stress, crumbling and losing nearly all contact with reality.

Kindred suffer from derangements even more often than mortals do in the World of Darkness, and no wonder. Their entire existence is one long battle between a human conscience and the drives of the Beast. Many neonates still think of themselves as mostly human, but they must feed upon mortal blood to survive. How can they commit assault — potentially murderous assault — night after night and still think of themselves as reasonably good people? As the decades pass, Kindred face other grief and traumas. Either they abandon all the people they love, or they watch them age and die. Society itself changes. What mortals once found unthinkable becomes accepted without question, and the old standards become quaint, rustic or crude. Kindred can also suffer more specific horrors. They include the stark terror of Rötschreck or killing loved ones during frenzy. Most insidious of all, the Danse Macabre takes its own slow toll. As Kindred enmesh themselves in the endless struggle for power, they can trust fewer and fewer of their fellows. Other people are the greatest of all reality checks. Denied any sort of healthy emotional connection to other people, Kindred lose themselves in their own thoughts and fears.

Ghouls are also prone to derangements. They love masters who regard them as slaves. They must move between a secret, supernatural world and mundane society. They are tainted with undeath while they yet live. Of *course* their situation can drive them crazy.

Gaining Derangements

Undead characters can fall into madness through several methods. Some are automatic. Others are largely a matter of the Storyteller's discretion. We have mentioned some triggers for madness elsewhere, but include them here for your convenience.

• **Failures and Dramatic Failures:** The character gains a derangement if the player fails a degeneration roll and a Humanity roll; or if he suffers a dramatic failure on a Resolve + Composure roll to resist frenzy, Rötschreck or Wassail. The Storyteller chooses a derangement that has some connection to the situation that leads to the roll.

Example: *A Kindred who suffers an extreme Rötschreck (the player gets a dramatic failure on the Resolve + Composure roll) incurs a permanent phobia about fire. He tries to prevent the slightest chance of any flame coming near. He checks power cords every half-hour to make sure that they aren't overheating, and searches through his haven to make sure no one left an oily rag anywhere. He demands that known smokers turn out their pockets to prove that they aren't carrying matches or lighters. He might not even ride in a car with a working cigarette lighter.*

• **Extreme Pain, Frustration or Horror:** Truly shocking events can topple a character's reason. Examples include killing loved ones in frenzy, a long period of torture by a witch-hunter, or (for elders) perhaps seeing centuries of work and scheming suddenly crash into ruin. Under such circumstances, the Storyteller may ask the player to roll the character's Resolve + Composure (at whatever penalty seems appropriate) to avoid a derangement.

• **Very Long Torpor:** Kindred who spend decades or centuries asleep wake up with confused minds. Sometimes a Kindred's mind clears, sometimes it doesn't. Very long torpor is not common among players' characters in most chronicles, so the Storyteller can use such a penalty to justify a crazed elder without worrying about dice rolls.

• **Impossible Conflicts:** Some Kindred find themselves under Vinculums to extremely cruel regnants. This condition can create a tug-of-war between love and hate that tears a subject's mind apart. Ghouls with loathsome or abusive domitors may also suffer derangements.

Roleplaying Derangements

Derangements present a great challenge to players. Most sane people have difficulty portraying crazy people; more often, the result is a giggle-producing caricature. Real mental illness isn't funny. The mildest forms can annoy other people. More severe cases can rip one's heart out with pity. Full-blown psychosis, however, can be scary as hell.

Nor are crazy people happy in their madness. Derangements are an attempt to deal with pain, but they often cause as much suffering as their root cause ever did. More often than not, insane people are desperately unhappy and would like to end their madness but don't know how.

The actions of the deranged often make no sense to other people, but they make sense to the subject himself. Other people don't see the reasons for the madman's behavior. Sometimes you can tell what "missing information" explains erratic behavior. When a schizophrenic rages against unseen presences, well, the hallucinations are plenty visible to him. Other times, the reason lies in a system of associations that the deranged person might not understand himself. For instance, an obsessive-compulsive might refuse to carry $20 bills. How does this refusal help the person? Perhaps he went to the bank just before he learned of his wife's death, and had received a stack of $20 bills. Therefore, he associates $20 bills with the death of loved ones. Or the chain of associations might be far more obscure than that. When playing deranged characters, players should come up with such hidden associations as a guide to portraying madness.

Curing Derangements

Removing a derangement is even more difficult for Kindred than it is for mortals. Modern psychiatry chiefly relies on drugs and "talk therapy." Some forms of mental illness, such as schizophrenia and manic-depression, seem to happen because of some defect in a person's brain chemistry. Various drugs can ameliorate the effects, and maybe a therapist can then teach the patient to think in healthier ways. Other illnesses, such as phobias and hysteria, seem to be created entirely by thought and stress. Finding and relieving the base anxiety can cure the disorder, though modern psychiatry generally prescribes antidepressants and other drugs.

Kindred cannot turn to drugs to relieve derangements. Talk therapy becomes feasible only if the city has a Kindred psychiatrist, as talking to a mortal would break the Masquerade. Anyway, most of the causes of stress in Kindred existence cannot be relieved.

For derangements acquired through degeneration, Kindred are much like mortals. A derangement is considered overcome once the character regains a level of Humanity one higher than the one at which he gained the derangement. So, if a character gains an addiction at Humanity 6, she needs to rise back to Humanity 7 to overcome that addiction.

At the Storyteller's option, a character can resist some derangements for a scene if the player manages an exceptional success on a Resolve + Composure roll and a point of Willpower is spent (which does not yield three extra dice to the Resolve + Composure roll). The character really tries to think straight and ignores his inner voice that screams that the sky will fall if he carries a $20 bill. He steps into the confined elevator car or faces the Prince himself instead of letting another individual do the job.

After a character successfully resists a derangement 10 *consecutive* times, the Storyteller can declare the derangement cured. This method does not work on severe derangements. A

true psychotic cannot control his own mind. Storytellers must decide for themselves whether extended use of Dominate or other mind-influencing supernatural powers can cure derangements. No method of treatment can ameliorate derangements acquired through moral degeneration. Those must be overcome by regaining Humanity. At the Storyteller's discretion, a character may resist such derangements for a scene, but he can never overcome them through sheer quantitative endurance.

Sample Derangements

Some of these derangements have already been described in the **World of Darkness Rulebook**. These descriptions focus on how Kindred (or, in some cases, ghouls) experience the ailments. We also add a few new ones.

Some derangements are severe forms of other conditions, but different from those discussed in the **World of Darkness** book. In such cases, after a character acquires the mild derangement, he and the Storyteller may choose what severe ailment might set in. For example, a character who already has the irrationality derangement gains another. According to the **World of Darkness Rulebook**, multiple personality is the severe form of that derangement. The character and Storyteller may decide, however, that the character is better suited to delusional obsession (see below). Of course, as the **World of Darkness Rulebook** also states, sometimes a single act or scene is so mind numbing that only full-blown insanity and dysfunction can result. In these cases, Storytellers may decide

that a character acquires a severe derangement whether or not she already has the mild form.

Some of the following derangements are mild in and of themselves, and have no progression to the severe form. These are marked as "mild only."

Bulimia (severe; follows Fixation): People with this neurosis try to drown their anxiety through activities that comfort them, especially food. Doing so leads to a binge-and-purge cycle. The bulimic stuffs himself to relieve stress, then self-disgust at his own gluttony drives him to vomit out what he's eaten. The bulimic soon seeks to feed again, though, and the cycle repeats.

Vampires face a special temptation toward bulimia because feeding is the strongest physical pleasure left to them. A bulimic vampire relieves his fear and guilt by gorging himself on blood, perhaps feeding several times a night and burning the Vitae as fast as he can. The character can augment his traits for frenetic activity or wound himself as a form of punishment, then heal the wounds so that other Kindred won't see his weakness and self-loathing. At severe levels, the vampire might even will himself to expunge Vitae by vomiting — no small feat and a noteworthy act of will, since vampires don't store blood in their stomachs.

Effect: A bulimic vampire becomes hungry more easily than other Kindred and has a harder time resisting the urge to feed. Whenever the character feeds, the player must succeed at a Resolve + Composure roll or the vampire feeds until full, whether or not he really needs the extra Vitae. Additionally, the character must use that Vitae frequently; the player must spend at least one Vitae per scene for the character until the character rests for the day, even if circumstances wouldn't otherwise warrant it. A player may, for example, devote Vitae to Strength for a turn in which no Strength roll is necessary, or spend a Vitae to heal a single point of bashing damage even though Vitae normally heals two points of bashing damage. A bulimic character also suffers an automatic -2 penalty to resist hunger frenzies. Forcibly preventing the character from drinking his fill might provoke a rage frenzy (no modifier to difficulty).

Delusional Obsession (severe; follows Irrationality): This derangement can emerge because of centuries of torpid dreams, or simply a strong desire for the world to be the way a character wants. Delusional obsession consists of a fanatical belief in something that just isn't true. Lots of people hold beliefs that other people find absurd, of course, but a delusional obsessive structures his life or unlife on them. Classic examples include the survivalist holed up in a cabin with canned beans and a shotgun, the street-corner preacher ranting that "The end is near," and the dotty old lady with a hundred cats. Nearly any hobby, belief or interest can seem dangerously crazed when it takes over a character's existence. Delusional obsession might be dismissed as fanaticism, but it is even more extreme.

Effect: A Willpower point must be spent to resist whenever an opportunity arises to act in accordance with the character's obsession, or whenever he must act in direct opposition to his obsession. For instance, a gardening fanatic might have to expend Willpower to stay out of a florist's shop. A Kindred who believes that every instance of a crescent or lunar reference indicates Lupine activity might need to expend a Willpower point to step into an Islamic cultural center or to stay in the same room as someone named Moon.

Dependent-Personality Disorder (severe; follows Irrationality): This emotional derangement most often afflicts ghouls or blood-bound Kindred. The character becomes utterly dependent on his regnant or domitor. He resists making even the most trivial decision for himself. This disorder might arise from fear of abandonment (especially strong in the case of ghouls who know that sudden aging or death awaits them if they lose their supply of Vitae). It might also grow from an exaggerated fear of displeasing a harsh or demanding master.

Effect: If a character has this derangement, the player does not include Resolve in contested dice pools when the domitor attempts to Dominate him (although Blood Potency still applies). Indeed, the character often follows up on any statement that might be construed as a request for the character to do something.

Phobia (mild): A person who suffers from a phobia has an unreasoning fear of something. A phobia can result from a traumatic experience associated with an object or condition, or might be a purely neurotic way of hiding from a real source of anxiety. Common phobias include a fear of open spaces, leaving one's home, of enclosed spaces or germs, but nearly anything can become the focus of a phobia. Kindred are especially prone to phobias of fire, sunlight or hunger. A phobic vampire might avoid going outdoors for fear of sunlight, even if she knows dawn is hours away.

Effect: Your character moves away from the object of her phobia. If she must be near it, she can tolerate being no closer than her Speed in yards. If it approaches her, she must move away at least her Speed in distance in her next action. She cannot easily target the trigger with close combat or ranged attacks. Such attacks suffer a -5 penalty as your character shakes just looking at it. If space or circumstances don't allow her to maintain her distance, she freezes like a deer in headlights until she finds an opening by which to escape. (Her Defense still applies if attacked and she can choose to dodge and can take cover from Firearms attacks, but she can take no other actions while "frozen.")

A successful Resolve + Composure roll must be made for a phobic Kindred to simply approach the subject of her fear. Any sort of shock or surprise associated with the subject of the phobia can cause Rötschreck. Roll normally for the character to resist, suitably modified by the degree of exposure.

Hysteria (severe; follows Phobia): Kindred hysteria operates much like that of mortals, except it rises to new heights, as would be expected for a mental ailment of the undead. The vampire's emotions run high and stressful situations can cause fits of rage, weeping, fainting or other emotional displays.

Effect: This condition operates as a phobia (see above), but on a failed Resolve + Composure roll your character cannot be in the same room with the object of her fear. She must run away from it immediately, and cannot tolerate being within sensory range (sight, sound, smell) of it. If the trigger comes within sensory range, she must move away at full running speed as soon as she can take an action. She cannot target it for an attack under any circumstance. If it touches her, make another Resolve + Composure roll for her to not freak out and run as far away as she can, thinking of nothing else until she's left the subject far behind. (Even if this roll succeeds, your character must still leave the room or area.) If any of your Resolve + Composure rolls suffer a dramatic failure or your character is unable to escape, she faints and loses consciousness for the remainder of the scene. If your character is unaware of the object's proximity until it touches her, a Resolve + Composure suffers a -3 penalty. If it touches her where she can't see it but she can feel it — a spider dropping on her neck or in her hair — the penalty is -5.

For a Kindred character, you must roleplay most aspects of hysteria, above, but also suffer a -1 penalty on all rolls to resist frenzy that relate to the object of fear. Any action that relates to the object and that results in a dramatic failure automatically causes your vampire to frenzy.

Manic-Depression (severe; follows Depression): Severe mood swings characterize this derangement. It occurs in two forms, one psychological and one a defect in brain chemistry.

The psychological form is a modified form of hysteria. The victim can swing from an enthusiastic, confident, even ecstatic state to lethargy and despair. The mood swings can happen any time, but any success can push the manic-depressive into exaltation, and any failure can plunge the person into depression.

The second form of manic-depression is an organic disorder. It follows a regular cycle that can range from hours to weeks. The manic phase begins with an excess of energy and confidence, then proceeds to a sort of ecstatic frenzy as the person's mind races faster and faster. Eventually the person calms down and then slides into a depression as lethargic as the manic phase was energetic. This form of manic-depression can mimic the effects of schizophrenia, and lead to a near-suicidal state.

Effect: Whichever form of the ailment your character has, whenever he fails a task, the Storyteller may secretly roll his Resolve. A failure means the character lapses into depression for the rest of the scene. The character also goes into depression whenever the player makes a dramatic failure on a roll, or the character has less than two Vitae.

While depressed, the character loses half his Willpower points (rounding fractions down), to a minimum of 1. A depressed vampire cannot expend Vitae to gain dice for Physical tasks, either.

Each scene thereafter, the Storyteller rolls one die. On a success, the character throws off the depression and becomes upbeat, energetic and obsessively active for as many scenes as he was depressed. He regains the Willpower points he lost before, and all rolls to resist frenzy suffer a one-die penalty.

Megalomania (severe; follows Narcissism): Clinical megalomania can consist of a delusion that the individual is some famous and powerful person, contemporary or historical, or even that he is God. A megalomaniac vampire might imagine that he is some famous or infamous Kindred, or the Devil himself.

A romantic form of megalomania might be called "James Bond Mastermind Syndrome." This sort of megalomaniac obsessively seeks ever-greater wealth and power. Such individuals hide their anxiety (even from themselves) behind a mask of arrogance and supreme self-confidence. The character may seek power by means ranging from intricate conspiracies to brutal murder and terror. To this sort of megalomaniac, everyone is a minion who should do what he's told, or a competitor who must be destroyed. This belief extends to even members of the vampire's own coterie.

Effect: If your character ever loses a contest to someone he feels is socially inferior, he loses one point of Willpower due to shame and self-loathing (which is at the heart of his megalomania; he secretly fears that he's a fraud).

Multiple Personality (severe; extreme; follows Irrationality): Multiple-Personality Disorder (MPD) results from traumas so severe and prolonged that the victim's mind splits into several personalities. When a vampire suffers this derangement, the Storyteller and player need to agree on a set of alternative personalities for the character, as well as on what situations call each personality to the fore. Each personality should have some connection to the trauma that fractured the character's mind. Alternate personalities might believe they belong to different clans, bloodlines or covenants, or even not be aware that they are undead.

Effect: A character with multiple personalities can manifest different Skills or perhaps increased or diminished Social Attributes for each identity (the number of dots allocated to your character's Social Attributes are rearranged by anywhere from one to three). The character does not actually possess more Skills than other characters, he merely switches personalities

when he needs to use certain Skills. For instance, a tough-guy "protector" persona might emerge whenever the character needs to fight, so the baseline identity doesn't need to face the moral and emotional stress of combat. The "protector" persona takes possession of the character's combat Skills, while the other personalities don't admit that they know how to fight.

This is an extreme derangement. The character must experience a life-altering trauma or supernatural tragedy to manifest it. The ailment cannot normally be acquired by failing a Humanity roll unless the sin performed is truly ghastly. MPD is an elaborate derangement, and a challenge to roleplay. Its symptoms are frightening and the suffering it exacts from its victim is monumental. It should not be an excuse for slapstick, wacky, foolish or childish behavior.

Obsessive Compulsion (severe; follows Fixation): A character with this derangement focuses her attention on a single repetitive behavior or action as a way to distract herself from feelings of anxiety or inner torment. The compulsive character turns everything into a ritual and feels utter dread of any disruption of her behaviors.

Many European vampire legends say the undead suffer from an obsessive need to count collections of small objects, and so a mortal can protect himself by leaving piles of grain where he sleeps. A marauding vampire, legends say, feels compelled to count the grain before he feeds, and this can keep the vampire occupied until dawn. Kindred who believe in the stories mortals tell about them might suffer from this kind of fixation.

Effect: Determine a set of specific actions or behaviors that your character follows to the exclusion of all else (even if doing so interferes with his current agenda or endangers his existence or others'). The effects of obsessive/compulsive behavior can be negated for the course of one scene by making a successful Resolve + Composure roll at a -2 penalty. If your character is forcibly prevented from adhering to his derangement, he may lose control among enemies or allies and attack either (or both) indiscriminately. An obsessive-compulsive vampire is subject to a frenzy roll in this situation.

Paranoia (severe; follows Suspicion): Paranoia is a species of delusion. The paranoid believes that enemies persecute her and make her miserable. As a paranoid's delusions intensify, she spins out elaborate conspiracy theories to explain who's doing the persecution, and why. Everything goes into the conspiracy. Do the neighbors stay up late? They must be spying. Does she have headaches? Her enemies have dosed her with some insidious toxin. Did she lose her job? The conspiracy arranged it… and of course, they want other people to believe she's crazy. As paranoia deepens, the sufferer might plot to strike back at her persecutors, whomever she imagines them to be.

This derangement can be hard to diagnose among the Kindred because they really do have enemies in the Danse Macabre. A paranoid vampire, however, can't tell a real enemy from one that exists only in his head. Imagined enemies can range from the CIA to Satan himself. Paranoid Kindred often turn obsessive-compulsive as well and adopt complex feeding precautions to prevent their enemies from "tainting their blood supply." They also parse every question or comment for hidden motives and meanings. Suspicion extends even to progeny and thralls subjected to Vinculums — maybe they're only pretending to be loyal!

Effect: A paranoid character has difficulty with all social interactions because of her reflexive suspicion of everyone. A character who suffers from paranoia automatically suffers a -2 penalty on Social rolls. The character is distrustful and wary of everyone, even close friends and family. The slightest hint of suspicious behavior is enough to provoke a Resolve + Composure roll to retain control (made at a -2 penalty). A failed roll indicates that your character flees or attacks an offender. Additionally, among Kindred, the slightest hint that someone might be an enemy can provoke a frenzy check, with the number of successes required set by how threatening the trigger event seems. A casual remark that seems to show someone knows a bit about the character's activities might require only one success to avoid frenzy. Finding an intruder in his haven would almost certainly require five.

Power Fetish Obsession (mild only): Although Kindred value their supernatural powers, their Disciplines and Vitae expenditures remind them of their undead state. Some Kindred project their powers onto an object, so they don't have to take responsibility for them. Other Kindred develop the "power fetish" delusion as a stronger form of good-luck superstition. Whatever the reason, the character believes she cannot use her supernatural powers without the help of a special object. In folklore, for instance, the Swiss vampire called the Alp became powerless without its hat. A character with this derangement might believe that she cannot use her undead powers without the dress she wore when she was Embraced, her lucky bracelet or some other article.

Effect: Any attempt to use Disciplines or expend Vitae without that object reduces any dice pools for an activity by three dice.

Sanguinary Animism (mild only): Only Kindred can suffer from this special derangement. This delusion grows out of a vampire's fundamental awareness of guilt about feeding on mortals. Kindred with this delusion believe they take part of victims' minds or souls along with their blood. For hours after feeding, the Kindred hears a victim's voice in his head, berating him, begging for mercy or making demands. The vampire even experiences ersatz memories from his victim's life, all concocted by the vampire's unconscious mind, but seeming very real. Weak-willed or especially guilt-stricken Kindred might even carry out actions on behalf of their victims. Whenever a sanguinary animist feeds on a mortal, the player makes an Intelligence + Composure roll. If the roll succeeds, the imaginary voice and memories of the victim torment the character for the rest of the night, but the character can function adequately. If the roll fails, the images in the character's mind are so strong that the other personality can influence the vampire's actions. The angry victim-personality usually means to harm the character, but the vampire might silence the victim's voice by doing something he imagines the victim would like. If the player cannot roleplay the possessing victim's personality, control of the character can pass to the Storyteller for short times. Control automatically reverts to the vampire just before dawn.

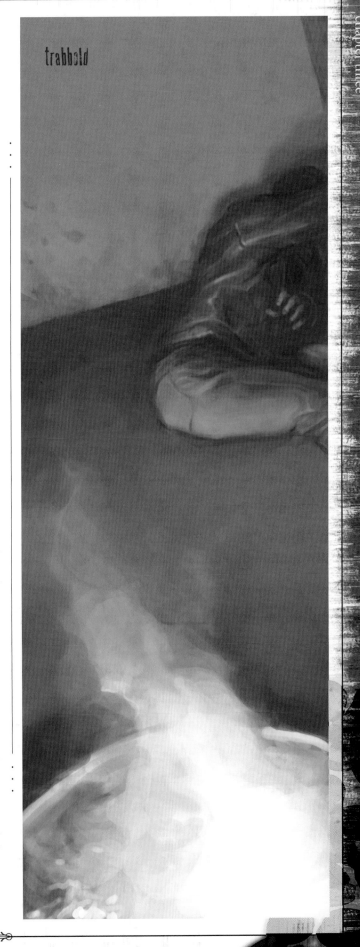

trabbold

For all the anguish that sanguinary animism causes, it illustrates how derangements work (badly) to relieve guilt and stress. As long as the victim's voice continues, she isn't really dead — or so it seems — while the vampire supplies her own punishment.

Effect: Sanguinary animism becomes particularly severe when a vampire kills his vessel. In this case, the Intelligence + Composure roll is at -3 dice. A dramatic failure means that the ersatz personality of the victim becomes a permanent fixture in the vampire's mind. Under stress, the victim's voice becomes more insistent. The Kindred might distractedly respond aloud to the voices in his head. Further shocks could drive the vampire into multiple-personality disorder (see above), with the Kindred taking on the fantasized personalities of victims. Diablerie is an especially bad idea for sufferers of this derangement!

Schizophrenia (severe; extreme; follows Vocalization): Schizophrenia is the most severe of all derangements. This mental illness includes hallucinations, delusions, radical mood swings, manic or obsessive babbling on certain themes, and outbursts of violence. The victim constantly hears strange hums, roars or voices in his head. People on TV or passing by seem to look at and threaten him. Delusions of grandeur are common: The schizophrenic thinks he's Jesus, Napoleon (no, really, it happens) or the president.

Unlike most lesser derangements, schizophrenia has a proven organic cause, an imbalance of brain chemistry that drugs can treat in mortals. Stress also plays a role in sending a latent schizophrenic over the edge, though, and mortals need both drugs and psychotherapy to recover from the disease (if they can at all).

Schizophrenia presents a formidable roleplaying challenge. The player must decide on a general set of delusions, hallucinations and behaviors that relate to the trauma that causes the derangement. The Storyteller, meanwhile, should prepare to include hallucinatory details in her descriptions to the player. The character doesn't know what's real, so the player shouldn't either. The player can probably guess that when the TV weatherman looks at the character and says, "Your sire wants to kill you. You have to kill him first," that isn't real. When he waits at a bus stop and someone pulls a dagger from under a coat, however….

Effect: A character with this derangement is unpredictable and dangerous. His player automatically suffers a -2 penalty on all Social rolls, and he might be aggressive or violent toward people who confront him with trauma such as accusations, disturbing truths or heated arguments. Make a Resolve + Composure roll for your character to avoid escaping or attacking the source of trauma. The player and Storyteller should also designate a set of conditions that trigger the character's mood swings and delusions. Under these conditions, a -2 penalty applies to resist frenzy and Rötschreck as the vampire's mind is racked by imaginary horrors.

Your character must experience a life-altering trauma or supernatural tragedy to acquire this extreme derangement. It cannot normally be acquired by failing a Humanity roll unless the sin performed is truly gut wrenching or horrific.

Golconda and Transcendence

The burden of undeath weighs heavily on most Kindred. Not only are they denied the sun, food and all the other simple pleasures of true life; not only are they trapped in a Danse Macabre with no beginning or end; but in the eyes of many, God Himself has cursed them. But why? Why punish thousands of mortals for an individual's crimes or bad luck? This bitter mystery forms the crowning injustice of their damnation.

The Lancea Sanctum gives the orthodox answer: original sin. Every son of Adam and daughter of Eve is born in sin, and what is mortal history but a tapestry of violence, greed, lust and deceit? Every man and woman deserves damnation a thousand times over for the crimes of their ancestors, and the crimes they did not oppose when they lived. It is not for mortals or Kindred to question the Almighty's will. The Kindred should bow their heads and accept their fate as sinners in the hands of an angry God. They have earned Hell, be it the fires of the afterlife, the torments of the Beast, or the hunger and the sheer ennui of centuries of existence.

Not all Kindred can accept this grim catechism. A few dare to hope that they can escape damnation. Some Kindred believe that they can win a pardon from God. Others hope for a more secular salvation, achieved through mysticism, self-discipline, drugs or alternative philosophy. Tantalizing rumors slowly spread through the Kindred race of vampires who became mortal again or who master the Beast. Elder Kindred scoff at such tales… but they still listen.

Of all these tales and legends, the most common theme is a mystical state called Golconda. The term's derivation is both simple and mysterious. Golconda is a town in India where diamonds were mined in ancient times. Its name became associated with anything distant and difficult to reach, but of immense value — a fitting name for the mystical transcendence that legend describes.

THE COVENANTS ON GOLCONDA

Individual views about Golconda vary widely, but Storytellers can take the following opinions as typical of the various covenants.

The Carthians: Fairy tales like Golconda serve only to distract the Kindred from political action.

The Circle of the Crone: Golconda may be real. We do not, however, pretend to know the secret ourselves.

The Invictus: Golconda is a childish fable for the weak-willed and weak-minded. Such a blessed state could not exist. Anyone who gives credence to such tales deserves mockery.

The Lancea Sanctum: Golconda is a cruel delusion at best, a wicked heresy at worst. Such tales lead Kindred away from accepting their place in God's plan.

The Ordo Dracul: Why bother with Golconda when transcendence can make one *more* than a vampire, instead of just enabling her to settle for what she is?

The Nature of Golconda

According to the tales, vampires who achieve Golconda defeat the Beast or pacify it in some way. They no longer suffer its relentless drive to rage and feed. They no longer require blood, or at least not as much. These spiritual masters retain all their Kindred powers, though. In fact, they can achieve the greatest heights of Kindred power without suffering the deadly thirst for the Vitae of other Kindred that afflicts the mightiest of the Damned. They abandon the Danse Macabre. They walk unharmed through the wilderness and Lupines bow to them. They walk through cities and the Kindred do not know them, for God has forgiven and blessed them.

Of course, no one can prove to have actually met such a redeemed vampire. Like any urban legend, the tales always come second or third hand, at least. A Kindred known in another city says his sire's broodmate met a vampire who worked wonders and talked of Golconda — that sort of thing. On rare occasions, Kindred claim to have achieved the blessed state and say they will teach others of their kind. Elders always expose these self-styled gurus as fakes working some sort of scam… at least, that's what the elders say.

Golconda legends describe a number of methods to achieve redemption. Cynics might observe that the purported methods tend to reflect the mystical ideas that were popular when the tale-teller lived. Older tales about Golconda emphasize the need for prayer, receiving sacraments, pilgrimages to holy places, tests of faith and resolve, and physical asceticism — fasting, flagellation and the like — to gain visions from God. In the Age of Enlightenment, philosophy and self-control became prominent in the stories. In the 19th century, the stories acquired Eastern elements such as meditation and paradoxical riddles. The 20th century gave the stories a quasi-scientific air, with drugs (or magic) to pacify the Beast, and a period of study with a mentor that sounded very much like psychoanalysis.

Most stories agree, however, that a Kindred who wants to find Golconda must pursue an existence of unblemished virtue and humanity. He must feed as little as possible to sustain his existence, and he must avoid any sort of harm to mortals or other Kindred. He must fight frenzy with all his might, never giving a moment's control to the Beast. Most of all, he must do penance for all his sins. If he cannot atone directly to a victim, he must perform some deed to compensate a victim's family, community or all humanity. Only then does he even have a chance that God might grant him forgiveness. The quest certainly takes years, decades or even centuries.

Most of the stories also say that Kindred cannot find Golconda on their own. They need a teacher who can guide them along the correct path, preferably a Kindred who has already achieved salvation. These undead spiritual masters hide themselves well, but a determined seeker can find one… or one of them mystically knows that a ready student emerges and finds the seeker himself. Some stories say that a Kindred who pursues Golconda might encounter other seekers. He might study under a series of tutors, each one more advanced, and he might teach other novices himself as he gains wisdom.

At the end of this long quest, a vampire experiences a mystical vision called the Suspire. Perhaps a mentor guides the Kindred through this ultimate spiritual test. Perhaps the seeker learns to conduct the test himself. Or perhaps the vision takes the seeker by surprise. In the Suspire, the vampire encounters God, the Beast or his own soul. As usual, stories differ.

The visionary encounter ends with a judgment passed on the Kindred. Not every seeker survives this judgment. Failure might also leave the seeker insane or merely wracked with despair at failing his one chance at salvation. The legends all agree on one thing: A Kindred experiences the Suspire only once. A seeker never gets a second chance. If the seeker passes the test, he achieves enlightenment and liberation from the curse of undeath.

Storytelling the Quest

We deliberately avoid specifying too much about Golconda and how to achieve it. By definition, Golconda pushes a character outside the rules that govern normal Kindred existence. Nailing down a state of mystical transcendence with trait scores and dice pools would cheapen the whole idea. Still, we offer a few suggestions on incorporating a quest for Golconda into your chronicle, assuming you want to include it at all. If you choose, the scoffers could be right and Golconda could just be a wishful fairy tale.

Before anything else, a character needs to learn that Golconda might exist. Stories about the blessed state are neither terribly rare nor brutally suppressed (in most cities, anyway), but they are not exactly common knowledge. Before a character can even think of seeking Golconda, she must hear a story or two about it.

If the character takes an interest in stories of salvation for the Damned, she can search for more information. Doing so involves broaching the subject with other Kindred who might not want to admit that they pay attention to such things, and it might expose the character to Harpies' derision. As the character hears more, she learns that attacks on her reputation are the smallest danger brought by the search. Not everyone survives the quest. The character also learns that the search takes a long time. As Storyteller, make it clear to players that if their characters seek Golconda, they commit to a long, ongoing subplot, if not a whole new direction for the chronicle. Salvation for the Damned is an epic story that one does not tell briefly.

Early in the quest, a character has nothing but tales to guide her. She doesn't know if Golconda really exists or exactly what she must do to achieve the state. Shee must proceed on faith and try by reason and intuition to sift truth from the cryptic hints available. As Storyteller, you need to supply those hints in the form of rumors and riddles. Some of these hints should contradict or just be mystical-sounding gibberish. The character might try to track a story to its source, asking each teller where he heard it. With luck, skill and perseverance, she might find a Kindred who says he personally encountered someone he thinks was a Kindred in Golconda, and he remembers a riddle or parable that was told. Another story might lead to an obscure mystical tract written by someone who claimed to

know the secret, or a meeting with another seeker who can pass on his own beliefs and research. Tracking legends to their source in this way certainly involves travel, with all the dangers it entails for Kindred.

The character soon learns the importance of remorse and atonement. The greater a vampire's sins, the greater the penance she must perform. The legends and rumors might suggest ways that Kindred can make amends for their crimes, but this is an opportunity for characters (and players) to explore the nature and limits of atonement. How do you make amends to the dead? Are some injuries beyond repair? Should a vampire even try to atone for some crimes or should she simply accept punishment, even unto Final Death?

Along the way, a character should also try to protect those weaker than herself and try to make the World of Darkness a better place. Through her efforts, she atones on behalf of all Kindred. If the Biblical metaphor is valid, Longinus' act that confirmed the faith of others proved his own damnation. Surely, any Kindred who seeks release from the curse of undeath must show that she is aware of the significance of that burden. Doing so necessarily involves maintaining (or recovering) a high Humanity, upholding every Virtue possible on every occasion possible, and resisting frenzy and Vice whenever those damning forces arise. Indiscriminate feeding, using one's powers to manipulate mortals and the cruel intrigues of the Danse Macabre are anathema to the sincere seeker.

If a character can consistently show penitent, abstinent and honorable behavior over many stories, she might be ready for the next stage in the quest. The character can finally locate a mentor, or one might locate her. This mentor tests the resolve, wisdom and ethics of the postulant through moral quandaries, enigmatic puzzles, strange tasks and dangerous missions. A Kindred who won't risk body and soul for salvation doesn't want it enough to earn it. Sometimes the challenge might be to teach another Kindred and help him begin the quest for Golconda.

The climax of the chronicle comes when a worthy character experiences the Suspire. To be ready, a character needs a Humanity of at least 7. No other traits really matter. As Storyteller, you decide upon the nature of the Suspire. It may be some sort of ritual. It may be a riddle or a seemingly innocuous task that nonetheless has its own metaphorical gravity. It may be a dream that comes over the sleeping character. Follow whatever scheme suits your sense of the mystical.

Tailor the Suspire to reflect the character's personality and whatever themes and conflicts evolved in the course of the chronicle. Potential themes for a Suspire include the character's greatest hatred, fear or sorrow, an overwhelming Vice, how much she wants to be mortal or a challenge to justify the existence of the Kindred and all their sins. This is entirely a moral challenge. Do not use any situation that calls for dice rolls. Work in a few hints, through references to past stories, what choice the character should make to pass the test. After all, the player isn't a spiritual master, to pluck enlightenment from nowhere. The Suspire should be difficult, even cryptic, but try to make it a *fair* challenge — one the player really has a chance to figure out.

If the character fails, that's it. The quest is over. The character can never try again. She can remain a highly moral vampire, but she can never hope to transcend that state. Maybe she can find a way to accept that, maybe not.

If the character succeeds and achieves Golconda… you have to decide what the legendary state actually *is*. Once again, we can offer only suggestions, which you may accept or reject as you will.

For a simple option, the character becomes mortal. She triumphs over the curse of undeath, so it no longer troubles her. Any Kindred who guided the character were vampires who failed their own Suspires or who had not yet dared to take the ultimate test, and who chose to guide other Damned.

For a more complicated option, the character remains undead, but is free from many of undeath's restrictions. The character never suffers frenzy again. The Beast no longer has the power to drive her into evil deeds. She may sin of her own volition, but never because the player failed a dice roll. A vampire in Golconda still needs to drink blood, but she need never fear taking too much because of the Beast's hunger.

Also, the character does not need to drink as much blood as before. The character loses one Vitae per week, instead of one Vitae per night. Her player still spends Vitae normally to heal wounds, augment Physical dice pools and power Crúac or any Discipline powers that require it. Perhaps best of all, the Kindred's Blood Potency can increase without the need to feed on stronger and stronger blood. Her feeding requirements are those of Kindred with half her Blood Potency. If she finds even that too much of a burden, she can voluntarily reduce her Blood Potency to a level where she can feed on animals. She cannot restore a higher Blood Potency, though, without using the normal means to do so.

All these benefits last only as long as the vampire keeps her Humanity high. Should her Humanity slip below 7 for any reason, the character falls from grace, loses the benefits of Golconda and can never gain them again.

Other Ways of Becoming Mortal

The Kindred tell stories about vampires who became mortal by other means than Golconda. Some tales are distinctly sentimental. They tell of Kindred who became mortal through true love for a living person; through miracles performed for exceptionally pious Kindred by mortal holy men and women, or holy relics; by nobly sacrificing their unlives for others (and becoming mortal as they died). Most Kindred cynically scoff at such stories. Then again, true love, perfect faith and selfless sacrifice seldom happen among the Damned (which might be part of what damns them).

Stranger and more sinister rumors speak of Kindred who became mortal by destroying their sires, their sires' sires and their sires' sires' sires, perhaps by diablerie or by drinking a potion of their dust. Other tales speak of powerful spirits who grant mortality for a price, or of blessed artifacts that can end the curse of undeath.

As with Golconda, Kindred never seem to have personal experience of such things. The legends are remote and dubious. The Storyteller must decide if any of these tales are true.

Other Forms of Transcendence

Another class of legends deals with other ways in which Kindred may gain powers denied other vampires, or to escape the limitations of undeath. As usual when the Damned discuss supernatural matters beyond their direct experience, tales tend to be so vague that no one can guess if they could be true. Or they supply a mass of spurious detail, and no one can guess what aspects might be true.

The most reliable stories concern the genesis of new Disciplines. Knowledgeable Kindred agree that many more Disciplines exist than the familiar powers known to all the clans (as described in Chapter Two). Rare, little-known Disciplines are most often invented and practiced by special bloodlines that arise among the clans. One popular theory attributes the invention of new Disciplines to occult contamination from other denizens of the supernatural world, such as werewolves and mortal mages. (See Appendix One for more information about Disciplines and bloodlines.)

Other stories speak of Kindred who gain special powers by selling their souls to the Devil. These legends say that demons can teach sorcery, confer unusual powers (another explanation given for new Disciplines), and release vampires from frenzy, the deadly effects of sunlight and other aspects of the curse. Lancea Sanctum leaders rigorously condemn all these stories. They insist that no Kindred ever profited from dealing with demons. The Lancea Sanctum's Inquisitors stand ready to expose and chastise any vampire who dares to take on a second damnation.

Sheer age might grant more powers. The Kindred know that their race has existed for many thousands of years, but vampires Embraced more than 500 to 1,000 years ago vanished into legend. Many of them certainly met Final Death, but what happened to the ones who didn't? Did they all succumb to the Beast? Do they sleep in millennial torpors? Such long sleeps should reduce the potency of their blood to that of mere neonates, but… the Kindred don't really know. Rare undead horrors such as the Unholy suggest that some elder Kindred escape the traps of their thirst for ever-stronger blood and the slow erosion of their *humanitas* to become something else, a creature that preys on the Damned as the Kindred prey on mortals.

Few Kindred would admit that they seek to become such monsters to monsters. In secret, however, many old (and not-so-old) Kindred pursue scraps of rumors in hopes of achieving a *verboten* transformation into something mightier, more fearsome and less limited. Among the Kindred, each is enemy to all. They spend their unlives learning to be wolves, and for all they profess to hate their condition, few accept the thought that other creatures still regard them as kine to be devoured at will.

"The Prince of whom you spoke, 'Dracula' — his name means 'Son of the Dragon' does it not?"
"Or 'Son of the Devil.'"
— Rites of the Dragon

Chapter Four:
Storytelling
and Antagonists

The wisest among the Damned have learned to ask questions

only when they want to know the answers.

Even so, it is always disconcerting to be confronted

with the fact that some questions have no answers.

The night has a will of its own,

and much as the Kindred might posture to the contrary,

we belong to it, not the other way around.

— Luther Franke, *Die Neuen Götter*

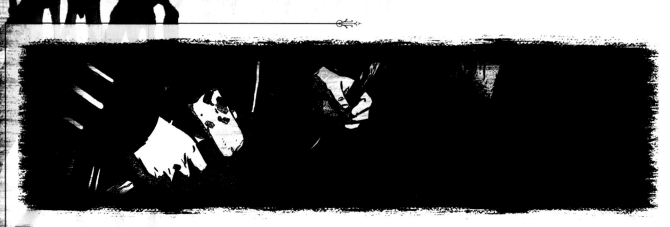

When I looked for good, then evil came unto me: and when I waited for light, there came darkness.

My bowels boiled, and rested not: the days of affliction prevented me.

I went mourning without the sun: I stood up, and I cried in the congregation.

I am a brother to dragons, and a companion to owls.

My skin is black upon me, and my bones are burned with heat.

My harp also is turned to mourning, and my organ into the voice of them that weep.

— Job 30: 26-31

Now you know the rules for **Vampire: The Requiem**. You know how to describe what characters can do. You can determine whether they succeed or fail at their actions. You also know what sort of world the Kindred inhabit. **Vampire: The Requiem** is not about rules, however, or even about a particular fictional world. It's about stories.

Specifically, stories about vampires. It's about a relentless hunger that makes one a monster. It's about having power over others but not over oneself. It's about secrets, madness and treachery. It's about making choices when no options are good, safe or easy. Most of all, it's a story you don't tell by yourself. You tell it in partnership with other players. One of you takes the role of Storyteller, but all of you work together to make the story complete.

Vampire: The Requiem is a Modern Gothic Storytelling game. This chapter tells you how to run such a game. Storytellers have the most need to read this chapter, of course, but some topics concern players, too.

The **World of Darkness Rulebook** already tells you what a Storytelling game is. So, what is a "Modern Gothic Storytelling Game"?

Horror comes in many flavors, from the blood-splattering shocks of a slasher movie to the eerie mysteries of a classic ghost story. **Vampire** can incorporate any sort of horror, but the game focuses on gothic horror, horror at one's own deeds, of one's self. In most horror stories, the protagonists are victims. Something bad happens to them and you're scared on their behalf. In **Vampire**'s particular brand of gothic horror, characters fill the roles of victim and monster at the same time. They do the bad things themselves and suffer the consequences, or they try not to do bad things, and suffer the consequences of that choice. The personal horror of **Vampire** is about realizing, beyond all doubt, that *you* are the monster. (Or at least your character is!)

You can tell all kinds of stories in a **Vampire: The Requiem** chronicle, from dark romance to gritty war stories. Your stories, however, should offer characters a chance to discover just how awful their existence as Kindred can be. Can the characters withstand the hunger and rage of the Beast and the ruthless demands of Kindred society? Can they maintain some moral standard when no mortal law can bind them and the Beast constantly goads them to assault and murder? Even if characters can affirm their humanity this time… there's always tomorrow night, the night after that, and the night after that….

Forever.

Getting Started

As Storyteller, you create a nightmarish reflection of the real world for the players' characters to inhabit, including all the people they meet. That means a lot of work. Fortunately, you don't have to create it all at once. **Vampire: The Requiem** presumes that most stories take place within one metropolitan area. At first, you don't have to worry about Kindred, mortals or other supernatural creatures elsewhere in the world. You only have to create the little bits of the world that affect the characters — and for Kindred, that's a lot less than it is for most mortals.

Even more fortunately, your players can help. Once a chronicle begins, every choice the characters make has consequences, good and bad, that can spark new stories. If you manage to fully engage the players' interests, they'll move beyond reacting to situations you create to initiating stories themselves. That's when a chronicle truly becomes a shared work of Storytelling — and, very probably, the most fun.

Building your chronicle starts with discussions with your players. What sort of chronicle do they want? Personal horror and a modern-gothic setting permit a wide variety of different plots and styles of play. A **Vampire** chronicle can range from a desperate struggle against implacable, marauding Lupines to elegant intrigue in Elysium. Do the characters want espionage, mystery, love stories or black comedy? Do they want to play neonates (the default **Vampire** chronicle), elders among the Primogen or something else? Does any aspect of the game or setting especially appeal to them? There's no point to running a chronicle that bores or irritates your players.

Also consider how long a chronicle you and your players want. A short one of four to six episodes demands quite different planning than a chronicle meant to continue indefinitely, through dozens of sessions and multiple story arcs. On one hand, players might try to give their characters every trait, Merit and personality quirk right away, since the chronicle won't have many opportunities to grow and change. On the other hand, players might generate more singularly focused characters, with less attention paid to their chances of surviving a long chronicle. As a Storyteller, you need to devise plots with clearly defined endings. Your own characters need to make an impression quickly, because they might not be on your imaginary stage very long.

Once you have some idea of what sort of chronicle you plan to run, you can flesh out vague notions into characters, a setting, plots, a theme and other details. Any of these factors can influence the others, so the process of building a chronicle is probably a lot less linear and systematic than it seems here. You might start with a particular theme and choose plots to illustrate it. You might begin with a character or set of characters and build the chronicle around them. Maybe you start with an image: a haughty Prince commanding everyone to kneel. A group of fearsome Nosferatu having a tea party, with blood in the china cups. A Kindred crucifixion. Don't be too quick to settle on just one idea, either. Jot down ideas as your fancy wanders, and look for connections among them. Eventually, bits of inspiration coalesce and you know what your chronicle is about.

Characters

Your players' characters are the most important part of the chronicle. After all, the stories are about them. (If they aren't, your players will be bored and probably won't continue the chronicle for long.) What sorts of characters do they want to play? How do they relate to the ideas you have percolating?

For instance, suppose you want to build your chronicle on the meteoric rise and equally spectacular fall of a Prince in a large city. You envision the characters as hip-deep in the political intrigue surrounding the Prince's career, with themes of treachery and corruption of power. One of your players, however, has her heart set on playing a Nosferatu who's chiefly interested in protecting his mortal family (without letting them see him), while another player wants to play an apolitical Mekhet who seeks mystical enlightenment through the Circle of the Crone. Neither seems very compatible with your concept. You shouldn't force the players to abandon characters they love and play characters they don't want. You want players to be your co-creators, not passive or resentful spectators.

So negotiate. Maybe you can shift the emphasis of your chronicle so the Prince's rise and fall plays out in the background and the characters deal with its side effects. Perhaps the central challenge is to avoid the machinations of elders so the characters can pursue their personal goals. Maybe the players hadn't fully considered how their characters could become involved in politics, and adjust their characters to suit the chronicle idea. The Nosferatu could be interested in the Prince's rise if he sees a chance to help his family through political connections. The Mekhet could sympathize with a Prince who also belonged to the Circle of the Crone. Mature players usually want to have some notion of a chronicle's premise in order to create characters that are suited to the story. This sort of give-and-take helps both sides, as players and Storyteller get a better idea of who takes part in the chronicle and what they do.

This process of cross-fertilizing ideas continues as the players write up their characters and flesh out the details of their personalities, backgrounds and social connections. As they build characters, you build a world the characters can inhabit. At the same time, you can suggest ways in which characters might fit into your world.

For instance, suppose one of your players wants her character to have been some sort of government agent before his Embrace — something in law enforcement, but maybe espionage. As you bounce ideas back and forth, you agree that a FBI agent in an organized crime task force could fit the bill: law enforcement, but with espionage too, thanks to undercover and surveillance work. The player gives her character Allies and Contacts in the form of other FBI agents, snitches and criminals who never knew he was really a G-man. He might even have had a double identity. The G-man character also receives suitable Skills, such as Streetwise, Larceny, Investigation, Subterfuge, Firearms, Academics (for law) and Crafts (to use electronic surveillance gear).

You, meanwhile, ponder how to fit an Embraced G-man into your chronicle. Perhaps one of the city's Primogen has secretly placed a mole inside the FBI task force and uses him to gain information about a rival's mob allies. That Primogen could be the character's sire, using him as part of his schemes to manipulate the task force — or perhaps the character doesn't know about the Primogen's subversion and is in for a nasty shock when the elder turns his ally against him! Perhaps the Primogen or some other Kindred plans to Embrace another person on the task force, a friend from the character's mortal days. Maybe someone plans to Embrace a mobster who hates the character for sending him to jail.

As the player develops more details about the FBI task force, she does some of your work for you. Each personality at the task force (or every criminal it builds cases against) becomes another character for you to blend into your world, and another hook with which to draw the character into stories. You gain allies for the character to protect, hide from, exploit, betray or slaughter in frenzy; enemies to hunt him or to reconcile with him; rivals; and potential helpers — all story material waiting for you to use it.

As the example suggests, Social Merits can play an important role in defining a character and providing impetus for stories. Newly Embraced neonates still have many connections to the mortal existence they left behind, so encourage players to buy these Merits for their characters. Brainstorm the details of each Merit and how the character acquired it. Why, for instance, does a character have high Resources? Does he come from a wealthy family? Did he make a fortune in business or through some well-paid profession such as medicine or law? Did he win the lottery? Does his money spring from dark sources, such as dealing drugs? Never let these Merits sit as abstract dots on a character sheet. Tie them back to something concrete.

Don't forget to ask how the Embrace affected the character's social connections. Did he somehow keep his mortal friends, relatives or co-workers from realizing he became a vampire? Does he maintain a completely false existence as a mortal, or does the world think he's dead and only a few people know he isn't? (Well… not *quite* dead.)

On the other hand, did the character try to walk away from his old existence, perhaps to the extent of faking his death? If so, how does he feel about this break with everyone he knows and loves? Can the character really stay away from his old home, family and friends, maybe even a spouse and children? Yet how can he not, knowing what could happen if the Hunger overwhelms him? Do the character's loved ones accept his disappearance, or do they try to find out what happened to him? Such broken connections offer their own opportunities for wrenching drama, pathos and horror.

Most dangerous of all, do some of his contacts, allies or other associates know what he really is? Such breaches of the Masquerade open wonderful Pandora's boxes of story opportunities. The character must prevent these people from telling anyone else. He must hide or defend them from other Kindred who would kill them to keep the secret, or he must justify his own connection to them. For their part, how do these people react to learning that vampires are real and that the character is one of them? Does a person turn against the "monster," freak out some other way, try to ignore the character's undeath or try to come to terms with it? Does one ask to be made a vampire too, because she sees the power and none of the horror?

Make sure that players don't ignore the Embrace itself as part of their characters' background. The Kindred don't sire childer lightly or often. What made this particular mortal so important to one particular vampire that she sacrificed part of her soul to bring him into the darkness? Such a deed suggests a great need for the character's abilities, great love… or great hatred. Odds are, the character dwells in the same city as his sire. If not, the character (or sire) made an extraordinary and dangerous effort to move to a different city. What drove the character to this desperate deed? Has he found acceptance among other Kindred despite his lack of a sire to vouch for him? More likely, the character's sire still plays an important part in his unlife. Even if both of them think the Embrace was a ghastly mistake and they never want to see each other again, other Kindred see them as linked. Each vampire's deeds reflect on the reputation of the other. Each vampire's enemies might oppose the other (and if the character and his sire are themselves hostile, the opportunities for opposition, alliance and treachery between them and their various enemies become downright Byzantine).

It's always tempting to gloss over a character's background and get on with the plot, so the game can begin. Some players also feel reluctant to develop social or emotional connections for their characters, out of fear that those connections will be turned against them. To be human, however, involves contact with other people. The struggle to hold onto a fading

humanity loses much of its poignancy and horror if no one else cares what happens to a character, and she doesn't care what happens to anyone else.

ONE COVENANT OR CLAN?

You might ask your players if they want to use the full range of clans in your game. A chronicle in which the coterie draws members from any clan provides the "default setting" for **Vampire: The Requiem**, but coteries in which everyone belongs to the same clan have their own points of interest. The same goes for covenants. A coterie can have members from more than one covenant, if that's what the players want, but a coterie that stays within one covenant has possibilities, too.

For one thing, it's easier to explain why the characters come together and choose to stay together. The players' characters might al be neonates of that clan or covenant in the city, drawn together by shared inexperience or pushed together by clan or covenant superiors who want them all in one group. For instance, a coterie could consist of Ordo Dracul Kindred who've formed their own house to share their occult knowledge and collectively bargain with other sorcerers for tuition. Or young Gangrel broodmates could strive to wrest recognition of their independence from hoary and corrupt elders of the covenants.

A coterie based on a single clan or covenant also gives players a chance to delve into the inner workings of that particular group and explore the range of possibilities it holds. How many ways can one challenge the social order as a Carthian? How many ways can one seek power as a Ventrue?

A limited coterie can also help players who have trouble deciding on a character concept. Simply saying, "Make a character" can overwhelm some players — the possibilities seem too wide. "Make a Daeva" or "Make a Lancea Sanctum character" might help such players by giving them a clear point at which to begin.

Setting

Where will you set your chronicle? The Kindred usually dwell in cities. The larger the city, the more Kindred it can sustain. The size of the city therefore has implications for your chronicle.

Vast urban conglomerations such as New York, London or Mexico City can support hundreds of Kindred, with every office of Kindred governance filled. Every clan and covenant has well-developed social structures with their own offices. No Kindred can claim to know all other Kindred, though. The politics of the undead start to resemble old-time mortal machine politics, with influence brokers promising the support (or enmity) of whole groups of Kindred in return for largesse from the leaders. The characters must work to stand out from their fellows. Conversely, they might be able to hide out or forge an alliance with a whole new faction if their current situation becomes too dangerous.

Large cities have the advantage that the Storyteller can always justify some new character appearing in her chronicle. He just moved from across town, or the characters just didn't happen to meet him until now. Of course, the characters don't know if that stranger is telling the truth… unless they investigate the stranger's claimed background, which could be a whole story in itself.

Second-tier cities such as Houston and Toronto sustain fewer Kindred, so the social structures are sparse there. A large percentage of local Kindred claim some sort of title, or many offices go unfilled because they aren't needed. Even if every clan and covenant finds representation, the numbers of Kindred within each group is low enough that clans and covenants need little internal organization. Individual personalities, grudges and influence can matter just as much as clan or covenant allegiance.

Mid-sized cities offer sufficient scope for Byzantine Kindred intrigue, while not overwhelming players' characters. It's easier to make a name for yourself when your coterie is itself a noteworthy group. On the other hand, if every coterie is worth cultivating for its support, every coterie is worth crushing in order to deny its support to one's rivals. The characters also have little trouble learning about other Kindred in town.

A third-tier city such as Las Vegas or Venice can support only a few dozen Kindred. Such cities might not contain members of all the clans and covenants, which can make their societies highly idiosyncratic. Actual clan and covenant politics hold little sway compared to the personal relationships between the undead. Everyone knows everyone else.

In a small city, the players' characters form a major demographic of the Kindred population. This keeps the characters in the center of plots, but the setting might feel constricted in play. If the players want to explore constantly evolving relationships between a limited cast of characters, a small city can work just fine.

Give thought to the city's age, too. In the New World, many major cities are less than a century old. The first Kindred to settle in the city probably still dwell there, and most other Kindred are their descendants within two or three generations. The alliances and rivalries between those founding Kindred probably still dominate undead politics.

In the Old World, by contrast, many cities are very old indeed. London and Paris have been metropolises for centuries (and significant towns long before that). Rome and Alexandria have flourished for more than 2,000 years. Baghdad is only the latest city in its location, in a series stretching back to ancient Babylon. Equally long Kindred histories can generate local bloodlines, bizarre customs, elaborate traditions, ancient secrets and vendettas whose origins are lost to even Kindred memory.

Many players and Storytellers like to set their chronicles in the nearest large city — perhaps the one they live in themselves — or some metropolis they know through books, movies or TV shows, such as Chicago or Prague. Such a setting has the advantage that players already know a fair bit about it and can easily learn more. Visits to the library can turn up all sorts of famous, notorious or merely eccentric people from the city's history, which might have influenced Kindred history as well. Every significant city also has weirdness in its past and present, from mass murders to quirky monuments that can inspire supernatural mysteries.

On the other hand, you might want to invent a fictional city. Doing so has the advantage that you can create whatever history, geography, local celebrities and colorful locations you want. That's a lot of work, though, and a lot to keep straight. Players do notice inconsistencies and might catch you in one if you don't take adequate notes during play.

Daring troupes might want to try out more unusual settings. In a small city, the coterie could be the only vampires in town. Such a chronicle consists entirely of their interactions with each other and the mortals around them. Here, especially, the players and their characters drive the chronicle. (The first story could be about how and why they come to town.)

The Kindred generally avoid both travel and the countryside, but that doesn't make a travel-based or rural chronicle entirely impossible — just challenging. The hazards of travel could fill a chronicle with suspense, as the characters juggle the logistics of their journey with hunting and staying safe during the day. They almost certainly need ghouls or other retainers, who might be played as full-fledged characters for this purpose. Unlife in a small town or in the wilderness might also be possible if the characters possess the right blend of Disciplines and a great deal of care. For a very unusual chronicle, perhaps the coterie tries to turn an isolated, small town into its collective herd. Even if these Kindred can succeed in conditioning, blood bonding or otherwise subverting community leaders, how do they persuade or frighten the rest of the populace into accepting a role as a food source? If they can do that, how do they keep the secret from the rest of the world? A wilderness chronicle, meanwhile, would focus almost entirely on raw survival: hunting for animals to feed upon, avoiding the sun, and possibly dodging other supernatural creatures who also hide far from mortal eyes.

A Darkened World

Once you decide where to set your chronicle, take that location and translate it into the World of Darkness. Exaggerate the negative in a real-world city to turn it into a hellhole.

Make the slums, barrios and other low-income neighborhoods poorer and more dilapidated. More buildings are vacant, except for squatters. Gang tags and other graffiti are everywhere, the only new paint any building has seen in decades. Many buildings, even people's homes, have broken windows covered with boards or plastic sheeting. The streets glitter with broken glass while garbage chokes the alleys. The only evidence of money comes from the pimps and drug dealers who cruise around in flashy cars. Most people don't meet another's eyes, and they talk as little as possible as they try to avoid the notice of the young toughs who swagger about in gang colors. Boom boxes, screaming arguments, car alarms and the occasional gunshot provide the soundtrack.

Affluent residential neighborhoods hold their own inhumanity. Blocks of apartments or condominiums are built like fortresses. Suburban homes look like they were cloned, with no trace of individuality. Anyone who can afford it lives in a gated community, behind high concrete walls topped with barbed wire or broken glass, and an armed guard at the gate. The very richest people can live in luxurious penthouse suites or private, walled estates — rather more common in the World of Darkness than in most real, contemporary cities.

Strip away any trace of beauty or humanity from the business districts. Skyscrapers become brutal monoliths faced with blank, featureless steel, stone, concrete or glass, or fearsome gargoyles jut from their crenellations. At night, the streets are deserted except for homeless people huddled on grates or in alleys. Let a businessperson have to walk a ways, though, instead of driving into and out of a skyscraper's guarded, underground parking garage, and human wolves appear like magic to demand money. Away from the financial towers, some businesses stay open: bars, strip clubs, nightclubs and X-rated video parlors, with the occasional convenience store or gas station. Out in the suburbs, massive iron security grilles turn the closed shops and offices of strip malls into lines of prison cells.

The industrial district becomes a barren wasteland of crumbling brick, concrete factories and warehouses. Most of the industries shut down long ago, leaving towering machines to rust and collapse onto poison-soaked dirt or asphalt.

Now and then, one comes across relics of a more gracious past, or at least a past with more ornamental tastes. An old church might nestle in between grim office blocks, its stained glass and carved stone more astonishing by the contrast. Older retail blocks still show fancy brickwork and molded concrete, albeit grimy and eroded by time and neglect.

As you design your World of Darkness city, think of places where Kindred might dwell or congregate. Museums, opera houses and other "cultural" locations work well for Elysiums, but so do old rail or bus terminals built in elegant Art Deco or earlier gingerbread style. Feel free to change your urban landmarks to make them more atmospheric: a derelict train station instead of a new one, for instance. Ruined churches are too perfectly symbolic to ignore. Buildings left unfinished and abandoned also convey the despair of the World of Darkness.

Look for other ready-made bits of symbolism, as well. In our sample setting of New Orleans, for instance (see Appendix Two), the entire city slowly sinks into the swamp that surrounds it. The Mississippi River now flows high above the city street level, held back by tall dikes. The city keeps building the dikes higher and higher, but someday the river must triumph and sweep away the Big Easy. Play up the giddy energy of the jazz clubs and Mardi Gras, as well as the city's reputation for sensuality and corruption, and you have a portrait of a modern Sodom or Gomorrah, with the hand of God already poised to destroy it in a new deluge.

General Features of the World of Darkness

As a general principle, keep the ambience of the World of Darkness in mind as you design your setting. For the Kindred, this world is even darker and deadlier than it is for mortals. Consider these guidelines for setting the tone of your chronicle:

• **The Death of Virtue:** People know they live in a decaying, vice-riddled world. They've learned it from centuries of greed and lies from leaders in business, government, religion and every other institution. Cynicism and despair saturate the culture, from tags on the walls to movies in the theaters. Everyone knows that virtues such as compassion and charity mark one as a sucker, ready to be victimized, while justice and faith are words used by scoundrels to hide their sins. True selflessness, love or honor is more rare and precious than diamonds.

- **No More Good Guys:** Did they ever really exist at all? Modern mortals certainly have no one to inspire them. The media has caught possible heroes in sex scandals or taking bribes, or maybe destroyed their reputations just to create a story. Local community leaders sold out or died in the endemic urban violence. The precious few people who genuinely seek to make the world a better place remain voices in the wilderness, their good works obscured by the torrent of cynicism and sleaze.

- **Violence and Fear:** Crime is omnipresent and life is cheap, especially for the young. The poor lash out from frustration and greed, with well-heeled criminals as their antiheroes. Bored rich kids look for thrills in violence and drugs. At every level of society, people find no shortage of other groups to blame — other races, other classes or just people who like other things.

- **Isolation:** Many families and neighborhoods adopt a siege mentality against the rest of the world, convinced that they live surrounded by enemies who want to strip them of whatever they have. Those who are well to do hide behind walls, gates and security systems, sending their children to private schools, careful to avoid anyone outside their class. The less affluent watch out for gangs and stay away from windows, especially at night, lest they become targets. Everyone watches TV instead of talking to neighbors. Churches, clubs and other social groups merely give people a chance to hide from the world together, with a few people who think like them.

- **Madness:** In a mad world, why not go mad yourself? Insanity takes many forms in the World of Darkness. Sometimes it's obvious, like a bag lady talking to herself as she roots through a dumpster, or a junkie ranting through his withdrawal on a street corner. Some forms of madness hide themselves, like the affable family man who molests his daughters. Other lunacies grow from isolation and fear, such as fanatical racism or other forms of bigotry. Many people seek escape through the temporary madness of drugs.

Xenophobia: A Good Thing (for Stories)

If any single emotion dominates Kindred behavior as strongly as the need to feed, it must be fear. Travel beyond city borders is never a safe prospect for the Kindred, even with all the modern advancements in transportation available to them. In fact, most Kindred are so opposed to the notion of travel that they'd rather remain in even the most hideous, dictatorial and oppressive domains and Princedoms than risk packing up and starting over elsewhere.

This section discusses reasons why the Kindred remain in urban domains. Any threat or encroachment to it can make

for an interesting plot twist. Setting these ideas in stark contrast to other story elements can also serve to highlight the unique situations in which the Kindred find themselves. They are masters of their domains, true, but they fear what lies beyond their spheres of control.

Loss of Influence and Status

The loss of allies, contacts and pawns the Kindred experience when they leave their centers of power is often a literal one. It's not just that they don't have access to these things, it's that they might very well be gone for good. No matter how vast their resources are, no matter how significant their influence is or how potent their allies are, many Kindred labor under the paranoid fear that their brethren constantly watch them from positions of superiority, ready to swoop down and consume those resources. More often than not, that fear is justified to an extent. It is much easier to suborn a rival's allies, compromise or eliminate his pawns and silence his contacts when he's not present. Underlings can be trusted only so far, and even those who will not betray their masters are often not strong enough to hold their own against more experienced adversaries. Many vampires have returned home after sojourns elsewhere to find that their fellow Kindred have seized a substantial portion of their untended holdings.

Status among the Kindred is even more easily lost than influence over mortals. Nobody need make any attempt to take it. It simply fades with disuse. An elder who steps away from a position of authority almost certainly finds it occupied by another when she returns. Older luminaries are forgotten, other names replacing theirs on the lips of the Harpies and Kindred on the street. Prime territories have been redistributed among those who please the Prince — after all, the original claimant to those domains wasn't using them. It's another paradox of the Kindred condition that such secretive creatures must forever keep themselves in the spotlight — at least in terms of those who hold power, if not the entire local undead population — or risk being passed over in favor of more noticeable and more useful contenders.

The Kindred Condition

Most wise Kindred do not set a single foot on an airplane that they don't personally own (or which is, at the very least, privately chartered). Commercial passenger jets are simply not an option for any but the shortest of flights. The Kindred circulate too many horror stories — presumably urban myths, since the Masquerade is intact, but powerful nonetheless — of vampires trapped on a plane by flight delays until after sunrise. Whether the Kindred bursts into flame as sunlight enters the plane or he simply collapses, is presumed dead and *then* bursts into flame when carried outside, the result is inevitably be the same.

Trains and ships pose less difficulty. As long as one pays for a sleeper car or a private cabin, one can usually avoid daylight, but these accommodations come with hazards of their own. Ships in particular provide only a limited pool of mortals from whom to feed. In the modern climate of sensitivity to the spread of illness, even a small number of people feeling weak or listless on a ship can draw substantial attention from authorities. A dead body is even worse, and in a confined population, the risk of discovery runs high.

In any case, plane, ship or train, the danger of frenzy is omnipresent. A Kindred in such a situation is surrounded constantly by the scent and the sound of pumping blood. All it takes is an instant's lapse in control for a vampire to literally go berserk in such circumstances, and the results are inevitably extremely messy, damaging to one's Humanity if not one's physical well-being (depending on how well the mortals fight back), and quite public. A vampire on a long train or boat trip is a Masquerade violation — to say nothing of a violent incident in the hands of the police — just waiting to happen.

One can avoid these particular hazards, but it isn't easy. Some Kindred have themselves literally shipped like freight to their destinations, but traveling thus requires hours (if not days) spent locked in a sealed, claustrophobic container. Most Kindred who wish to travel choose to drive, but doing so is slow, and travel is limited to nighttime hours unless a trusted associate capable of handling the task comes along. Even then, the Kindred must find some means of avoiding daylight, and the trunk of a car is neither the most secure nor most comfortable haven.

In any case, the vampire in question must trust her safety to someone else, something most Kindred are loath to do. Ultimately, even those Kindred who are willing to travel on a (relatively) regular basis usually limit their range to those areas that they can reach in a single night's drive.

In a Strange Land

Perhaps the most difficult part of traveling outside their home territory, as far as the Kindred are concerned, is the simple fact that they don't know the area as well. Finding a safe haven in the middle of open territory is hard enough. Surprisingly, it's equally hard to find one in an unknown city.

Certainly, a vampire can rent a hotel room. Even in the best hotels, though, Kindred run the risk of discovery. Sunlight itself isn't the greatest danger, as it's fairly easy to cover the windows and take shelter in a bathroom or closet. Yet, cleaning staff workers tend to call the police when they find corpses in bathtubs.

Even if one finds a relatively secure haven, it's easy — more so than most people realize — to become lost trying to navigate a strange city. The comfy hotel room doesn't do a damn bit of good when it's downtown, the vampire who rented it is lost in suburbia, and the eastern sky is beginning to redden.

Just maybe, if one talks very fast and offers a great number of favors, a fellow Kindred might be willing to provide a few square feet of sleeping space in a darkened room. Of course, phone books don't list vampires, and the Kindred have spent millennia learning how to hide. If one doesn't already know at least one Kindred in the city, the odds of locating one are slim to none.

Where does a stranger feed? Almost certainly, all the prime feeding grounds are somebody else's territory. How long can a newcomer poach without being caught? How does she locate the locals to ask permission? What if they refuse? For that matter,

Kindred aren't the only danger when it comes to feeding. Which parts of town have a heavy police presence? Sure, a neighborhood looks like a slum where nobody would care what happens, but what if the cops have constant surveillance there due to the crack house on the corner? That neighborhood there, how good are the alarm systems? Is the neighborhood watch armed?

Perhaps the greatest threat in an unknown city lies not in violating the rules one knows, but the rules one doesn't. Does the Prince demand that all visiting Kindred present themselves to her? How would one find her to do so? Does she require that all visitors inform the Sheriff of where they're staying? Is a specific covenant in charge, and does it have its own rules? Are members of certain covenants or clans even permitted? Can one feed on the Sabbath? (And for that matter, which Sabbath, Saturday or Sunday?) Are Boy Scouts off limits? What about postal workers? Such esoteric and oblique laws are not common, but neither are they unheard of in domains of particularly tyrannical Princes.

Monsters in the Dark

The notion might surprise most mortals (assuming they knew vampires actually existed), but certain things lurk in the dark and the wilds that even Kindred fear. Despite all the previous reasons for staying home, ask any random Kindred why she avoids leaving the city, and even money says the answer is "Lupines."

The hideous werewolves are the bogeymen of Kindred lore. Kindred fear mortals, true, but mortals are dangerous only in great numbers. Kindred fear other vampires, but that sort of fear usually operates on an abstract level. While it's possible that a vampire attempts to kill his chief rival or arrange her assassination, it's far more likely that he suborns her allies, badmouths her to the Prince or frames her for a violation of the Traditions. The fear Kindred feel toward one another usually has to do with loss of position, status, reputation and resources, not imminent loss of unlife and limb. Certainly exceptions exist — the Prince in most domains has the power to call for the execution of a condemned criminal, and some elder Kindred feed only on the blood of their own — but these are special cases, normally avoidable if one watches one's step.

Werewolves, however, are something else entirely. Most Kindred who have been undead for more than a few years believe in Lupines, even though most have never encountered one personally. Are they brutish animals or intelligent, conniving fiends? Are they a purely physical threat, or do they possess mystical capabilities to match Kindred Disciplines? Do they hunt alone or in packs? Are they dangerous on any night other than those of the full moon? Are they really vulnerable to silver, or is that just a myth on par with the Kindred's own false vulnerability to garlic or running water? Stories and legends among the Kindred differ on all these issues, and one vampire's "truth" is another's urban legend. What nearly all Kindred myths agree on, however, is that werewolves do lurk in the wild, that they have the physical prowess to tear even some elders limb from limb, and that they are both swift to anger and extremely territorial — more so, perhaps, than Kindred themselves. This idea, in turn, leads vampires to wonder what it is that Lupines try to hide.

Werewolves are therefore the most voiced reason why vampires hesitate to travel between cities by car or on foot. Panicky vampires can work themselves into a real state, watching for snarling beasts to leap out from behind every tree. More level-headed Kindred acknowledge that werewolves probably have better things to do than sit around watching highways and back roads on the off chance a vampire should happen to cruise by — but then again, why take the chance?

Of course, while they are by far the most feared of the night's other denizens, Lupines are hardly the only mysterious creatures that Kindred might encounter abroad. Mortal witches and warlocks exist who possess spells and abilities that make them a threat to all but the most powerful vampires. In some ways, they're even more dangerous than Lupines, because a vampire can usually at least see a werewolf coming. Demons summoned from God knows where manifest in the foulest, darkest places of the world, threatening not merely one's unlife but one's soul. And beyond even these are other, more esoteric and unnamable things with which the Kindred have little or no experience.

Sure, many of these creatures may be found in cities more so than in the wild, but at least a Kindred can be fairly sure such horrors don't exist in her home city — or, if they do, they keep to themselves. After all, they haven't bothered her yet, have they? Travel elsewhere and all bets are off. The possibility of violating some obscure rule or poaching an elder's territory is danger enough. The risk of crossing paths with a ravening demon or blood-boiling warlock, though less likely, is more terrifying.

A Shrinking World

As implied by the Kindred need to remain in the cities, each Kindred domain is its own sovereign territory, a kingdom in miniature in which — for the most part — an absolute ruler and hierarchy reigns over the inhabitants with unquestioned authority. That said, the modern world is not the Middle Ages (no matter how much it might resemble them from inside certain domains). Not even the Kindred can escape the fact that technological advancements have bridged the global community as never before. Despite their instincts (and in some cases, desires) for isolation, Kindred do interact with their counterparts in other cities.

Contact and Communication

Throughout most of history, if a Ventrue in one city wished to send a message to a Nosferatu confidant in another, he had no choice but to trust his words to a messenger who could easily wander astray or be ambushed by brigands, enemy soldiers or monsters in the wild. Even if a couriers won through, it required weeks if not months to conduct a conversation or negotiation. It was enough to convince most Kindred to keep to their own domains and not concern themselves with what went on elsewhere unless it became absolutely necessary.

Tonight, the Kindred need merely pick up a phone, type in a password or — if they're feeling nostalgic — lick a stamp, and whatever they need to say is said. Modern innovations provide a means for Kindred the world over to tighten the bonds between them. For the first time, the potential seems to exist for the undead community to actually be a community, rather than a string of individual and independent fiefdoms scattered across the world.

Such unity is unlikely, however. Phone conversations and email are wonderful ways to establish personal connections and to acquire a basic sense of events elsewhere. But they are not sufficient to truly understand the situation in another city.

Consider a hypothetical ambitious Ventrue. She "knows," thanks to her contacts, that Atlanta is an Invictus city. Fine. But what she doesn't know is that it's Invictus only because it has an Invictus Prince, whose actual dirty work is done by Lancea Sanctum zealots. The Prince hates the Carthians, and in the interests of maintaining their own power, Lancea Sanctum Kindred root Carthians out for him. The Prince suffers unbound to dwell there only if they submit to a Vinculum to him, making them more thralls than independent. Unknown to the Prince, a number of hidden (and still free-willed) independent Kindred scheme to sneak in a contingent of Carthians (at which point they might reconsider their own covenant abstinence if the Carthian coup goes anywhere). Meanwhile, a few vampires have turned to Pagan cults out of a debased sense of taboo. It's a far cry from "Atlanta is an Invictus city."

If our Ventrue doesn't travel there personally, she's not likely to uncover much of this intrigue. Her contact might mention some of it if he really tries to be thorough. Odds are, though, he leaves out large portions because he's involved personally, because he's so accustomed to them that he doesn't think to mention them, or because he doesn't know — or doesn't want her to know.

Imagine the difficulties involved in trying to iron this all out; for the Ventrue to get it all straight in her own mind. It's difficult enough even for the Kindred who actually dwell in Atlanta. Now think, "Why should she bother?" Atlanta's not our Ventrue's home domain. She's based in Chicago, for crying out loud. She's got her own mess to worry about. Who gives a damn about Atlanta, anyway?

This, then, is why the advent of modern communications has not drawn the Kindred community that much closer together and why it's not likely to do so any time soon. This sort of thing is wonderful for personal contacts and private arrangements, but nothing on a domain-wide scale. It also helps explain the perspective of some elders who, concerned by the dangers that video cameras and satellite feeds pose to the Masquerade, feel that modern technology is a far greater danger to the Kindred than it is an advantage.

Travel Arrangements

As mentioned previously, the idea that no Kindred ever travels simply isn't true. Obviously, they have done so, for they have expanded alongside humanity until they can be found in every region of the globe. Modern conveniences and conveyances do not offer foolproof means of travel, but they make it far easier than ever before. Maybe a certain Kindred flees a blood hunt, he has to conclude an arrangement with a clanmate in Toronto that requires face-to-face contact, or maybe he just feels the need to begin anew elsewhere. Sometimes, no matter the hazards, a vampire just has to pack up and go.

A trip to another city requires extensive preparation. Optimally, retainers are involved in every step of the process. The wise Kindred sends proxies ahead to locate a safe haven or three, and if possible some of the local vampires to whom the Kindred might present himself and from whom he may learn the basic rules of the city.

The second step is to plan for the trip itself. Whether they involve the purchase of passage or the planning of routes, travel arrangements must be absolutely meticulous and must allow substantial time for error. Being lost on a back road in unfamiliar territory is bad. Being lost on a back road in unfamiliar territory less than an hour before dawn is worse. Only the most foolish of Kindred travels without easy access to blood, whether in the form of willing vessels accompanying her or a cooler full of blood stolen from the local Red Cross.

Many Kindred, if they have the resources, prefer to travel by medical transport, where all their requirements — blood, privacy and a number of attendants — can all be explained as part of the package. Others ship themselves as freight or even travel as a corpse inside a coffin.

All these options, unfortunately, require both money and retainers, and many Kindred have neither.

Themes

This is a world in which virtue cannot count on a foreordained triumph. In fact, most evidence suggests that virtue hasn't got a chance. The only question left would seem to be whether the world will choke and die on its own corruption or just grind on the same vicious round forever — a horrible ending, or horrors without end.

Most people have given up. They merely want a little comfort in the short lives allotted to them. Only blind fanatics seem to care about the world's future, and they would rather cast the world into fire than bend one inch on their ideologies. The few people who achieve real power have chosen to reign in Hell instead of struggling to make the world a better place.

As a race, the Kindred fall in that last category. In some ways, the curse of undeath gives them great power. In other ways, it makes them weaker than the mortals upon whom they prey. Deep down, they know this. If the mortals give in to despair, why would the Damned hope they could make a difference?

Regardless of clan, covenant or setting, the players' characters face the choice between striving for virtue or surrendering to vice. The choice doesn't have to be stated openly, but it lies at the heart of **Vampire**. Can the characters work to become something more than monsters? Especially when they know that they must sometimes fail? "Doing the right thing" is difficult during the Requiem. It is often dangerous. Sometimes it's hard to tell exactly what the right thing is. Nevertheless, characters might achieve heroism during their tragic unlives by struggling to find courage, compassion or other values in themselves.

Within that broad theme of moral choices and their consequences, you can develop a variety of other themes for your chronicle. A theme gives your game a central idea that organizes stories and ties them together. A theme isn't a "moral to the story" — nothing so cut-and-dried. A good theme is a question. The characters supply their own answers in the choices they make as they react to the situations you present. Suitable themes for **Vampire** chronicles include:

• **The Danse Macabre:** Kindred existence is a ghastly, undercover war of each against all, with power over mortals as both weapon and prize. Young vampires struggle to gain some power and security despite the greed of their elders. Older vampires struggle to keep the power they've acquired and gain more, to use against their rivals. Young and old are both willing to betray other Kindred of their age in order to better their own positions, all the while striking alliances of convenience.

Can the characters avoid the Danse Macabre, or must they participate for their own survival? Can they escape the vicious cycle of needing ever more power to deal with enemies made in past gambits? Can they use their power for virtuous ends? Do virtuous ends even exist in the World of Darkness? Most importantly, can they trust each other, or do they betray each other for the sake of individual reward?

• **Bound by Invisible Chains:** The Requiem brings power and freedom from mortal laws and limitations… or does it? Many Kindred believe that they are the undying masters of the night, at least within their cities. But they bind themselves through favors owed and their own laws — especially the authority of the Prince and the need to observe the Traditions. The intrigue of the Danse Macabre traps them as well, though the tar baby makes a better metaphor here than chains. Kindred grab for power and find themselves caught by the need to direct and defend their mortal pawns from jealous rivals. Their own nature binds them even more thoroughly. The Kindred cannot escape the Beast Within, they can only struggle to restrain it lest it capture and destroy them. Their Vices provide another level of entrapment, and few Kindred manage to escape the grip of their own selfish passions. In this light, is even a Prince truly the master of his fate?

This theme works best in a chronicle about a group of ambitious neonates who want to win offices and titles in their covenant, clan or city's hierarchy. Perhaps they want power for its own sake. Perhaps they merely want to escape the Danse Macabre by winning it, achieving sufficient rank and influence that no one dares to command or threaten them. They must scheme to escape the grip of their sires and parry the attacks of their equally ambitious peers. Eventually, they must challenge the influence of the elders they hope to supplant. Along the way, however, the characters must cut deals and incur debts, make and break alliances, acquire short-term partners and long-term enemies. If the characters ever reach the pinnacle they seek, they might find that they are still not free. They have simply raised the stakes by entering a higher realm of competition. Of course, they must also defend themselves against younger Kindred who want to supplant them in turn.

• **Dark Redemption:** Undeath horrifies some newly Embraced Kindred. They struggle to reclaim as much of their lost humanity as they can and redeem themselves to their own consciences, if not necessarily to God. Characters who seek redemption might try to use their Kindred powers to do good. That could involve anything from destroying a predatory street gang to intriguing for the power to shape the mortal city government's policies toward the poor and homeless. Of course, such characters find plenty of other Kindred to oppose as well. Most vampires consider such altruistic campaigns foolish at best, a threat to their own power and food supply at worst. The characters' own nature presents the most immediate and ineradicable threat, however. One moment of surrender to the Beast could turn a mission of mercy, justice or other virtue into a horrific bloodbath. Can the Damned truly do good in the world, or are they doomed to corrupt and destroy everything and everyone they touch? Can any number of good deeds make restitution for the evils that vampires inevitably commit?

• **Home Lies the Heart:** A vampire's existence is lonely and full of horrors, and a coterie makes a poor substitute for true friends and family. Some neonates try to cling to the relationships of their mortal lives. Can a vampire really go home and reclaim her mortal relationships, or does she merely set herself up for worse tragedy and desolation?

This theme examines the Kindred's separation from humankind. Vampires can never reclaim some aspects of mortal existence, such as daylight and becoming a parent. The Hunger presents a constant danger to any mortal around them. Other Kindred surely condemn the characters for endangering the Masquerade. If a character clings to mortal family and friends whom he may have taken for granted in life, is he just being selfish? Or has he found the only thing in the Requiem that really matters? As for the character's mortal loved ones… what sort of choices do they make, and what are the consequences? Are they blind to their danger or do they bravely risk their lives to help the character hold onto his humanity?

Themes help you focus the events and actions of your stories around a single idea. Your chronicle gains consistency and emotional resonance as the characters see your theme from different angles. As the chronicle reaches its resolution, you can provide a climax by presenting the characters with a situation that forces them to answer, once and for all, the questions raised by your theme.

A chronicle can explore more than one theme. In fact, it's best not to tie every story too closely to a single theme, at least in a long chronicle. If you make your theme too omnipresent or you spoon-feed particular answers to the players' characters, the chronicle might seem forced or preachy. You might choose one major theme but build occasional stories around other themes. You can also combine themes. For instance, the members of the coterie might hope to resume as much of their mortal lives as possible, with all the difficulties that entails, but find themselves drawn into the Danse Macabre by the need to defend their loved ones from the machinations of other Kindred. Quite possibly, each character might explore his own theme. You are limited only by how much work you and your players are willing to devote to developing themes.

Drama 101

Most roleplaying games could fairly be described as "action-adventure." Characters pursue goals and face dangers along the way. It doesn't matter whether the game bills itself as high fantasy, science fiction, western, wuxia, talking animals or even horror. The characters have a problem and try to solve it.

You can run **Vampire: The Requiem** that way, too. The World of Darkness offers characters no shortage of dangers to get in the way of their goals, from mortal authorities that must be kept ignorant to crazed Lupines out to destroy all vampires.

As a Storytelling game, **Vampire** is designed with drama in mind. Drama differs from action-adventure in that characters must make difficult decisions. "How do we stop the Lupine?" is action-adventure. "What should we do about the Lupine? Kill it, hide, try to reason with it, or steer it at our enemies?" is drama.

In drama, there's no obviously right answer, or it's one that characters don't want. For instance, maybe the characters discover that the witch-hunter who's destroying the Kindred is also somebody's best friend from his mortal days. Do they try to stop him, and maybe kill him in the process? The hunter is a murderer. He kills mortal retainers as well as their Kindred masters. He used to be a friend, though. So do they try to reason with him and invoke old ties of friendship? That would be a humane and forgiving approach, but it would deny justice to the slain mortals, aside from being incredibly dangerous if the witch-hunter sees his former friend as just another vampire. On top of all this, the Prince certainly asks hard questions if he learns that the characters have some connection to the hunter. He might even think they planned the murders together.

One simple way to generate drama is to figure out what situations the characters least want to be in — not for reasons of danger, but based on their fears, shames, ambitions and other emotions. Then place the characters in those situations.

As the chronicle proceeds, your list of emotionally taxing situations changes as the characters themselves grow and develop. Old situations drop off the list as the characters resolve personal issues, and new situations are added to the list as the characters make decisions and form new relationships.

A character's Virtue and Vice provide a shortcut for designing dramatic situations. Create a situation in which a character must sacrifice his cherished Virtue to uphold some other aspect of his unlife, such as Humanity or a social debt. Less virtuous characters can find their Vices in conflict with other aspects of their identity. For instance, a Kindred known for pride might find that to achieve revenge (driven by pride), he must humble himself before a rival (going against pride). With a little work, you can devise situations in which characters must indulge Vices in order to achieve Virtuous goals, or even stranger juxtapositions.

For the climax of a chronicle, or at least a story arc, pick the most dramatically extreme situation possible — the situation you think a character would least like to face. Pit the character against her greatest fear, or tempt her with multiple rewards offered by different parties — possibly including herself. If your players are willing to face such situations, they might have the most intense roleplaying experience of their lives, as well as a story they'll recount for years to come.

Plots

As the examples show, themes often suggest plots all by themselves. Your chosen themes can also help you turn a vague notion for a chronicle into a complete plot, by suggesting what sort of choices and challenges the characters face. Like a movie or novel, a chronicle should have a beginning, middle and end, so players know that their characters' actions build to some sort of climax and resolution. You'll have a better idea of how to design individual stories if you start with a clear idea of where the entire chronicle should go.

For instance, let's take another look at that idea of a chronicle built on the rise and fall of a charismatic Prince. The premise sounds political, so you might select "Bound by Invisible Chains" as the chronicle's theme. The neonate characters see the apparent freedom and power of older Kindred, compared to the oppression they experience in their own unlives. Then the would-be Prince offers them a chance to grab that power and freedom for themselves. The attempt at revolution draws them into an ever-deepening mire of intrigue, favor-trading and deceit.

Once in power, however, the new Prince turns out to be just as despotic as her predecessor. The characters have gained the power and influence they sought, but at the price of obligations to the Prince and her other allies. If they break those promises and alliances, they could become hunted outcasts. As the Prince's rule becomes more harsh, the characters must decide where their loyalties lie. Do they join the new crop of rebels that arises, thus risking their power and unlives? Do they stick with their Prince and try to improve the regime from within? Do they sell out their old principles? Do they run away? What you do know is that you want the chronicle to end in a blazing finale of a Kindred civil war, forcing the characters to commit completely to whatever course they choose.

If the characters support the Prince, they must burn with her or slaughter fellow Kindred who are just as idealistic as they once were. If the characters turn on the Prince, they lose the influence they built. They also gain a reputation as turncoats and fair-weather allies. Such a reputation ensures that no one trusts them for a long time, no matter how principled they feel the choice was.

Now you can go through this skeletal plot and block out its beginning, middle, climax and end, along with the sorts of choices you present to the characters. Remember that your actual stories may change from what you plan; this is still just a slightly more detailed outline.

The chronicle should start simply, just because the characters need some time to learn about the city and its other Kindred. (New players also need time to get comfortable with the Storytelling System and the special powers and weaknesses of vampires.) You decide that the first stories center on the characters' Embrace and relationships with their sires, each other and the remnants of their mortal lives. The characters' reactions to undeath and the Kindred they meet can give rise to conflicts and goals that you develop in later subplots. Along the way, the characters discover how much power the older, better-established Kindred have over them — especially the iron hand of the existing Prince.

As the chronicle develops, you show the unrest growing among the city's Kindred as they chafe under a tyrant. Doing so calls for stories, scenes and encounters that give the characters firsthand experience with tyranny. For example, one character might try to continue running a business he started as a mortal, only to have one of the Prince's cronies seize it under the pretext that the character's continuing involvement risks the Masquerade. Another character might see his sire, who has tried to treat him fairly, forced to abase himself before the Prince in order to gain some trifling favor. To cement the image of the Prince as a despot, have the characters ordered to take part in a blood hunt against another neonate whom they've already met. They know the victim well enough to realize that the charges are trumped up or false (or other Kindred mutter as much to the characters). The neonate's real crime seems to be that she insulted the Prince to his face. Older Kindred find ways to weasel out of the blood hunt, but they make clear to the characters that any neonates who refuse to join will be suspected of collaboration with the "criminal," and could face blood hunts themselves.

The introductory phase of the chronicle ends with the characters' first big decision, their response to the blood hunt. If they participate, you arrange for them to be the ones who corner the fugitive. If they don't, the fugitive ends up coming to them. In the end, they join in murdering the fugitive (with all the consequences for someone's Humanity), they turn away and let other Kindred kill the fugitive, or they try to find some way for the fugitive to make the dangerous journey out of town, with full knowledge that if anyone else finds out, they too will face Final Death.

Some time in the introductory phase, the characters also meet an ancilla — probably a Carthian, but any covenant would do — who cautiously opposes the current regime. She speaks eloquently about how the Kindred should govern themselves, while barely avoiding direct accusations about the Prince's deeds. She helps neonates cope with the trials of joining the undead, such as giving advice on setting up a new identity or getting permission to hunt in an older vampire's territory. After the blood hunt, this ancilla becomes bolder and sounds out the characters about forcing changes in the policies of the Prince and Primogen. In this middle phase of the chronicle, the characters might join the ancilla in seeking ways to undercut the Prince's clique and gain power at its expense. Eventually, it becomes clear that the ancilla wants to become Prince herself, and she promises fellow conspirators that her new regime will be far more humane than that of the current leader.

In this phase, the major choice facing the characters is whether to join the ancilla's conspiracy, to denounce her, or to back away and try to avoid the conflict. Becoming a revolutionary sounds more heroic, but as Storyteller, your job is not to force the characters in a particular direction but to present them with choices.

If the characters try to avoid commitment, once again, force the choice on them. Maybe a rival threatens to denounce them as conspirators unless they do what he says, or maybe someone in the Prince's clique demands they prove their loyalty by betraying someone else.

If the characters denounce the ancilla, she goes into hiding and the burgeoning revolution is quelled… for the moment. The

Prince rewards the characters with hunting territories, minor titles or other privileges. Of course, they also gain a reputation as snitches and toadies, and they keep their new privileges only as long as they continue to please the Prince. The ancilla continues her agitation from hiding, and the revolution eventually arises anyway. The characters just happen to be on the other side.

If the characters join forces with the ancilla, they face the challenge of lining up support from other Kindred who might be dissatisfied with the current regime. They find, however, that other Kindred want more than a promise of better leadership. Everyone says they want some more immediate reward or guarantee before they risk their status, influence and possibly unlives in a coup. The characters must do a series of favors for other Kindred in the city. Most of these have nothing to do with political reform and could involve the characters in sleazy dealings. One potential ally might want the characters to help him enslave a prominent mortal bureaucrat or businessman. Another might want the characters to sabotage the plans of her rival. They both want assurances of more favors in the future. They might even insist on oaths to that effect, backed up by curses or Vinculums if the characters or their ancilla patron defaults.

The climax of the chronicle's middle phase comes with the revolution against the Prince. You've already decided that the revolution succeeds whether the characters join it or fight it. Since the revolution involves most of the other Kindred in the city, you can justify its success through the deeds of other undead. Of course, it's best from a dramatic point of view if the characters play some vital role in the coup's success, whether it's a lightning raid to capture the Prince or a dangerous negotiation to secure the backing of a powerful sorcerer. Even if the characters defend the Prince, the ancilla generously offers them a chance to redeem themselves in the new order.

The final phase of the chronicle deals with the new regime's fall from idealism into a new tyranny. Your first thought might be to have the new Prince simply reveal the full extent of her ambition, and that the whole coup was a cunning scheme to seize power. The famous dictum about power corrupting springs to mind. The chronicle's theme, however, is supposed to be one of disillusionment and entrapment. Instead of simply revealing the new Prince as a villain equal to the one before, you could lure the characters themselves into becoming part of the "corruption" and "abuse of power."

In the previous phase of the chronicle, the characters made a lot of promises. Now the Kindred who supported the coup want payoffs. Whatever reforms the Prince and the characters propose, someone whose support they need says, in effect, "What's in it for me, and what's it worth to you?" Someone else finds that the reform hurts his own interests and opposes it no matter what sweetener the characters offer. The characters also find that fulfilling their earlier promises means bending their reformist principles a little… then a lot, as other Kindred test the limits of what they can claim or extort from the new Prince. The various demands and promises inevitably conflict, too. What do you do when you find that you've promised two Kindred your help in destroying the other one?

Eventually the new Prince decides that she needs to make an example of the most troublesome and demanding Kindred in the city, to show the rest that her administration won't be pushed around. You can make the target a real son of a bitch, so the characters don't feel so bad about hauling him in for a forced Vinculum or some other penalty. That makes it easier when they find that two Kindred have irreconcilable differences and one of them has to go, for the good of the domain. Let each story show the Prince giving a harsher response to challenges to her power and a more abrupt, less diplomatic answer to disputes. For a sub-climax, let her order something very much like a command of the old Prince's that especially offended the characters. Maybe she orders a blood hunt against some neonate who has made himself inconvenient, or as a way to pay off a political debt.

Once the characters realize that the new regime is turning as bad as the old one, they face their final tests of loyalty and integrity. Another group of Kindred starts lining up support for another coup, using the same techniques that worked for the coterie, while avoiding their mistakes. After all, the characters showed how it could be done and made it no longer unthinkable. They might even face multiple coup plots, as ambitious Kindred think, "Why shouldn't *I* be Prince?"

Thus does the chronicle come full circle. The characters have become the authority figures they once hated and envied, except they are less powerful since they lack their predecessors' age and experience. How do they respond to the new revolution? Try to fight it? Join it, try to convince the new young firebrands that it isn't a devious plot to destroy them, and then hope that they can do it right this time? Say, "A plague on all your houses!" and try to destroy all the Kindred scrambling for power? Where, finally, does honor lie in the world of the Damned?

Now you have a framework for your chronicle's plot, with the main challenges and choices the characters face. As you play through the chronicle, the characters' individual goals and backgrounds will spawn smaller plots. You can tie some of those subplots into your main one. Other subplots will surely remain separate, but provide added conflict and character development. For instance, while the would-be usurper gathers support, she might decide that she could undercut the Prince's power by Embracing a key mortal at a company under the Prince's sway — a company that supplies much of the Prince's wealth and other social connections. But that mortal is also close to one of the players' characters. Alternatively, the characters might oppose the Embrace on grounds of principle, even though they support the idea of overthrowing the existing tyrant. At least one character faces a significant choice with far-reaching consequences no matter what he decides.

Stay alert for potential subplots, both at the start of the chronicle and as it develops. Incorporate them when they enhance the game, and resolve them quickly when they distract the characters too much. Of course, you might find that a number of subplots unexpectedly converge into a new, major plot that the characters follow on their own. If that happens, don't be afraid (or too proud) to chuck your carefully planned thread and follow the new one to its own conclusion. If you and your players find the new story entertaining and dramatic, you have still done your duty as Storyteller.

Other Sample Plots

Other ideas for potential chronicles, and the themes they incorporate, include the following:

• **The Search for Truth:** Secrets and lies permeate the World of Darkness, and the Kindred possess more than their share. Seeking the truth can be both difficult and dangerous.

Some secrets are straightforward: The law-and-order Prince once committed diablerie, and doesn't like anyone probing too deeply into his past as a result. Indeed, the Kindred of other cities form a mystery few Kindred dare to investigate.

Other secrets are more arcane: What is the nature of the Beast and can it be tamed or excised? Even the most metaphysical inquiry can feed back into the game's moral and political themes if someone else thinks that the characters should not ask such questions, or doesn't like the answers they find. For example, the leader of the local Circle of the Crone isn't pleased if the characters find that some cherished mystical notion she espouses simply isn't true.

Such a chronicle centers on mystery and deception. Themes include the conflict between truth and social harmony, the past not being dead after all, and discovering the truth about oneself.

• **Liberty or Death:** The characters are unaligned Kindred who rebel against the heavy hand of their sires. They cannot tolerate the idea of remaining beholden to elders for decades or centuries. Their sires insist that the characters toe the line for the common good, because only strict order and obedience can protect the Masquerade, keep the Lupines at bay, or fulfill some other overwhelmingly important goal.

By going independent, the coterie drives its sires to put aside their own differences to support the traditional order. The characters find most of the city's powerful Kindred against them or at least unwilling to help them, because they don't want their own childer forming notions of rebellion. The Carthians might help or might want to drag the characters into some unfavorable agenda. Can the coterie carve out a niche for itself despite the hostility the characters face?

Relevant themes for such a chronicle include the price and nature of freedom, self-will versus the common good, and how far one will go to get one's way.

• **Golconda:** Rumors spread of a mysterious new Kindred in town who claims she knows the secret of salvation from the Beast. Does the stranger speak the truth, or is she spinning lies to lure local Kindred into some diabolical scheme? Is it all just big talk in hopes of conning the Prince and Primogen into letting her stay? The characters decide to find out. Along the way, they face the temptation of Golconda and the intrigues of Kindred who feel threatened by the message of salvation.

Potential themes include faith justified or betrayed, trust, and the search for redemption.

• **Angels of Death:** Horrified at what they have become and how they were drafted into the Kindred race, the characters set out to destroy their sires and all other vampires — or at least all others who dwell in the city. They fight against their fellow Kindred for the sake of mortals, yet they might find themselves feeding on mortals, too — and of course the mortal populace would destroy the Angels of Death as readily as any other monsters. Existing vampires might even mistake the character for members of the Seven (see p. 71) and fight fire with fire.

Suitable themes include honor and betrayal, the nature of humanity and monstrosity, the limits of justice, prejudice, and becoming what you oppose.

Supporting Cast

Unless you plan a quite unusual chronicle, the players' characters will interact with many other people, both Kindred and kine, in the course of your stories. Before you begin the chronicle, you need to define at least some of those people. It's not possible (or necessary) to write up everyone the characters might meet. If you set your chronicle in a large city, you probably need not bother detailing every vampire in town, at least not right away. The Kindred and kine who matter most for your plot, however, should be designed with as much care and detail as the players' characters. Boring Storyteller characters can weaken the cleverest plot, while interesting, three-dimensional characters can make even the oldest, most familiar story into something that seems fresh and new.

Start with the Storyteller characters who matter most to the coterie, and who appear in the earliest stories. This probably includes the sires of the players' characters. The relationship between sire and childe is one of the deepest, strongest and most enduring among the Kindred, whether they like it or not. Even if a character and his sire loathe each other, Kindred society doesn't let them avoid each other forever. Give considerable thought to the characters' past and present mortal associates, too. Remember that your players can help you brainstorm the histories and characteristics of their characters' loved ones, acquaintances, relatives and important social contacts. The city's Prince and a few other prominent Kindred also probably play important roles. As the chronicle progresses, you can fill in other individuals as needed.

When you design important Storyteller characters, keep these guidelines in mind:

• **Envision the Role:** Each character performs one or more functions in your chronicle. Establish what role you intend a character to play and figure out what qualities he needs to fill that role. In the preceding sample plot, the old Prince needs to seem both tyrannical and powerful so that the players' characters have reason to hate him while believing that they must garner widespread support before they dare to attack him. The ambitious ancilla revolutionary, on the other hand, needs to show sufficiently admirable qualities so that the characters believe she would make a better Prince. She must seem compassionate to the characters' problems, sincere in her devotion to reform, and smart and strong enough to pull off a coup and to govern the other Kindred afterward. Even a minor role such as the anonymous clubber or vagrant who falls to a character's hunger should receive a few moments' thought. When the characters feed, you want to remind them that they commit an ugly deed against people with lives and feelings, not against cardboard cutouts or "blood batteries."

• **Paint a Picture:** Try to form an image of what each Storyteller character looks like. A character's appearance can evoke

the qualities you assign to the role, or can surprise by their apparent inconsistency. If the tyrant Prince is a tall, broad-shouldered man with crew-cut gray hair, who wears a gray silk suit, and who has a retinue of young men in black suits and sunglasses, you evoke the contemporary image of power and authority. If he looks like an aging hippie or a young Jazz-Age dandy, you might have to work to convince the players that their characters should fear him. On the other hand, sometimes the contrast between appearance and reality forms the point of the character. Consider the image of a burly man with a square jaw and a prominently broken nose. This image suggests strength and aggression. Now make this man a member of a character's herd and shift the image to this powerfully built man on his knees, submitting to the Kiss from a smaller vampire. The new image evokes the power and horror of the Kindred.

• **Choose a Name:** Carefully chosen names can enhance the image and role of a character, while inappropriate names can detract form a character. Avoid names that make the players giggle, as they spoil the mood of horror. If you name the tyrant Prince Aloysius, he sounds more pretentious than frightening. A common, abbreviated name like Tom or Billy makes him sound too ordinary. A slightly unusual name such as Brandon or Lorimer helps this important character stand out.

Before you run your chronicle, spend some time flipping through the phone book. Write down any memorable names you find. Not only can you assign these names to the Storyteller characters you've designed in advance, but you have a supply of names ready for cast members who appear without warning. If a member of the coterie suddenly decides to talk to a gangbanger instead of eating him, or chats up a clerk to gain access to city records, you aren't left fumbling for a name.

• **Age:** Both mortal age and the length of time spent undead can matter for Kindred characters. An appearance of either callow youth or enfeebled age can lead characters to underestimate a Kindred. Most importantly, the time since a character's Embrace has bearing on her attitudes to mortals and other vampires. As the decades pass, everyone the Kindred cared about in life grows old and dies. Eventually the character has spent more time among the undead than she has among the living, and her attitudes inevitably shift to match. What insights can a mortal who has seen just a few decades offer to a creature who considers World War I a recent upheaval, and the rise and fall of Communism a short-lived fad? After a century or so, Kindred tend to regard mortals as domesticated animals. They have their uses, and some might be likeable, but they remain creatures of limited life span and awareness… and one shouldn't feel too bad when turning them into food. Elder vampires become inhuman. Not only does their Humanity drop, they develop a detached, ruthless sense of expedience that renders them more alien than any mortal stranger. An elder's passions grow from hopes, fears and habits that have had decades or centuries to grow into obsessions that would seem insane to mortals.

• **Personality:** Pick a few words to describe each character's personality. To make your characters more interesting, pick personality traits that don't obviously fit together or that run against players' expectations. For instance, if you plan for an adversary who will dog the coterie at every turn, you might make him cunning, ruthless… and affable, or even compassionate. Sure, he believes that he must destroy the characters, but he regrets the necessity and hopes he can persuade them to cease their opposition to his plans.

- **History:** Every major character needs a background, just like a player's character does. What conflicts has this character already faced? Who has she loved, hated or feared? Could former friends or enemies appear to complicate her unlife and that of the players' characters? If she's a vampire, why was she Embraced? How did she reach her present status, whatever that is? Design as much of the character's past as you feel her role demands. A character who fills a limited role in the chronicle, such as a street contact or the mortal pawn of a Kindred character, might not require much background. The unlife of a 200-year-old Priscus who plays an important role in a story deserves a fair bit of attention.

- **Quirks:** Little quirks of behavior can help players remember a cast member. Kindred, like kine, accumulate odd habits over time. A mortal who picks his nose while talking to the characters stands out as a disgusting slob. A Kindred who enjoys feeding on mortals to the strains of *Die Fledermaus* establishes himself as a twisted creature of the night.

- **Flaws/Weaknesses:** Everyone has some sort of flaw or weakness that he struggles against… or that he cannot perceive and refuses to admit exists. At the very least, everyone in the World of Darkness suffers temptation from at least once Vice. Define it for major Storyteller characters.

In particular, you need to establish a few weaknesses for the major adversaries of the coterie. An enemy who fears nothing and never makes mistakes is not only discouraging to the players, he's boring, almost as boring as a hero who never does anything wrong. The players will enjoy discovering and exploiting an enemy's blind spots, obsessions or other flaws, while a well-chosen weakness adds pathos or tragedy to a hero who must battle inner demons as well as outer dangers.

- **Traits and Statistics:** Do these last. They're just numbers, and if your characters aren't unique and interesting, the best traits in the world won't help your chronicle. For many Storyteller characters, traits won't even come up — you don't need to supply dots for every herd member or the snitch who tells characters the word on the street. Only important Storyteller characters deserve the same detail you would apply to the players' characters. Most of the time, you can settle for writing down the traits that matter most, such as, "Jackson the Snitch: Intelligence 2, Streetwise 4, Street Contacts 4."

Always try to avoid Storyteller characters who are nothing more than stereotypes. It's easy to get lazy and fall back on a few well-worn images such as the Ventrue businessman or the unbound Gangrel. Sure, many Ventrue are in business, and it's hardly rare for Gangrel to be independent. All too often, though, every Ventrue businessman or unaligned Gangrel starts looking the same and acting the same.

Defy players' expectations. The stereotypes for each clan exist for a reason. The clans do tend to select certain sorts of people from certain walks of life. Those are only tendencies, though, not ironclad rules, and even tendencies are vague enough to hold many variations in the details. A character who seems to fall squarely into the mainstream of a clan's image can be personalized to become a unique and interesting individual.

Consider that stereotypical Ventrue businessman who wields a controlling share of one of the city's major corporations. He (of course a he) should be cool and arrogant in his power, refined in his tastes. Yawn. Now let's put a few spins on the stereotype.

Ventrue One spent most of his mortal life as a surfer. Daddy dragged him into leading the family business' branch office in the city, and then a Kindred turned him into a vampire to strengthen a stranglehold on local industry. Ventrue One still has long, sun-streaked hair and lounges around in shorts and a T-shirt whenever he can escape the office… and when the wind blows strongly at night, he's out with his board again, riding the waves.

Ventrue Two is a woman. She graduated from business school and clawed her way up the corporate ladder until she hit the glass ceiling. Her sire saw her as an eternal secretary, but she had other ideas. Now she has her own company, and she ruthlessly competes to crush every former boss whom she feels has held her back. Her herd consists of her own secretarial pool… all young, male, fit, tan and looking scrumptious in identical bespoke slacks and sport jackets.

Ventrue Three made his fortune in real estate. He became successful enough that his sire saw him as a way to become the one-stop supplier for Kindred in need of havens. The fact that Ventrue Three already had a wife and children did not matter to his sire. Some years later, Ventrue Three's sire suffered an accident that destroyed him. Ventrue Three now holds back from political machinations, though many Kindred still request his help in securing havens. Ventrue Three's great secret is that he drank his son dry in frenzy… and, mad with horror and remorse, Embraced him immediately afterward. The rest of his mortal family now serves as his blood-bound and conditioned retainers, hiding and protecting his undead son.

Yes, they are all Ventrue businessmen, but players would never forget who's who.

Crafting Stories

You've outlined the chronicle you want to tell, designed a setting and detailed the major Storyteller characters who inhabit your World of Darkness. For their part, your players have created their own characters and made suggestions that you've incorporated into your plot and setting. It's time to begin play and turn this mass of notions into actual stories. Now all that background work starts paying off because you know your world well enough to concentrate on telling stories and to improvise when the players' characters do something that you don't expect.

Preludes

As an introduction to your chronicle, you might want to run a brief, solo story about each character's Embrace — a set of preludes. Some Storytellers prefer to just talk over these details with their players, so they can launch straight into the main plot. The Embrace is perhaps the most important event in a character's unlife, though. It deserves a little extra attention. A prelude helps players get to know their characters before the chronicle really begins. It's a chance to establish relationships with the supporting cast members who matter most, especially a character's sire, and to find out how each character feels about his Requiem.

It's also tremendously dramatic. Indeed, you can't get much more dramatic than your own death. The Embrace occurs in a moment of hot pain and spurting blood as the sire does the deed. Does the character accept the Embrace willingly, seduced by his sire's promises? Does he even ask for it? Or is he taken by force, violated as if by rape? Whether the character wants to become a vampire or not, the Kiss quickly turns terror into ecstasy, wiping away any resistance. As the character's blood drains away to feed his sire, he feels himself dying, but it's far too late to struggle, assuming he could think past the pleasure of the Kiss. He sinks into darkness and death. And then…

…he's back. Back in a body turned cold, with his sire's Vitae in his mouth. And he's so empty. So *hungry*. He smells blood in the air, the warm blood of the living. Driven by instincts he cannot yet name, he rises to attack his first prey, to feed for the first time, perhaps to make his first kill. And then what does he do? By playing out the story of the Embrace and the character's first victim, you can show the conflicts and urges that set the Kindred apart from the kine.

Assembling the Coterie

After launching the characters into their unlives, you need to bring them together into a coterie. Since **Vampire: The Requiem** is so much about interactions among the characters, you can't just have the characters meet in a bar (or an Elysium) and decide to go on an adventure together. That works fine in some genres, but not here. The characters need some reason to associate with each other. Establishing this reason could be the subject of your first story, though you can begin a chronicle with the characters already together. As with preludes, playing out the characters' meeting can help the players develop insights into their characters and how they interact. It might also lay the groundwork for possible conflicts in the future.

How you bring the characters together depends in part on the type and purpose of the coterie. Internal factors such as camaraderie, belonging to the same clan or running a business together can pull members together. External factors such as a common enemy or a shared duty assigned by the Prince can push them together. Some examples include:

• **The Gang's All Here:** The characters knew each other before the Embrace, so they stay together afterward. This decision does raise the question of why a number of vampires would choose to sire childer more or less at the same time and pick a particular group of mortals. (The Willpower cost of the Embrace almost guarantees that no single vampire would Embrace all the characters together, though a creative Storyteller can devise a justification for such a deed.) If the characters form a group with impressive abilities, perhaps a whole faction of Kindred could agree to recruit them as childer and minions, as in…

• **The Sire's Ready Hand:** A group of allied Kindred carefully choose the characters to form a group of elite agents. Each character brings special skills and mortal connections to the coterie. The characters probably had little choice about their Embrace or about working together. They might have been manipulated, deceived or coerced outright. Such a situation can link all the character preludes into one tale of terror, while introducing the characters to the goals and conflicts that drive the chronicle.

• **As the Prince Commands:** For a variation, the characters might be Embraced for personal reasons, but the city's Prince (or some other powerful Kindred) calls them together some time later and assigns them a particular task or responsibility. The characters might be tied together by nothing more than a handshake or by the power of a common Vinculum to the one who assembled them. Aside from this shared duty, the characters do not need to have anything in common. In fact, they might hate each other. Such a coterie can be difficult to play. If the players and Storyteller work to find ways for the characters to set aside or work through their differences, it can lead to some intense roleplaying and Storytelling.

Both of these premises for a coterie have the advantage that they can accommodate characters of any clan and covenant. The players and characters also receive a well-defined goal. (Of course, the stated goal might not turn out to be the real challenge of the chronicle.) On the other hand, some players deeply dislike playing characters who have to take orders. If that's the case, don't use this premise at all, or quickly lead the characters out of their subordinate position. The Kindred who oversees them might meet Final Death, or the characters might find a reason and opportunity to rebel.

• **Outcasts:** The characters are pariahs in Kindred society. Perhaps each character did something so shameful that other vampires despise him. Perhaps a character's sire was destroyed for some crime, and her childer inherit her disgrace. Perhaps a character exiles himself to escape a tyrannical sire. Whatever the reason, the characters have no one to rely on but each other, at least among their fellow vampires. Some characters might seek to acquire enough power or prestige to rejoin Kindred society or to clear their names of a false accusation. Others might simply band together to carve out their own hunting turf, and to defend it from other Kindred. A coterie of outcasts might even declare war on other Kindred. For instance, a coterie of diablerists is outcast the moment any other Kindred discover its goal. Stalking and slaying older Kindred offers such a coterie a fast track to supernatural power, at least in terms of their Blood Potency, but it carries grave risks and exacts a terrible price on the characters' souls.

• **Spirits of Like Mind:** The predatory and territorial nature of the Kindred does not prevent them from forming relationships based on shared experiences or common interests. A shared belief or goal could draw together Kindred from diverse clans, and perhaps even from different covenants (though the covenants are themselves based on common interests).

A coterie might share a relatively straightforward goal, such as the aforementioned outcasts who work together to seize a hunting ground. Common enemies, such as a force of Lupines or mortal mages systematically destroying the city's Kindred, offer another simple reason to work together. A coterie could also follow political goals, such as the sample plot's revolt against a tyrannical Prince, or protecting mortal society from undead manipulation. Characters might feel conflicts of loyalty between their common goal and any ties to clan, covenant or sire.

Conflict Within the Coterie

Some of these coterie premises assume a greater or lesser degree of conflict among the characters. You and your players might want to discuss the degree of internal conflict and treachery you can accept in a chronicle. Tastes differ. For some players, having characters at each other's throats (when they aren't stabbing each other in the back) offers unparalleled roleplaying opportunities. Other players prefer characters to cooperate, and think that betrayal among the characters is an insult to other players. They would rather see treachery limited to Kindred outside the coterie, while their characters remain honorably loyal to each other.

Ambition and manipulation, however, are built-in parts of the Kindred condition. While you should never force betrayal on characters (and players) who don't want it, the mere possibility of treachery, deception and hidden agendas is a powerful theme that a Storyteller can draw upon to evoke the ultimately lonely, isolated horror of being a vampire. It's enough to assemble a group of characters with potentially opposing goals. In proper dramatic fashion, you offer choices. At various points in the chronicle, set up situations in which characters could follow personal agendas at the expense of group's objectives, and let them decide what to do.

Consider a coterie in which one character sees diablerie as a way to take revenge on other Kindred for being dragged into undeath. Another member has political ambitions and wants to curry favor with the city's older and more powerful vampires. A third member thinks he's fallen in love with one of the city's Primogen. Each of these three characters might face some temptation to exploit another member's goals. The diablerist could pretend to help the would-be lover pursue his passion, in hopes of gaining unguarded access to the Primogen. The lover could feel bound to expose the diablerist for the sake of the Primogen, or he might see the social climber's schmoozing as a way to get close to his love. The political aspirant, meanwhile, could see a chance to manipulate the other two, first assisting in the destruction of the Primogen and then betraying the diablerist in hopes of winning a place among the city's elite. Or they could keep faith with each other. All three might decide that their personal goals aren't worth hurting an ally. The choice is theirs.

Interlocking Backgrounds

Whatever the justification for bringing a coterie together, the Storyteller can strengthen the ties among characters by interweaving the people and events of their backgrounds. Two players might say their characters worked for a major corporation before the Embrace. Could it be the same corporation? One character's sister could be the woman who broke another

character's heart. The drug dealer who ruined one character's life worked for another character's sire.

You can overdo this connectivity, though, making it seem like a city contains only a dozen people apart from the characters, and too many soap-operatic interconnections can make the players roll their eyes. Still, it can be convenient to give each character an indirect link to one or two other characters. For instance, you can use one Storyteller character as a hook to draw two players' characters into a story, instead of just one. In the end, the more the characters feel they have a personal stake in a story, the better the chances are that the other characters will go along.

Storylines

Plot is the chain of cause and effect that links the events of a story.

Just like the chronicle as a whole, each story needs a central idea that you develop through a beginning, middle and end. In the story's beginning, you present a situation that drives the characters to act. The middle consists of what the characters do about the situation and how other characters respond to their actions. The situation resolves itself at the story's end.

A good plot needs focus. You should be able to sum up a plot's premise in a sentence or two. For instance:

- The leader of the coterie's covenant asks the characters to convey a gift to the Mekhet Priscus, with whom he wants an alliance. The Nosferatu Primogen, however, wants to block the alliance by stealing the gift.
- Members of a character's herd are disappearing. A Dragon whom the characters have never met before approaches them to say he has a clue.
- A character's mother, who thought he was dead, discovers that he still exists and wants him to come home — but she doesn't know that he's a vampire.

If you cannot explain a plot in a sentence or two, you are probably trying to do too much at once. Very likely, you actually have two or three plots in mind. Pare your idea down into one or two central actions, then work out what causes these central events and what happens once the characters get involved.

Primary Plots, Secondary Plots and Subplots

Not all plots serve the same function. Primary plots advance the overarching focus of the chronicle. They form chapters in a longer story. Secondary plots are more self-contained. They might have nothing to do with the chronicle's main plot, but they provide entertaining diversions. A subplot is a small story that runs alongside other plots and concerns just one or two of the characters.

A chronicle should intersperse primary and secondary plots, with a few subplots now and then. Unless a chronicle is very brief and focused, it just doesn't make sense that *everything* that happens to the coterie revolves around one conflict or situation. Secondary plots and subplots let you develop aspects of the characters that the main story might not call upon. Diversions from the main plot also keep the players on their toes, because the characters don't know whether a particular story has some wider significance. Events that look unconnected to the main story might later turn out to be very important indeed — maybe even if you didn't plan them that way. For instance, the coterie could make an enemy in a secondary story who returns to oppose them in a primary plot.

For your primary plots, refer back to your chronicle outline. Where are the characters in this overarching story? What's the next step the characters must take to advance the plot, or what special challenges or decisions should they face? At the start of a chronicle, most primary plots might involve meeting the city's other Kindred and deciding upon allies and enemies. Returning to the "Revolution" chronicle, one primary plot might involve a character's sire bringing the coterie on a visit to another influential vampire. In the course of this meeting, the characters incur the jealousy of the other vampire's childe, who becomes an ongoing rival to one character, but the coterie also sees the first hint of unrest under the Prince's heavy-handed rule.

Anything goes for secondary plots. They might serve as a change of pace. If the characters have sweated through a series of grim and difficult moral dilemmas in the primary plot, maybe it's time to break the tension with a simple brawl or something darkly humorous. Perhaps they meet a band of enthusiastic, would-be vampire-hunters that possesses more weaponry and enthusiasm than skill, knowledge or sense. The challenge becomes to survive these lunatics and maybe, if the characters feel generous, persuade them to quit before they kill themselves with their extremely unsafe, improvised weapons. If the characters have become a bit complacent about their undeath, maybe it's time to hit them with a story about a mortal family member or lover who becomes a victim of cutthroat Kindred intrigue. Secondary plots also offer a chance to experiment with different Storytelling styles and techniques, and provide transitions between one major story and another.

Subplots are good for character development. They provide extra conflicts and obstacles that can complicate the resolution of a main story. A character's subplot about her attempt to provide for her mortal children without revealing that she still exists as a vampire might conflict with her obligations to her coterie or sire. Another character's attempt to gain favor within a particular covenant might draw her into conflict with a clan leader with whom the coterie seeks an alliance. Such conflicts provide more chances for characters to make decisions that influence the course of the main story.

If you and your players developed characters in sufficient detail, many of your stories will easily spin off additional complications for individual members of the coterie. Use subplots based on a character's background or current activities to further enmesh the character in your setting. Subplots also give players a chance to contribute more ideas and deeds into how your World of Darkness develops. One subplot per character at a time is usually enough, and you don't have to bring every subplot into every story. If your subplots don't leave enough time for the main story to advance, trim a few subplots or put them on hold for the time being.

Stories usually revolve around some sort of conflict. A conflict consists of some obstacle or opposing force that characters must overcome in order to achieve their goals and resolve the plot. This doesn't have to mean a fight, though that's one possibility. Some conflicts take place within characters, rather than between them. Suppose that a characters' patron, a member of the Primogen, asks the coterie to eliminate several key mortal servants of a rival Primogen — without revealing who did it, of course. The characters face external conflict in the form of the mortals' bodyguards and security systems, the need to preserve the Masquerade, and the equal need to conceal their involvement. They may also face internal conflicts. Characters with a high Humanity could balk at cold-blooded assassination, which could spark another layer of conflict within the coterie or between the characters and their patron. Even if murder *per se* no longer bothers the characters very much, one of them might object if he has a personal connection to the victims.

Storytellers should watch closely for chances to present the characters with such ethical conflicts. More than any other conflict, an internal one presents the coterie with a problem that the characters cannot solve through brute force. Indeed, the very point of an ethical dilemma or internal conflict might be that characters must decide what constitutes an acceptable solution. It makes the players think, and it can produce superb drama and roleplaying.

The usual sorts of conflicts break down into a number of categories.

• **Kindred vs. Himself:** The character faces divided loyalties or conflicting desires. He might follow two goals, but achieving one means abandoning the other. The character must therefore decide where his priorities lie: Keep faith with one ally, or another? Seek power, or preserve his Humanity at all costs? Protect mortal loved ones by staying close to them, or protect them by staying away? Even a character's Vice can produce conflicts. For instance, a character known for pride (as a personality aspect) and Greed (as a game trait) might encounter a situation in which he can make a lot of money, but only if he abases himself to another person, or in which he can humiliate a rival but at great expense to himself.

• **Kindred vs. the Beast:** Vampires cannot avoid this conflict, and they never know when it might erupt. Storytellers can exacerbate the conflict with the Beast by creating situations in which a character must resist frenzy, Rötschreck or Wassail to achieve a goal, or in which surrender to the Beast could destroy something (or someone) held dear. In the long term, the struggle to retain or recover Humanity — maybe even to seek Golconda — can form the basis of an entire chronicle.

• **Kindred vs. Kindred:** Individual Kindred might oppose each other because of clashing ambitions, competition for hunting grounds, moral differences, or because they just don't like each other. We've already given several examples of reasons for characters within a coterie to disagree and need to resolve differences.

trabbold

• **Weak vs. Strong:** Differences in status and power can drive conflict between Kindred. On one hand, young Kindred fear and envy the power of their elders, and unaligned Kindred with more attitude than experience chafe at the rule of the Prince, Primogen, covenants and clan leaders. On the other hand, old Kindred fear their resentful childer — but what can they do? If they give away any of their own power and influence, their rivals might gain an edge. The powerful also stick together out of conviction that their childer lack the prudence that comes with experience and could endanger the Masquerade if they were not ruled with a firm hand.

• **Clan vs. Clan:** The clans have their own cultures, interests and viewpoints, which give them grounds to disagree. The Ventrue tend to think they should be in charge; other Kindred often disagree. The unnerving nature of the Nosferatu frequently makes them unwelcome in polite society; they seek to claim the power and status they feel they deserve. The Mekhet yearn to give the whole system of Kindred society some greater meaning, if only they could agree among themselves what it is. All too often, though, the conflict between clans within a city grows from some personal slight that one clan member offers another. Both clans close ranks out of pride, the members of one demanding an apology, and the others refusing to knuckle under.

• **Covenant vs. Covenant:** Each covenant espouses a particular ideology of how vampires should organize and comport themselves, from the strict hierarchy and formality of the Invictus to the modern populism of the Carthians. Believing that you are right usually involves believing that people who disagree with you are wrong, so that gives any covenant grounds for conflict with any other covenant. Any alliance between covenants is most likely temporary, at least as Kindred reckon such things, but a covenant that shows too much hostility could unite the others in a coalition against it. Within covenants, conflict can arise over different interpretations of doctrines and practices. Most obviously, some covenant members may be more willing to compromise with other Kindred, while other members demand strict adherence to ideology.

• **Clan vs. Covenant:** Although Kindred of any clan might join any covenant, each clan favors some covenants over others. The leaders of a clan or covenant within a city might oppose each other and drag their followers into a conflict. That conflict becomes awkward for any character who falls within both groups. You can build a conflict between any other factions or centers of power, too: Prince vs. clan, covenant vs. Primogen, and so on.

• **Individual vs. Society:** Kindred society, like mortal society, has its rules. Some rules, such as the Traditions and the prerogatives of sires and Princes, are explicitly stated. Some are not. Even the Carthians, who deny the traditional primacy of Princes, and the unaligned, who deny any authority beyond their own coterie leaders or even themselves, follow their own standards of conduct. Anyone who challenges the rules of his society, be it Kindred, kine, covenant or clan, gets into trouble with the people who believe in those rules and have a stake in enforcing them. Kindred who endanger the Masquerade by letting mortal associates know they are vampires violate the most important taboo of Kindred society and set themselves and their loved ones up for a potentially deadly conflict. So do any characters who try to change the nature of Kindred society itself, or at least the current regime of the city's vampires.

• **Kindred vs. Mortal World:** The Kindred defend the Masquerade with such zeal because they know that in a concerted war between Kindred and kine, the mortals would easily win. Kindred power depends on mortals not knowing how the undead manipulate their lives. The Masquerade therefore imposes serious restraints on a coterie's actions. Maybe a group of Kindred can use its supernatural powers to subvert, work around or kill any mortal who gets in its way… but every use of supernatural power is potentially a Masquerade breach that the group's members must cover up.

Some mortals do know that the Kindred exist, and hunt them. Some of these people support the Masquerade in order to preserve their own secrets, to prevent panic or to prevent a far more dangerous fascination with the power of the undead. Other vampire-hunters simply lack credibility in the public eye. All sorts of vampire-hunters pose an obvious threat to the unlives of any Kindred they encounter. Hunters who want to expose the existence of vampires present a further challenge, in that characters must discredit or silence them as well as survive their attacks.

The most gripping conflicts, however, arise when Kindred come into conflict with the mortals they once loved. How do you explain to your parents, your best friend or your spouse that you are worse than dead? How do they react if they discover what a monster you've become? When it comes to mortal loved ones, the options for Kindred range from bad to worse.

• **Kindred vs. Other Supernatural Creatures:** The Kindred share the World of Darkness with a variety of other supernatural creatures. They know that ghosts, Lupines and mortal mages exist. Dubious rumors tell of everything from elves to demons to creatures of pure nightmare. Very few Kindred actually meet other supernatural beings, and most would like to keep it that way. Now and then, however, Kindred are challenged by encounters with other dwellers of the hidden world. Sometimes the challenge consists of surviving and escaping (the usual course with Lupines). Sometimes the challenge consists of recognizing the very existence of a supernatural force, figuring out its powers and motives, and carefully working out boundaries that both sides can respect.

Developing the Story

You have an idea for your story; you know which players' characters and Storyteller characters will be involved; you've decided what challenge or conflict the characters will face. Now it's time to plan the structure of the story and block out possible scenes. Most importantly, you need to figure out why the characters get involved.

Character Hooks

"Hooks" are story jargon for factors that draw a character into a plot. In some games, the players readily accept that their job is to throw their characters into whatever situation is presented for them, but a Storytelling game demands a little more attention to the characters' motivation. Kindred don't go haring about, possibly risking their unlives, because some mysterious sixth sense tells them a story has begun. As a Storyteller, you possess a vast arsenal of ways to draw characters into stories. Here are some of the more common sorts.

• **The Carrot:** A character sees a chance to get something she wants. It might be anything from blackmail information about a Priscus to meeting her favorite writer at a late bookstore signing. The character tries to acquire what she wants, and thus places herself on the scene as the story begins. For instance, the person who has the blackmail information wants $10,000 in return, which the character doesn't have, or a fan who's a mage also comes to the bookstore and realizes that the character is a vampire.

• **The Stick:** Some external threat forces the characters to take action. A typical example is the Prince telling the coterie to perform a mission, or suffer the consequences. Or an enemy attacks a character (physically or by slander, personally or by proxy, or perhaps she attacks someone close to the character). Or a character gets involved in a situation to prevent something worse from happening to him.

• **It's My Job:** The character has a professional obligation to get involved. A Sheriff, Whip or Scourge doesn't ask for a motivation when her Prince, Priscus, covenant leader or other superior gives an assignment. This being the World of Darkness, the job might turn out to be something quite different than the character initially thought. For instance, does the Invictus Prince really want the Circle of the Crone Hierophant's murder solved?

• **Curiosity:** If a character possesses a special interest in some subject, any event that relates to that subject might attract her attention. A Circle of the Crone blood sorcerer might want to investigate strange events that hint of magic at work.

• **Personal Connections:** Someone close to the character — a mentor, rival or one of those mortal friends, relatives, partners or other contacts you made the player define — is already involved. This person needs help or has attracted attention that extends to the character. The person might want something from the character, or the character might want something from the person. A character might learn that his old girlfriend is deeply in debt to a loan shark who now demands that she work as a prostitute, or the character's sire draws him into her plot against a rival.

Early in the chronicle, you need to work especially hard to provide hooks for all characters. Character One wants to investigate the museum burglary, because one of the stolen items might be magical. Character Two helps, because he used to be a cop and still doesn't like thieves. Character Three has a contact who works as a museum guard and who was injured in the burglary. The coterie is still new, so the characters might not possess very strong reasons to work together. As the chronicle progresses, the characters probably build up some trust and a sense of obligation to each other. If they don't especially like each other, they might still accept that they have to help with each other's problems and schemes in order to receive help in return.

In the long term, you need to give characters reason to care about the challenges that drive the chronicle as a whole. That was the whole point of negotiating with the players about their characters and the rough premise of the chronicle. It couldn't hurt, though, to review the chronicle now and and ask yourself how well your stories have drawn the characters into the overarching plot. Using the "Revolution" sample plot, for instance, if the characters don't already loathe the tyrant Prince by the time they meet the revolutionary ancilla, you haven't made the Prince's tyranny matter enough to the protagonists. It's past time you had the Prince do something truly vicious to maintain his power at the coterie's expense.

Setting the Stage

As you pique the characters' interest, you need to draw them into the story and set out the challenges they face. You shouldn't reveal everything at once, though. Give them only part of the situation. The players need some goal for their characters to accomplish. To accomplish that goal, they need to follow leads that you plant. If you present them with a mysterious death (that they cannot leave to the police for some reason), they can interview people who knew the victim and search for physical clues. If they try to forge an alliance with an influential Kindred, they need to figure out what she wants and how they can serve each other's interests. Clever players look ahead and anticipate where the coterie's actions might lead. If they don't, they leave their characters open to all sorts of complications and plot twists.

Early in the story, you also present the important characters, if only by implication. For instance, if the point of the story is the search for an unknown person who kidnapped a character's mortal brother, the coterie might never have met the kidnapper before. They know they're after someone, however, so the mystery kidnapper counts as "introduced."

After the first hour of play, the players should have a pretty good idea of what challenge the characters face, what conflict awaits and what other characters matter in the story, even if they haven't met all those people yet. They could, of course, be mistaken on several counts. In the World of Darkness, matters are seldom how they seem. The characters have a direction, though, and the story is begun.

Building the Action

The bulk of the story consists of the characters' reaction to the situation they discover in the introduction, other characters' responses to those actions, and the coterie's deeds in return. The characters learn more about the situation, including a few surprises. They meet other characters, gather information, implement plans and face challenges.

Not every surprise necessarily comes because someone lied to the coterie. Supporting cast members might be misinformed, ignorant or outright deluded. Other characters might blunder into someone's careful plan and disrupt it. For instance, the mystery kidnapper might demand that the characters rob a certain art dealer in order to get the abducted brother back safely. When the characters open the dealer's vault, they find no trace of the piece they were told to steal.

Was the whole situation a complicated setup? Was the kidnapper misinformed about the art dealer or the item? Did someone else buy the piece the day before? Whatever your devious mind has planned, the characters have just experienced a plot twist. The challenge they thought they would face (burglary) was replaced by another challenge. (Where is the art, and what the heck is really going on?). Yet, the main challenge of the plot (secure the brother's return or rescue) still needs resolution.

When you design the middle portion of a story, you need to decide who knows what and who does what, but you also need to leave room for the characters to make their own decisions, including multiple possible courses of action. Storytelling the middle of a game demands some flexibility since everyone reacts to everyone else and you don't really know what actions the characters will choose. You can (and should) furnish hints that some courses of action are more useful than others. Just as you should try to surprise the players at least once in a story, you can expect that they'll surprise *you* now and then. If you know your World of Darkness and your Storyteller characters, you can work out how other people respond to the characters' unexpected choices.

Climax

At the story's climax, all the chains of cause and effect come together. The characters face the biggest challenge and succeed, fail or decide what constitutes success. Their decision and actions resolve the central conflict. Mysteries are explained. They find the missing piece of art and exchange it for the brother. Or they go after the kidnapper directly to succeed or fail in a rescue attempt. Or they discover who pulled the kidnapper's strings, or whatever the real story turns out to be.

Make sure your climax is worth the effort the players and characters invest to get there. This is a golden rule of Storytelling. Arty modern novels might get away with anticlimax now and then, but a group of players who spend hours trying to achieve a goal feel cheated if they learn it was all for nothing. Give them something spectacular at the story's climax: the most wrenching ethical decision, the most dangerous fight, the most enigmatic puzzle, the most difficult social challenge. The rewards, of course, are proportionately great, whether they consist of money, victory over an enemy, social prestige or a brother rescued. Conversely, the price of failure is high as well.

Aftermath

After the climax, the story probably still has a few loose ends. The characters learn the consequences of their choices. Other people react to their deeds. Remaining questions might be answered. The aftermath phase might not need much intensive roleplaying. Much of it can be portrayed in downtime, which you simply describe. You might include a question-and-answer period in which the characters can explore points of special interest, such as, "What does my sire say about this?" or, "What can we find out about that piece of art's history?" Some scenes, such as receiving a reward (or dressing-down) from the Prince, should still be roleplayed — but briefly.

The aftermath connects the coterie's actions back to a wider world. Doing so reinforces the sense that the characters' actions matter to other people, and that they dwell in a greater environment. This, in turn, sustains the players' interest and curiosity. Meanwhile, you may also plant the seeds of future stories. Not every question is necessarily answered, and some Storyteller characters might react to the coterie's achievement by setting their own plans in motion. Such connections between stories turn a series of events and challenges into a chronicle. You already know how your stories fit together into a greater whole. The ties between one story's aftermath and another story's introduction show your players how it all fits together, too.

Technical Matters

There you have the basics of constructing stories and chronicles. Storytelling is a performance art. It's not enough to have a great plot. You must also try to present a story in an interesting, exciting way that draws in your players and makes them feel the horror of their characters' existence.

You learn the craft of Storytelling by doing it. Just as with stories and chronicles, you can prepare for your "performance" by practicing some simple techniques that make your story more vivid. This section also tells how to avoid a few of the pitfalls that can make your chronicle less enjoyable.

Description, Setting and Mood

Horror, especially personal, gothic horror, depends on what you feel more than what you do or what sorts of props are available. How you present people, places and events goes a long way toward making your setting a World of Darkness instead of a World of Action Movie With Vampires or, even worse, a World of Campy Humor. (If you *want* an action-movie or camp-humor style, go ahead. You bought this game, you can play it how you choose. We assume, though, that you bought **Vampire: The Requiem** because you thought a "Modern Gothic Storytelling Game" sounded interesting — so that's what we tell you how to do.)

How you describe a scene determines how the players feel about it. Flat, colorless descriptions of a location or people's actions tend to make the game seem like a tactical exercise. Engage your players' senses through the details you describe. Suppose a player decides that her character spends an evening hunting. If you say, "After a few hours stalking the streets, you find a mortal leaving work late. How many Vitae do you take?" the incident turns cold, abstract and meaningless.

Instead, you could say, "Sick, yellow light from the streetlamps glints off the patches of dirty gray ice on the cracked sidewalk. The hard December wind moans as it blows through the power lines and rushes between the skyscrapers. The cold cuts right through your coat and pants, chilling your flesh all the way to your dead heart. You keep to the shadows when you can, peering into alleys where homeless people might huddle, and sneaking into parking garages where a few cars still wait for their owners. You force your lungs to draw in the icy air, wincing at the reek of garbage and car exhaust while you seek the scent of warm flesh. Hunger sharpens all your senses. Then you hear it — the echo of a door closing in the

depths of one of the parking garages. One set of footsteps tap-tapping on the concrete floor. You break into a run as your hunger rises. He looks up as you dash around the corner. He's a middle-aged man with a comb-over. You can smell his fear mingled with his hair oil as he fumbles for his keys, and then you're on him. He's so warm as you grip him, and your hands feel so cold."

A scene like that makes it clear that the character doesn't just take some Vitae on the hoof. He preys upon a living person. The precise details of the events, the victim and the character's actions make the scene come alive and be meaningful. Sure, you can overdo the descriptions and bore your players with too many adjectives. You can spare 30 seconds or a minute now and then, however, to give your players a vivid scene.

You can also choose details to evoke specific moods. This is especially true when describing locations — and don't forget how a location itself can suggest ideas and associations. Select the details that suggest the mood you want, and minimize anything that detracts from the mood. For instance:

• **Fear:** To evoke fear, provide details that suggest helplessness and vulnerability, or harsh menace. *The children stare at you with round, glassy eyes beneath the single bare bulb hanging from the ceiling. They scamper away as you approach, retreating into the shadows. None of them go near the iron door at the other end of the cellar, and when you approach it, some of them whimper.*

• **Anger:** Actual or implied violence suggests anger better than anything. *Your sire slams the door and stalks, stiff-legged, into the living room. He stands by the cold fireplace, slapping the poker in his hand as he stares into the mirror's blurred reflection of himself. Suddenly, he steps back, swings the poker and smashes the mirror into a thousand glittering shards.*

• **Loneliness or Despair:** To evoke these moods, use images of isolation, abandonment and ruin. *Rank upon rank of dusty, ripped velvet seats descend into the darkness of the theater. As you swing your flashlight about, the beam picks out fragments of time-dulled, golden scrollwork, an old poster of a movie star who died when you were still alive, an empty bottle left on the floor. As you walk down toward the stage, your feet make no sound on the stained carpet and the darkness and silence close in around you.*

Don't simply tell players, "Your sire looks angry," or, "The kids are scared." Use concrete details to *show* them anger, fear or whatever other mood you want to establish.

All this goes for characters, too. Show some detail that individualizes each Storyteller character, that suggests how the players should feel about him or her. You have a tougher job of this than the players do, since they have to create only one vivid character each, while you have to manage a world (or at least a city). Minor characters who appear only once need only one or two details to keep them from seeming like identical drones. Important Storyteller characters should receive all the detail that you can gracefully convey to the players. Get inside their heads to work out how they talk and react to the players' characters. Give them quirks in dress or in how they talk. One character might always wear immaculately polished black shoes and tap the side of his nose whenever he makes a point.

Above all, remember that Kindred characters are vampires. Their bodies are pale and cold, they don't breathe except to talk, they don't eat, and they might not have seen daylight in a long, long time. The older a vampire is, the less contemporary — maybe even the less human — her personality seems. Your description can include manners of speaking, clothing or customs that the character acquired in her mortal life and that went out of fashion decades or even centuries ago.

Dialogue

Nothing reveals a character better than how he talks and what he says. Dialogue is perhaps the most important skill a Storyteller can learn. When characters talk to each other, either within the coterie or between a player and Storyteller character, act out the conversation whenever possible. Actual dialogue reveals more than the bare facts of what a character conveys. It shows how he thinks and feels. Giving each major character a distinctive voice and mannerisms appropriate to his personality helps players remember who's who… no small matter in a lengthy chronicle that might include dozens of cast members. If you can act out a character's expression and body language as you sit at the game table, so much the better. Don't be afraid to ham it up. The Kindred exist in a modern-gothic world of dark passions, madness, extravagant ambitions and bloody horror. Let them act the part.

Acting out dialogue doesn't come easily to everyone, especially when you have to improvise a character's lines in response to something another character says. It also takes a bit of courage for a self-conscious or shy player (or Storyteller). Fear not. Just like your characters, you can improve your skill at conversation with practice. Remember, too, that you are playing a game with friends who will forgive any fumbles. Encourage the players to speak in character. You might even grant an extra experience point at the end of a session for an especially good bit of in-character interplay.

Action and Violence

Remember that these two concepts are not the same. Do try to keep the pace fast and the characters busy doing things, whether they run through alleys or discuss the significance of an enigmatic postcard. You don't achieve much horror with one fight scene after another, though.

Violence is an important part of the World of Darkness. Vampires are consummate predators in a cold and brutal reality. They can't avoid violence, whether it takes the form of grappling with mortal prey or an assassination attempt from an enemy's hired knives.

Combat is seldom an optimum way for Kindred to resolve their differences or other challenges. Leaving aside the game-mechanical effect of Humanity loss, fighting is dangerous. Kindred can look forward to centuries of continued existence. Should they risk those centuries and all they have built and could achieve? This is especially true for old vampires who have spent decades or centuries acquiring rank, alliances and mortal influence as means to get their way.

Even in the World of Darkness, open violence tends to attract the police. If a Kindred slaughters a punk in an alley, the cops probably shrug and chalk it up to a gang vendetta. If gunfire erupts in the home of an eccentric tycoon (who doesn't come out during the day…) and he is never seen again, the cops ask questions. Police asking questions can endanger the Masquerade. Heaven help the vampire who kills a cop. The authorities *never* stop hunting a cop-killer. Again, such a pursuit can endanger the Masquerade… and in the World of Darkness, police who catch up to a suspected cop-killer might decide to save the taxpayers the cost of a trial by killing the quarry themselves.

Most of all, **Vampire: The Requiem** is a game of drama. Characters face challenges that are tests of, well, character, not their ability to rack up a body count. Having someone trying to kill you tends to inhibit moral questioning.

When combat does happen, though, give it the same vivid, concrete description you've practiced for settings and characters. Make it dynamic and brutal, not an abstract exercise of dice rolls and Health points. Bones splinter, blood sprays, gunfire shatters objects, characters run and dodge, leap for cover or collapse in pain. Take the dice rolls as a guide, then quickly turn the results into pulse-pounding action.

"The longshoreman leaps out from behind the stack of crates and screams with rage as he swings the crowbar at Solomon Birch."

(The Storyteller rolls the dice for the longshoreman's attack. Solomon Birch's player declares his intent to intercept the blow. The attack dice produce a dramatic failure.)

"One end of the crowbar slaps into your hand. You hold one end of it, he holds the other. A sick grin spreads across the man's face. What do you do?"

"I whip the bar around to hurl him across the warehouse," the player says. "With Vigor, of course." (The player rolls an attack, then counts up damage: many points.)

"The longshoreman's grip slides off the crowbar and he flies through the air, screaming with terror. He smashes into another stack of crates. The stack falls over and two of them break, spilling portable CD players across the concrete floor. The man lies among the wreckage, bleeding from his scalp, and… his arms shouldn't bend that way. A dark red stain spreads through the sleeve of his shirt. Is that the jagged edge of a broken bone poking through his flesh and shirt? The smell of blood fills the air."

Mystery and Intrigue

In the World of Darkness, few people — Kindred or kine — are entirely what they seem, or seek exactly the goals they say they do. Much is hidden, whether because it's criminal or shameful, or just because someone wants an edge by deceiving the people around him.

So never show the characters everything that's going on. Keep them guessing through plot twists, betrayals, hidden complications and surprising revelations.

Running an actual mystery story presents challenges to Storytellers as well as players. The players might not know how to look for clues, gather testimony or construct a chain of reasoning and evidence. As Storyteller, you need to make an extra effort to give the characters leads so that stumped players don't just sit around in frustration, spinning theories without knowing how to check them out. Know your players. If you have a group of Agatha Christie fans, feel free to present them with challenges to their logic and insight. If they prefer the Mike Hammer approach, make deceptions a bit less cunning and ensure that the characters can find the answer if they show the determination to follow one lead to the next.

Intrigue among the Kindred demands discretion, too. If the players feel they can't trust *anyone*, you've overdone the hidden agendas and betrayals. After all, a betrayal is shocking only when trust existed before. Before one character's treachery can outrage another, the first character must have shown faith in other matters, so the reversal comes as a genuine surprise. An excess of hidden agendas can also convince players that they can never predict anyone's motives or actions. In the most extreme case, Storyteller characters are "plot-bots" whose only motive seems to be to do whatever the Storyteller wants at the moment, with no regard for any sort of consistency. One moment a character helps the coterie, the next he screws it over. Make sure your Storyteller characters have consistent motives in various intrigues, even if those motives have more than one layer.

Plot Derailment

Now and then, players throw you a curve by making a choice that takes their characters way beyond anything you planned. Perhaps they ignore the clue you thought would be obvious. Perhaps they decide to change their relationship to an important Storyteller character without warning, or to each other. Maybe one of the players has a brainstorm and guesses the central mystery of your plot long before you thought anyone could — or maybe the players come up with a completely wrong theory and refuse to accept any evidence of what's really going on. Maybe a freakish dice roll lets them kill a character who is supposed to remain an adversary for the next several stories.

Such situations have no easy or consistent answer. When the characters' choices take the chronicle in an unexpected direction, you should probably let them follow the new story and watch for chances to nudge them back to the plot you had planned. Since you did all that preparatory work to invent the details of your World of Darkness, you should be able to improvise something to keep the characters occupied. If necessary, you can frankly admit that you need a little time to think about what happens next, and this is a good time for snack and bathroom breaks.

Changing your plot in mid-story so the characters can't jump to the resolution pleases some players and angers others. Some players don't really want to short-circuit the *sturm und drang* of their characters' unlives. As long as you provide a gripping story, they don't care if you cheat. Other players want you, the Storyteller, to act as a strictly neutral arbiter of an objectively defined world. If they anticipate the plot, they want their characters to profit by their lucky guess, even if it means ending the story on an anticlimax. Likewise, if they blunder or completely miss what's really going on, they want their characters to suffer the consequences of the mistake, even if it means their characters fail completely.

The same goes for rolling dice. Some players don't mind if you fudge a dice roll to keep the plot moving, whether it's to save the unlife of an adversary who's not yet scheduled to die or to help the characters find an important clue. They simply don't want *systematic* dice-fudging to thwart or help their characters. Other players find such fudging outrageous and insulting.

Talk to your players about dice-fudging and plot-shifting before you start the chronicle. Give them a story they consider both fair and entertaining. If you ever feel you absolutely must violate the standards they want for your chronicle for the sake of their entertainment… make sure they don't catch you at it. Even if the players don't mind you cheating now and then, make sure you exercise this privilege as seldom as possible. If you use it too often, the players will soon feel that their characters can never really accomplish anything. Success or failure is foreordained.

The Commandments

Like any artistic endeavor, Storytelling is a process and skill you develop with practice. At first, the task might seem overwhelming. The main elements to remember break down into five "dos" and five "don'ts."

• **Involve the Players Whenever Possible:** Work their ideas and their character backgrounds into your city and chronicle. Doing so not only reduces the amount of work you have to do to build your World of Darkness, it gives the players a greater sense of involvement in the story.

• **Work with the Players' Expectations:** Remember that it's their game, too. Try to get some idea of what sort of game your players want before you throw them into your chronicle.

• **Work Things out in Advance:** The better you know your setting and characters before game time, the more attention you can pay to telling the story and presenting interesting characters. When the players throw you a curve, you'll be better prepared to respond if you've already worked through your story's twists and turns and pondered possible alternative events.

• **Story First, Rules Second:** The rules are here to help you tell the story, not to get in the way or to turn the game into a tactical exercise. Use the rules you need when you need them. When you can get by with narration and common sense, do so. It saves time that you can spend on more interesting things.

• **Description, Dialogue and Action:** Bring your world to life with exciting descriptions using sight, sound, smell, taste and touch. Act out character interaction through dialogue, with different voices and mannerisms for each character. Keep something happening at all times, and give the characters important choices to make.

On the other hand:

• **Avoid Stereotypes:** An endless parade of identical, cardboard characters can drain the interest from your chronicle.

• **Keep the Focus on the Players:** Don't let your Storyteller characters take over the plot, leaving the players' characters with nothing important to do. Remember that the players' characters probably aren't the most powerful or important figures in the world, but they must be the most important characters in their own story.

• **Don't Forget the Payoff:** If the players work hard and make smart decisions, their characters should overcome challenges and achieve something. If the characters' success is not in proportion to their effort and the challenges they face, the players will feel cheated.

• **Don't Tell Them Everything:** One of the biggest "hooks" in a story is actually for the players, not the characters. They want to discover what's going on! Part of the fun of any story is the suspense of not knowing how it will turn out. Make the characters work to figure out who's really doing what.

• **Don't Abuse Your Power:** As the final arbiter of events, your word is law in your chronicle. Don't use this power to beat the characters into doing what you want. You're playing a game. It's for fun, and everyone wins if they have a scary, good time, whether they follow your script or not. If the players pull the rug out from under your story, call a break to collect your thoughts. This might happen a lot at first, but with practice, you can handle every surprise they throw at you.

Designing and Using Antagonists

When creating antagonists for a **Vampire** chronicle, it's best to keep a few key principles in mind. This section explores those points. It's important to know *why* we recommend certain practices, as well as *how* to implement them. Also remember that you will need to make some adjustments of your own, based on your troupe's style of play, your chronicle's theme and other concerns. If your troupe likes action-oriented stories and your chronicle's theme is "violence is its own vicious cycle," creating an antagonist who never leaves his Edwardian mansion and prefers to fight by stealing his foes' assets out from under them likely leaves your players frustrated.

And that's as good a place to start as any.

Suit Antagonists to the Chronicle

Antagonists need to be a vital part of the story in which they appear. They should help tell that story, not work at cross-purposes to it. A story about back-room deals needs to have a suitable back-room dealer as one of its antagonists. A chronicle that emphasizes the age differences between different groups of Kindred should have an antagonist who's notably older (or younger) than the players' characters. The antagonist is the vehicle by which a story's conflict occurs, and conflict is what makes the story exciting. Mismatching an antagonist with the type of story told only weakens the significance of both.

Vary Antagonists' Methods

Only a fool tries the same methodologies time after time, especially if they fail. Allow your antagonists to learn from their mistakes. If the players' characters soundly thwart your antagonists in one scene, have those opponents wait in ambush the next time. Have them hire additional muscle. Have the antagonists lead with a ruse, hoping the characters move to foil it — and then have them make a well-prepared countermove. These tactics need not apply only in physical combats. An effective ruse can be a political feint made before Prince and Primogen that the antagonist really *wants* to fail, but that tricks the characters into wasting their efforts. An ambush can be a high-politics situation in which the antagonist reveals he has more support than the characters thought, and he wins the vote.

Vampires are Rare

While enough Kindred exist to necessitate a society in which they operate, and to facilitate the formation of various factions, not every antagonist in a **Vampire** chronicle needs to be one of the undead. It takes a conscious act of will to create a Kindred, so most sires have chosen childer who have something to offer the world of the Damned. While your main antagonists are probably vampiric, there's little need for a gun-wielding thug to be Kindred. "Extras" probably shouldn't be Kindred; rare is the vampire who has so many Willpower dots to spare that he surrounds himself with undead cannon fodder. Ghouls, vampire-hunters, mortal vigilantes and regular people who are in the wrong place at the wrong time can all run afoul of vampires, as can other supernatural creatures with whom the Kindred share the shadows. The more the condition of vampirism remains mysterious and rare, the more special players feel as their characters are members of that exclusive culture. No one should ever be "just another vampire."

The Value of Undeath

Antagonists want to improve their own lot in unlife. That's why they're antagonists. Their efforts to do so intrude upon the protagonists' own desires. Such being the case, not every conflict with an antagonist should result in a showdown to the death. Vampires almost certainly want to survive until another night — they potentially have forever in front of them. Likewise, minions don't necessarily put their lives or unlives on the line for the master. Even the most devoted ghoul who *is* willing to die for his regnant knows the difference between dying when it wouldn't help the situation, and dying in an effort of helpful sacrifice. Attackers can make tactical retreats. Political enemies can withdraw from the arena for a while to secretly cultivate influence and return to threaten the characters again. Generic guardians and other extras probably aren't paid well enough to take a bullet for some cruel or aloof employer.

Do the Math

Make sure that you take the protagonists' abilities into account when assigning traits to antagonists. Antagonists shouldn't necessarily mop the floor when they come in conflict with the players' characters, but neither should they be pushovers. It's fine for an antagonist to exceed the characters' abilities (as challenge makes for interesting stories), but she shouldn't be unassailable on all fronts. In her realm of expertise, a good antagonist is probably more capable than two or three of the players' characters combined, but when other members of the coterie come into play, the odds even out or possibly favor the players. Such is the value of teamwork —

which lets you mine the inherent untrustworthiness of the Kindred to add tension to the story.

Beware Incongruous Antagonists

Incongruous characters serve a few purposes, some of which are bad while others are good. Regarding the poor use of incongruous characters, they're either thrown in at the last minute to create some sort of conflict where none existed before, because the players were getting bored, or they're "swerve" characters, whose only purpose is for the Storyteller to lord over the players by saying, "Aha! You fell for the red herring!" Incongruous characters can fit into a story if their alien status helps the story along or illustrates by way of contrast some aspect of the chronicle. Consider an antagonist sent by a greater rival to confound the characters. The rival knows the characters and attacks them where they're weak. The incongruous character initially seems out of place, but some relevant characteristic makes him, in fact, very apropos. An apolitical character in a very political chronicle, say, might seem out of place, but his defeat at the hands of the better-connected characters reinforces the theme that politics are important, and those who exist outside them will be overrun.

Sample Antagonists

The following sections contain profiles of a number of Storyteller characters that you can drop into your stories as you need them, or as models for creating your own characters. As with the antagonists in the **World of Darkness Rulebook**, non-combatant characters are individuals who fill minor or "walk-on" roles. They serve as contacts, they sell secrets and they become vessels. They have a basic description, Storytelling hints to help you convey them as distinct characters, and a basic description of their pertinent abilities. Combatant characters are individuals that, as the name implies, could pose a threat to the main characters of the story. They can be all sorts of physical threats. In addition to a basic description and roleplaying hints, they also have a much more detailed breakdown of their relevant abilities. Note that combatant characters do not always have to be involved in combat — the encounter might have a nonviolent resolution, or the contact between characters might result in some resolution other than bullets and fangs.

These antagonists complement those in the **World of Darkness Rulebook**. The antagonists found there help round out a cast of enemies whom characters can encounter during the course of a chronicle. Remember, however, that meaningful interactions between characters make for satisfying dramatic situations. These antagonists and those in the **World of Darkness Rulebook** aren't meant to be the central foes in a game, or even major figures. They're just here when you need an archetype quickly and on the spot. A wise Storyteller builds his chronicle's central antagonists long before play begins, custom-tailoring them to the chronicle he wants to tell.

Animals

The following examples list some animals commonly found in urban or rural environments. Note: Unlike humans, Defense for animals is determined by selecting whichever is *highest* between Dexterity and Wits.

Specialties are listed in parentheses following their associated Skills. Add one extra die to a dice pool whenever a Specialty applies. Each animal's attack is listed with a total dice pool (including natural weapon modifiers) for the Storyteller's convenience.

Hell Hound

Description: Hell hounds originate as normal dogs who gain supernatural prowess over the course of their lives. In most cases, this is due to being fed vampiric Vitae (thus turning them into ghouls), but in other cases, certain magics of the undead twist them into these brutish beasts. Hell hounds have far shorter tempers than their normal counterparts, except toward their masters. Hell hounds are fanatically loyal, even more so than most canine companions.

The Attributes listed here represent a large guard dog (80-100 pounds) as the base stock from which the beast is created.

Attributes: Intelligence 1, Wits 4, Resolve 4, Strength 4, Dexterity 3, Stamina 3, Presence 4, Manipulation 1, Composure 3

Skills: Athletics (Running) 4, Brawl 3, Intimidation 3, Stealth 1, Survival (Tracking) 3

Willpower: 7

Initiative: 6

Defense: 4

Speed: 14 (species factor 7)

Size: 4

Disciplines: Vigor 2

Vitae/per Turn: 2/1 (this is just Vitae usable for a creature's Discipline; it does not represent the entirety of the blood within a hell hound's body)

Weapons/Attacks:

Type	Damage	Dice Pool
Bite	2 (L)	9

Health: 7

Homunculus

Description: A homunculus is a magically conjured servant that might be found in the service of a Pagan or some other sorcerous type. Its appearance varies. In some cases, homunculi are stunted, impish likenesses of their masters. In other cases, they're animal "familiars" with an outstanding degree of intelligence or loyalty. In still other cases, homunculi are wholly freakish things — disembodied hands that scramble about doing their masters' business, small tentacled horrors that scuttle from sight when the lights come on, or even things less describable with words.

Homunculi can take simple orders and even communicate on a limited basis with their masters. They're not capable of meaningful communication with other intelligent creatures, however.

The following Attributes are typical for a small homunculus, perhaps 10 pounds or so. Storytellers should come up with physical descriptions for exactly what each homunculus looks like. For animal "familiars," Storytellers may wish to consult the **World of Darkness Rulebook** and use the animals presented there instead of an artificial description.

Non-animal homunculi are not designed for heavy-duty tasks. They have a -1 dot penalty to their Health.

Attributes: Intelligence 1, Wits 2, Resolve 1, Strength 1, Dexterity 5, Stamina 3, Presence 2, Manipulation 1, Composure 2

Skills: Athletics 2, Crafts 1, Investigation 3, Stealth 3

Willpower: 3

Initiative: 7

Defense: 5

Speed: 10 (species factor 2)

Size: 2

Weapons/Attacks:

Type	Damage	Dice Pool
Bite or Claw	2 (L)	2
Throttle or Strangle	2 (B)	2

Health: 4

Gargoyle

Description: Gargoyles are large, man-shaped creatures that look like their namesake architectural features. They have minimal intelligence, being mostly designed for the purposes of serving a master or sorcerer. Indeed, some gargoyles truly are architectural features, perching atop their masters' havens and coming down only when beckoned or when they've seen something about which a master might wish to know. Gargoyles are unliving automatons, crafted from stone or some other substance.

Gargoyles are dense, heavy creatures, with rocky skin and features. A gargoyle might weigh anywhere from 250 to 1,000 pounds. This entry assumes a man-sized gargoyle, weighing about 450 pounds.

Not being truly alive, gargoyles are immune to being knocked out, bleeding to death, disease and wound penalties caused by damage.

Attributes: Intelligence 1, Wits 3, Resolve 2, Strength 5, Dexterity 2, Stamina 5, Presence 3, Manipulation 1, Composure 2

Skills: Athletics 2, Brawl 3, Intimidation 3, Occult 1, Stealth 1, Weaponry 1

Merits: Danger Sense

Willpower: 4

Initiative: 4

Defense: 3

Speed: 10 (species factor 3)

Size: 5

Weapons/Attacks:

Type	Damage	Dice Pool
Slam	2 (B)*	10

* Special: Knockdown (See the **World of Darkness Rulebook**, p. 168.)

Certain gargoyles may also use weapons, whether by design or their masters' instruction.

Health: 10

Non-combatants

The following are examples of non-combatant characters commonly encountered over the course of a typical story.

Blood Doll

Quote: "Why do you only call me when you need something? Wait — don't get mad. I need you. Do you hear me? *I* need *you!*"

Background: Some people know about vampires without truly knowing about the Kindred. Of these, some actually yield up their blood to those who would drink it, craving either the thrill of the taboo or genuinely experiencing pleasure from the act. People like these who are subsequently drawn into the vampire scene are known as blood dolls, and they unknowingly walk a dangerous line. As close to real vampires as they are, they are only ever a Prince's decree away from destruction as a possible Masquerade breach.

Description: Blood dolls can have any appearance, but many find themselves among those subcultures traditionally associated with vampires, such as goths, punks, riveteheads and the like. Among these, many wear heavy makeup to accentuate the deathly pallor that their lack of blood produces.

Storytelling Hints: Although they represent great boons to vampires who are in dire straits for sustenance, few vampires truly like to hang around blood dolls. Most don't like the notion of consorting with their food too closely, while others find blood dolls whiny and effete. Not surprising, given that many dolls are addicted to the feeling they receive from the Kiss. Many also become codependent, feeling that they share a bond with "their" vampires, at which the Kindred usually sneer. And yet, a vampire who drinks from the same vessel frequently might genuinely have an affection for her — or the vessel might be part of a certain vampire's preferred feeding stock. Given that many vampires hide their blood-drinking activities with acts of passion, some degree of "pillow talk" occasionally happens, and another Kindred's secrets might not be as safe as he thinks, even if the one who holds the secrets doesn't know that her paramour is a vampire.

Abilities:

Expression (dice pool 6) — Many blood dolls come from performing arts backgrounds, or are otherwise "creative types" with whom the Kindred can stoke their feelings of vitality.

Occult (dice pool 4) — Some blood dolls dabble in "black magic," pagan faiths or other sources of eldritch lore, often bunkum, but occasionally valid.

Socialize (dice pool 5) — Blood dolls are often well read, very experienced or have specialized knowledge that makes for good conversation. Many of the subcultures from which blood dolls often hail have Byzantine social structures and pecking orders not unlike the Kindred's own, giving them an edge, or at least a bit of practical understanding.

Doting Thrall (Ghoul)

Quote: "Whatever you want, my love… whatever you want."

Background: The Vinculum wreaks havoc on those subjected to it. In the case of ghouls, they often have little choice, given that they rely on the same domitor to provide them with Vitae. They don't know that their love is artificial — and even if they do, many don't care. Doting thralls are almost like lapdogs to a master, hanging on his every word and doing their best to please him in the weird, codependent, surrogate-sexuality submission fantasies their lives have become. Still, their love has limits. The doting thrall is presented as a non-combatant because, even though her love for her regnant is extreme, she won't throw herself at impossible odds if she believes she can run away and help her master from afar. Master doesn't want her dead, after all. He wants her… he *needs* her alive.

Description: Thralls come from all walks of life, but almost all have weak wills (the better to be suborned by the Kindred). More than anything else, a doting thrall's appearance suits her purpose. A perverted domitor who simply wants a ghoul to provide sustenance might make a thrall of a kidnapper. A refined Ventrue who uses his thrall as an aide and chamberlain might deck his ghoul in tailored suits. A thrall can appear as anything or anyone, and often does.

Storytelling Hints: As might be expected, many ghouls know more than their share of secrets regarding their domitors. In fact, many Kindred regard their ghouls affectionately and possibly even lovingly. As such, thralls make for excellent moles (almost always unwittingly) or hostages.

Abilities:

Investigation (dice pool 5) — Ghouls seek to look out for their masters and protect them from harm.

Socialize (dice pool 5) — Those Kindred who bring their servants to Kindred functions find that their ghouls are eager to learn about the ways of Kindred society, and often pick up the nuances of its relationships rather quickly.

Rack Visitor

Quote: "Buy me a drink?"

Background: Rack visitors are those nightlifers who prowl the hip, trendy bars, or who while away their lives in the less glitzy but no less popular drinking joints.

Description: Rack visitors fit a wide range of descriptions depending on the local culture and the kind of establishments they frequent. They can range in age and appearance from teenagers with fake IDs to salty old drunks, from glamorous club-wear to blue-collar shirts and denims.

Storytelling Hints: Rack visitors aren't in it for deep conversation or epiphanies of enlightenment. Most of them go out primarily to socialize or to booze themselves numb. Still, much "networking" goes on in bars throughout the Rack, and gossip is the nightlife scene's stock in trade, whether among countercultures or in mainstream whiskey bars. Secrets and leads might issue from Rack visitors' mouths as little more than idle chatter, and enough of them are looking to hook up that the scene is practically a buffet for Kindred looking to feed.

Abilities:

Carousing (dice pool 5) — Rack regulars know how to party, and most are well versed in the art of drinking the night away. These characters are adept at dragging others along on their club-hopping escapades, often to the detriment of hangers-on. (See "Carousing," p. 85 of the **World of Darkness Rulebook**.)

Street Preacher

Quote: "I look, and here before me stands a pale horse! Its rider is named Death, and Hell follows close behind in his wake!"

Background: Among the ranks of the homeless, some find salvation from their desperate lot by turning to religion. Granted, their notions of religion don't necessarily correspond to those of any organized denomination, but as long as it gives them a bulwark for their humanity, few of these street-corner prophets care about the regularity of their "congregations." Heavy on doom, brimstone, fire and damnation, many preachers rant about the imminent end of the world. Others preach a neo-Gnosticism, ranting against the evils of material things and the soulless fools who pursue them.

Description: Wild-eyed and filthy, the street preacher has a windburned face. He might wear a sandwich board proclaiming that the apocalypse is nigh, or he might clutch a tattered Bible close to his chest.

Storytelling Hints: Because they're homeless and often insane, street preachers frequently find themselves ignored. Thus, they might be witness to certain events to which those witnessed don't even consider a prophet a credible witness. When a street preacher speaks about "darkened angels who have fallen to walk among the living," there might just be something to it.

Abilities:

Survival (dice pool 4) — Many homeless people have learned to be acutely aware of their environment, quick to take advantage of whatever opportunities fate tosses their way.

Occult (dice pool 3) — The homeless witness some strange stuff amid the streets, and the preacher is attuned to weirdness and events of Biblical significance. His skewed insight might be just what's needed to gain a fresh perspective on a problem for which the jaded Kindred think they already have all the answers.

Streetwise (dice pool 5) — Homeless people develop an intimate knowledge of who and what goes on in their territory, mostly as a matter of personal survival. With the right incentive they can be persuaded to share what they've observed.

Combatants

The following are examples of combatants against whom your principal characters might come up against at one time or another during a story.

Rogue Ghoul

Quote: "You can give me what I need or I can take it from you. It's your choice."

Background: The rogue ghoul knows what it's like to serve a vampiric regnant as a thrall — and she's had enough. Somehow, she escaped thralldom to her master and made it out on her own. The problem is, she's addicted to or dependent on what being a ghoul does to her. As such, she's taken to a lonely path. She seeks out vampires, either to slay them or barter with them, but always to take their Vitae for her own use. She's savvy and quick and more than a little paranoid, but that's what her path demands.

Description: The rogue has a haunted, hunted look about her. She might go days without a shower, or even longer without access to a mirror. She spends her life hunting vampires, but knows she is weaker than her prey, and she looks it. While she's not frail by any means, she's no match for a vampire in a fair fight, so she skulks about the shadows and dresses the part.

Storytelling Hints: The rogue ghoul's story hooks are as broad as one might expect a soldier of fortune's to be. She's probably under Lextalionis in at least one domain, so helping her probably means courting disaster in more ways than one. Still, she probably knows a great deal about individual Kindred and travels more than most vampires do, so she might have news of outside territories and domains. Is her information worth the danger, though?

Attributes: Intelligence 2, Wits 3, Resolve 4, Strength 2, Dexterity 2, Stamina 4, Presence 2, Manipulation 2, Composure 2

Skills: Brawl 2, Crafts 3, Drive 2, Investigation 1, Larceny 1, Persuasion 2, Stealth 3, Streetwise 1, Survival 2, Weaponry 2

Merits: Resources 2

Willpower: 6

Morality: 6

Virtue: Prudence

Vice: Pride

Initiative: 4

Defense: 2

Speed: 9

Vitae/per Turn: 4/1 (this is just Vitae usable for the ghoul's Disciplines; it does not represent the entirety of the blood in her body)

Weapons/Attacks:

Type	Damage	Size	Special	Dice Pool
Stake	1 (L)	1	Must target heart	1

Armor: None

Health: 9

Disciplines: Auspex 1, Vigor 3

Belial's Brood Fanatic

Quote: "Burn, motherfucker!"

Background: Members of the demonic undead faction known as Belial's Brood despise the established social order and do whatever they want, the Prince's will be damned. Their methods vary from the subtle to the blatant, but their recklessness never wavers. While a few members of Belial's Brood will speak with more "civilized" Kindred, no peaceful resolution between the two groups has ever been corroborated. Sooner or later, any interaction between these disparate vampires turns bloody.

Description: Because they are on such poor terms with the other covenants, the vampires of Belial's Brood are almost always seen dressed for a fight. Their demeanor varies from furtive to aggressively hostile, but they're always ready for a conflict to begin. On the other hand, members of Belial's Brood rarely carry modern weapons, because they rarely have the connections to procure such things. Whether this is a matter of personal preference or because melee weapons tend to harm the Kindred severely is a matter of academics.

Storytelling Hints: While Belial's Brood might be a numerical minority, its activities are not so easily overlooked.

This group lends itself to a search-and-destroy type of Storytelling, one in which an obvious enemy fits the bill rather than the more shades-of-gray intricacies of most **Vampire** stories. Belial's Brood members serve as excellent enemies, or as the impetus to forge alliances with previously rival groups in the face of a common enemy.

Attributes: Intelligence 2, Wits 3, Resolve 3, Strength 3, Dexterity 2, Stamina 3, Presence 4, Manipulation 2, Composure 2
Skills: Athletics 2, Brawl 3, Drive 1, Larceny 2, Stealth 1, Streetwise 2, Weaponry 3
Merits: Allies (Satanic Cult) 3
Willpower: 5
Humanity: 5
Virtue: Fortitude
Vice: Wrath
Initiative: 4
Defense: 2
Speed: 10
Blood Potency: 2
Vitae/per Turn: 11/1
Weapons/Attacks:

Type	Damage	Size	Special	Dice Pool
Machete	2 (L)	2		8
Stake	1 (L)	1	Must target heart	

Armor:

Type	Rating	Defense Penalty
Reinforced/thick clothing	1/0	0

Health: 8
Disciplines: Celerity 2, Resilience 2, Vigor 1

Experience

People learn from their experiences and gain new abilities. They pick up new skills and knowledge, either through deliberate study or through the school of hard knocks. The undead are no exception. Over years and centuries, vampires learn from their successes and failures, hone their Disciplines and mundane skills, and even change their force of will and personality as they compete in the Danse Macabre. Vampires use a similar experience system to the one presented in the **World of Darkness Rulebook**. See p. 35 of that book for more information.

Much of what a character learns falls outside the scope of traits and game mechanics. Really, it's what the *player* learns about the Kindred, the World of Darkness and the Danse Macabre as it plays out in the Storyteller's chronicle. If a character learns the hard way that you don't tell the Prince he's a moron, you don't need some game trait to reflect his new wisdom. Ditto for a character who learns that even a mother's love has its limits when a child is undead. You roleplay transformations like that.

Some changes and improvements are quantifiable, though. A character can become a better driver with practice, or become more persuasive, or learn how to use a computer or fire a gun. She can even become stronger, quicker-witted, stronger-willed or better able to resist the Beast. The character's traits change. **Vampire: The Requiem** uses experience points to represent such change. The Storyteller gives each character experience points for participating in stories. The player spends those points to improve his character's traits or to buy new traits, reflecting what the character gained through deeds and efforts. The character thus becomes more competent and better able to meet challenges in subsequent stories.

Awarding Experience Points

The Storyteller gives out experience points at the end of each chapter — usually at the end of a game session. If a particular chapter takes more than one session to play, the experience points come at the end of that unit of the story. If a particular story is just one chapter long, that's it. The Storyteller may award more experience points at the end of a longer story or story arc that takes many sessions to play through (see "After a Story" on p. 217 of the **World of Darkness Rulebook** for more suggestions on this method). Characters gain experience points for the following reasons:

• **Automatic:** We learn from success and failure alike, both our own and those of the people around us. Each player therefore gets one experience point for her character for participating in the chapter's events.

• **Learning Curve:** Ask each player what his character learned in the course of the chapter. The character might have gained information about another Kindred's deeds, about a bit of mortal society that he didn't know before, or some other tidbit or fact. Alternatively, he might have learned a lesson about his own personality, his limits or his true goals. If the Storyteller agrees that the character learned something important, the player gets an experience point.

• **Roleplaying:** A player can win one experience point for playing the role of her character exceptionally well. Not only did her performance entertain the other players, she showed the strengths and weaknesses of the character's personality. Nothing was out of character. The player stuck to what the character knew, without bringing in the player's out-of-game knowledge, or stuck to the character's motivations even when they became inconvenient.

• **Danger:** The character took risks and showed courage. Dangerous situations challenge a character's ability to think on his feet and use all of his resources. The danger might involve combat, or might be entirely social — a risk of humiliation, financial ruin or personal grief deserves recognition as much as a shoot-out or a brawl. The player receives one point for the character's bravery. On the other hand, don't let players turn this into an excuse for characters to pick pointless fights or to take idiotic risks. Seeking out danger without reason isn't a brave response to a challenge, it's suicidal lunacy… or an attempt to play the system, instead of the character. (For some characters, of course, suicidal lunacy may fall under the rubric of roleplaying.)

• **Coolness:** Sometimes a character comes up with a solution to a problem that's positively brilliant. Sometimes a character does something that has everyone else at the table standing and applauding. Sometimes a character takes an action that unexpectedly heightens the drama or opens a whole new avenue of interest for the entire troupe. When a player is just this damn cool, he should earn an extra experience point or two as a reward.

• **Resolution:** At the end of a long story, the Storyteller might award additional experience points if players and characters did especially well. Did the characters face down significant trials? Did they achieve most of their goals or push the story to a dramatic conclusion? Did the players (and thus the characters) come up with a cunning plan or a brilliant insight that enabled the coterie to survive and succeed? In such cases, the Storyteller can award each player an extra one to three experience points.

Storytellers should keep in mind that the number of experience points they award can influence the success of the chronicle as a whole. If you award too few, the characters advance in competence very slowly. The players might find this frustrating. Their characters go through all this grief, and what do they have to show for it? Awarding too many experience points can cause other problems, as characters rapidly become more powerful than their erstwhile rivals. The 200-year-old Prince doesn't seem very impressive when each of the characters has more dots of Disciplines than he does. Earning two to four experience points per chapter enables players to raise one trait every two or three chapters, giving a slow but steady increase in competence. If you want the characters to gain power more rapidly, for whatever reason, hand out more experience points.

Be very careful to maintain balance among the players and characters when you award experience points. If one character (and therefore player) keeps getting more experience points than the others, the remaining players might suspect that you play favorites. If one character consistently receives fewer experience points, that player might think you hold a grudge. Some characters can receive more experience points than others after a single chapter, but try to make sure that the awards aren't too radically disparate over the course of a chronicle.

Sometimes that might not be easy. Some players genuinely are better roleplayers than others. They come up with better plans or have other strengths that help whatever character they play. Set the bar higher for them. A clever plan from a player who consistently comes up with brilliant plans doesn't merit as much notice. Or if it does, make sure that you recognize other players for their unique contributions as well.

Spending Experience Points

Each player keeps a running tally of how many experience points her character has earned. (The character sheet includes a small section just for this.) As the tally climbs, she can spend those points on traits for her character. She can raise the value of traits the character already has or buy new Skills or Disciplines.

The Experience Costs chart shows how many experience points it costs to buy various dots, or to raise existing traits. Some traits cost a lot more than others. This disparity represents the ease or difficulty of gaining dots. Skills, for instance, are comparatively easy to learn. Characters often develop Skills by using them. Teachers are easy to find. For some Skills, characters can actually go to night school to improve their knowledge and technique. Disciplines, on the other hand, require great effort to learn. The community college doesn't offer courses in Dominate or Theban Sorcery. Characters need to find other Kindred who are willing to teach them, or they must embark on a long process of trial and error.

The cost of improving an existing trait is a multiple of the new dot total sought. To raise a character's Strength from 3 to 4, for instance, costs 20 experience points: 4, the goal, times a factor of five. Buying the first dot in a Skill costs three experience points (1, the goal, times a factor of three).

Willpower presents a special case. Vampires can lose dots of Willpower through siring childer or a few other circumstances. Players can regain that lost Willpower by spending experience, but they cannot raise Willpower dots over the sum of their Resolve and Composure dots. A character who seeks a higher Willpower overall must raise one of those two base Attributes (at which point, Willpower increases for free). Willpower dots cannot be purchased directly with experience for mortals, and therefore ghouls. Their Willpower dots can be raised only by increasing Resolve or Composure dots.

Players cannot spend experience points in the course of a story. A character simply doesn't have the time to study a new Skill, acquire a Merit or practice a Discipline. This restriction also prevents players from spending their way out of difficulties by having characters pull new traits out of nowhere.

EXPERIENCE COSTS

Trait	Cost
Attribute	New dots x 5
Skill	New dots x 3
Skill Specialty	3 points
Clan or Bloodline Discipline	New dots x 5
Other Discipline*	New dots x 7
Theban Sorcery or Crúac Ritual	Ritual level x 2
Merit	New dots x 2
Blood Potency	New dots x 8
Humanity	New dots x 3
Willpower	8 points

* Includes Coils of the Dragon. See p. 149 for more information in increasing Coils of the Dragon.

Where to Spend Experience Points

Although players decide where to spend their characters' experience points, the Storyteller has a veto. When players improve traits, they should spend experience on traits that characters actually used in the last few stories. If a character hasn't done anything scholarly lately, why would his Academics increase? If a character hasn't had an opportunity to use his Animalism in the last few stories, how could he advance his mastery? Even a failed attempt to use a trait could justify an increase, because the character learns from his mistake, but greater aptitude requires some justification.

Storytellers should particularly enforce this rule for Humanity. A character who recently burned down an orphanage, devoured his mother and tortured people for information just doesn't qualify for improving his Humanity.

Most of the time, Storytellers can let players buy whatever traits they want, particularly new traits, as long as a player presents some plausible justification. Players should never feel that the Storyteller usurps their characters and forces them to develop in directions the players don't want. Simply ask each player what her character has done to try to repress the Beast and become more humane, how the character sets out to hone his scholarly credentials, or why he's better connected than he was last month. Best of all, a player can tell the Storyteller of her intent to raise a certain trait in the future. In that case, the Storyteller can work learning experiences and opportunities to use that trait into the next story. The character's desire to improve her abilities or ethics can even provide the driving force for part of the story.

Physical Attributes are a special case. The vampiric form is resistant to change, so when a player spends experience points here to become quicker, tougher or stronger, the character doesn't actually become any more lithe (as with increasing Dexterity) or bulky (as with Strength and Stamina). Rather, the Kindred's body remains the same, and the character's potential increases as a manifestation of her undead nature.

Note that improving a character's Attributes also raises any figured traits that depend on them. For instance, raising a character's Stamina also permanently grants him another Health dot, while improving the character's Resolve likewise raises his Willpower.

New traits such as Skills and Disciplines present special story challenges. A character might pick up some traits, such as a new language or the rudiments of computer programming, all by herself. Such courses of self-study take time,

though. A player should be ready to explain how her character goes about learning a new trait. How does the time she spends on training affect hunting and other aspects of supporting her Requiem?

Many Skills, Merits and Disciplines require a character to find a teacher. For instance, a character who has never held a sword can't just learn fencing (a Weaponry Specialty) without a trainer and sparring partners. This goes double for Disciplines other than Celerity, Resilience and Vigor. Learning a new Discipline means forcing the power of the Blood to manifest in new ways that the character has never felt and can hardly imagine. No mortal can possibly help a character, either. The vampire absolutely must find another Kindred willing to teach her how the Discipline works. A mentor helps a great deal, but mentors are limited by their own knowledge. What's more, mentors demand some sort of compensation for their time and trouble.

Learning a new Discipline, ritual or Coil of the Dragon can become a story in itself, as a character seeks a tutor, negotiates what favors she will perform in return, and tries to uphold her end of the deal. Does the tutor have enemies? They become the character's enemies. Does the character's sire or existing mentor object to her turning to some other Kindred? She might have to soothe someone's wounded pride. Perhaps the character's promises to her tutor conflict with her existing obligations. For some Disciplines, training itself might be an exercise in trust or terror. Suppose a tutor says that to learn the rudiments of Dominate, a student must herself feel what it's like to have her mind controlled and her memories altered. How far does she trust her teacher? What stratagem can she devise to ensure that her mentor does not use her as a pawn?

Lastly, some Merits cannot be taught. Physical Merits, in particular, must be bought during character creation or not at all. No one, for instance, can set out to become a giant and gain that extra Size.

As Christ had his Golgotha, so do I have mine:
Night and hunger and the voice of the Adversary tempting me toward greater evils.
These are the mount on which I dwell, the walls of the house in which I sleep.
— The Testament of Longinus

appendix one: bloodlines and Unique disciplines

I have heard it said that the Embrace is like the original sin,

that as it passes from sire to childe,

and from that childe to his own progeny,

the taint of undeath remains the same throughout.

What such defeated and pious doggerel fails to take

into account is the power inherent in the Blood itself.

We are not bound by the sins of the father.

We can change each individual sin,

make it one of our own choice.

— Dr. Miranda Estes, "Beyond Post-Mortem"

Blood doubly unites us, for we share the same blood and we have spilled blood.

— Jean-Paul Sartre, *The Flies*

While every vampire belongs at least ancestrally to one of the five great clans, some Kindred diverge from those lineages into their own unique bloodlines. Also, Disciplines favored by those five clans hardly exhaust the possibilities of Kindred power.

Some bloodlines exist as purely social divisions. Certain Kindred prefer to identify themselves as descendants of some esteemed vampire from centuries past, instead of being just an ordinary Mekhet, Nosferatu, Gangrel or whatever. Other bloodlines come about because of shame. A Kindred suffers some disgrace in the eyes of clanmates, and that disgrace passes to his childer and their childer in turn. An elder who joins a covenant that is not usual for his clan, and draws his childer in likewise, might also cause other Kindred to call his descendants a bloodline. Such "bloodlines" have no consequence in terms of game mechanics.

When most Kindred talk about bloodlines, they mean a lineage whose nature or inclination genuinely differs from that of its parent clan. True bloodlines stand out because their members favor at least one different Discipline than their parent clans, they suffer a different blood-borne weakness, or both.

Most remarkably of all, some bloodlines practice Disciplines known to few other Kindred. Some bloodlines actually introduce new Disciplines that have never been seen before.

Using new bloodlines and Disciplines is a way for the Storyteller to customize your World of Darkness. The five clans and their Disciplines portray vampires more or less as they appear in fiction and pop culture: the sinister aristocrat, the sensual predator, the deformed monster and so on. Bloodlines can embody narrower or more exotic images of the vampire, whether inspired by folklore, fiction or your own imagination. Most importantly, new bloodlines and Disciplines add mystery to your World of Darkness. Even players who read every supplement cannot assume they know it all.

We begin with five bloodlines and two specialty Disciplines that you can add to your chronicle. This appendix continues with advice about designing your own bloodlines and Disciplines, using the Bruja, Burakumin, Malkovian, Morbus and Toreador as examples.

PLAYING A BLOODLINE MEMBER

Being part of a bloodline allows a character access to that lineage's Discipline (which thereafter counts as a fourth "clan Discipline"). It also adds that bloodline's weakness, which complements a character's existing clan weakness.

For more information, see p. 256.

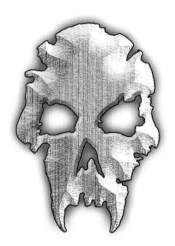

Bruja

Shit, the guy's still back there after a mile and a half! Now that's some quality barbwire!

The bloodline known as the Filhos des Bruja (or Bruja's Sons, or simply the Bruja) seems like something out a nightmare or drug trip from the '60s. It's a motorcycle gang of vampires, ghouls and a few handfuls of blood dolls — all dirty, mean-as-hell, leather-wearing monsters tearing up the American Southwest on roaring black American motorcycles when the sun goes down. It might almost be funny to those who've never seen the Bruja in action, but this isn't some bullshit Sunday-afternoon club for impotent middle-aged men, or another over-commercialized Big Red Machine. These guys are locusts who hate you and who have no respect for notions of domain or the Kindred Traditions.

The gang first formed in the late '40s around a charismatic punk bastard named Carlos Saavedra. Growing up a lazy, no-account orphan during the Depression, Saavedra kept himself amused with petty crime, animal cruelty and a burgeoning love of violence. Yet, no matter how many of his friends got roughed up or hauled down to juvenile detention for going along with his illicit whims, Carlos was never caught, arrested or even so much as charged for anything he did wrong. His uncanny luck earned him the nickname Hijo de Bruja ("witch's boy"), which later became just Bruja. His knack for staying out of trouble couldn't last forever, though, and shortly after he was drafted into the army to fight in the war, he was drummed right back out for drunkenness and incompetence. He was sent back home in disgrace, where he fell in with the Booze Fighters motorcycle gang.

It was some years later when Carlos caught the attention of an iconoclastic Gangrel who became obsessed with transforming Carlos "Bruja" Saavedra into a compliant but violent weapon who could threaten the established Prince in the Gangrel's home domain. He Embraced Carlos and tried to urge him toward the Carthian cause, only to learn that his childe would have none of it. Bruja saw his cursed condition as a newfound power, and immediately went back to his gang to "gift" his six closest friends and accomplices with more of that same power. The seven of them then broke off from the Booze Fighters to form their own gang, the Filhos des Bruja. When Carlos' sire tracked his errant progeny down and tried to correct his mistake, the entire gang jumped him and Carlos diablerized him on the spot.

Since then, the gang's been growing slowly and getting worse. Where it once comprised just seven troublemakers whose nastiest crimes included vandalism, assault and disturbing the peace, it's now become a fairly widespread criminal organization. It makes money in drug-trafficking, prostitution, illegal arms dealing, extortion, smuggling, murder for hire and transporting illegal immigrants across the border, just to give a handful of examples. These activities draw customers and potential victims to them, but they also risk drawing Masquerade-shattering attention from local and federal authorities.

What's worse, Bruja himself has disappeared in the last five years, which hasn't helped to calm the gang down one bit. Before he left, Carlos demanded at least a modicum of restraint when the gang pulled in somewhere to feed — he even advocated keeping the gang's Blood Potencies low in order to maintain the option of feeding on animal blood to take the edge off the Hunger. Without him, though, that restraint is dust in the wind, and it's only a matter of time before the Bruja start descending on isolated Southwestern towns like modern-day Vikings, murdering everyone in sight and razing everything to the ground. It's possible that a more mature Carlos Saavedra saw this potential arising in the gang and rode away from it all in disgust, but it's just as likely that one or two of his treacherous cronies took that option out of his hands.

Regardless, the bloodline remains, and even the youngest, meanest, most ignorant members proudly uphold the values of greed, willfulness and sloth that Carlos espoused before he disappeared. In his name, they do what they can to make his gang a symbol of fearsome power and hell-bound eternal freedom.

Parent Clan: Gangrel

Nickname: Rabble

Covenant: This bloodline is really too small and too young to include members representing all the covenants. In fact, most members' only loyalty (half-hearted and cloudy though it might be) is to the gang and to the ideals of the founder. While that technically makes the entire bloodline unaligned — or unbound, which is the term Bruja preferred — the odd member drifts away and winds up with one of the established covenants. Some members

of the gang have gotten it into their heads somehow that Bruja hooked up with the Ordo Dracul and won't come back until he's become something else altogether. Their conviction inspires some jaded or gullible deserters to follow in his supposed footsteps. Others try to hook up with the Circle of the Crone, convinced that Bruja's nickname *means something, man.* More rational Bruja make contacts with the Carthians when members of that covenant work hard to unseat power players and are willing to turn a blind eye to what the gang is up to in exchange for help. Sometimes said Carthians' passion turns into revolutionary fervor, and a particularly charismatic movement-leader can lure away young, excitable Bruja. No Bruja has ever hooked up with the Invictus or the Lancea Sanctum, though, except as a result of brainwashing, blackmail or forced conversion and acceptance of the sacraments. For the most part, the Bruja try to stay the hell away from those two covenants, lest powerful elders of either (or both) crack down on the gang's whole operation. Not even Bruja himself pushed his infamous luck that much.

Appearance: Most Bruja are black, white, Hispanic or of mixed heritage, anywhere on the spectrum among those three. They're generally big, loud, hairy, tattooed, unkempt, bristling with body piercings and covered in road dirt (if not blood from a sloppy feeding). The way they dress comes across as an homage to every outlaw biker movie that's ever been made since the '50s. They wear heavy leather or denim jackets, hobnail boots, metal helmets (if any), torn-up jeans and T-shirts, with "accessories" like aviator goggles, studded fingerless leather gloves, chain epaulets and bandanas to ward off flying dust. None of them wears any insignia to indicate what gang they belong to, but the bloodline is still small enough that most Kindred members recognize each other on sight. No self-respecting Bruja would ride anything but a burly, growling American bike — no rice rockets — or keep it in anything less than prime running condition. They might be rabble and scum, but they still have standards.

Haven: The Bruja own and/or subsidize several out-of-the-way roadhouses and all-but-abandoned motels out there across the wastelands of the Southwest. They paid for the places with drug money or took them over as a result of too-successful protection rackets, and they've converted them into serviceable, sunlight-proof flophouses. These places aren't much to look at and they have a fair market value of zero dollars, but they aren't on any maps, and they're within easy riding distance of (if not each other, at least) some great places to hang out, to have a drink or to get into a fight.

Background: At its current size, the Bruja gang has adopted a fairly strict rule about not Embracing anyone else unless existing vampires drop out. It happens, though, and when it does, it usually happens to people who are already like the rest of the gang. That is to say, big, tough, hard-riding sons of bitches (or just actual bitches) who want to drink blood and kick ass for the rest of eternity. They're not above occasionally Embracing (or at least creating Vinculums for) criminal contacts for the sake of expediency, and a handful of the really tough hangers-on were random hitchhikers, family men or police officers who got picked up and turned on some cruel whim.

The Bruja are somewhat lax about taking Gangrel they've never met before into the gang, since it hardly ever happens anyway. All a prospective Bruja has to do is earn the local head man's respect (likely by surviving a surprise Bruja beatdown), prove he's connected by blood to Bruja himself, then pony up a bike and get ready to ride out and meet the other boys and girls. Sounds easy, but if the rest of the gang doesn't like him, the Bruja-wannabe starts back over at step beatdown.

Character Creation: Bruja vampires don't tend to be intellectual powerhouses, but neither are they entirely thuggish, apelike brutes. Granted, the bloodline does boast a high percentage of that ilk, but its nominal leaders are just as charismatic and commanding as they are powerful and tough (if not more so). As such, Physical and Social Attributes run a tight race with each other, with Mental ones lagging behind. Most Bruja rely on Physical Skills above all others, followed by Social and Mental as the individual sees fit. Various Social Merits help represent the breadth of the Bruja's criminal operations and the influence and impact they have on the communities they terrorize. It also makes sense to buy at least a second dot of Blood Potency since a character's just a punk Gangrel without it.

Bloodline Disciplines: Animalism, Protean, Resilience, Vigor

Weakness: Founded in indolence and caring little for anything other than their own well-being, the Bruja are given to the same feral urges that infect and overtake their Gangrel forebears. Their predatory laziness has a more serious effect on them, however, when it comes to feeding. Like many predators in the animal kingdom, the Bruja would rather stuff themselves as soon as the opportunity to feed presents itself than hunt carefully every night to maintain a baseline satiation. As a result, a player suffers a -3 penalty on rolls to resist the Wassail (hunger frenzy).

Organization: The extended pack mentality of the gang is the extent to which the Bruja adhere to any form of organization. The founder's closest companions are nominally in charge for now, but only until Bruja deigns to come back and start tearing up the road with his boys again. Said companions constantly vie for dominance among one another, and their bickering polarizes the followers around them, but the gang as a whole puts up a pretty unified front. They're practically of one mind against outsiders who try to give a Bruja any shit, and even the occasional knock-down, drag-out between Bruja rarely results in more than somebody getting a baseball bat across the teeth or a switchblade under his collar bone.

Concepts: Bar brawler, blood-doll pimp, coyote (in the illegal-border-crossing sense), dealer in drugged blood, drag-racer, drug dealer, loan shark, motorcycle mechanic, perpetual omega wolf

BURAKUMIN

DO YOU CONSIDER ME UNCLEAN BECAUSE YOU FIND MY PROFESSION OR MY NATURE ABHORRENT?

REGARDLESS, I M PREPARED TO FIND YOUR ANSWER IRONIC.

The Nosferatu bloodline that has come to be known as the Burakumin originated in feudal Japan within the social stratum of the same name. Beneath the samurai and the soldiers and the priests and even peasant farmers were those mortals whose professions were considered "spiritually unclean" by the tenets of the Shinto and Buddhist religions. Such professions included tanning, leather-working, butchery and the handling of dead bodies. People who made their living from these professions were declared unclean and legally worth less than other people, and grouped in small hamlets far from their spiritually poor neighbors. (Roughly translated, in fact, the word *burakumin* means "hamlet people.") Considered equally impure and valueless by the Kindred Princes of the Eastern domains, Japanese Nosferatu were restricted from feeding on or Embracing from anyone outside that same class of mortal. In time, all of Japan's Nosferatu were referred to as Burakumin, and the name and stratification spread throughout much of Eastern Asia as Burakumin Nosferatu expanded their influence under the cover of various Japanese imperialistic advances.

Strictly enforced by Kindred of higher station, these mandates kept Burakumin numbers small and hemmed in what influence they could garner over mortal politics. Their low numbers and popular concentration greatly aided in the development of their uniquely grisly necromantic Discipline. As more Burakumin throughout the Eastern Courts learned it, they found that they were able to exert greater influence in their society and even to wrest occasional grudging concession from their superiors. One such concession was the right for their Prisci to petition the Princes of their domains for redress of grievances committed against individuals by younger Kindred of higher station.

The Meiji Restoration abolished official discrimination against mortal *burakumin* in Japan in the late 1800s, but where mortals have been slow to do away with their prejudices, vampires are stagnant. The changes in the social climate that have swept past them in the century since have not alleviated the restrictions and conditions placed on Kindred Burakumin. Instead, they have had to strike out on their own and forge their own destiny. Leaving their home domains by the handful ever since Commodore Perry "helped" open trade with the West to Japan, Burakumin have worked subtly to insinuate themselves into positions of influence over major exporters of raw materials. They also worked to gain a small but significant degree of influence over certain manufacturing concerns in the early 1900s as Japan became thoroughly industrialized.

Although their status in the East was limited, the Burakumin's wealth and influence in the West grew considerably. And when Japan struggled to rebuild its collapsed economy and industry after World War II, the Burakumin's various holdings and enterprises were best suited to bouncing back and achieving relative stability. It was also the Burakumin who were most willing to leave their home domains and seek wealth and influence overseas in areas of exporting and industrial outsourcing. In the West, they've come to find status and respect that has long been denied them, and the support they are able to lend their compatriots back East has greatly improved their standing in the eyes of many local Princes.

And in domains where the Burakumin's industrial and financial influence (or meddling, depending on who you ask) is not as welcome, they can still earn respect and recognition for teaching their unique Discipline or using it to profitable effect.

Parent Clan: Nosferatu

Nickname: Unclean

Covenant: In the Far East where it originated, this bloodline has traditionally been forced to remain unaligned. Most remnants of the Circle of the Crone covenant were wiped out long ago in favor of Shinto and Buddhist belief structures (or ones as similar to them as local Kindred could bring themselves to uphold). For much the same reason, the Lancea Sanctum has only very recently taken root there, and thus has never been of much interest to the Burakumin — though Kindred roundly disapprove of the unwholesome practice of their necromancies. The local version of the Invictus still proves resistant to accepting the Burakumin, but Western members of that covenant are considerably less so. Many Western Princes fear the strange power that the Burakumin wield, so they graciously invite Burakumin into their domains and grant them rights undreamed of back home. They do so largely to distract and placate these outsiders in an attempt to keep them docile, content and under control, but most Burakumin have been slow to realize how they are being played. The Ordo Dracul goes largely unnoticed by the Burakumin, but the ones who know about it find it baffling and more than a little oblique. The covenant that has had the most impact on Kindred of this bloodline, though, is the Carthian Movement. It proposes a state of true equality in which every vampire is entitled to an equal share in the spoils of the night, which is what the most vocal and active Burakumin have fought for since well before the Meiji Restoration. Carthian ideals have caught on like wildfire in the once-closed Eastern domains, and the Burakumin who introduced them enjoy an up-welling of underground status and influence unlike any they have ever known.

Appearance: All Burakumin Kindred tend to exude the same disturbing, unclean, inhuman presence, which grows more obvious as their age and Blood Potency increases. As they age, they begin to reek of grave soil, and a stifling tomblike quiet emanates from them when they don't consciously speak or make noise to counteract it. What's more, their bodies take on a corpselike aspect that no amount of Vitae can ever banish completely. Over time, their skin withers and grows leathery until it's no more than a parchment-thin veneer stretched taut over knobby bone.

Out of dignified indifference to this condition (or sometimes out of a sense of perverse irony), most Burakumin dress and comport themselves with fastidious attention to detail. They do the best they can to make favorable impressions on Kindred around them so as to set prospective allies and business partners at ease (in the West) and to keep from giving anyone specific evidence to support unfavorable prejudices (in the East). Elder Burakumin in the East tend to favor garb that harks back to the mortal styles of the late Tokugawa Shogunate and early Meiji Era, while younger and more progressive Burakumin prefer more severe and formal Western professional attire.

Haven: Eastern Burakumin have traditionally been restricted to communal havens in isolated hamlets populated by those mortals who are considered "unclean" by the tenets of the Shinto and Buddhist religions. Young and more urbanized ones dwell in and beneath large cities, yet well away from Kindred of higher station. Westward-looking Burakumin often wind up competing with local Nosferatu for havens, but as they grow more successful, their new homes come to rival those of the Daeva and the Ventrue.

Background: Elder Eastern Burakumin mostly select progeny from among the societal class of the "unclean"

from which they themselves were once chosen. More cynical, bitter ones choose from among the beautiful, noble, powerful or traditionally pious in order to spite those who consider themselves so much more pure than the Burakumin. Bloodline members in the West have not made it a habit by and large to Embrace childer, but when they do, they choose those who can help them achieve their business and political goals and to adapt to their foreign environment.

Character Creation: Burakumin don't tend to have high Social Attributes, especially those who remain in Eastern domains. Neither do they place a particularly high priority on Physical Attributes. Their mental prowess has won them the niche in which they thrive, which leads them to favor Mental Attributes and Skills. Many of them tend to value Social Skills as well, although those propensities do not come as naturally to them. According to their weakness, Status is not a particularly economical buy up front, but other Social Merits (as well as certain Mental ones) can be worthwhile. It also makes sense to buy a second dot of Blood Potency since a character can't officially join this bloodline or learn Getsumei until then.

Bloodline Disciplines: Getsumei, Nightmare, Obfuscate, Vigor

Weakness: Despite the unique power that the Discipline of Getsumei grants, and the relatively newfound wealth and influence it enjoys beyond its traditional cultural borders, the Burakumin bloodline is a decidedly unlucky one. Not only does it share the weakness of its wider parent clan (though a specific variety of it), but it also suffers social stigmas unrelated to its ghastly appearance. Like other Nosferatu, players of Burakumin cannot re-roll 10's for additional successes on Presence- or Manipulation-based rolls, and 1's subtract from successes on those rolls. This weakness is due to the fact that Burakumin closely resemble the decaying corpses that they should be. Upon the Embrace, the Burakumin take on the appearance of cold, hours-dead bodies, and they cannot mimic the appearance of vital life with the expenditure of Vitae. As their Blood Potency increases, their bodies appear to wither and decay as per the natural stages of human decomposition (only matching the pace of the vampire's progression). This appearance of decay does not hinder the physical functions of the vampire's body (even though flesh might constrict and split, revealing bone beneath).

Aside from this physical affliction, the Burakumin must deal with a social penalty as well. Try as they might to build up resources and increase their influence among mortals, line members have trouble fitting in and earning a standing comparable to that of their fellow Kindred. In their cultural homeland, they suffer the long-standing prejudices of an undying elite that cannot keep up with the pace of modern society. While they earn more respect in the West, they suffer a different sort of prejudice for being not only an offshoot of the Nosferatu, but foreigners as well. Young Kindred don't tend to hold such prejudices, but they don't tend to be the ones with all the power and influence in the domains in which the Burakumin seek to insinuate themselves. As a result of these various prejudices, purchasing the Status Merit (in all of its forms) costs double.

Organization: In their Eastern homes, Burakumin have little choice but to come together with others of their own kind, lest they face a Requiem of maddening solitude. Individual Burakumin defer to regional Prisci, who communicate with ministers responsible for passing on edicts from local Princes. Priscus is usually the highest station to which a Burakumin can hope to rise in the East, and though it conveys significant status among other Burakumin, that status isn't worth quite as much to anyone else. Moving West, these Kindred stick together for the sake of familiarity among strangers and in strange lands, but they adhere to no established internal hierarchy. Some scatter to the four winds, never looking back, while others fall in with other kinds of Nosferatu, lacking the ability to adapt sufficiently to their new environments to forge their own destinies.

Concepts: Ancestral avenger, aspiring upstart Primogen, blackmailer, forensic pathologist, grave robber, importer, mortician, private investigator, spectral intercessor, tanner

Malkovians

Forgive me for distressing you, dear lady. I regret my habits have become rather less healthy since my death. I suppose that only stands to reason, doesn't it? But perhaps you have been more fortunate — thus far.

Most Kindred are still unaware of the so-called "Malkovian" bloodline and its peculiar, threatening gifts. The Lunatics are few — a state of affairs that those who *are* aware of them would like to perpetuate, by whatever means necessary.

Among worried Ventrue elders, the story of the Malkovians' origins is now verified. It seems that a certain Dr. James Griffin Hartleigh of England's Broadmoor Criminal Lunatic Asylum once became a bit too interested in one of his patients, an Anton Malkov. Malkov was rumored to be related to the czars of Russia, which was a chief reason, Hartleigh believed, why Malkov had been transported to Broadmoor under cover of night. (After all, the asylum hosted many such inmates whose whereabouts were a secret to all but their embarrassed and wealthy families.) Hartleigh never learned the details of the wretch's crime, but the director had strictly enjoined him never to touch Malkov nor look him in the eye. Moreover, despite being a recluse who rarely left his dark cell, Malkov seemed to exert a strange fascination over the other madmen. Hartleigh found him an intriguing case, and their rambling interviews only fired his interest. Evidently Malkov felt the same way. Or, at least, it's the only reason anyone can think of why he chose to Embrace the staid doctor.

Hartleigh stumbled home that same night and murdered his wife. Even now he cannot precisely recall what moved him to do so. True, he had always entertained certain doubts about her and the cook, but… well, never mind that. When he came to and found himself greedily sucking her blood, even such a font of Reason had to admit that something was much amiss. After hastily covering up his deed (which unfortunately required a further murder), Hartleigh stole back to the asylum to demand an explanation from Malkov. The lunatic drove him away with his mocking, echoing laughter. The doctor never dared return.

After some months of painstaking investigation, Hartleigh tracked down a solitary old gentleman whom he had seen mentioned in Malkov's papers. This worthy was, alas, unforthcoming. Indeed, he seemed quite piqued to learn where the errant Malkov had secreted himself, and he waxed outright wroth as Hartleigh inquired whether he and Malkov were kin and whether there was any family history of insanity or blood-diseases of which he was aware. At last the

Ventrue grew exasperated with this embarrassing mistake of a grandchilde and reached into Hartleigh's mind. But in the intimacy of psychic contact, Hartleigh reflexively reached back — and found something he could *twist*. With startling ease, he sent the elder Kindred into a fugue state not at all unlike the one in which he himself had behaved so regrettably.

Hartleigh has since Embraced several childer — doctors to "consult" and lordlings to infiltrate the Ventrue to seek the answers he himself was denied by his scandalized clanmates. In time, some of those childer have gone astray from the fold, much as Malkov did, and begotten lineages of their own.

To date, the bloodline has made no serious attempt to claim the status theoretically due it as an innovation of the Blood; its particular creation seems profoundly unwelcome. The Ventrue resent the attention the Malkovians draw to their own mental instability, and since Ventrue and Malkovians are sometimes hard to tell apart, few Lords dare discount the horrifying possibility of a hidden contamination of the entire clan. Many vampires of other broods are also inclined to go mad with time, and they certainly don't want any "help" in doing so. For those who aren't so inclined, their minds are the last sanctuary they have, the one thing they can still rely on after their bodies have transformed so monstrously and their instincts have fallen prey to the Beast. And so most Lunatics wisely endeavor to pass their Requiems in such a way as to avoid rousing their fellow Kindred's ire. Of course, even the most unassuming Malkovian occasionally find himself plagued by someone who seems to deserve a taste of the curse he's tried so hard to bear nobly.

As for Malkov, Broadmoor records claim that a fellow inmate killed him in 1889.

Parent Clan: Ventrue

Nickname: Among those rare non-Ventrue who know of them, the Malkovians are nicknamed Lunatics. When the Ventrue mention them at all (generally only to other Ventrue), they refer to them obliquely as "our most charming cousins," or sometimes as "the escapees."

Covenant: A fair majority of Malkovians pretend to be something else (generally Ventrue), so they usually favor whatever covenant allegiance makes the most sense for their assumed identities. As a result, many (if not most) belong to the Invictus. The fanatical bent of the Lancea Sanctum also appeals to some Malkovians, particularly those who suffer obsessions or visions. Some petition to join the Circle of the Crone or the Ordo Dracul, hoping for the relief that mystic wisdom might bring, but they are usually marginalized sometime during the initiation process. Rare indeed is the Malkovian whose madness strikes either covenant as an aid to enlightenment rather than a sad liability. After all, the tests and trial periods that both covenants set are explicitly designed to ferret out just such inner obstacles. As Malkovians grow weary of vainly searching for acceptance in the more established circles of Kindred society, it's likely that more and more of them will show up in the ranks of the Carthians and the unaligned.

Appearance: Malkovians with enough self-command to recognize what they are and what afflicts them often go to some trouble to appear as anything but. Clothes might be fastidious and well coordinated — indeed, even suspiciously pristine. Among those who aspire to Ventrue status, styles appealing to elder tastes are favored. Other Lunatics are too… preoccupied with other matters to attend to such trivialities as vestment. Some can explain the etiquette of gloves and soliloquize on why stirrup pants are an abomination before God and man, but they haven't the slightest idea what's wrong with a morning coat that hasn't been dry-cleaned or mended since 1932.

Haven: Discretion is the key consideration for a Malkovian haven. After all, most Kindred require privacy, but should a Malkovian start to have a bad evening, he *really* needs a safe retreat where neither easily shocked mortals nor judgmental Kindred can pry. Many Lunatics adapt family homes or vacation homes to this purpose. Such places are often left to slide into a sort of genteel decay, which helps the isolation along. Others rely on the comforting anonymity of cookie-cutter apartment complexes. More outré domiciles like old fallout shelters or church attics aren't unheard of. In any case, once settled, a haven quickly comes to enshrine its resident's quirks, manias, idols and fears. While one area within might be scrubbed clean of incriminating detritus and kept suitable for entertaining, the greater part of any Malkovian's home is a veritable treasure trove and museum on the subject of him.

Background: Motivations for Malkovian Embraces vary as widely as those for any other clan or bloodline. Company in misery is a frequent one. Sometimes a Lunatic hopes that his new childe (be that childe a psychiatrist, priest, mother or simply someone who made the mistake of being kind to the vampire once) will be able to help him with his ailment, or at the very least will have the psychic strength to somehow overcome the madness and so purge the bloodline of its taint. Other sires, like their Ventrue forebears, pride themselves on selectivity, so erudite scholars and folk of "quality" are inducted.

At present, the very idea of a willing Ventrue seeking adoption into the ranks of the Malkovians is an absurdity to both bloods. Occasional rumors surface, however, of Malkovians who have made "converting" a certain Ventrue — in other words, fracturing her mind to the point where joining the Malkovians seems like a good idea, or the only idea — their pet project. So far, no such catechumens have shown up on the doorstep of Dr. Hartleigh. Much to his relief.

Character Creation: Mental and Social Attributes are usually primary. (After all, there's no correlation whatsoever between being *mad* and being *dumb*, though ignorant Kindred frequently make the mistake. The line hosts many an adroit manipulator and charming psychopath.) Malkovians whose Physical Attributes predominate are uncommon but not unheard of. Malkovians generally favor Mental and Social Skills as well; Academics, Science, Expression, Empathy and Investigation are particularly useful. Malkovians often possess the same Social Merits as their Ventrue cousins. Most Mental Merits are appropriate (except for Common Sense). Also, be sure to take at least a second dot of Blood Potency, to allow the character to be at all eligible for a bloodline.

A Malkovian's core derangement is key to her makeup. Mortals with mental illnesses are far more than the sum of their ailments, but a Malkovian's curse is no mundane affliction. It runs in her very Blood. In all likelihood, it eventually consumes her soul. Accordingly, much care should be given to choosing and understanding it. Read up on mental illness; steep in literary traditions of madness, particularly the gothic tradition. Mental illness is a serious real-life issue that should be regarded respectfully, but don't feel obliged to make your character a textbook DSM-IV diagnosis. It's more important that derangement amplifies and enriches character, theme and story (rather than derails them).

Bloodline Disciplines: Auspex, Dominate, Obfuscate, Resilience

Weakness: Malkovians suffer the Ventrue clan weakness (-2 penalty to Humanity rolls to avoid acquiring derangements after failing a degeneration roll). In addition, all Malkovians must take a "core" derangement that is theirs for eternity. This derangement may not be cured, reduced in severity or bought off no matter how high the character's Humanity soars. It could certainly become more severe, however.

This core derangement is also susceptible to being "set off" or aggravated whenever the character uses Dominate. If a Discipline roll is *anything other than an ordinary success*, the character experiences a bout of his core derangement at some point that night (or first thing the next night if the roll in question occurs too close to dawn). In other words, failures, dramatic failures and exceptional successes all cause this effect. Furthermore, in the case of a dramatic failure, a mild derangement is upgraded to its more severe version for the remainder of the night. (Storytellers, be sensible about this. The middle of a combat in which four goons attack a Malkovian with napalm is not a good time to decree that he curls up into a fetal ball on the floor. The middle of the Prince's salon later that night is a different story.)

Organization: The relative level of cooperation among Malkovians varies. There are now Malkovians who don't consciously realize their true heritage. In some lineages, a series of desultory or irrational Embraces has produced neonates who feel only disregard for others of their bloodline — or even outright hatred for them. In others, however, sires and grandsires still maintain a more secretive version of the age-old bonds. They gladly provide mentoring, counseling and comfort in exchange for their descendants' compliance in their schemes. Malkovians with sires who are too distracted to cultivate them often seek out an "aunt" or "cousin" to fulfill that role instead.

Occasionally, sophisticated collaborations to study and cure the bloodline's maladies arise. Doctors, pharmacologists, psychologists, mystics and historians keeping each other informed of their discoveries through discreet correspondence. Of course, close contact among Malkovians has other hazards besides just the danger of interference from fearful Kindred. Madness can be contagious, and often it only takes one brilliant mind's descent into unreason to drag the entire effort down.

Concepts: Absinthe-addled roué, *Arsenic and Old Lace*-style death angel, conspiracy theorist, eccentric scholar, failed suicide, health professional, idiot savant, mumbling beggar, religious visionary, scion of decaying noble line, tortured artist

Morbus

For as long as the Kindred have been aware of the existence of the Morbus, bloodline historians and vampiric genealogists have been frustrated by them. Owing largely to the rarity of extensive records cataloguing Mekhet lineage over the centuries, no one can pin down exactly who the founder of this bloodline might have been or where the first niche was in which the Morbus began to thrive. The idea of constructing a truly inclusive history of the Kindred (especially as regards the Mekhet clan) from which one might solve this mystery conclusively is a pipe dream at best, but some aspire to it nonetheless. Those Morbus who choose to concern themselves with the subject consider this ongoing failure a relief and a legitimatization of their entire existence. They see themselves as simply Mekhet who are afflicted or cursed with a singular variety of rarefied tastes.

The particular preference to which the Morbus are all suspect is that they must feed on the blood of the ailing and diseased in order to sustain their vital undead state. In fact, the name Morbus comes from a Latin root meaning "diseased," which was ascribed to afflicted Mekhet by non-afflicted ones during the reign of Justinian in the sixth century AD. According to records from that period unearthed centuries later by Kindred archaeologists, the Morbus were suspected of either spreading or helping to spread a virulent plague across the Mediterranean in one domain after another. Less solvent data has linked named Morbus from Roman records with Mekhet who were active in Greece and Egypt as far back as 430 BC, a year in which plague was said to have struck Athens. The connection this data implies is tenuous as best, and possibly wholly fabricated as propaganda against the Morbus. Nonetheless, it might have been possible for the Kindred to accept the Morbus condition as just a peculiar feeding preference if it were not for records recovered from Constantinople dating back to AD 1334. At that time, one of the most widespread plagues in history swept across Europe and Asia, aided by large numbers of soldiers and captives returning from the Crusades. The records in question describe the "righteous wrath" of a Mekhet pilgrim who traveled in secret with the Christian army. He returned to his domain once the campaign was ended to find his Kindred subjects in rebellion and his mortal herds mired hopelessly in sin. To punish them, records say, he blighted his people with a wasting sickness from within him that killed everyone for miles within a matter of days. This incident blended in with concurrent reports of blight and plague that swept the continent at the time, but Kindred historians pin it down as the first known instance of the use of the Morbus Discipline known as Cachexy.

When captured and put to the question by Kindred Inquisitors for the act, this Kindred denied being the founder of a bloodline at all. He claimed that he had learned his unusual abilities from his sire, who had long since succumbed to the sleep of ages. When he awoke much later, the Kindred's sire also denied developing the Discipline or founding a bloodline, but his memories of his own sire or brood brethren were too hazy to offer any more definitive leads. These records are the closest any historian has come to finding the bloodline's true founder or tracing its evolution.

Tonight, most Morbus are not as concerned with their origins as they are with survival. Once they discover their condition and the unique power that derives from it (or they have both explained to them by an older Morbus), they must decide whether to hide it or admit what they are and try to redefine their niche. Their ability to do either varies by domain, but if nothing else, periodic outbreaks of severe infectious diseases throughout history and all over the world provide sufficient vessels on which to thrive. All they have to do is keep informed and be willing to risk travel to areas in which untreated strains of infectious disease defy the cutting edge of First-World medicine.

Parent Clan: Mekhet

Nickname: Carriers

Covenant: Many Carriers find it difficult to make a respected name or to carve out a fruitful place among the undead of the Invictus or the Lancea Sanctum once their affliction becomes known. Kindred consider them threats to the Traditions and claim that hundred-fold damnation awaits any Morbus who breaks the Third Tradition. Princes of the Invictus simply don't want Carriers polluting their domains and weakening the mortal pillars of their power structure with careless feeding. Some Morbus take perverse pleasure in testing the limits of Carthian egalitarian tolerance, but most would just as soon cultivate as much power and influence as they can and tell the Carthians to go to hell. Repentant or remorseful Carriers turn to members of the Circle of the Crone in hopes of finding some way to undo the curse they've wrought upon themselves, but no member of the bloodline or the covenant in general has yet uncovered any hope that such is possible. Others join the Ordo Dracul in an attempt to progress beyond the weakness that their blood inflicts, but no Morbus has yet achieved the true transcendence that the Order espouses. The rest of the bloodline hide out among the Kindred of the Invictus or the Lancea Sanctum — guarding the secret of their heritage for all their unlives are worth — or go it alone among the unaligned.

Appearance: Most Morbus adopt attire based on how they intend to interact with Kindred society vis-à-vis their condition. Those who try to pass as "normal" often play to the stereotypes that they feel are expected of their clan in their chosen covenant and domain. In fact, they often overdo said stereotypes and give themselves away. Those whose nature is fairly common knowledge try to keep a low profile in "urban camouflage" (i.e., plain, baggy, off-brand clothes in neutral colors), so as to not stand out and risk being social lightning rods. Those who are outright cavalier about their bloodline — and have found acceptance in a Prince's domain — often play to Mekhet stereotypes. They do so out of a desire to show how successful they can be despite their condition.

Haven: Whether they're covert or open about what they are, Morbus make just as much of an effort to make their havens a reflection of their personal purposes as other Mekhet do. The only way in which they choose havens that differs is they look for ones among or offering easy access to diseased mortal vessels.

Background: It is a more frequent for a Mekhet to Embrace a childe who then realizes he is a Morbus than it is for a confirmed Morbus to Embrace a childe. Most Morbus childer therefore have the same backgrounds as non-afflicted Mekhet. When the Morbus do Embrace deliberately, they tend to choose doctors (whom they vainly hope can help cure them), dying vessels to whom they've formed obsessive attachments, or people with influence over policymakers.

Character Creation: The priority assigned to Physical Attributes and Skills is largely a matter of personal taste, as these vampires do not necessarily need sterner constitutions to balance the diseases they carry. The choice between Mental and Social Attributes and Skills should depend on how open a character is to revealing his lineage and how he intends to adapt to his condition. It is also wise to buy up or sell off Humanity dots based on how cavalier uses of Cachexy will be, or how humane a function he considers feeding from the sick and infirm to be. Also, don't forget to buy a second dot of Blood Potency since a character can't officially join the bloodline before then.

Bloodline Disciplines: Auspex, Cachexy, Celerity, Obfuscate

Weakness: The Morbus are slaves to a highly rarefied palate. Only the blood of diseased and dying mortals sustains them, while healthy blood turns to ash in their mouths (though they may take Kindred Vitae and be nourished by it as normal). They can feed from other vessels only when frenzying, but doing so does not replenish their Vitae to any degree whatsoever. Some Morbus feel compelled to drink blood infected with only one specific disease, but this restriction is only a matter of taste or a psychological limitation. Should such a member be brave or desperate enough to drink from a victim with a different affliction than his preferred one, he suffers no penalty. While these diseases don't adversely affect the Morbus themselves (usually), they can occasionally be transmitted when the Kindred feed, share blood with their ghouls or have sex.

The Morbus bloodline is a shameful aberration in the eyes of most Mekhet, which makes it all but impossible for a confirmed Morbus to gain any Status Merit or clan offices among the non-afflicted. What's more, a surviving descendent of a confirmed Morbus who is not a member of the bloodline stands to lose standing by association, both from Mekhet who expect him to follow in his ancestor's footsteps and from other Morbus who wonder why he's afraid to do so.

Organization: The tradition among certain elders and Kindred genealogists of tracking descent and lineage both informs and works against the Morbus. A few members trace lineage and determine intra-bloodline status based on the relative fame or notoriety of sires and grandsires. Some consider the achievements of only their confirmed Morbus forebears worthy of consideration, while others uphold any Mekhet ancestors' accomplishments. Morbus who manage to keep their membership in this bloodline a secret, and earn status and respect from other Mekhet, earn the same again (and more) from their Morbus peers for their cleverness.

Concepts: Angel of mercy, cult leader, demon of retribution, doctor, hospice manager, medical researcher, New-Age holistic healer, plague dog, retirement-home orderly, seemingly philanthropic political activist

Toreador

You actually expected me to buy this modernismo trash that Alphonse Mucha inflicted on the world? I'd rather see you cleaning windshields on a street corner with it. In fact, go do that right now.

To the unwashed, ignorant masses, the Daeva are sleek, haughty, alluring, idealized predators who've been gifted with eternal youth, beauty and undying *style* because they're just that much better than regular mortals. The Kindred of the Toreador bloodline see themselves in much the same way, only they elevate themselves above the thrashing, hedonistic, uncultured Daeva as well. They're too well mannered and aloof to say as much *to* the Daeva, but what they leave unsaid in mixed company could fill volumes.

The name "Toreador" reflects not only the bloodline's noble history, but its members' fascination with the fine arts that they hold dear even tonight. Its founder, Garcilaso de Castillejo, was the second son of a moderately influential Spanish nobleman and a peer and rival of the innovative *torero* (bullfighter) Francisco Romero, whose grandson Pedro carried on the tradition and is legendary even today. Castillejo might have even surpassed Romero in skill and innovation in the eternal *escalafon* of Spanish bullfighters had he not been seduced and Embraced by an influential Andalusian Daeva while he was still in his prime. He adapted quickly to his undead state and impressed his Kindred peers with his charm, wit and grace. He even continued to fight bulls in secluded, hidden arenas for the delighted Kindred nobility until King Philip V decried the sport as barbarous and pressured a compliant pope to threaten willful noble *toreros* with excommunication. Fickle Spanish Sanctified chose to enforce Philip's will among their own kind, denouncing the entire spectacle as a sacrilegious mockery of Abel's sacrifice, largely at the urging of a Daeva Bishop in Seville who was jealous of Castillejo's growing fame.

Yet Castillejo disregarded this slight with his characteristic aplomb and looked for other ways to fill his time at ease. He became a patron of the arts and a nigh-obsessive student of them, arranging travel into Italy, France, Greece, Portugal and even England to track down artists or to follow exciting new movements that caught his fancy. His adventurous spirit and unshakable will attracted cultured, indolent Daeva from all over Europe to his side, and they emulated every opinion and behavior of their charismatic *torero* in attempts to curry his favor. In time, amused outsiders came to refer to not only Castillejo but his growing cult of personality as *El Toreros*. When Castillejo finally chose to Embrace childer and those progeny demonstrated an aptitude for Dominate — which iron-willed Castillejo had learned from a Ventrue patron and lover in Venice — the nickname was applied to them as well.

When the bloodline gained recognition among European Kindred societies, it was known as the Torero line, and it remained thus for almost a century. Then, in the last quarter of the 19th century, Castillejo's favorite childe, Cristóbal de la Vega saw the opening-night performance of Bizet's opera *Carmen*. He was so profoundly moved by the performance of Jacques Bouhy as the bullfighter Escamillo that he convinced Castillejo to come see the performance with him the next night. When he did, Castillejo was so pleased by Bouhy's performance that he insisted upon the adoption of the inexpertly translated word "Toreador" in place of Torero in reference to his bloodline. Ever eager to please their founder and paragon, vampires of the line and associated Daeva hangers-on eagerly followed suit.

In the century-and-a-quarter since then, however, Castillejo has grown jaded and bored by the evolution of what passes for fine art. He has withdrawn into seclusion somewhere in the mountains of Andalusia to pray that the inspired artists of the Age of Enlightenment will be reborn soon so he'll have a reason to travel the world again as he did as a young Kindred. Yet his haughty sycophants can be found all over the world, insinuating themselves among the mortal elite in cultural centers of high art (such as New York, Paris, Milan and Madrid). Many of them spend their nights seeking inspired, classically trained artists and attempting to groom them into talented Kindred prodigies whose works will shake Castillejo out of his ennui. Others slavishly try to hone their own talents to perfection in hopes of doing the same thing. Some have even realized they don't need Castillejo's constant attention and approval to enjoy the status and influence they've garnered as Toreador. Possessed of their inceptor's will, determination and grace, they've set their sights on supplanting the disconsolate old Kindred in the affections of their adoring brothers and sisters.

Parent Clan: Daeva

Nickname: Patrons

Covenant: The Toreador believe any covenant would be lucky to have them, but not every covenant is worthy

of them. Nonetheless, no self-respecting Toreador is so gauche as to go slumming among the unaligned. (*Honestly....*) The closest many Toreador come to thumbing their noses at established authority and going their own way is joining the Carthians, though they usually do so only to spite a rival in an opposing covenant or because the Carthians have the most sway in the Toreador's chosen domain. Members of the bloodline traditionally shy away from joining the Circle of the Crone because of a story their elders hand down about a member of that covenant whom their founder held in particular contempt and openly derided at court. Likewise, they both fear and respect devout members of the Lancea Sanctum, though they are wary of the intentions of certain hypocritical or overzealous Sanctified. And yet, piety and passion have inspired some of the most profoundly moving works of art in history, so finding the odd Toreador among the Lancea Sanctum is not unheard of. Many Toreador can be found among the Ordo Dracul, although many members of the Order consider the Toreador effete dilettantes who don't have the capacity to master the Coils of the Dragon (which is not generally an inaccurate estimation). The covenant that attracts most Toreador is the Invictus. Not only is the Invictus accepting of them, but it aspires to the ideal of the undying feudal elite, of which the Toreador naturally account themselves.

Appearance: The eldest and most influential Toreador come from Spanish or Italian stock (including Sardinia and Corsica). They show the same range of appearance as south European mortals, from the duskiness of a part-Moorish Andalusian to the blonde hair of a part-Nordic Lombard. Young Patrons display a wider variety of ethnicity, but all of them represent the ideals of classical or exotic beauty to which men and women of the era in which they were Embraced aspired. In public and among their few accepted peers, they dress as paragons of the styles most popular at the time. In private, many Toreador cling to the by-gone high-style fashions of their breathing days.

Haven: Toreador havens come in two varieties: the disarrayed studio of the self-absorbed artist, or the lavishly appointed haven of the elite socialite patron. The latter is far more common, and all such spaces have at least a couple of *objets d'art* on display. Most Toreador consider it gauche to display their own artwork (or not to display that of their guests) when entertaining fellow Kindred.

Background: The Toreador aren't quite — *quite* — as picky about selecting physically beautiful people for the Embrace as the Daeva are. Charm, wit and grace are far more important than simplistic concerns about symmetry or bone structure. They also look for artistic talent that inspires them or at least a consummate love and learned understanding of the fine arts. The Toreador are just as prone to Embrace out of guilt or passion as the Daeva, but they don't make a habit of welcoming those illegitimate childer into the bloodline afterward.

As for adopting other Daeva into their august ranks, it simply isn't done. It takes at least two Toreador in good standing to propose and second a *novillo* (a neonate Daeva of Toreador lineage) for inclusion within the bloodline, and a Toreador elder (known as a *diestro*) must give his blessing in a ceremony called the *alternativa*. If the *novillo* doesn't have a traceable pedigree of respected Toreador ancestors leading directly back to the founder, it would take a miracle for him to get a Toreador to even acknowledge him, much less support his dreams of adoption.

Character Creation: The Toreador rely primarily on Social Attributes across the board, although few can be accused of lacking in Wits or Resolve. Intelligence and the Physical Attributes are not quite as important to them as making a powerful and lasting first impression, but few Kindred can honestly claim to have met an especially weak, stupid or clumsy Toreador. Social Skills are often primary, with a notable preference for Expression, Socialize and a haughty, unspoken style of Intimidation. Social Merits predominate, as do ones such as Status, Haven and Herd — all of which reflect the decadent opulence with which the Toreador surround themselves and the allure such trappings have for mortal victims. It also makes sense to buy a second dot of Blood Potency unless you intend to play the character as a *novillo* Daeva struggling for acceptance among his Toreador betters.

Bloodline Disciplines: Celerity, Dominate, Majesty, Vigor

Weakness: Like the Daeva, every Toreador finds it difficult to resist his hedonistic impulses. When he opts not to indulge his Vice, a Toreador Kindred loses two Willpower points.

In addition, all members of the Toreador bloodline share their inceptor's peculiar obsession with fine art. Whether this obsession is imposed culturally or inherited mystically is unknown, but most Toreador hardly recognize it as a weakness at all. When a Toreador is exposed to a work of art in a particular style (chosen at character creation), he becomes intensely fascinated with it and is unable to divert his attention. (General examples include sculpture, painting, music, drama, dance, jewelry and fashion. Most Toreador also focus on the work of specific artists, styles or movements that were popular among the cultural elite when they were Embraced.) The player must spend a Willpower point or succeed at a reflexive Resolve roll to break the spell, or the Toreador does nothing but focus on the object of fascination for the rest of the scene, or until said object is taken away. The character also regains control if he is attacked or otherwise physically broken from his reverie.

The nature of this obsession need not necessarily be rapt appreciation. While the average Toreador is entranced by beauty, some focus all of their scornful energy on the work of a particular artist, period or movement that they despise, criticizing it vehemently and mercilessly for as long as others are willing to listen.

Organization: Since the Toreador don't strive as a unified front to achieve a specific goal, they don't tend to hew to a strict hierarchy. A handful might gather in an informal group called a salon, a *peña* or simply a clique until jealousy or petty disagreements drive them apart. These groups most often form around particularly charismatic *diestros*, and the internal pecking order is determined by each member's status. These groups sometimes include fascinating or promising *novillo* Daeva, but only in the minority. The fickle, flighty nature of the Toreador doesn't lend itself to long-term compatriot loyalty, so the thing that best holds a Toreador group together is an enemy or victim in common.

Concepts: Bullfighter, buyer for a museum, character assassin, gallery owner, Harpy, Master of Elysium, promising young artist, reclusive retired maestro, sycophantic courtier, vicious critic

Disciplines

The following section details the secrets of two new Disciplines wielded by bloodlines found in this Appendix. Getsumei is the province of the Burakumin, while the Cachexy Discipline is a special talent of the Morbus bloodline.

Cachexy

Facility with this Discipline is considered the dividing line between what makes a Kindred a Mekhet with a peculiar feeding habit and a confirmed member of the Morbus bloodline. Any Kindred can choose to feed from diseased mortals if he's willing to risk spreading infection to the rest of the herd, but only the Morbus can turn the effects of their feeding predilection into this formidable and dangerous Discipline.

Cachexy allows the user to selectively spread, inflict or worsen the effects of any of the myriad diseases he carries at any given time. Some of the effects require the character to touch his intended target, while the dangerously high-level ones eliminate that impediment and render users walking biological hazards.

When a Morbus intentionally spreads a disease with Cachexy, the player decides which of the diseases his character has sampled is inflicted. The specific disease isn't important as far as rules are concerned, but the choice should have some sort of resounding effect on (or be driven by) the themes of your story. For the basic rules on diseases, see p. 176 of the **World of Darkness Rulebook**.

• Diagnose

Probably the most important power of this Discipline, Diagnose helps Morbus vampires identify suitable vessels from the throngs of the kine. The power reveals the taint in someone's blood as it moves through his body, and it calls out to the Morbus' Beast.

Cost: None

Dice Pool: Intelligence + Medicine + Cachexy

Action: Instant

Roll Results

Dramatic Failure: The character receives a completely false or misleading impression of the subject's condition.

Failure: The character receives no impression at all of the subject's condition.

Success: The character receives a sense (lasting a scene) of who in his line of sight carries infected blood.

Exceptional Success: As per success, but the character can also intuitively identify what diseases people carry.

A Morbus can also use Diagnose to identify Kindred who've been feeding on tainted blood (and whether those Kindred are Morbus themselves). Uses of Obfuscate, however, confound this power as surely as they confound the naked eye. Diagnose detects only those diseases that are currently active in a creature's body. Pathogens that travel through the air, that are sealed in biohazard containers, that grow in a test tube or that thrive on a dirty countertop are undetectable.

•• Contaminate

Contact with the blood of a Morbus might result in infection from whatever diseases he has sampled, but this power ensures it. By smearing a hand-held object or a small area (up to a square yard) with a point's worth of his Vitae, the Morbus contaminates that object with a supernaturally resistant strain of one of the diseases he carries. Should a mortal or Kindred (other than the Morbus who activated the power) touch the affected area with bare flesh or touch or ingest the affected object, that person risks being infected.

Cost: 1 Vitae

Dice Pool: No roll is required to activate this power. The disease remains hardy and viable from the time it is applied to the object or area until the sun rises the next morning, or until someone touches it and is infected. While the disease remains in waiting on the object, it cannot be washed away or sterilized by any normal means except fire, but neither can it be spread through the air. After the sun comes up, it dissipates completely as if it were never there.

Once contact or ingestion transmits the disease, a reflexive Stamina roll is made for the victim. If it fails, the disease takes hold and thrives, affecting the character as per the normal rules for diseases. (Kindred victims become carriers only.) Should the roll succeed, the victim eradicates the disease from his system. If an exceptional success is rolled, the subject is immune to further mystical attempts to inflict the same disease. Victims who are affected can transmit the disease normally.

Action: Instant

••• Inflame

Once a Morbus successfully infects a victim with Contaminate, or identifies a pre-existing disease with Diagnose, he can call out to it with the power of his Blood and intensify its effects.

Cost: 1 Vitae

Dice Pool: Wits + Survival + Cachexy – subject's Stamina

Action: Instant

Roll Results

Dramatic Failure: The Morbus accidentally sends the disease into remission for the rest of the story. If the victim is only a carrier of the chosen disease but is not affected by it (be he Kindred or just a semi-lucky mortal), a dramatic failure scourges the disease from his system entirely.

Failure: The character is unable to affect the victim in that turn.

Success: The character inflames the victim's condition temporarily, inflicting a -2 modifier to all of the victim's rolls for a number of turns equal to successes rolled.

Exceptional Success: As a success, plus the victim collapses before he can take an action in the first turn. He is unable to rise or otherwise act until the next turn.

Invoking this power imposes certain effects on the subject at the Morbus' discretion. The exact details of those effects are best left to the player and Storyteller to decide based on what disease is inflamed, but they have a generic, quantifiable impact. Be it due to a splitting headache, overwhelming nausea or intense muscle pain, the victim suffers a -2 distraction penalty on all rolls for actions (except reflexive actions) for a number of turns equal to the successes achieved on the power's activation.

A Morbus cannot use this power on a single victim more than once at a time. It can be used repeatedly to extend the effects of the disease on the victim, however.

The power affects only mortal carriers or sufferers of a disease.

Plague-Bearer

Although it is not the most immediately deadly application of Cachexy, this power is the one that is most widely feared by other Kindred. A Morbus can use it to infect a rival's entire herd out of spite, turn an entire coterie into plague-dogs like him, or taint broad swaths of victims at the local Rack so that they're suitable vessels for only his ilk.

Cost: 1 Vitae per turn

Dice Pool: Intelligence + Medicine + Cachexy

Action: Instant (That is, initial use is instant, but the effect can be multiplied over several turns as long as the player is willing to keep spending Vitae.)

Roll Results

Dramatic Failure: The character infects no one, and he cannot use any Cachexy power for the rest of the night.

Failure: The character infects no one, and he cannot use Plague-Bearer again for the rest of the night.

Success: The character infects up to three mortals *or* one Kindred with a chosen disease per success rolled. The same number of victims can be infected in each turn thereafter when Vitae is spent.

Exceptional Success: No additional effect beyond the staggering number of people who can be infected.

By concentrating and burning the blood within himself, a Morbus can spread one of the diseases that he carries to a crowd of unsuspecting victims. Those victims (be they mortal or Kindred) can then go on to spread the disease themselves until the Morbus is the epicenter of a potentially devastating outbreak.

If the player spends one Vitae and succeeds on the activation roll, the Morbus infects up to three mortals or one Kindred per success. If the first attempt is successful, another Vitae may be spent per turn thereafter to infect the same number of people. No rolls are made in subsequent turns, but perpetuating the infection requires all of the character's concentration. The character can perform simple actions such as standing up, looking around or pretending to drink a beer at a bar. He can even move up to his Speed in a single turn. He cannot engage in combat, walk from room to room looking for people to infect, engage in conversation or even so much as tie his shoes while using this power. The effective range from which a character can infect victims is 10 yards per dot of Stamina that he has.

So, if three successes are achieved when this power is activated, up to nine mortals or three Kindred can be infected in the first turn. Each turn thereafter, another nine mortals or three Kindred can be infected if a Vitae is spent.

Once Vitae expenditure stops or the vampire's concentration is broken, the disease cannot be spread any further. The power must be activated anew if the spread is to continue.

Once the Morbus has begun to use Plague-Bearer, his chosen victims are affected as per Contaminate with concomitant reflexive Stamina rolls and subsequent effects.

Accelerate Disease

Once a Morbus infects a victim with Contaminate or Plague-Bearer (or identifies an infection with Diagnose), he may wreak havoc with the person's health. By calling on the power of his tainted blood and its sympathy with that of the victim, he can send the subject's disease into a destructive frenzy that more than likely proves fatal.

Cost: 1 Willpower

Dice Pool: Wits + Survival + Cachexy – subject's Stamina

Action: Instant

Roll Results

Dramatic Failure: The Morbus sends the disease into remission for the rest of the story. If the victim is only a carrier of the chosen disease and is not affected by it (be he Kindred or just a semi-lucky mortal), a dramatic failure scourges the disease from his system entirely.

Failure: The character has no effect on his chosen victim.

Success: The character automatically inflicts a point of lethal damage per success rolled.

Exceptional Success: As a success, with no additional effect.

If the Morbus activates this power successfully, he accelerates the pace of the disease eating away at a victim to such an extent that the subject starts to die immediately, regardless of any medication he might be on or how advanced the disease is. For every success rolled, the victim suffers one point of lethal damage automatically as buboes or bloody lesions erupt on his flesh, ulcers spill stomach acid, or what have you. This effect occurs in the space of a single turn and the disease returns to its normal pace thereafter, assuming the victim survives. The power has no effect on other Kindred.

Getsumei

The name of this Discipline comes from the Japanese phrase *getsumei no michi*, which translates roughly as "the moonlit path." It comes from an apocryphal poetic exchange between two Tokugawa-era Burakumin who were master and student. Out of revenge for an undeserved slight, the bitter, ill-tempered student considered desecrating the body of a deceased son of an influential governor whose wealth had long supported a haughty Ventrue Prince. The Burakumin's wise master replied only, "We can't do as you say. The governor's son is already picking plum blossoms along the moonlit path." As the story goes, the shambling corpse of the son returned to the governor's mansion late that evening to kill three of the governor's concubines and four of his remaining children before being cut down by the mansion's guards.

As the exchange relates to the story, so does the name relate to the Discipline in the way its genteel seeming refers to something distasteful and ugly. This Discipline arises from the profession of handling and preparing the dead for burial, turning an already spiritually unclean undertaking into a perverse and ongoing desecration. With it, a Burakumin can learn secrets from the corpses of dead men, harvest parts of corpses as disgusting tools, and even imbue dead bodies with a false semblance of life.

• Moonlit Preservation

This most basic application of Getsumei grew from one of the traditionally accepted responsibilities of the *burakumin* class. It mystically halts the effects of decomposition in a dead body and renders it suitable for other effects of higher levels. A recently deceased body can be perfectly preserved for years without need of chemicals, and even a badly decayed body can be granted a solid structural integrity that makes it useful for the high-level effects of this Discipline.

Cost: 1 Vitae

Dice Pool: Composure + Medicine + Getsumei

Action: Instant

Roll Results

Dramatic Failure: The body (or parts) that the character tries to preserve rot instantly into useless dust.

Failure: The corpse is not mystically preserved.

Success: The corpse is mystically preserved (or held together) for a period of one month per success rolled. After that time is up, the character must use the power again, lest the corpse pick up rotting where it left off.

Exceptional Success: As a success, but the duration of the effect is one year per success.

Moonlit Preservation does not repair damage done to a corpse, nor does it make a corpse any more resistant to damage, but it can (for instance) hold every bone of a skeleton together in its proper orientation without requiring any ligaments or other tissue. It is not strictly necessary to use this power on corpses in order to use high-level effects on them — nor does doing so confer any bonuses to corpses affected by high-level powers. If the Burakumin does not use Moonlit Preservation, however, he has to connect any disjoined flesh and bone by mundane physical means such as bolts, needle and thread, leather straps or wire, lest his animated creations fall apart under mundane physical stress.

This power has no effect on Kindred, only on actual, dead corpses.

•• Crow's Harvest

This power allows a Burakumin to stare into the eyes of a corpse and see reflected there the last thing the dead man witnessed. The vision appears only in the eyes of the cadaver and is visible to no one except the character using this power. This effect cannot be used on the corpses of supernatural creatures (such as other Kindred or werewolves) or on those of animals, and at least one eye must be relatively intact to reveal the vision. This power does not work on corpses that are currently under other Getsumei effects of a higher level.

Cost: None

Dice Pool: Wits + Investigation + Getsumei

Action: Instant

Roll Results

Dramatic Failure: Rather than gaining a clear impression of the circumstances of the subject's death, the Burakumin is possessed by the confused and angry spirit of the dead man for the rest of the scene. The effect is similar to that of the sanguinary animism derangement (see p. 191).

Failure: The Burakumin sees nothing more than the sightless eyes of a corpse staring at him.

Success: The character receives a clear impression of what the corpse saw as it died, as well as the few moments that led up to the event.

Exceptional Success: The character witnesses the entire scene leading up to the victim's death just as the victim saw it, including up to an hour's worth of time.

Should the character choose, he may go so far as to pluck out and devour one of the corpse's eyes whole when using this power. If he does, he experiences the events that the dead person did (as described previously) as if they happen to him, based on the degree of successes rolled. Such a vision lasts only a turn's time for the user, but can transmit up to an hour's events in the dead person's life. While experiencing the subject's last moments, the vampire's undead body enters a trance state similar to that of daytime slumber for one turn.

The Storyteller might require a player to roll Intelligence + Investigation after using this power successfully to interpret confusing events or ones that might have taken the victim completely by surprise.

••• Corpse Skin

The Burakumin slices away a token of a corpse's flesh and uses it to mystically enhance his physical resistance. The token can be a one-inch by one-inch wafer of flesh, a whole adult tooth, a toe, a knucklebone or something comparable in size, and the character must hold it in his mouth or in a closed, bare fist for the duration of the effect.

Cost: 1 Vitae

Dice Pool: Stamina + Athletics + Getsumei

Action: Instant

Roll Results

Dramatic Failure: The character's flesh bloats and imposes penalties as per success, but he gains no Armor for his efforts, and the token of flesh is consumed.

Failure: Nothing happens, but the token of flesh is consumed.

Success: The character suffers the penalties described below, but achieves one additional point of (grotesque) Armor per success, which lasts until the end of the scene.

Exceptional Success: No additional effect, but the extra Armor is its own reward.

When a character employs this power, his flesh thickens, discolors and bloats like that of a decomposing corpse. The player suffers a -1 penalty on all Presence- and Manipulation-based rolls (excluding attempts to use Intimidation, and in addition to restrictions imposed by the Burakumin bloodline weakness and Nosferatu clan weakness). In exchange, the character receives the benefit of temporary Armor. Despite the somewhat uncomfortable bloating, this effect imposes no Defense or Speed penalties, though a character might find it difficult to fit his finger into the trigger-guard of a small pistol. Each success on the activation roll counts as Armor for the rest of the scene. The protection applies against all attacks types, whether melee or firearms. A character can use this power only once per scene, and only on himself. When the effect wears off, the token of necrotic flesh disintegrates and cannot be used again. This effect does not add to other armor the character might wear — the player must choose one or the other to employ as protection.

•••• Channel of Hasu-Ko

One of the most bizarre and useful powers available to the Burakumin, the Channel of Hasu-Ko enables a character to construct a tiny, autonomous servitor from the bodies of dead men. These servitor creatures appear as grotesque insects or deformed homunculi, and can be exceedingly useful as spies.

Cost: 1 Vitae

Dice Pool: Dexterity + Crafts + Getsumei

Action: Instant (The act of building a Channel of Hasu-Ko takes hours, of course, but the actual roll and expenditure that occurs at the end of that period is considered an instant action.)

Roll Results

Dramatic Failure: The character builds and animates the creature, but it goes berserk and attacks him.

Failure: The character is left with an inanimate lump of rotting castoffs.

Success: The creature comes to life and obeys the character's spoken commands to the best of its ability and is able to verbally relate to its creator what it sees and does.

Exceptional Success: Not only does the character create a Channel of Hasu-Ko, he may link his perceptions to its — seeing, hearing, smelling and tasting what it does. The character sacrifices awareness of his own surroundings, but is able to give the creature telepathic orders over any distance. Rolls to notice events transpiring in the vicinity of the vampire's body suffer a -3 penalty, and he can do nothing else when sensing through his creation.

A creature animated by the Channel of Hasu-Ko travels with an eerie hopping gait, can climb walls like a spider and can speak in a tiny, hissing voice. Its traits are the same as those for a homunculus, listed on p. 225, with the following exceptions. The creation remains active for an entire night, breaking down into its component corpse parts as soon as the sun rises. It is as intelligent as the character who created it, capable of understanding conditional spoken orders, and capable of acting on its own out of self-preservation. A creature is also loyal to the Burakumin who creates it, and control cannot be usurped by another user of Getsumei. Mind-affecting Disciplines such as Animalism and Dominate do not work on a servant, nor does the Telepathy power of Auspex. The creature is largely unaffected by Nightmare and Majesty, but is unable to resist the effects of the Sovereignty power. It is also unable to penetrate the veil of Obfuscate. Additional Vitae

expenditures may increase any of a creation's Physical Attributes by one dot per Vitae.

A creature's actions can be determined by the Storyteller to the player's specifications, or the Storyteller may allow the player to determine the creature's actions and make its dice rolls.

••••• Convocation of Hotoke

With this power, the Burakumin can command a number of dead bodies to rise and perform relatively simple functions. He can command them to carry heavy objects, attack individuals or groups, guard a door, dig a ditch, build a wall or do other fairly menial tasks. The corpses carry out their orders with rudimentary intelligence until the effect wears off or they are destroyed. Accomplishing the latter normally requires dismemberment, fire or utter pulverization.

Cost: 1 Vitae + 1 Willpower minimum (see below)

Dice Pool: Intelligence + Occult + Getsumei

Action: Instant

Roll Results

Dramatic Failure: The character animates every corpse he intends to, but the unquiet spirits of the dead take control and wreak vengeance on him. Should they succeed, they collapse into lifelessness once again. Otherwise, if they aren't destroyed, they collapse at the end of the night.

Failure: The character does not animate any of the corpses.

Success: The character animates one corpse per success on the activation roll, and they remain active until the next sunrise.

Exceptional Success: As per success, but the corpses remain active until the next time sunlight actually touches them.

When the player makes the activation roll and requisite expenditures, the character must speak his commands immediately, and they must apply to every corpse animated in that use of the power. If the character wants to change orders later, before the effect of the power wears off, another Willpower point must be spent. If the character wishes to give corpses individual orders, one additional Willpower point must be spent for each corpse. Giving orders requires that the Kindred speaks to the dead in person — a Burakumin cannot change a corpse-servant's orders from half a continent away or by telephone, for example.

Corpses animated with this power have Strength 3, Dexterity 2, Stamina 4, Brawl 2, Mental Attributes of 1 and Social Attributes of 0. Their Size and Speed factors equal those of a normal human being. They do not talk or respond to people who talk to them, but their eyes do track targets of their attention and they retain the basic awareness to perform such necessary actions as turning doorknobs, climbing steps, crawling through tight spaces and searching for hidden intruders. Animated corpses suffer only bashing damage from all attacks except fire, which causes aggravated damage. They do not suffer from wound penalties.

Mind-affecting Disciplines such as Animalism and Dominate do not work on corpses, nor does the Telepathy power of Auspex. Corpses are not affected by Nightmare or Majesty, but are unable to penetrate the veil of Obfuscate.

Characters cannot use this power to affect corpses that are already under the effect of someone else's use of the Convocation of Hotoke. Nor can it be used on other vampires.

Story Functions of Bloodlines and Disciplines

Bloodlines fulfill a number of story functions within a chronicle. Most simply, they expand the range of options for players. Five clans might not be enough for some troupes. Perhaps a character concept just doesn't fit specifically enough within one of the standard clans. Bloodlines offer a chance to play "something different," as well as a way in which players and Storytellers can customize the setting to their own tastes. Each clan focuses on a particular aspect of vampire mythology — vampire as secret master, as tragic counterculture icon, as bestial predator and so on. With a bloodline, you can create an undead subculture that explores other aspects of vampirism, or you can just create an interesting new Kindred group to add to your chronicle.

Bloodlines can also specialize in narrower aspects of a clan's basic concept, throwing them into sharp relief. For example, the Morbus represent the ugly side of exclusivity and portray the Mekhet in a debased and even vulnerable form. For the Carriers, the Mekhet affinity for darkness has turned in on itself to become a literal sickness, while the clan's long history has curdled into desperation to remain hidden.

New Disciplines can play a similar role. Some players like to give their characters unusual powers. Sometimes they do so to give their characters some edge over other characters. Sometimes they use powers as a substitute for personality. Those are not reasons to forbid new Disciplines, though. As Storyteller, you can help players use bloodlines and Disciplines to make their characters individual and unusual while retaining play balance.

Bloodlines and Disciplines make the World of Darkness more mysterious. Kindred who think they know it all are in for a shock when a new vampire in town leaves pestilence in his wake, or he confronts them with the ghosts of their parents.

This is especially true for bloodlines from distant lands. Since vampires do not travel much, the clans often striate into bloodlines. Just as each city has its own political structure of covenants and personalities, so each region of the world might have a special bloodline or two. Regional bloodlines can highlight cultural or historical elements. The Burakumin illustrate Japan's historic slowness to abandon custom and tradition for more modern forms of society. The Malkovian draw upon a fantasized tradition of foggy Victorian England and grim aspects of gothic madness. The Bruja is a biker gang that remains locked in a cultural perception and a kind of villainy that originated at the time of the line's creation.

As you create new bloodlines, think about where they come from and what regional quirks they can embody. If you like, read up on a region's vampire legends. Every part of the world has its own stories about blood-drinking witches, ghosts and demons that can help inspire new bloodlines. Other parts of

the world, such as Africa and Asia, almost certainly include different covenants. When characters encounter Kindred from other parts of the world, with strange customs and powers, they realize just how little they know about their World of Darkness. The Burakumin, for instance, preserve a cultural tradition long forgotten by modern Japanese custom, while the Toreador retain neoclassical beliefs about patronage and artistry.

New Disciplines, like new bloodlines, expand the range of stories you can tell. Each Discipline enables vampires to perform certain feats; a new Discipline results in a character who does things that no one else can. Such a character can set events in motion that no one else could, provide novel mysteries and challenges for other characters, and generally shake up a chronicle. What happens when one character can talk to the dead? Kindred high and low realize that secrets they thought were lost and scandals they thought were buried have become accessible again. A character with Getsumei can expect bribes and threats galore as other Kindred try to exploit her power or protect themselves from it. You could build an entire story arc around learning what a new Discipline can do and how it shakes up a city's Kindred.

Clan and bloodline weaknesses, on the other hand, supply a challenge to players' ingenuity and roleplaying. A different weakness imposes different challenges for players and Storytellers to explore. How does a Morbus establish a domain after moving to a new city? If other Kindred learn of his connection to the near-epidemic that has sprung up, they can veritably hold him for ransom.

Storytellers can feel the same temptation as players to use bloodlines and Disciplines as substitutes for personalities. Keep in mind that you don't need to invent a whole new bloodline to justify one unusual character. Many Kindred simply don't act the way other vampires expect from members of their clan, and vampires can learn unusual Disciplines without belonging to a bloodline.

Watch out for "super-bloodlines," too. You might feel tempted to create a bloodline with the most ass-kicking kickass set of Disciplines you can devise. This temptation can become especially strong if you intend for the members of a bloodline to serve as adversaries to the characters. Resist this temptation. **Vampire: The Requiem** presumes that *all* undead lineages are equally worthy for players' characters. No vampire lineage in this book or any supplement receives a black hat and an "Enemy — Do Not Play" stamp along with the Embrace. We recommend that you stick to this rule as well. If one bloodline possesses clear advantages over other lineages, however, a character from that bloodline holds an intrinsic advantage over other players' characters. That might seem fun for one player, but the other players will probably object.

Creating a Bloodline

Designing a bloodline has two parts. The first consists of the "story" aspects of the lineage: the clan from which it emerged (even if characters could not know this aspect of its history), how the bloodline came to be, its distinctive culture and its interaction with other Kindred. The second part consists of the "game" aspects: the Disciplines favored by the

bloodline and the special weakness that all members of the line inherit from their sires.

Players might want to invent bloodlines. Not only might a player want to play a character from a bloodline she created, a character can establish a bloodline in the course of the chronicle. As always, the Storyteller has final say on whether to allow a bloodline. Founding a lineage is one of the greatest feats a Kindred can achieve, however, so we do not recommend that Storytellers forbid this deed. Instead, work with the player to make the new bloodline interesting and balanced with the standard Kindred clans.

How Bloodlines Appear

Bloodlines do not appear from nowhere. Someone has to start them, and that someone can shape the entire identity and culture of the lineage. New bloodlines can appear in a number of different ways. Storytellers can devise any number of variations on these basic stories and combine them to form a unique and interesting background for a line.

Deliberate Intent

Any Kindred can work a change in her Vitae once she achieves sufficient age and power. In game terms, any vampire can start a bloodline once her Blood Potency reaches 6 or higher. The process does not require any special ritual, but it does cost the character a dot of Willpower and some amount of time during which her Blood takes on the new characteristics. A new weakness also arises, adding to that of her original clan. Any childer the character sires after that point have the potential to inherit her new weakness and new set of favored Disciplines.

A Kindred might change herself to reflect some special interest. The founder might prefer some Discipline outside the roster of her in-clan capabilities. By changing herself, she makes that Discipline easier for her to learn. Her childer may then inherit the altered set of bloodline Disciplines. A founder also suffers some special flaw in addition to the normal weakness of her clan, and she passes that weakness on to her childer when they "activate" the line.

The Bruja provide an example of a deliberately created bloodline. The founder of the lineage wanted to be remain true to his outlaw biker gang roots, not serve as a pawn in some other Kindred's maneuverings in the Danse Macabre. The line acquired Vigor, a Discipline considered most applicable to a pack of blood-drinking, hell-raising, ass-kicking outlaws who had little to depend on other than their own capabilities. The creator's choices defined the strengths of his new bloodline.

Exactly how "deliberately" a lineage's founder changes the Blood varies from character to character. One might change her Blood in a calculated attempt to secure greater advantages for herself or her childer. Another might act unconsciously, her Blood responding to her obsessions. Kindred scholars suspect that the Toreador split from the Daeva through an unconscious but undeniable sense of self-esteem. The bloodline's founder developed closer ties to the society to which he found himself drawn while honing his tastes and predilections to a level of indulgence that exceeded the main clan's predilection for vice. Many Kindred suspect the Malkovians of having a similar reason for diverging from their parent clan. In some cases, more than one member of a clan decides to change her Vitae and begin a bloodline. A number of bloodlines began as cults or secret societies within a clan.

ACCIDENTAL BLOODLINES?

You might wonder how a Kindred could exert an act of will so great that we represent it by the loss of a Willpower dot, yet not know it. Please remember that Kindred do not have access to their character sheets. Game mechanics might suggest that a character has a Willpower dot one minute and does not the next. The change must take place during downtime, when we do not track time minute by minute. During downtime, it's quite possible for an action that we represent with a single dice roll or a quick pencil-stroke on a character sheet to actually take several nights. A character can therefore engage in the prodigious effort of will needed to change her Blood a little at a time, and no one can say — not even the character herself — exactly when the change took place.

Curses

A vampire might change because someone else changed him through magic. Kindred refer to this as "cursing," no matter how the magical alteration occurred.

Sometimes the change happens because of an actual curse. At its highest levels of mastery, accessible only to Kindred of the most potent blood, Theban Sorcery includes curse-rituals that can impose flaws on a Kindred and all her descendants, even childer who have already been sired. The most powerful mortal mages might also be able to curse Kindred in this manner.

Curses can also happen because a bloodline's founder meddled with the powers of other supernatural beings. Wise Kindred warn their fellows to avoid the blood of Lupines, mortal mages and the stranger creatures that stalk the World of Darkness. Some Kindred develop new powers through contact with such beings, but that power usually comes with an unexpected price in the form of some new flaw that adds to the character's existing clan weakness.

Any character can suffer the effects of a curse, no matter how high his Blood Potency, and the curse can be passed to any childer. If the character achieves a Blood Potency of 6, he might be able to throw off the curse… or maybe not. At least, he can mitigate and select the effects on himself and his childer.

Tainted Embrace

Some mortals are touched by the supernatural before their Embrace. No mortal mages are known to have suffered the Embrace, but some reputed "witches" or other aberrations of the supernatural world have founded bloodlines from the moment they became undead. Mediums and possessors of other spiritual gifts can also join the Kindred with Blood differing from their sires'. All such instances are quite rare, though. More often, a mortal mystic simply becomes a Kindred with an unusual talent.

The Burakumin provide an example of a bloodline that began through a tainted Embrace. The bloodline originated as a caste of mortal pariahs before their sire dragged them into undeath. They retained a degree of traditional power over the dead and passed it through their Kindred descendants.

Very Old Bloodlines

In some cases, a bloodline has existed so long that no one remembers how it began. A bloodline's derivation might be a matter of pure guesswork based on a characteristic weakness, the Disciplines that its members favor, or just an indefinable similarity between cultures. That, in itself, is an important factor in the bloodline's history and character. In its home region, Kindred might consider the bloodline equal to any clan, especially if its numbers are large. Storytellers should pay special attention to how the bloodline selects and trains childer, so as to explain why its culture has lasted so long.

No one remembers, for instance, exactly how or when the Morbus bloodline diverged from the Mekhet. Culturally, the Mekhet left the Morbus behind centuries ago. The bloodline could retain its archetype as shadowy figures who prowled through darkness and left plague in their wake because such situations occurred even among mortals in the same domains that hosted "stock" Mekhet. The Morbus bloodline (though it is more of a faction, really) still strives to hide its identity, rather like other Kindred observing the Masquerade.

Indeed, the clans themselves might be nothing more than "bloodlines" of ubiquity. In the extreme case, perhaps a bloodline isn't really a bloodline at all. Perhaps it is a fading clan, once numerous and widespread but now shrunken and confined to a particular locale. A supposed "clan of origin" might actually be an offshoot that grew to supplant an older lineage. The ancient history of the Kindred hints at many such mysteries that undead scholars despair of ever solving.

The Founder

Design the founder of a bloodline with as much care as you would any other character in your chronicle. Even if the founder is destroyed or in torpor, he remains the most important figure in the bloodline's history.

Work out why someone Embraced the founder in the first place. What attracted his sire's notice? What did his sire want from him? Is the founder a player's character?

How did the founder feel about his parent clan? If he felt out of place, that supplies a motive to split from the clan.

What circumstances led this Kindred to found his bloodline? Was it deliberate, accidental, completely unasked for? Did any other Kindred react to the event in any notable way?

Why did the founder sire childer? What does he want from them? What demands did he place? How did his childer react?

Does the founder still exist? Does he still wield any influence over the rest of his bloodline? If he's been destroyed, how did it happen, and how did it affect the bloodline?

Joining or Realizing a Bloodline

A character's ability to join a bloodline or create one of her own depends on several factors, including her clan, specific lineage and Blood Potency.

Joining the Sire's Bloodline

At Blood Potency 2, a character may "activate" his sire's bloodline, becoming a part of it. Doing so allows him access to that bloodline's Discipline (which thereafter counts as a fourth "clan Discipline") but also saddles him with that bloodline's weakness (which also complements his existing clan weakness).

Joining a sire's bloodline requires the expenditure of a Willpower dot.

Joining Another Bloodline

At Blood Potency 4, a character may align himself with an existing bloodline to which his sire doesn't belong. The character must belong to the bloodline's parent clan, however. For instance, a Ventrue could become a Malkovian, or a Gangrel could join the Bruja, but a Nosferatu could never become a Morbus, nor could a Mekhet join the Burakumin.

Normally, a character needs the permission and patronage of a vampire who is already a member of that bloodline to join it. This patron is known as the Avus (from the Latin for "grandfather"). When the Kindred seeks to join the bloodline, she must drink at least one Vitae from the Avus (though drinking at least a point of Vitae from any member of the bloodline will suffice, including acts of diablerie…), so that she knows what mystic form she must force her blood to take. Cruel, domineering or overly careful Avuses occasionally subject their proxy "childer" to Vinculums, just to be sure that no later treachery occurs. At no time does the Avus directly become a blood-relation to the Kindred in question (unless he already is…). The Avus is not subject to blood ties or blood sympathy as described on p. 162-163 (again, unless he already is). Without the support of an Avus it is almost impossible for a Kindred to join a bloodline to which she is not directly connected or that she creates on her own.

Becoming part of the Avus' bloodline allows a character access to that bloodline's Discipline (which thereafter counts as a fourth "clan Discipline") and also bestows upon her that bloodline's weakness (which complements her existing clan weakness).

Joining the Avus' bloodline requires the expenditure of a Willpower dot on the character's part, and the expenditure of a Willpower point and at least one Vitae on the Avus' part.

Creating a New Bloodline

If a player does not "activate" a sire's bloodline or join another clan bloodline, she may create a bloodline for her character at Blood Potency 6. Many bloodlines have a unique Discipline, and all have a unique weakness. As with activating prior bloodlines, the Discipline becomes a fourth clan Discipline and the weakness layers on top of the existing clan weakness.

Creation of a new bloodline requires the expenditure of a Willpower dot.

Universal Concerns

A character can engage only one of these options: become a member of his sire's bloodline, join another clan bloodline or diverge into his own unique bloodline. He cannot do two or all three.

Any time after a character achieves Blood Potency 2, he may "activate" his sire's bloodline. That is, if a character has Blood Potency 6 and hasn't started his own bloodline or joined another, he may then join his sire's latent bloodline. Any time after a character reaches Blood Potency 4, he may join a clan bloodline (provided he has the proper patronage or is willing to commit diablerie). For example, if a character has Blood Potency 6 and hasn't started his own bloodline or joined his sire's, he may join a clan bloodline. The same holds true with regard to starting a character's own bloodline and Blood Potency 6. Again, only one choice is available; you can't do all three or even your choice of two.

Joining or creating a bloodline doesn't "just happen." The character actually forces her Blood to take on new characteristics or to conform to the characteristics of another. Needless to say, effecting a change like this in the static Kindred takes time, to say nothing of entreating an Avus for the distinction of joining his bloodline. Creating a new bloodline or joining an existing one isn't something that should happen overnight. Storytellers are recommended to allow players' characters to transition to new bloodlines between chapters of a chronicle, not simply between scenes, or even in the same game session (unless some unconventional pacing takes place). Alternatively, a Storyteller may allow characters to begin play as members of existing bloodlines, so long as those characters have the requisite Blood Potency of 2 or more.

A character who has met bloodline requirements and whose Blood Potency later drops due to torpor does not lose those bloodline privileges. For example, a vampire who creates a bloodline at Blood Potency 6 and later drops to Blood Potency 5 does not have his bloodline, Discipline, et cetera suddenly vanish. He has already forced his Blood to take on the bloodline characteristics, so even if his Blood later loses some of its inherent power, the deed has already been done. At the Storyteller's discretion, it may be difficult for a character to learn further levels of the bloodline Discipline when Blood Potency drops, but this is usually suitable only if the Discipline isn't yet known completely or has yet to be codified.

Not only do the answers to such questions help you make the bloodline's background seem more real, you probably find story hooks popping up. To give the simplest example, a surviving bloodline founder might take an interest in the remarkable achievements of a descendant — a player's character. The founder might become a mentor, a patron, a jealous enemy or anything in between.

The Bruja and Toreador offer case studies of a bloodline founder's influence. The Bruja founder, Carlos Saavedra, was a hellion in life who retained his criminal commitment in undeath. He helped his childer gain power among the outlaw community as well, giving his bloodline a focus that survived his own disappearance. The first Toreador Embraced only those who suited the founder's growing cult of personality. This practice gave the Toreador a degree of consistency (if not internal cohesion) that is rare among Kindred. The founder or his childe presumably still has immense sway over the bloodline's tastes, and few of his descendants would dare to tempt his wrath (as the whole point of the Patrons is to demonstrate bloodlines as a clique). A Toreador character might even receive occasional messages from Castillejo or de al Vega, as the first Patrons keep tabs on their heirs.

Of course, the founder becomes especially important if she is a player's character. In this case, the bloodline's origin is an ongoing subplot within the chronicle. Storytellers can build stories around the circumstances that lead to a character's change, the reaction of other Kindred (especially those in the character's clan) and the choice whether to sire a childe or not.

Recognition of a Bloodline

Any Kindred might say that he founded a bloodline, but do other Kindred believe him or care? Bloodline founders can receive a fair bit of prestige in Kindred culture. It takes more than an odd power — or a signature weakness — to win respect.

A Kindred must prove that her special aptitudes pass to her childer, and to their childer in turn. Kindred tradition holds that no change in the Blood can be certain until two generations pass. One generation of childer might learn a new set of Disciplines because their sire drove them to make a special effort. If a second generation shows similar aptitude, the Blood has surely changed. Inherited weaknesses can be even harder to detect, especially if they produce no overt mark such as the Nosferatu's palpable otherness.

If they want, the Kindred can consult a sorcerer to establish whether a self-proclaimed founder has truly changed her Blood and that of her childer. Hiring a blood magician to perform occult tests means owing that sorcerer a boon, however, and prudent Kindred do not promise favors lightly. Anyway, what if someone bribed the sorcerer to lie? Prudent Kindred do not take another vampire's word for anything.

More simply, Kindred can taste the Vitae of an alleged founder's childe and compare it to the parent clan. (See "Blood Ties" on p. 162 for more about this.) Vampires who drink the blood of fellow Kindred risk addiction and take the first step to a Vinculum, however, so wise Kindred would not perform this test themselves. In another few decades, the matter will sort itself out.

A bloodline's founder also needs to amass enough power that other Kindred fear and respect — or at least acknowledge — her. Two generations of childer who retain some connection to their forebear form an impressive reserve of power all by themselves. A would-be founder can also establish her power through the normal means available to vampires, such as wealth, mortal minions and high office among a city's Kindred. Garcilaso de Castillejo possessed more than a fourth Discipline and a few childer to back up his assumption of a founder's rank. He also "possessed" a unique subculture that grew around him, and inspired an *esprit de corps* that was fervent enough for his lineage to claim its own under penalty of crushing social retribution.

Mere time also plays a role. The undead see many small upsets in their long existence. They do not waste much attention on the short term. So what if a Kindred wants to say he's founded a bloodline? Will he still make that claim in a hundred years? Will he still *exist* in a hundred years? A new bloodline must persist for decades, if not centuries, before other Kindred consider it worth serious attention. The slow pace of communication among Kindred of different cities also makes sure that word of a new bloodline takes centuries to reach vampires who dwell far away. News of the Bruja still has not reached all the Kindred of the United States, let alone the rest of the world. The Kindred of California took decades to acknowledge that Saavedra had founded a bloodline, and he was already infamous in a context that eclipsed the secret world of the Kindred.

For much of their history, the Kindred did not especially care about bloodlines in distant lands. Foreign vampires could not affect them, so most Kindred did not bother learning about them. Modern travel and communications have changed that to some degree. Travel remains difficult for Kindred, but a journey across continents is not much harder than a trip of a few hundred miles. As a result, rare Kindred visitors to a city might include members of bloodlines formerly limited to distant regions, such as the Burakumin. Some elders now want very much to know who or what might come to their city, so that they can exploit, avoid or destroy an intruding member of a foreign bloodline.

Thus, when you design a bloodline, give thought to how much other Kindred know about it. Do they consider it a minor, idiosyncratic group within an existing clan, or do they recognize it as a distinct lineage? How many Kindred even know that the bloodline exists? Has word of the bloodline spread very far? If so, how? The Kindred react in different ways to an envoy from a known bloodline than to a wholly mysterious vampire threat.

Just as importantly, how much information on a bloodline is accurate? Rumor might ascribe any sort of strange powers and horrible customs to an obscure and distant line. Consider that 500 years ago, educated Europeans seriously believed that central Asia held one-eyed giants, dog-headed cannibals and pygmies who lived off the smell of apples. The Kindred travel less than their mortal ancestors did 500 years ago. Any "foreign" Kindred might be suspected of diablerie, sanguinary sacrifice to strange gods or any other foul practice, just because

bloodlines and unique disciplines

someone's great-grandsire said it was the custom of Kindred in that part of the world or among that bloodline.

Size and Population

Approximately how many members does a bloodline have? The Tradition of Progeny keeps Kindred from siring childer very often, so a bloodline's numbers probably do not grow quickly. A bloodline might take centuries to build up respectable numbers. The Morbus, for instance, probably number at least a hundred, but the bloodline is more than a few centuries old. The Bruja, at just a handful of decades, number rather less.

Cultural factors and historical events can slow a bloodline's growth even further, or actually reduce its numbers. The bloodline's founder might not want to sire many childer, or he might forbid progeny to his childer in reverence of the Traditions. A bloodline's members might think that very few mortals deserve the Embrace. Conflicts with other Kindred, other supernatural beings or with mortal witch-hunters might result in the destruction of many members of a line. For example, the Toreador Embrace only those who fit into their social clique, and they limit their numbers to maintain a sense of rarity and therefore significance and uniqueness.

Storytellers should not say exactly how many members a bloodline has unless it's so small and localized that every member can appear in a particular story arc. Rough estimates, such as "a pittance," "a few dozen" or "maybe a hundred," preserve the setting's sense of mystery and the unknown.

Age and population also tend to correlate with how far a bloodline has spread. Since vampires seldom travel, a bloodline could take decades to spread from the domain in which it began, and centuries to reach other nations or continents. A populous, old bloodline might have spread through several countries, and the odds are better that some member takes the risky step of moving far away to the young cities of the New World.

The Rules Stuff

At some point, you must define a bloodline's favored Disciplines and inherited weakness. This is usually the easiest part of designing a bloodline, and it's very often the point of inspiration. Storytellers shouldn't let a Discipline be the *only* inspiration, though.

Bloodline Disciplines

A bloodline favors *at least* the same Disciplines as the parent clan. In case it doesn't, a bloodline may replace one or two favored Disciplines, and one of them is usually a somewhat similar Discipline. For instance, the three "physical" Disciplines of Celerity, Resilience and Vigor easily substitute for each other. So do the "psychic" Disciplines of Animalism, Auspex, Dominate, Majesty, Nightmare and Obfuscate, which all affect the mind in some way. The Bruja, for instance, seem to have decided that they'd like to wield brute strength in addition to the supernal hardiness of their parent clan.

A bloodline has four favored Disciplines. Of them, three almost always remain the same as the parent clan's. The fourth is either unique to the bloodline — unable to be learned by Kindred who are not of the bloodline — or is one of the "common" Disciplines practiced by vampires across clan lines.

Theban Sorcery, Crúac and the pseudo-Discipline of the Coils of the Dragon may never be a bloodline's fourth Discipline.

The change to a bloodline never replaces all three clan Disciplines. The Blood just doesn't change to that degree, no matter what influence works upon it. If you design a bloodline and find that you want to replace all three of the parent clan's Disciplines, re-examine your reasons for choosing that particular clan. Some other clan is probably more appropriate.

This goes for players, too. A player whose character has developed all three clan Disciplines to the limit set by his Blood Potency might want to move the character onto a bloodline so that the character gets an experience-point break when learning another Discipline. We recommend that Storytellers not allow this because it's cheap and tacky point-mongering, instead of serious character development.

We also recommend that you do not allow any bloodline to favor more than one unique Discipline. This is a point of story design, not an innate property of the Blood. Special Disciplines should relate to the core idea of a bloodline — its very reason for existence as part of your chronicle. More than one exotic Discipline suggests a lack of focus in the concept of the line… or an attempt to create a "super-bloodline" or a simple desire to be strange for the sake of strangeness. For comparison, note that of the sample bloodlines, the Burakumin and Morbus have just one unusual Discipline each. The Bruja, Malkovians and Toreador stick to familiar Disciplines.

Under no circumstances can a character have more than four bloodline Disciplines. Changing the Blood to favor a new Discipline always means honing one's affinity for *one* other Discipline. No power in the World of Darkness can change this iron law.

Bloodline Weakness

A bloodline may keep the same weakness as its parent clan. Additionally, bloodlines develop new flaws or focus the clan's existing weakness. The Morbus, for instance, have very specific tastes while the Malkovians suffer from a refined madness even more crippling than that of members of their parent clan. Storytellers should examine proposed weaknesses closely, to make sure that they actually handicap a character. Compare the new weakness to the standard clan weakness. Does the new weakness limit or hinder the character just as much?

We recommend that any new weakness include some aspect that you can objectively represent through a dice roll or some other game mechanic. Good players roleplay their characters' weaknesses, but a well-designed weakness does not depend entirely on the player's willingness to roleplay or the Storyteller's fiat for when it affects the character. Arguing slows down your story and usually isn't much fun. Make sure that player and Storyteller agree when the weakness affects the character, how it affects the character and what the character can do to resist or compensate for its effects. For example, the Bruja weakness plays out as a severe form of hunger frenzy that affects those Resolve + Composure rolls. If a player proves reluctant to roleplay her Rabble's thirst for Blood, the Storyteller penalizes her those three dice and lets them arbitrate the situation.

OPTION: A HOARY SECRET

Theban Sorcery, the Coils of the Dragon and Crúac might include rituals that enable a Kindred to join or renounce a bloodline without the normal prohibitions or prerequisites. These rituals are immensely rare and obscure. Storytellers who wish to allow such false bloodline potential are advised to require exceedingly potent mastery of the various blood magics to perform them: rituals of level six, at the very least.

Creating a Discipline

New Disciplines, like bloodlines, don't appear from nowhere for no reason. Just as with bloodlines, give thought to both the origin of the Discipline and what role you want it to play in your chronicle. Sure, every exotic Discipline is a mystery, an opportunity and a threat to all the Kindred who don't have it and who don't know what it can do. What sort of an opportunity or threat do you want the Discipline to present?

Consider Getsumei. Most simply, the Burakumin's trademark Discipline enables them to manipulate the energies of death. Since most other vampires understand very little of death beyond their own Requiems, that gives the Burakumin a unique reserve of informants and assets. More than its direct applications, though, Getsumei extends a chronicle into a new realm. Why would one suppose that the dead just mope around their haunted houses and graveyards, waiting for someone to hold a séance? The realms of the dead might hold their own secrets. Kindred who use Getsumei to interact with the corporeal dead necessarily involve themselves in the culture and concerns of their unquiet realm. They can acquire allies — or enemies. This is a whole new world of stories for a chronicle to explore.

Most new Disciplines probably don't broaden a chronicle as much as Getsumei does. When you invent a new Discipline, however, try to think of different ways to apply its powers and what implications it holds for other Kindred and your chronicle. What at first seems like just a cool trick might actually prompt many Kindred to change their nightly unlife. Certainly, any Kindred who learns about Cachexy never looks at illness the same way. Is that the latest flu to arrive from some exotic port of call… or a Morbus in the domain?

PROPRIETARY KNOWLEDGE

Unique Disciplines are impossible for anyone to learn unless they belong to the bloodlines that created them.

In some cases, similar Disciplines arise among different bloodlines. Even the "common" Disciplines might manifest a similarity among certain bloodlines. A snake-themed lineage might speak with a forked tongue whenever it uses its powers of Dominate, for example, while members of a bloodline renowned for divinatory abilities

might lapse into an oracular, trance-like state when they put their Auspex powers to use. Players should feel free to make a certain aspect of the "common" Disciplines a signature of their own bloodlines, if they so wish.

Not-Really-New Disciplines

Some "new" Disciplines are not really new or unique to a bloodline. A Discipline might have existed for millennia but remained little known because no surviving lineage carried it. When a bloodline that favors the Discipline grows in number, however, other Kindred have a better chance of seeing the Discipline. By the same token, not every new Discipline needs a bloodline to practice it. If you think that a particular Discipline would improve your game and your stories, bring whispers of it into your chronicle. You don't have to invent a bloodline if you don't want to — let the tales of the Discipline carry the mystery. You can invent the bloodline later as rumors of the Discipline circulate, or you can use them as very effective red herrings. Don't overdo it, though. Too much abuse of rumor without enough to substantiate it can make players feel misled, and it smacks of smoke and mirrors rather than good plot design.

Origin Stories

New Disciplines appear along with new bloodlines, so the stories of their origins usually bear some connection. A curse or contamination from some other supernatural race can provide the stimulus for a new Discipline as well as a bloodline. The effort to invent a Discipline might change a Kindred's very being, thus resulting in a bloodline, rather than stemming from it. Two broad patterns turn up again and again, with many possible variations. You could work either of these patterns into the history of a bloodline.

Variations on a Theme

A rare or new Discipline might be a variation on a more familiar Kindred art. Such a variation could appear because a Kindred wanted to use the original Discipline for some unusual or specialized purpose. He might even develop unique Devotions or level-six+ powers, so the Discipline would perform more of the feats he really wanted. Such a Kindred might find that his childer learn his idiosyncratic variations instead of the more common version, creating a new Discipline. For instance, an elder with mental problems might use Dominate to inflict his delusions on other people, as with the Malkovian bloodline. Further than that, however, his childer might not learn to use Dominate for anything else, and their childer might actually learn a new Discipline that can't be used for anything *but* to derange the mind.

Crossover Contamination

Kindred can also develop new Disciplines based on the powers of other supernatural beings, such as Lupines, mages or ghosts. A vampire who sets out to do so deliberately certainly needs to study the other supernatural race — a precarious activity, to say the least. His research subjects surely object, since

Kindred tradition holds that one must drink another being's blood to claim its power, as with diablerie. Still, a Kindred manages to pull it off now and then and manifests a Discipline, the effects of which resemble one of the magical gifts of another supernatural creature.

Such "crossover" Disciplines can also appear spontaneously. Embraced mortal magicians might manifest novel Disciplines based on the sorcery they practiced in life. Getsumei provides an example of mortal sorcery potentially transformed into a Kindred Discipline. More dubious rumors speak of exotic creatures of legend giving rise to novel Disciplines. In rare cases, Kindred can also manifest strange powers if they repeatedly feed upon other supernatural creatures or survive deadly encounters with their powers. When different supernatural powers clash and end in death, anything might happen.

WHO INVENTED IT?

When you work out the back story for a Discipline, give some thought to who invented it, or at least who made it more widely known. This is usually the founder of the bloodline that uses the Discipline. Not only does this character set the style for the bloodline, he might still exist. Quite possibly, a character who wants to master the last one or two powers in the Discipline needs to learn them from the inventor himself. This requirement might lead to a travel story as the character searches for his bloodline's founder, with all the difficulties and dangers that travel always holds for the Kindred. Once he finds the Discipline's inventor, the character still faces the challenge of persuading him to share his secret. What compensation, threat, bribe or plea can be offered?

Select a Theme

Creating a Discipline is rather more complicated from the point of view of a player or Storyteller. First, give thought to what the Discipline is about. Every Discipline sticks closely to a theme or effect, such as "strength" or "fear" or "concealment." Be careful that you don't just create a grab bag of cool powers, even if they would all be useful for a certain purpose. Remember that a Discipline is really just one linear progression of power that a character learns to use better and in different ways.

Not every theme or effect is really appropriate for the Kindred. Can you tie a Discipline to some aspect of the undead condition? Is it something a vampire could really use? The Kindred are undeniably powerful, but they aren't superheroes. Think about creepy, moody, gothic ways that the secret lords of the night could use a proposed Discipline to maintain their power, not how the Discipline would work in a flashy monster smackdown.

Neither of our sample unique Disciplines, for example, are much use in a fight. A Morbus could use Cachexy to sicken an opponent, but that's about the limit of its combat use. If a

Burakumin has advance knowledge that he will be attacked, some corpse-minions could prove helpful, but he probably doesn't have enough prepared cadavers lying around to animate them on the spot.

Very few Disciplines directly cause damage to an opponent. Of the "old standards," only Protean, Vigor and one specific power of Nightmare increase a character's capacity to deal physical damage. Vampires can already harm each other (or mortals) using their claws and fangs… or plain old guns and knives. They don't need much more. Instead, most of the standard Disciplines enable the Kindred to influence the actions of other creatures (Animalism, Dominate, Majesty, Nightmare), gain information (Animalism, Auspex), enhance their own physical capacity (Celerity, Protean, Resilience, Vigor) or hide themselves from threats (Obfuscate, Protean).

Don't feel too constrained by existing legends and fiction about vampires. Like bloodlines, Disciplines offer a chance to extend the vampire myth. Your new Discipline might affect some common aspect of Kindred experience. For instance, vampires are creatures of darkness, barred from the light of day. A new Discipline for a member of the Mekhet bloodline might help a vampire thrive in darkness and master it. Other Disciplines might show a more symbolic link to undeath. Vampires exist in a state between life and death. The unique Discipline of Getsumei enables Kindred to interact with death-energies, which exist beyond the living and close to oblivion. Bringing Getsumei into your chronicle gives you a chance to explore the Kindred's place as mediators between life and death.

New Disciplines should probably be less powerful than the familiar Disciplines. The "old favorites" became the standards because they were especially useful. The Kindred spent thousands of years learning how to use them to great effect. A new or obscure Discipline has not received such unilateral refinement. From a story point of view, a rare Discipline's value lies in its ability to surprise other characters, not in its raw power. A character with a new Discipline is a mystery to other Kindred. Perhaps she's a resource to exploit or a menace to destroy, but not matter what she's someone to watch.

Although novel Disciplines might be more specialized than the "old favorites," don't let them be *too* specialized. Think of how many ways you can use increased strength, influence over people's emotions, or communication with animals. Since discovering clever uses for a Discipline is part of the fun of having them, a Discipline that's too narrowly focused might be boring.

On the other hand, watch out for Discipline arms races. New Disciplines might come from a desire to build characters who are more powerful than anyone else's. If a player succeeds, other players could want to play characters of the same bloodline or create their own super-characters with even more powerful Disciplines. Such escalation can ruin your chronicle.

Alas, Storytellers can fall into this trap just as easily as players. You can feel a great temptation to create a bloodline of Kindred that is tougher than the standard clans, especially if you intend a member to oppose the players' characters. This falls into the category of adversarial Storytelling, which gives you reason enough not to do it.

Killer Disciplines?

One form of specialized Discipline presents a special danger. You might feel tempted to create a Discipline geared toward combat, which enables its possessor to slaughter all opposition. Resist this temptation. This goes for Storytellers as well as players!

"Killer Disciplines" really aren't as much fun as they sound. For one thing, they usually aren't good for anything *but* killing enemies. They don't offer many opportunities for the devious cunning and intrigue that forms so great a part of Kindred existence.

Slaughtering your enemies is also not a great strategy for characters. A Kindred who racks up a body count of other vampires — or even mortals — might frighten his elders enough that they plot his elimination. Elders have lots of ways to destroy a loose cannon without getting into a fight.

Most importantly, **Vampire: The Requiem** is a Storytelling game. Combat has its place, but it's fundamentally a game about making choices, not about how many foes one kills before being destroyed.

Select the Powers

Assuming your Storyteller likes the concept of your Discipline, you can move on to defining the specific powers gained at each level. Your Storyteller might not let you design the whole Discipline. She might want to leave some of the powers a surprise for your character.

The first power is always the weakest, though it can be very useful. Look at the initial powers in the standard Disciplines. Extra-keen senses (with occasional psychic flashes) or issuing one-word commands does not crush all opposition and establish one as a blood god of the night. They can be awfully handy, though, and give your character a crucial edge in her endeavors.

The first power in a Discipline tends to be subtle. These capabilities add a drop of the supernatural to some natural ability, or at least to some feature common to all Kindred. For instance, the first level of Majesty makes its user seem very interesting and attractive… but some people are that way naturally. A single level of Celerity lets a Kindred be frighteningly quick… but anyone can try to be quick, it's simply difficult for those who aren't inherently inclined toward it. In the sample unique Disciplines, the first Getsumei power allows one to preserve a corpse indefinitely. The first Cachexy power lets one diagnose latent diseases. All certainly have their applications, but an onlooker could not tell that anything really out of the ordinary happens when they're used.

As a Kindred masters a Discipline, its applications often become flashier and more explicitly supernatural, as well as more powerful. No one could mistake the effects of Sovereignty for anything less than a magical effect, while no mortal could ever achieve the blinding speed of five levels of Celerity. Ordinary people certainly don't summon waves of plague or conjure legions of walking corpses, either.

The fourth and fifth powers are, naturally, the most formidable. At this point, a Discipline should grant some crushing advantage over mere mortals. Kindred who possess four levels

of mastery in a Discipline are deadly fiends whom mortals defeat with difficulty. This potency does not need to involve combat, either. A Kindred with four dots of Auspex, for example, can learn a mortal's secrets and goals by listening to his thoughts — very useful for extortion, temptation, or for getting the hell out of the way before the mortal attacks. A Morbus with four dots of Cachexy can cripple a mortal by ravaging him with disease, or can cause him to be the focus of an epidemic investigation.

Try to avoid overlap with existing Disciplines unless you explicitly design your new Discipline as a variation on one of the old standards. If a Discipline leaves players thinking, "I've seen that before," it just doesn't seem very exciting.

In particular, don't make your new Discipline better at something that a standard Discipline already does, especially at the same level. If your new Discipline is better at concealment than Obfuscate, why would anyone learn Obfuscate? If it permits greater changes of form than Protean, who needs Protean?

Watch out for redundant powers within a Discipline, too. Unless you run an "elders" chronicle, you have to define the Discipline with just five powers. That's not many. If one power is merely a stronger or more complete version of an earlier effect, players might feel that the lower-level power is a waste of experience points.

Game Mechanics

After you work out the general effect of each Discipline level, work out the details by assigning game mechanics.

• Does the power require a dice pool? Not all of them do. Some Discipline powers have fixed effects. Vigor, for instance, simply adds dice to Strength-based dice pools, Speed and jumping distances.

• If the power does require a dice roll, what traits go into the pool? A Discipline's powers usually all stem from the same Attribute category, be it Mental, Physical or Social. Attribute + Skill + Discipline level is the basic combination. You should have a strong and cogent reason for ever using Resolve, Composure or Stamina proactively as part of the user's invocation roll, though it can happen.

Note that most Disciplines use the same category of Attributes throughout. Mental Disciplines use Mental Attributes, social Disciplines use Social Attributes. If you break with this custom, address the fact and give a sensible reason other than, "My character has lots of dots in that Attribute."

• What modifiers apply? As noted previously for many Discipline powers, you add or subtract a modifier from the dice pool to reflect how some Kindred (or other supernatural creatures) might be harder to affect than others, situational distractions, how much information is sought, or other concerns. The power might receive other modifiers, increasing or decreasing the dice pool, to reflect special circumstances. Is the power affected by the presence of blood ties (see p. 162) between user and subject?

• Does the number of successes rolled have any influence on the power's effect? Some Disciplines have all-or-nothing effects or effects in which the difference between success

and exceptional success is merely a matter of degree. Others can unpredictably produce greater or lesser effects on a target. One success, as always, indicates a weak, marginal effect on the target. Three successes indicate a more pronounced effect. Five or more successes represent an exceptional success with greater than normal effect. Dramatic failure always results in something bad happening to the character if any potential for it exists. Resistance Attributes usually modify the activation roll based on the Discipline's function as a Mental, Physical or Social power, or they serve as the basis for a defensive dice pool in a contested roll. (Unless some overwhelming circumstance applies, any roll to resist a power should be reflexive).

For example, a power that uses Intelligence as the invoker's base Attribute is modified by Resolve. This means the subject's Resolve is subtracted from the user's dice pool or is rolled as a contested dice pool. The rule of thumb is that if a power has gradations of effect, in which each success individually accounts for increasing results, the subject's Resistance trait is subtracted from the user's dice pool. If the power has an all-or-nothing effect, the subject's player gets a roll of his own that is compared to the user's activation roll. See p. 202 of the **World of Darkness Rulebook** for more on this design principle. (Note that mortals typically have limited capacity to resist the supernatural abilities of the undead, as the living are traditional victims of Kindred power. It's part of their job in the chronicle. At the very least, they have no Blood Potency to bolster contested rolls. Even if they are entitled to a

contested roll, it's probably a dice pool of a single trait because their Blood Potency is effectively zero.)

• What subjects does a power affect? Some Disciplines, such as Celerity, Resilience and Vigor, affect the user herself. Others affect a single person, a number of people or everyone in an area. Still others might change a Kindred's surroundings in some way. See the following for a set of standard tables that relate a Discipline's effect to the number of successes rolled.

• Does the power cost Vitae? Many powers of the standard Disciplines do not cost Vitae to use, or one Vitae fuels the power for a full scene. Disciplines that only one faction favors, such as Crúac or unique bloodline Disciplines, generally cost Vitae to use. The powers of a novel Discipline should probably cost Vitae, too, to reflect their lack of development. Only the most lethal or efficacious powers, or powers that never fail to have full effect should cost Willpower points.

Standard Models for Disciplines

As a convenience, we offer some of the more common design models for Discipline powers. These tables can help a new Discipline stay roughly equal to the "old standards." The successes rolled indicate a character's degree of success.

The effects of a power can vary in several ways. Most simply, they can cause damage in proportion to successes rolled, just like a mundane attack. Discipline powers can also vary in duration, the number of targets they affect, and their area of effect.

Direct, Single-Target Attacks

Discipline powers that inflict actual points of damage work just like mundane combat. The player rolls for the character to strike the target, which determines the amount of damage dealt.

Disciplines, however, can employ traits other than the Strength or Dexterity used in mundane combat, and can call upon various traits for the subject's protection. For instance, a "psychic attack" power might use Intelligence + Skill + Discipline level for the "attack" or invocation roll, with the target's Resolve for the Resistance modifier. The invocation roll may succeed, fail or yield disaster, with appropriate effects.

Dramatic Failure: The power rebounds and harms the attacker in some way.

Failure: The power doesn't activate, or it doesn't affect the target.

Success: The power causes damage normally.

Exceptional Success: The power causes damage normally. Extra successes are their own reward, since they increase the potential damage.

If the attack succeeds, each success indicates one point of damage.

The ability to inflict aggravated damage should never be less than a level-three power.

You can also use this system for attacks that reduce a target's combat abilities in some way other than Health. A power might reduce one of a character's Attributes for a time, or strike him blind. Dominate and Majesty are examples of "attacks" that do not cause harm at all — they just change the target's thoughts or emotions.

Duration

Duration can be a factor for a power in one of two ways. The invocation roll of a power might indicate a duration. Alternatively, the player can modify an invocation roll. Attempting a longer duration than normal means subtracting dice from the pool. Sacrificing duration may add dice to the pool.

An attack might have a fixed effect on the target, regardless of successes rolled — for instance, a power to strike a foe blind. You can't make someone *more* blind, so successes on an effect roll indicate a duration instead of a degree of damage, such as:

Successes	Duration
1 success	Two turns
2 successes	Five turns
3 successes	20 turns (1 minute)
4 successes	10 minutes
5+ successes	One hour or scene

Powers that affect the target in particularly subtle or non-damaging ways may last much longer.

Successes	Duration
1 success	Two turns
2 successes	One hour or scene
3 successes	One day
4 successes	One month
5+ successes	One year or indefinitely

No handicap is ever permanent — at least not for vampires. If nothing else, a victim can restore lost traits with experience points. A vampire can remove many other indirectly damaging effects if she is willing to suffer lethal damage. A Kindred could cure his blindness by putting out his eyes and re-growing them, for example.

If a character wants to try for an extra-long duration for a power, the player subtracts one die from the effect roll for every step up the duration table that he wants. If a character wants to try to blind a foe for a full minute (two steps up the duration table), the player subtracts two dice from the activation dice pool. If he succeeds at all, he's sure the blindness lasts at least one minute.

Area Effects

Some Discipline powers affect an area rather than a person or object. A curse could make everyone within an area get sick. Decide whether you want a fixed area, in which the effect on targets may vary, or a fixed effect on targets but a greater or lesser area depending on the number of successes rolled. For instance, a power that creates a patch of darkness has a fixed effect: It makes an area dark. Depending on how many successes a player rolls, the patch of darkness might cover a greater or lesser area.

You can define an area of effect in terms of radius, affecting everything within a circle. Alternatively, you might prefer to say that a power affects everything within a given area, but the character can define the shape of that area each time he uses the power. Use this table when the number of successes determines the power's area of effect.

Successes	Radius	Undefined Area
1 success	1 yard radius	5 sq. yards
2 successes	2 yard radius	10 sq. yards
3 successes	5 yard radius	50 sq. yards
4 successes	10 yard radius	250 sq. yards
5+ successes	30 yard radius	1000 sq. yards

If the player wants to be sure that a power affects a larger area, he subtracts dice from the effect pool: one die per step up the area of effect table. If he gains even one success, the desired area is affected, as with duration.

Use a similar system if the power has a base area, while the degree of effect on subjects depends on the successes rolled. In such cases, the Storyteller picks a default area for the power from the table. If the player wants to increase that area, he subtracts one die from the effect roll per step up the table from the default area. By this system, attacks on wide areas are less likely to succeed at all, and they deal less damage on average to the victims caught within them. Characters must choose whether they want to attack many targets with a greater chance of failure, or a smaller number of targets with a greater chance of success and damage.

Multiple-Target Effects

Some powers affect a number of people or other targets — potentially as many as are within range. The power's effect is otherwise fixed. See the Majesty power of Awe for an example.

The player can roll for the power's effect and hope that many targets succumb, or the player can subtract dice and hope for an all-or-nothing effect on the desired number of people.

Successes	Targets Affected
1 success	one person/other target
2 successes	two targets, or a quarter of targets
3 successes	six targets, or half the targets
4 successes	20 targets, or almost all targets
5+ successes	all targets in the appropriate area

Doubly Variable Effects

In certain rare cases in which a power's effect can vary in two ways — number of targets and degree of effect — Storytellers may choose to use an invocation roll and an effect roll. Doing so breaks with custom, so it shouldn't be used frequently, but it can make for some interesting and dramatic powers, and is especially suitable to those at high levels. One factor modifies the invocation roll, and the effect roll describes the second factor. For instance, a power could blind multiple people for a varying length of time. The Storyteller could apply a penalty to the invocation roll based on the number of targets the character wants to affect. Say, -1 die for two targets, -2 dice for six targets, and so on. If the attack succeeds, the effect roll could use the duration table to determine how long the targets remain blind. In other cases, the Storyteller might prefer to modify the invocation roll based on the severity of the desired effect, and let the effect roll determine how many people succumb to the power.

DESIGNING DEVOTIONS

Devotions are combinations of Disciplines that yield unique effects based on the interactions of those powers. Unlike regular Disciplines, Devotions do not progress — they're single-purpose capabilities that stand by themselves. For more on Devotions, see p. 150.

Designing a Devotion works much like designing a Discipline and is subject to Storyteller approval. The guidelines for designing other Disciplines in this section can help you with Devotions, at least as far as power and function are concerned. The first step is to decide what a Devotion does. The second step is to decide which Disciplines are necessary to create the effect. The final step is translating the Devotion into the rules and deciding its costs.

You don't need any help in satisfying step one. If you want to create a Devotion, you need an idea for its function. Where this transitions to step two is in deciding how to break the Devotion down into two or more Discipline influences. Use the Disciplines themselves as guidelines. A Devotion that involves preternatural senses probably requires some degree of Auspex, while a Devotion that invokes the power of personality likely requires Majesty or Nightmare, depending on what the power is designed to do.

This process is imprecise, more art than science. Because Disciplines generate linear, static effects, sometimes a bit of guesswork has to be done. Take Auspex, for example. If your Devotion focuses on supernatural perception, how much Auspex is necessary? If perception is the focus of the power, one or two dots worth of Auspex probably suffice, based on the first two levels of that Discipline's powers. If projection of the senses or consciousness is required, three or more dots are likely required, judging by the focus of levels three through five of the Discipline. A simple but uncanny projection of senses is probably level three, an overt application of sense or awareness is probably level four, and a full, revelatory condition probably requires level five. Again, you have a lot of leeway here. Devotions are very much instinctual, so go with what you both determine to "feel right."

Most Devotions are combinations of only two Disciplines, but that precedent shouldn't limit you. It's not unheard of for vampires to have Devotions that require knowledge of three or even four Disciplines. More than that, however, and the power becomes so obtuse or specific that it's probably outside the Kindred realm of potential.

Devotions always have an activation cost, usually one Vitae unless their effects are particularly grandiose for their ease of learning.

The experience-point cost to learn a Devotion is roughly three times the total number of Discipline dots among its prerequisites. A Devotion that requires Dominate 2 and Vigor 3 of its would-be possessor costs about 15 experience points. Particularly powerful Devotions might cost as much as three experience points more, while particularly limited or specific Devotions might cost as many as three experience points less.

Also, Devotions that require activation rolls use the power's highest-rated prerequisite Discipline as the basis for those rolls, depending on what the power is designed to do. That Discipline is the most advanced needed to master the Devotion's intricacies. So, the aforementioned power that requires Dominate 2 and Vigor 3 probably calls for Strength in its dice pool. If the Dominate aspect of the power were higher than the Vigor requirement, it would likely call for Intelligence or Wits. If the highest requisite Disciplines are the same, decide which is most important to the Devotion's function and choose that one.

May those who fear us, fear us. And those who hate us, may the Crone turn their hearts.
And if she doesn't turn their hearts, may she turn their ankles so we'll know them by their limping.
— A Circle of the Crone proverb

Appendix Two:
New Orleans

This domain is mine, and so it has been for two centuries.

None but God Himself is fit to take it from me.

— Augusto Vidal, Prince of New Orleans

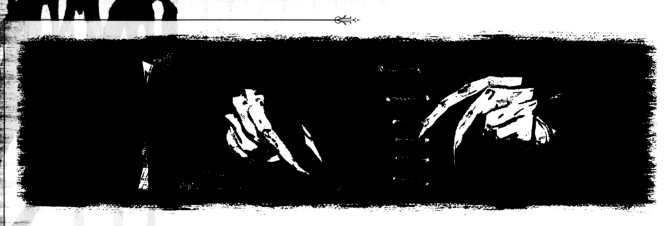

Arrive at New Orleans, a city of ships, steamers, flatboats, rafts, mud, fog, filth, stench, and a mixture of races and tongues. Cholera, "some." [At] Planters' Hotel. Mem: — Never get caught in a cheap tavern in a strange city.

— Pres. Rutherford B. Hayes, diary entry December 21, 1848

What more perfect environment could there be for the nocturnal Kindred than the glorious city of New Orleans? It is a place — perhaps the only place — that fully embodies not only the feel but the very essence of what it is to be damned to darkness. Even the paradox of unlife itself is mirrored in every contradictory facet of this roiling city that is at once gaudy and genteel, pious and perfidious, daring and discreet. Here, in the bloated belly of the Deep South, the wine flows, the dice roll and the pleasures come slow and steady as molasses. Nothing is difficult here, unless it has to be, and yet nothing is free, either.

Nothing is ever free.

Some readers might think they are familiar with such a place. Some might even have been there, a fair number on more than one occasion. But the New Orleans you think you know, though it seems to be the city of which is spoken here, is not the New Orleans of a modern-gothic world. No, the New Orleans of the World of Darkness is a significantly darker place, filled with more people, more crime, more vice, more wine, more desire, more despair — more everything than its real-world counterpart. This is where it all hangs out, for both Kindred and kine, where dreams intercourse with reality, begetting nightmares most unreal — where even the dead must toss in endless, fitful sleep.

Welcome to New Orleans.

Theme

Stories set in New Orleans should strive to hew to what lies at the heart of all modern-gothic tales, for in many ways, the Big Easy is the consummate locale for the evocation of that aesthetic. Indeed, this is precisely the reason for its inclusion in the book you hold. Few cities can so accurately encapsulate the feel of the World of Darkness, especially with regard to vampires, as can New Orleans. As such, the primary themes of the city (and any stories set therein) are the themes of the World of Darkness at large — with one addition.

The primary theme at work in New Orleans is the ubiquity and perversion of paradox. The city was built on religion, and yet it has become synonymous with depravity and sin. It is a glittering Mecca for the living and for life, yet the dead continue to hold as great a sway as they ever have. Like the striking harlequin masks one sees floating through her streets, New Orleans wears a dual face — the light and dark, the agony and ecstasy.

This stark juxtaposition parallels itself again in the world of the Kindred, where the city's devoutly faithful Prince tries to enforce order amid a sea of chaos. Through unwavering enforcement of the Traditions, he has managed to keep overt Kindred conflict to a minimum, but at a mortal cost some believe too high — New Orleans is the murder capitol of the world and has been for many years. Given the Prince's increasingly extreme policies, the city seems intent on carrying its title into the foreseeable future, and given the barbarity that exists elsewhere in the World of Darkness, this grim claim only grows all the more unsettling.

Mood

As it cannot help but do, the city's theme plays into its overall mood. Perhaps the best metaphor to ascribe to New Orleans would be to liken her to a manic-depressive partygoer, one who experiences wild temperamental swings between positively Alpine highs and the lowest of abyssal lows, all in the course of one long night of saturnalia. The difference is that in New Orleans, the party never stops — and neither do the mood swings. This manic disposition engenders some truly frenzied revelry, but it also results in tragedy. Those who wish to partake of the city are wise to be wary of on which side of the pendulum they stand, lest they get caught in its path.

An Historical Overview

It's impossible to truly understand the current state of affairs in New Orleans without knowing how things developed as they did. Presented here is a brief overview of the most important events in the history — Kindred and kine — of the city. For a substantially more detailed look into New Orleans' past, as well as the various secrets and conspiracies unknown to most of its undying population, see **City of the Damned: New Orleans**.

- **1682:** The French explorer Sieur de La Salle arrives at the Mississippi River and claims the region for France. If any Kindred activity existed in the area prior to the arrival of the French, it has been lost among the legends of the Choctaw.
- **1701:** Sieur de Bienville becomes governor of Louisiana and first begins planning for what will become New Orleans.
- **1717:** France grants John Law's company a charter for controlling Louisiana.
- **1718:** Bienville selects a capitol site on the river and names it after the Duc d'Orleans.
- **1719:** The first large importation of slaves arrives in New Orleans. The first evidence of Kindred presence in New Orleans dates to this time, as found in legends of the local slave population.
- **1721:** French engineers lay out the street plans of the city. Anton Savoy claims to have arrived around this time, but no evidence of his presence can be found before the late 19th century.
- **1722:** Official capitol of the Louisiana Territory moves to New Orleans.
- **1727:** Pearl Chastain arrives in New Orleans in the midst of a group of French settlers.
- **1729:** Indian massacre at Natchez. Local legend maintains that newly arrived Kindred used the French/Indian hostilities as a cover to strike at a venerable Choctaw elder.
- **1731:** Louisiana officially becomes a colony of the crown.
- **1757:** Pearl Chastain begins to make a name for herself in and around the city. Although she does not claim the title of Prince, she is the closest thing the Kindred of the city have to such an authority.
- **1762:** France secretly cedes Louisiana to Spain via the Treaty of Fontaine. A cabal of Cordoba Ventrue claim credit for influencing the governments involved into making this deal, but this might be little more than Kindred arrogance.
- **1763:** Treaty of Paris confirms the cession of Louisiana to Spain.
- **1766:** Don Antonio de Ulloa arrives to govern Louisiana; the people revolt.
- **1768:** Under pressure, Ulloa departs for Spain, abandoning New Orleans.
- **1769:** Alexander O'Reilly, an Irishman in the employ of the Spanish government, arrives with 3,000 troops. In a bloody series of engagements, they secure the city for the Spanish government.

Along with O'Reilly comes Augusto Vidal, the childe of one of the Cordoba Ventrue. Intended to oversee both Spanish and Ventrue interests in the region, Vidal swiftly determines to rise out of his sire's shadow and bring order to the anarchic Kindred of the region.

- **1770:** Vidal formally stakes a claim to the Princedom of the area. Using his influence with O'Reilly's men and rumors of "insurgents," he uses available soldiers to eliminate or drive out most Kindred who would challenge his rule. Chastain wisely offers Vidal her support.

Over the next several years, Vidal is first exposed to vodoun, the faith espoused by many of the Haitian and Caribbean slaves. Due to both his upper-class breeding and severely Catholic faith, Vidal takes an instant dislike to the religion and discourages its practice among the Kindred.

- **1779:** Spain goes to war with England; Louisianans ordered to act against British. The remaining Kindred who oppose Vidal's reign launch a guerrilla war against his supporters.
- **1780:** Spain gains control of all the former Louisiana Territory from England.
- **1782:** Maria Pascual, Daeva Priscus and wielder of powerful influence among the growing sugar cane industry, becomes a powerful ally of the new Prince. Her support inspires many of the "rebel" Kindred to accept Vidal's rule.
- **1788:** Fire destroys nearly every building in New Orleans.
- **1793:** Pope Pius VI establishes the Louisiana Diocese. The Ventrue claim a hand in this decision as well.
- **1794:** New fires destroy 200 buildings; Church of St. Louis rebuilt as a cathedral. These fires also destroy many of the havens of the remaining rebels. The survivors, led by the Mekhet Francois Nicholas du Valle, believe the fires to have been a deliberate attack. They redouble their efforts against Vidal.
- **1795:** Vidal Embraces the Catholic architect Emmanuel Costa.
- **1799:** Baron Cimitiere first arrives in New Orleans, along with a population of Haitian slaves.
- **1800:** Treaty of Ildefonso provides for retrocession of Louisiana back to France. Vidal, horrified at the notion of French rule in his domain, immediately sets about pulling what strings he can to change the situation.
- **1803:** Thomas Jefferson buys Louisiana from France for $15 million. While it would be foolish to claim Vidal responsible for the Louisiana Purchase, he does press for it with what influence he holds.
- **1805:** New Orleans is incorporated as an American city.
- **1812:** Louisiana admitted to the Union; the War of 1812 begins.
- **1814:** Under cover of the battles of the War of 1812, du Valle begins a rebellion against Vidal's rule.
- **1815:** Andrew Jackson defeats British troops at the Battle of New Orleans. Du Valle attempts an assassination of Vidal, aided by the Prince's own childe, but the attempt is thwarted by the efforts of Pascual and Vidal's ally and Seneschal from the Old World, Philip Maldonato. Both du Valle and Costa are put to Final Death. To this night, Vidal has never taken another childe due, some say, to the shame of Costa's betrayal.
- **1835:** Creole-American hostilities divide the city into three municipalities. Vidal begins parceling out various neighborhoods and areas to his allies, granting them their own territorial rights.
- **1838:** First Mardi Gras parade takes place on the streets of New Orleans.
- **1849:** Baton Rouge becomes the new state capitol.

- **1852:** Three municipalities once again consolidated into a single city. Vidal allows his allies to maintain domain rights.
- **1853:** More than 11,000 people die of yellow fever.
- **1862:** New Orleans falls to the Union during the Civil War. Roger Halliburton, a Northern Gangrel, arrives and attempts to establish a power base in the city. He woos both Baron Cimitiere, who has attained a sizable following among the vodouisants population, and Miss Opal, the Nosferatu Priscus, but both are wise enough to remain neutral.
- **1865:** Pascual steps down from Primogen council and becomes the first holder of what has become known as the French Quarter.
- **1870:** Historic steamboat race between the *Natchez* and the *Robert E. Lee.*
- **1877:** Reconstruction officially ends. Vidal relents his class biases enough to cease fighting the integration of slaves into society. He also stops opposing the entry of certain elders to the Primogen based on clan; Miss Opal declines to become the first Nosferatu Primogen of New Orleans so that she may carry on her (self-imposed) duties as Priscus.

With the departure of Union troops, Vidal increases his efforts against vodoun practitioners and against those Kindred forming a power base among the newly freed slaves. This includes Baron Cimitiere on both counts. Cimitiere finally begins negotiations to ally with Halliburton.

- **1894-95:** Both Roger Halliburton and Maria Pascual are destroyed — the Gangrel at the hands of a crowd of vodouisants angered at his predilection for preying on their children; the Daeva by assailants unknown.
- **1896:** Antoine Savoy steps in as Pascual's "heir," becoming lord of the French Quarter. He claims to be a close compatriot of Pascual's and has sufficient access to her knowledge and political allies that Vidal is unwilling to challenge his claim to the Quarter.
- **1897-1913:** Vidal and Savoy clash frequently as the Lord of the French Quarter expands his influence into other neighborhoods and builds a substantial power base among New Orleans' disenfranchised. The city develops the three-way stalemate between Vidal, Savoy and Cimitiere, which persists to this night.
- **1914:** Rumors spread that Vidal and Cimitiere hold a series of meetings. Most local Kindred dismiss these rumors as highly improbable, given the hatred between the two Kindred.
- **1915:** A rash of killings, called the Storyville murders, takes place in the city's poorest districts. Both Cimitiere and Savoy investigate the possibility of Kindred or occult influence, but if either party finds anything, they do not make their knowledge public.
- **1925:** The Nosferatu known as Sundown opens his first Kindred-friendly club in New Orleans. Vidal and Savoy begin jockeying for Sundown's support, but he remains neutral.
- **1931-36:** The French Quarter blossoms into a tourist Mecca, granting Savoy a substantial increase in power.
- **1935-41:** Vidal and Cimitiere's influence in industry wanes a bit, as many of the individuals with whom they were accustomed to dealing depart for war.

- **1949:** Miss Opal disappears, leaving power among the local Nosferatu in the hands of several hand-selected proxies.
- **1957:** The 24-mile-long Lake Pontchartrain Causeway opens.
- **1974:** New state constitution adopted.
- **1975:** Miss Opal returns from torpor. This time, in hopes of improving her clan's standing from within Vidal's government, she claims a seat on Vidal's council of elders when it is offered.
- **1977:** "Dutch" Morial is elected the first black mayor of New Orleans.
- **1991:** Riverboat gambling legalized. Some Carnival krewes stop parading.
- **1992:** Coco Duquette is invited to join Vidal's Primogen, to the surprise of many.
- **1994:** Hotel building boom begins with word of expansion of convention center.
- **1996:** Statewide referendum on gambling rejects further casino development. Purportedly, Savoy and Cimitiere cooperated (reluctantly) to influence this decision, as much of Vidal's power in the modern era comes from those tourist industries not connected to the French Quarter.

New Orleans Tonight

Remarkably little has changed among New Orleans Kindred since the 1970s. The city has continued to expand, drawing an ever-larger population of vampires to the domain. The Masquerade is relatively easy to maintain here. The French Quarter in particular, and many other neighborhoods as well, boast an astonishingly high crime rate. The constant influx of tourists, especially during Mardi Gras, represents nothing so much as a walking buffet for the Damned. Given the city's occult reputation (as well as its association with vampires, thanks to a certain well-known novelist), it is very easy for witnesses to dismiss unusual phenomena as a hoax, a drunken hallucination or "some weird voodoo thing." All of these factors, as well as the presence of three separate Kindred factions all seeking support and alliances against the others, combine to create a city with a Kindred population vastly larger than the worldwide average would suggest.

New Orleans is very much a domain of conflict for the Kindred, and while much of that conflict stems from political factions specific to the Crescent City, a good portion of it comes from the interaction of the covenants. As in so many domains, the dominant covenant is not so fully in control that it has completely pushed out the others, and while no covenant has the might to truly challenge the Lancea Sanctum's supremacy, none of them are likely to back down any time soon.

The following discussion of politics, current events and most specifically the major movers and shakers of New Orleans is broken down by covenant. It is vital to remember, however, that covenant affiliation is not the only — or even necessarily the most important — indicator of loyalty and allegiance among New Orleans' Kindred. Above and beyond devotion to covenant, three different factions claim the loyalty — in lip service, if not always in behavior — of the vast majority of the city's Kindred. These are the factions headed by the city's three most powerful Kindred: the formal Prince, Augusto Vidal; the usurper Lord of the French Quarter, Antoine Savoy; and the inscrutable and fearsome Baron Cimitiere. These factions are discussed in subsections beneath the covenant headings that follow.

The Lancea Sanctum

The Lancea Sanctum is undeniably the single greatest Kindred power in New Orleans. In addition to claiming both the Prince and his most potent political rival, a majority of New Orleans' Damned population count themselves nominally among the Lancea Sanctum. Because they believe in the same God, even if their views toward Him differ, members of the covenant often bear a resemblance to the faithful of the various Abrahamic faiths. This overlap is even more pronounced in New Orleans than in many other domains, as Prince Vidal is a devout and practicing Catholic and has been so for longer than he's been a vampire. The trappings of the Lancea Sanctum in the Crescent City are thus even more heavily influenced by Catholicism than they are elsewhere.

It's an unmistakable presence to any Kindred who have been in New Orleans for more than a few nights. Signs of such Sanctified Catholic ideology are everywhere, if one knows how to look. A great many Kindred offer regular prayers or devotionals, and it's not even terribly uncommon (circumstances permitting) to see a vampire offer a prayer of thanks over a vessel. For those Kindred not averse to the symbols of the divine, churches and cathedrals are sources of many herds, contacts and retainers, as the Kindred feel most at home among those who share some aspects (if certainly not the specifics) of their faith. Many of New Orleans' Kindred pride themselves on their knowledge of scripture, from *The Testament of Longinus* to the Bible. One's familiarity with the tenets of those holy texts and the various interpretations of the Traditions is actually a mark of status in some of the domain's territories. It surprises many Kindred visitors (and discomfits many secular or superstitious Kindred) to learn that crucifixes, rosaries and pendants with the faces of saints are not uncommon accoutrements for many of the city's vampires.

The religious influence is even more obvious in gatherings of the court and formal Elysium affairs. Vidal chose the secular title of Prince, rather than Archbishop or Cardinal as is common in many Sanctified domains, because he did not feel he had earned the right to an ecclesiastical title. Nevertheless, every formal affair begins with a solemn religious ceremony. This is sometimes as simple as a brief prayer but more frequently involves a number of traditional Lancea Sanctum rites performed by multiple priests and, on occasion, the Prince himself. Any Kindred who attend are expected to participate in the rituals, as an enthusiastic audience if not as actual contributors. No exceptions are made for Kindred of differing beliefs. They participate or they depart. This is particularly true on Catholic holidays, which the Prince insists be honored with both Latin mass and Kindred rites.

Perhaps the single largest sign of the Lancea Sanctum's dominance in New Orleans is the makeup of, for lack of a better term, the ruling class. Prince Vidal is fanatic about granting territories to only his allies. Doing so has always been a major concern with him, and he has grown more restrictive since the rise of Antoine Savoy. While it is not unheard of for him to grant a small territory to an Invictus or Carthian ally, the overwhelming majority of domain-holding elders in New Orleans are Sanctified Kindred in general, and loyal to Vidal specifically. Given that even the normally opposed followers of Vidal and Savoy often cooperate to make sure that a non-Sanctified Kindred fails to obtain any true authority, it seems unlikely that the balance of power will shift any time soon.

Prince Vidal's Faction

Vidal and his court still hold the largest amount of power in the city. The greater portion of New Orleans is Vidal's domain. Certainly, he has divided the parishes up among his favored and most faithful vassals, but he exerts ultimate authority. Only in the French Quarter and the poor (and predominantly black) neighborhoods does the Prince's reach falter.

It certainly appears that Vidal has little to worry about, as his efforts to date have prevented both Antoine Savoy and Baron Cimitiere from swiftly expanding their own territories. In recent years, however, Vidal has grown almost fanatical about retaking those portions of his city he has lost. As his attention focuses ever more closely on his rivals, much of the night-to-night duties of managing the domain fall to his Seneschal, Philip Maldonato, and the Primogen. All efforts by his allies to encourage the Prince to seek some sort of accommodation with Savoy and/or Baron Cimitiere have been violently rebuffed. For whatever reasons, known perhaps only to him, Vidal has determined that Savoy and Baron Cimitiere must be eliminated. He has put no specific plans in motion in recent years, but all who work with him know it is only a matter of time. If something isn't done, the Prince could plunge his own city into open Kindred war.

Augusto Vidal, Ventrue Prince of New Orleans

As a devout Catholic and a devout Kindred, Vidal sees the maintenance and growth of the Lancea Sanctum's rule as one of his primary duties. He selects his vassals and grants territories based on personal allegiance, certainly, but also on covenant affiliation. Vidal is canny enough to elevate an allied member of the Invictus or Carthians over a Sanctified loyal to Savoy, but this circumstance is practically the only one under which he would aid in the ascension of a non-Sanctified Kindred to a position of power.

Despite his claims of loyalty to the Lancea Sanctum's beliefs and ideals, Vidal is not above using his authority among the Kindred to further his personal goals and to execute his own vendettas. For decades, Vidal supported first the institution of slavery, and then the persecution of freed slaves in his domain. This was due partly to his own archaic ideals regarding class and social status, but also due to his utter hatred for the religion of vodoun, brought to America by Haitian and Caribbean slaves. Vidal considers the faith an abomination, not merely because of its "pagan" aspects, but because its practitioners often incorporate Catholic saints into the pantheon of loa.

The Lancea Sanctum of New Orleans devotes substantial energy to maintaining its position of dominance. Members of other covenants are required to participate in the rites conducted at formal gatherings and to adhere to the laws and traditions of the covenant. Lancea Sanctum Kindred often work together to harass non-Sanctified vampires who attempt to claim or enforce domain rights over parishes that were not formally granted them by Vidal (or, in some instances, Savoy). Vidal himself uses these activities as a cover for his own personal crusade against Baron Cimitiere, his supporters and the vodouisants community in general. Vidal is a great believer in letting the masses of the kine do his work for him. Through his ties to the Catholic Church, he spreads messages of intolerance toward vodoun, denouncing the religion's "usurpation" of the saints. Through subtle messages and willful ignorance of their parishioners' actions, those priests over whom Vidal holds sway encourage harassment and even violence against vodouisants.

The Prince makes similar use of his influence in local government circles, a task made unfortunately all the easier by the fact that a majority of vodoun practitioners — followers of Baron Cimitiere or not — are among both the poor and minority populations of the city. Local police are encouraged to raid *hounfours* (vodoun temples) and arrest practitioners on trumped-up drug, gang-related or even indecency charges. City funds for charitable and outreach programs and for urban repair are funneled elsewhere, leaving vodouisant-heavy neighborhoods in poor condition or even without reliable utilities. Kindred newcomers to New Orleans involved either in vodoun or in actual trafficking of narcotics are likely to find themselves swept up in the Prince's personal vendetta, one that a substantial portion of the city's Sanctified aid in carrying out.

In recent years, Vidal has stepped up his activities even further, to the point of foisting off some of his other responsibilities on his allies and advisors. Whatever he plans, it most likely involves a major offensive against Baron Cimitiere (and possibly Antoine Savoy) in the very near future.

Vidal is technically the local Bishop, as well as the city's Prince — that is, he is formally the leader of the Lancea Sanctum of New Orleans, as well as the governor of the domain. As mentioned previously, however, Vidal refuses to take on any ecclesiastical titles, and he objects strongly to anyone referring to him as "Bishop," even when dealing with him in that capacity.

Philip Maldonato, Mekhet Priscus and informal Seneschal

Prince Vidal's oldest companion and staunchest ally, Maldonato serves a rare purpose in the ranks of the local Lancea Sanctum — that of example. Maldonato conducts himself by the precepts of the covenant and *The Testament of Longinus* and encourages others to do likewise. He also serves as one of Vidal's bodyguards, and few Kindred can remain in New Orleans for long without hearing tales of the Mekhet's martial prowess.

In truth, Maldonato is involved in very few political gambits or machinations. He is far more concerned with preventing Vidal's reign from imploding under his master's personal vendettas. Maldonato serves as Seneschal as much as he does as simple advisor. Many of the night-to-night decisions of running the city's Kindred government have recently fallen on his shoulders. Between this responsibility, his efforts at ensuring Vidal's safety from his many enemies, and the constant efforts of the Mekhet Primogen Coco Duquette to unseat him (see the Carthian section, p. 277), Maldonato has little time to involve himself in much else.

"Gutterball" Gus Elgin, Nosferatu Master of Elysium

The strange, twisted creature known, thanks to his rounded head and small, sunken features, as Gutterball, is an odd sight indeed standing at the Prince's side. Gus Elgin is a devout Longinus-worshipper, a scholar of scripture and an expert on all matters of politics and etiquette. As Vidal's Master of Elysium, Elgin has free reign to travel through many territories that are only nominally under the Prince's sway. Elgin even travels into Savoy's domains as both envoy and occasional consultant on matters of formality. Since Savoy is anxious to be seen respecting the tradition of Elysium as fully as Vidal does, he extends that respect to the Master of Elysium.

What the Prince is not aware of is that Elgin has ambitions beyond his station. If Vidal uses his Master of Elysium as a means of policing and spying on certain neighborhoods, Elgin himself uses his attendance at all major court and political functions to accumulate a frighteningly complete knowledge of the city's movers and shakers. Vidal would undoubtedly be surprised to learn that Gutterball actually has a greater knowledge of the Kindred of all three primary factions, their strengths, their weaknesses and their goals than does the Prince himself. The fact, then, that Gutterball has been working to compile even more data of late, and seems to be building up to some action, suggests that he has found a cause behind which to rally at last. What that cause is, however, is anyone's guess.

Caitlin Meadows, Gangrel Hound and Inquisitor

This broad-shouldered, heavily muscled woman is one of the most feared weapons Prince Vidal wields. Although she is not his only enforcer, hers is the fiercest, most ruthless reputation. Any vampire who has dwelt in New Orleans for long knows full well that when Meadows comes to see you, the Prince has already decided he doesn't care what you have to say.

Or at least, all this was true until a few seasons ago. Meadows disappeared for a stretch of perhaps four months — too short for torpor to be a likely culprit. Since then, the brutal Kindred has utterly abandoned her fealty to Vidal. Instead, she seems to have made it a personal mission to obliterate those who violate the precepts of the Lancea Sanctum as she sees them. She has destroyed at least three vampires since her return and has made attempts on the unlives of Antoine Savoy, Baron Cimitiere, Lidia Kendall and Gus Elgin. She has appeared at several Elysium gatherings, participated in various religious rites, even spoken to Vidal and the Primogen, and then disappeared into the night. She has always succeeded in losing any pursuers well before she departs Elysium grounds, making it impossible for them to take action against her. Rumor suggests that Vidal is very near to calling a blood hunt on Meadows and has so far refrained only because her targets are mostly Kindred he himself wouldn't mind seeing destroyed (her abortive attack on Elgin notwithstanding). Until she moves against one of Vidal's allies, or against someone with enough clout that he cannot afford to remain still, it is likely that the Prince will allow Meadows to continue dealing with those irritants that he has either not been able to eliminate, or who have not made themselves so aggravating that he can justify an official reprisal.

Other Sanctified of Vidal's Faction

In addition to those already discussed, other Lancea Sanctum Kindred of the city include the Primogen Gabriel Hurst (Ventrue), Mr. Dimanche (Mekhet) and Martin Bowler (Gangrel), the priests Remy Albright (Daeva) and John Polk (Ventrue), and the so-called Storyville Coterie.

Lord Savoy's Faction

Whether by accident or design, Antoine Savoy has positioned himself as the second-most powerful vampire in New Orleans. While tonight he is certainly in no position to challenge Vidal for dominance, few have any doubt that such is his ultimate aim. Savoy acts like a campaigning politician, coaxing Kindred to his cause one at a time. For the time being, his greatest areas of influence do not greatly overlap Vidal's. Where the Prince focuses on the mortal politicians of the city, Savoy moves among socialite circles and charitable organizations. Vidal's business contacts are mirrored by Savoy's ties to organized crime. Both have substantial influence in the tourist industries, though Savoy's tend to be localized to a few specific areas. Even the Prince's connections within the Catholic Church are somewhat reflected by Savoy's ties to vodoun, though Savoy really holds only a small amount of influence in that arena compared to Baron Cimitiere.

Savoy seems content to wait and build his power base slowly. He holds his own court, which is attended by a small but growing number of Kindred to whom he has granted feeding rights and other consideration in exchange for loyalty.

As Vidal is the true Prince, Savoy has a much smaller number of Kindred supporters. In fact, those vampires who actively serve or support Savoy probably number barely more than a quarter the number of those who have sworn fealty to the Prince. Still, considering that the French Quarter and other neighborhoods over which Savoy holds dominion represent but a tiny fraction of New Orleans, his support among the Kindred is far larger proportionally than would be expected.

Antoine Savoy, Daeva Lord of the French Quarter

A few of Savoy's vassals have taken to referring to him as the "Prince of the French Quarter" in order to give him equal legitimacy to Vidal, but Savoy himself rejects the honorific. Until he is Prince of all New Orleans, he maintains that he will take no such title.

This general attitude is perfectly representative of Savoy's demeanor and general tactics. Where Vidal is a powerful and forceful leader, emotional and yet dignified, Savoy is a slick politician — or, according to his detractors, a used car salesman. Everything hides behind a façade of humility and good humor that's engaging enough to charm even many who know it is a façade.

As might be expected, Savoy's strength comes in making allies and acquiring debts. His greatest authority, and the single most brilliant political move he made in his early years, was his use of the French Quarter in the nights following his claim of dominion over the neighborhood. He almost immediately began offering feeding rights in the area and the surrounding neighborhoods without waiting for Vidal or anyone else to confirm that he had the authority to do so. He asked only a few moderate promises of favors returned in exchange, nothing so minor as to appear suspicious, but nothing outrageous either. By doing so, Savoy instantly built up a following of Kindred who would support his bid to remain in power. After all, if Vidal removed him and replaced him with someone else, they would lose their rights to the area as well. Savoy has since extended that same tactic to other neighborhoods, particularly those that are too impoverished for Vidal to pay much attention to, yet not so heavily vodoun-dominated that they fall under Baron Cimitiere's influence.

Even tonight, Savoy relies on these tactics more than any other in his struggle against Vidal. His position is simple: Vidal has more power, so Savoy needs to coax allies from Vidal. He sends constant messengers, envoys and even offers of aid to members of the Primogen and Vidal's government, pointing out ways in which they might help each other, ways in which his rule would be preferable to Vidal's. To date, few powerful Kindred in the city have heeded the messages, but a great number of neonates on the street listen. Savoy plays up his message of tolerance and faith without the level of oppression offered by Vidal, and he focuses on building power where the Prince has neglected it. On multiple occasions Savoy has attempted to ally himself with Baron Cimitiere, but the Nosferatu has invariably rebuffed him due to Savoy's use of vodoun as a political tool and marketing ploy.

John Marrow, Daeva Priest and Inquisitor

While Natasha Preston (see p. 276) is Savoy's Seneschal, right hand and operative in the neighborhoods of New Orleans that fall outside his domain, "Father" John Marrow is at least as important to the smooth running of Savoy's territories. Marrow is a priest in both senses of the word. He conducts Lancea Sanctum rites for Kindred and offers them spiritual guidance, but he is also the priest of a small Catholic church located in the Tremé District.

To most of Savoy's followers and foes, Marrow is known as nothing more than a religious advisor and a community leader of the local Kindred. According to the rumor mill, however, Marrow is also Savoy's informal spymaster. They say a unique mastery of vampiric powers has allowed Marrow to develop information-gathering procedures to make even the Mekhet sit up and take notice. Those who would betray the Lord of the Quarter or the precepts of the Lancea Sanctum are marked. Those who prove truly dangerous might even disappear at the hands of Marrow's coterie. Whatever happens in the Crescent City, odds are good that Marrow has caught at least some wind of it. And if doing so doesn't negatively impact Savoy's standing or the local Lancea Sanctum, the priest is not above using it to advance his own agenda.

Other Members of Savoy's Faction

In addition to John Marrow, the French Quarter lord's supporters include Natasha Preston (Ventrue), Savoy's own Master of Elysium, Reynaldo Gui (Daeva) and homicide detective Peter Lebeaux (Mekhet).

The Invictus

The New Orleans Invictus bitterly resents the dominance that the Sanctified exert over the city. New Orleans has passed through the hands of multiple governments during its history, any one of which could have provided the occasion for a change of power among the Kindred as well. The Crescent City is one of the centers of power for the "Southern Nobility," the old plantation families that still practice the customs of, and survive on the monies from, the days when they owned not only the fields but also the people who worked them. Further, while no records survive to prove any such thing, most local Kindred believe that the first European Kindred to arrive, in the nights before the coming of the Spanish and Prince Vidal, were Invictus. A great many members of the First Estate in this city honestly believe that New Orleans is rightfully theirs. Of course, Invictus Kindred tend to believe that every domain is rightfully theirs, but in this instance they feel particularly strongly about it.

For the most part, Invictus vampires in New Orleans grit their teeth and follow the Lancea Sanctum's customs and traditions, especially in Elysium. It chafes them to do so, but the alternative is banishment from court functions, and cutting off their own access to what little power they wield would be foolish. Some of the city's Invictus are slowly but surely drifting toward Antoine Savoy's camp. Since the Invictus is nowhere near a position where it can yet put one of its own in charge, many of its members prefer to at least support someone less fanatical than Vidal. Still, showing too much loyalty to Savoy is frowned upon — the Lancea Sanctum is still the Lancea Sanctum, after all. Some Invictus Kindred have even gone so far as to attempt alliances with Carthian factions or gangs of unbound in order to oust the Lancea Sanctum, but have obtained only limited success so far. Baron Cimitiere and the Carthians are willing to exchange occasional information with the Invictus, but are unwilling to actually work alongside those whose objectives they trust no more than they do Vidal or Savoy.

At its own covenant gatherings, the Invictus looks and feels very much like a gathering of traditional Southern ladies and gentlemen. Its meetings have an air of refinement about them, of the last keepers of a lost noble tradition. Only a few of the eldest and most eccentric actually still dress in the garb of the 19th century, but the customs and etiquette of the Old South are alive and well. Unfortunately, many of the other attitudes of the time survive as well, and a significant minority of the city's Invictus Kindred maintain their old racial prejudices. This isn't to say that no Creole or black vampires have joined the New Orleans Invictus, only that a select group of the covenant's most affluent and influential make a point of snubbing these "lower-born" members.

Pearl Chastain, Daeva Primogen and Member of the Inner Circle

The sad truth is, the woman who was once the greatest and most dynamic force in New Orleans' Invictus is now largely impotent. Her spirit crushed under the weight of years that could not touch her physically, Chastain still makes efforts toward improving her own lot and the lot of her covenant in the city. From her position on the Primogen, she argues against Vidal's successes and is routinely ignored or defeated. As the eldest of the Inner Circle, she proposes plans and procedures intended to cement what influence the Invictus has, but her methods are too slow and cautious for many of the other members. If not for the support of her compatriot Opal, who is not even a member of the Invictus herself, Chastain might have long since given up trying.

Only on one point does Chastain remain adamant. She refuses to grant her approval to any official alliance with Savoy. She lacks the power to prevent the informal and personal arrangements that grow stronger and more common night after night, but she neither acknowledges nor lends her weight to them. Why she prefers Vidal is a mystery to most of her fellow covenant members — and indeed, possibly to Chastain herself. It's entirely possible that she supports Vidal over Savoy for no better reason than she has always done so, and is too old to change now.

Pierpont McGinn, Ventrue Member of the Inner Circle

McGinn, who was born during the American Reconstruction, is the absolute epitome of the archetypal Southern businessman. He is remarkably polite, speaks with a pronounced accent and is utterly devoid of anything approaching compassion or sympathy. McGinn is a strong believer in the notion that quality is inherited, and both his mortal birth and his Embrace as a Ventrue prove that he is well suited to lead. He intends to become the driving force in the New Orleans Inner Circle, and as Chastain grows increasingly distant and McGinn gathers an ever greater number of allies and supporters, it appears as though he'll do just that.

Behind Chastain's back (though this is an open secret), McGinn is in talks with Antoine Savoy in hopes of forming an alliance against Vidal. He's also in talks with the Carthian members of the Primogen, laying the foundations for an eventual alliance against the Lancea Sanctum. He's even in talks with Vidal's own people (or so rumor states), in case it ever appears that the Invictus can better profit by turning on the Prince's other enemies. He refuses to treat directly with Baron Cimitiere due to lingering social attitudes from his mortal youth. Further, McGinn is fond of manipulating events so that newcomers to the city invariably clash with Vidal — up to and including framing them for violations of the laws and Traditions — thus forcing them to seek allies and allowing him to "ride to the rescue," as it were.

Natasha Preston, Ventrue Seneschal to Lord Savoy

Preston is in an unenviable position in the New Orleans hierarchy. She belongs to the Invictus, because that's the covenant with whose values she most identifies. She has, however, little or no loyalty to the other Invictus vampires of the city. Her fealty is to Antoine Savoy. Yet, neither can she afford to utterly alienate other members of her covenant, for they can be both powerful allies and dangerous enemies.

Preston walks a fine line indeed. The other members of the Invictus ply her for favors almost nightly, and McGinn expects her to use her influence with Savoy to advance Invictus objectives. While she cannot afford to refuse them outright, neither can she (or will she) take any action even remotely disloyal to her chosen patron. Savoy seems to trust Preston as much as any Kindred trusts another, but he's not foolish enough to let her go unwatched. Both sides keep a careful eye on the young vampire, waiting for her to make the slightest misstep one way or another that will shatter what trust she has built up and earn her at least one, if not two, powerful enemies.

The Circle of the Crone

Baron Cimitiere holds a rather unusual form of power in New Orleans, one that allowed him to go largely unnoticed in the political arena for a substantial amount of time. Cimitiere informally holds dominion over even fewer neighborhoods than Savoy. He does not dominate (in Kindred terms) many specific industries. He has fewer Kindred followers than even Savoy can claim.

No, Baron Cimitiere's power base is made up largely of mortals. Where Vidal and Savoy can claim a large handful of mortal pawns, proxies, contacts and servants, Cimitiere has literally hundreds of mortals at his beck and call. Baron Cimitiere himself serves as *houngan* (a vodoun priest) for several congregations, and some of his closest Kindred and mortal followers serve as *houngans* and *mambos* (female *houngans*) for others. Entire neighborhoods of vodoun practitioners — or vodouisants — consider Baron Cimitiere a religious and cultural leader. While an overwhelming majority of these followers remain ignorant of Cimitiere's undead nature (though less fanatic about it than some, Baron Cimitiere is not unconcerned with, or careless of, the Masquerade) they do consider him a *houngan* of substantial power. It would be exaggeration to say that these vodouisants would do *anything* for Baron Cimitiere, but they would do much — as much as could be expected of any devout community with a popular and respected religious leader.

Thus, while Baron Cimitiere has influence over the management of few industries, businesses or political organizations, he has extremely loyal people throughout New Orleans. Vidal and Savoy are both aware of the potential for rampant bloodshed should Baron Cimitiere ever bestir his followers to violence. So far, Cimitiere has shown no inclination of drawing that much attention or putting his followers in such danger, but his rivals remain fearful of the possibility. Out of respect for this influence, Vidal has reluctantly granted a loose Regency over the vodouisant community to the Baron. This Regency infuriates Savoy, who has made much public show of his acceptance of vodoun. As much as it incenses Vidal to recognize the "bastard faith," his acknowledgement of Baron Cimitiere's supremacy in that arena serves to keep Savoy from devoting his full attention to the Prince, thereby preserving the balance of power for the time being. Baron Cimitiere really cares little for the formality of the Regency, but it does give him some basis of legitimacy in the city's power structure.

Baron Cimitiere espouses a belief that the vodoun loa are the source of the Kindred race — that each clan, and indeed each distinct bloodline, is the scion of a different spirit. This belief directly flouts the precepts supported by the Lancea Sanctum. So long as the Sanctified dominate New Orleans, Baron Cimitiere's struggles will continue. They will never leave him or his followers to go their own way. On the other hand, Cimitiere's enormous sway over a specific group of the city's mortal residents makes him a force to be reckoned with. More than once, Cimitiere has subtly urged the local vodouisants to activity, whether gathering on the steps of City Hall to oppose an unpopular law or rising to near-riotous fervor after an unfair court verdict. Such demonstrations come and go in the eyes of the mortal populace, but among the Damned, the message is clear: Baron Cimitiere can crush any single Kindred in town by focusing mortal attention on her. Neither Vidal nor Savoy can move overtly against him for fear of being snuffed out in a single act of reciprocity, so they must move subtly. Indeed, word has spread among Kindred loyal to neither Savoy nor Vidal that the Baron could be Prince if he so chose, claiming the title by denying the ability to make any move to his rivals. Whether this is true — and whether the Baron acts upon it — remains to be seen.

Baron Cimitiere, Nosferatu *Houngan* and Regent

Perhaps the most enigmatic figure in New Orleans, Baron Cimitiere is a savior to some, a threat to others and a mystery to all. This strange Kindred arrived in New Orleans 1799, having left Haiti during the revolt against French colonial occupation. Of his days before, he speaks little, even to his most trusted followers. None know if he was native to Haiti or traveled there at some point from elsewhere. He says only that he faced Final Death in Haiti and was restored to his current incarnation through the aid of the great loa Baron Samedi. Whether he speaks metaphorically or literally is another detail of which he does not speak, but he ascribes his devotion to vodoun to that event. Cimitiere claims to have no fear at all of Final Death, if by that death he can accomplish his goals. To hear him tell it, he has faced death once already and Baron Samedi returned him to the world. If his task is incomplete, he has no doubt that the Baron will do so again — though it should be pointed out that he is in no rush to test this belief. Baron Cimitiere is therefore unwilling to back down from his principles, even well past the point where other Kindred might do so. This, more than anything else, makes him a threat to both Vidal and Savoy, and a frustration to the unaligned.

Other Members of Cimitiere's Faction

Several other devoted followers of Baron Cimitiere include Lidia Kendall (Gangrel; see p. 278), the *mambo* Malia Eliza Curry (Mekhet), and the hulking Doctor Ephram Xola (Gangrel).

The Carthians

While the Carthians have a smaller presence in New Orleans than even the unbound do, they're actually doing better — at least in terms of hanging together as a single unit. The Carthians have managed to do what Jennings' independents are unwilling, and Baron Cimitiere's faction is unable: work from within the system, side-by-side with Prince Vidal, in hopes of effecting change. They have actually managed to insert themselves into a few fairly important positions in the city hierarchy. Two of the city's Primogen are Carthians. One of them, Coco Duquette, is also the local Prefect. Between their efforts, they have managed to restrain Prince Vidal from oppressing the local Carthians to quite the same extent that he throws his weight against the Invictus and the unbound. (Of course, some argue that his tolerance of the Carthians is based less on the efforts of these two Primogen and more on the fact that the Carthians simply don't pose much of a threat.)

Ultimately, the Carthian goals in New Orleans are similar to the covenant's objectives elsewhere: to establish a Kindred leadership based on more democratic (or at least egalitarian) principles than rule by eldest or by divine right. Neither Duquette nor Miss Opal has any delusions, though. Their positions simply aren't strong enough to push for any sort of major change. For the time being they perform a balancing act, arguing and maneuvering to restrain the worst of Vidal's excesses (as they see them), while never opposing him so strongly that he considers them actual enemies.

In the interim, they recruit, speaking often to young Kindred of all the covenants — and other factions besides Vidal's when they can get away with it. They've actually succeeded in bolstering their numbers of late, though the overwhelming majority of new recruits comprises neonates, many of whom do not even dwell in New Orleans proper, but in the surrounding parishes and communities. The Carthians also make a habit of playing intermediary, carrying messages between and working with multiple opposed parties, even hosting the occasional meeting between Vidal's, Savoy's and/or Baron Cimitiere's representatives. By doing so, they hope to make themselves useful to all three factions. If they can maintain their position, they prevent any of the primary factions from turning against them, and have already proven themselves a valuable ally should one faction finally gain a true victory over the others.

Coco Duquette, Mekhet Prefect and Primogen

Duquette intends nothing less than to supplant Philip Maldonato as Vidal's primary advisor, thus placing herself in the perfect position to steer his government in a more enlightened direction. The young Kindred is not naïve, or at least not as naïve as her goals might indicate. She knows that this will be no easy task and that it won't happen for decades, if ever. Until then, she works as hard as she can to ingratiate herself with the Prince in order to make herself a vital cog in the workings of his government.

Unfortunately, she is starting to realize that doing so might interfere with her duties as Prefect and force her to bend (if not break) the very precepts she tries to bestow upon others. More and more often of late, Vidal asks for her support in matters that force her to choose between her values and his good graces. She has managed to avoid violating either to any great extent, but she's sullied her hands with a few activities — mostly in terms of information gathering — that she'd prefer to have avoided. She has begun to wonder if Vidal isn't fully aware of her discomfort and puts her in such situations deliberately to determine where her ultimate loyalties lie. Duquette grows desperate for something to take the pressure off, some means of proving to the Prince that not only she but the Carthians as a whole are worth having around. Should newcomers to the city present a notable threat to Vidal, it's entirely possible that the Carthians will stand against them as well, simply because Duquette cannot afford to do otherwise.

Miss Opal, Nosferatu Primogen

The obese Nosferatu Miss Opal is a Carthian, and an ally to Duquette, but these are secondary concerns at best. Opal's highest priority is her own clan. The former Priscus to the Nosferatu, Opal finally took a seat on the Primogen because she could accomplish more for her clan from that position. She supports the Carthian cause primarily because it would allow the Nosferatu — who are often excluded from the Kindred hierarchy — an equal share of power. As both a member of the Primogen and still the de facto Nosferatu Priscus (though she no longer answers to that title and constantly seeks a replacement), Opal is one of the most well informed Kindred in the city (along with John Marrow and Desirae Wells). She uses that knowledge to aid the Nosferatu first, the Carthians second, and Prince Vidal a distant third.

Miss Opal is known to have had several under-the-table dealings with Baron Cimitiere in the past, though she has refrained from contacting him since Vidal truly began focusing on ridding the city of his two main rivals. Some channels remain open between them, and an alliance between Opal and Cimitiere, should the two of them find themselves with compatible goals, is not outside the realm of possibility.

The Ordo Dracul

The Order of the Dragon has only one objective in the city of New Orleans — survival. Given the enmity the Lancea Sanctum in general, and Prince Vidal in particular, holds for this covenant, it would require substantial personal power and luck for members to acquire any true influence in the city. Alas for them, the Ordo Dracul numbers only a bare handful of Kindred in New Orleans. They are too few to amass any real power, and luck can take them only so far.

The Dragons tend to stay as far below Vidal's radar as possible. They gather for rites when their faith demands it and otherwise avoid each other for safety's sake. They have only one true ally in the city. For all that he rejects their philosophies, Baron Cimitiere recognizes the Dragons as sympathetic spirits against Vidal. In fact, one of Baron Cimitiere's most devoted followers is a Dragon who still works on perfecting her own personal mesh of Ordo Dracul and vodoun beliefs.

Lidia Kendall has revealed to Baron Cimitiere that the Order of the Dragon is a large enough presence in New Orleans, albeit just barely, to claim its own Kogaion. She does not, however, actually know her covenant leader's name, or even his face. He appears only at the Order's gatherings — if three or four Kindred can be called a gathering — to conduct their ceremonies, and he (or she, for that matter) remains masked or otherwise Obfuscated throughout the entire proceedings. Only through the use of pass phrases, mystic scripture and personal knowledge can the cultists recognize their leader at all. Whether the local Kogaion remains anonymous to avoid Vidal's wrath or for some other, more personal reason, is unclear.

Lidia Kendall, Gangrel Novice

A devoted follower of Baron Cimitiere and a loyal member of his faction, Kendall is nevertheless a devout believer in transcendence through the Coils of the Dragon. She struggles to make her conflicting belief systems work as one, but remains a follower of Baron Cimitiere due more to personal loyalty than any religious connection. Lidia is anxious to please her mentor and see him rise above those who would oppose him. To date, she has proven one of Cimitiere's most reliable followers, but her religious zealotry and personal faith make it difficult for her to understand the need for patience and subtlety. It's only a matter of time before her actions anger the other forces at work in New Orleans to the extent that Baron Cimitiere will have to bail her out — or possibly be dragged down with her.

The Unaligned

The independent Kindred of New Orleans are a disorganized, factionalized lot, even for the unbound. The "true iconoclasts" of New Orleans, as Shep Jennings and his allies think of themselves, bitterly resent Baron Cimitiere. (This is especially true of Jennings himself, who despite — or perhaps because of — his mortal life as a slave, carries a grudge against vodoun and its practitioners.) They hate that he harbors what amount to sectarian goals, given his membership in the Circle of the Crone. At the same time, he is still their greatest ally when it comes to fending off the machinations of the Lancea Sanctum and the less powerful covenants, so they occasionally ally with him. This arrangement leads to grudging cooperation at the leadership level but occasional frustrated skirmishes (both influential and physical) among individual unbound.

Cleavon "Shep" Jennings, Mekhet Voice of the Disenfranchised

Cleavon sees himself as a man beset by enemies on all sides — and in truth, his situation is almost as bad as he believes. He despises everything Vidal, Savoy and the Inner Circle all stand for, and thus finds himself with a severely abridged list of potential allies. His cooperation with Baron Cimitiere is grudging at best, and it occurs only when he feels that he has literally no other choice. Jennings has made occasional overtures to the Carthians, but given that the Carthians attempt to remain at least somewhat in Vidal's good graces in order to effect change from within, the unbound are normally unwilling to consider any such alliance. The paradox that afflicts all Kindred who hold little authority — namely, that it requires power to obtain allies and requires allies to obtain power — weighs heavily on Jennings, and he finds himself growing ever more frustrated as the nights wear on. So far he's remained level-headed enough to prevent his few followers from doing something stupid (read: violent) and attracting the Prince's direct attention, but he's swiftly becoming too frustrated and too tired to maintain that stance. If violence does erupt from the independent Kindred of New Orleans, it might be with Jennings' tacit approval.

Desirae Wells, Gangrel Emissary

The young Gangrel companion of Jennings fell into the role of emissary almost by default. While devoted to the unbound's notions of freedom, Wells has an even stronger, more personal ambition: figuring out who she is. According to local rumor, Wells has little if any memory of her past. She wanders the city to which she feels an attachment, seeking anything to spark her lost memories. Knowing that Vidal and Savoy would respect the position as long as the unaligned didn't abuse it, Jennings made her his emissary, to excuse and explain her presence in their territories. In exchange for that consideration, Wells takes time out of her search to occasionally handle actual political business. Uncertain how genuine her memory loss is, both Vidal and Savoy attempt to put watchers on her whenever she's in their territory, with only mixed success. It's entirely possible that, due to her semi-free reign, Wells knows almost as much about the city as Marrow, Elgin or Miss Opal does. Whether she cares enough to make use of that knowledge is an entirely separate question.

Sundown, Nosferatu Harpy

Since Prohibition, at least one of New Orleans' Kindred has managed to not only survive but to come into his own without involving himself in the numerous political or philosophical factions. With the rise of Jazz in the 1920s came the appearance of nightclubs, and the Nosferatu known only as Sundown took advantage of the opportunity. He began with a single establishment, a club that happened to be Kindred-hospitable, with private rooms (even made available as emergency havens, for the right fee) and a rather unusual selection of beverages in the "members only" section. Sundown not only thrived during Prohibition, opening several additional establishments, but his focus on Kindred customers allowed him to make it through the Depression with no noticeable loss of income or prestige. In fact, as both Vidal and Savoy became regular patrons of his establishment, the apolitical Sundown found himself wielding more potential influence than he ever wanted. Tonight, he has the ear of nearly every powerful

Kindred in the city, and a powerful bargaining chip — that is, the use of his establishments — to boot. So far he has rarely taken advantage of that position, but should he ever side specifically with one of New Orleans' three factions, that support could tip the balance of power.

Sundown, however, pointedly refrains from doing just that. The Nosferatu has less interest in claiming allegiance to any existing faction than probably anyone else in New Orleans, and he has fallen in among the unbound by default rather than due to any active gesture on his part. This is yet another frustration for Jennings, who believes that Sundown should use his influence to aid his own band of "fellow" independents. The fact that Sundown does not — that, even worse, he extends his hospitality to Vidal, Savoy and every other Kindred in power — has marked him as an enemy of Jennings' own followers. To date, they have not moved against him for the same reason they have not moved directly against Vidal. They cannot afford the hostile attention that such an action would bring. Nevertheless, Sundown's clubs are occasionally subject to vandalism, and his customers to harassment while entering or exiting the property.

On the other hand, as a Harpy not appointed by any Prince, Sundown's opinion carries great weight among the Damned of New Orleans. He enjoys a position of shaping Kindred tastes to some degree, so naturally he esteems his own establishments, which in turn makes his opinion worth all the more. Other Kindred would describe it as a vicious cycle, but for the fact that there's nothing vicious about it.

The Crescent City

The city of New Orleans lies at the heart of Orleans Parish, one of the 64 theopolitical districts into which the state of Louisiana has been divided over the course of its existence. The city proper lies at the same latitude as Cairo, Egypt (30 degrees north of the equator), occupying the east bank of the Mississippi River about 90 river miles above the Gulf of Mexico. It was given its nickname the "Crescent City" for the way the city splays out around the edge of the land.

The entire region was a swamp when the first colonists arrived, and were it not for the ingenuity (and determination) of man and his technology, it would look much the same tonight as it did back then. The average elevation is two feet below sea level (which is why most corpses must be entombed above ground), with the most elevated areas, formed over time due to the flooding of the Mississippi, resting near the city's many levees. These levees, surrounding the city for a total of over 130 miles, act as the informal, crescent-shaped boundary to the south.

The Greater New Orleans Metropolitan Area (which includes but is not synonymous with Orleans Parish) actually comprises 24 different districts besides New Orleans proper, including such places as Abita Springs, Port Sulpher and Slidell. These areas are considered suburbs of New Orleans for geographic and economic purposes, but many are no more beholden to the city than, say, some Maryland or Northern Virginia towns are to the nation's capitol. When censuses are taken and statistics compiled, the

results are usually rendered relative to the Greater Metro Area, rather than to the city limits proper.

New Orleans at a Glance

Climate: New Orleans is hot and humid, with summer temperatures reaching upward of 100 degrees. The Gulf of Mexico provides the region with a great deal of moisture, and the city receives more than five feet of rainfall annually. New Orleans has no "dry season," and locals know to expect rain at any time of year. The city's greatest natural threat comes from hurricanes, which buffet the Gulf of Mexico at regular intervals in the months between June to December.

Curfew: No person under the age of 18 is allowed on the streets after 11:00 PM.

Economy: In addition to tourism, which brings in millions every year, New Orleans trades extensively with Latin America. The city is strong in grain, steel and coffee beans, and it saw a boom in offshore oil rigging during the 1970s. Average wages lag behind all states but two, even with plenty of white-collar jobs and lucrative waterfront trades. One in four people lives below the poverty line.

Government: New Orleans has an elected mayor and a city council. Parishes (Louisiana's version of counties) were geographically ordained by the Catholic Church and became political districts under Spanish rule.

Population: Just over one million in the Greater New Orleans Metro Area, but nearly twice that number visits from out of town each and every month.

Religion: Roman Catholicism predominates. Slaveholders were required by Bienville's Code Noir of 1724 to baptize and instruct their slaves on Catholicism, but slaves and other immigrants brought vodoun to the city, where it has thrived. Protestants are slightly more common uptown, especially around St. Charles Avenue.

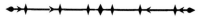

No discussion of New Orleans would be complete without mentioning the city's biggest festival, Carnival, an extended party season that begins every year on January 6th (the Feast of the Epiphany). The culmination of the festival is a day called Fat Tuesday (from the French "*mardi gras*"), which can occur on any Tuesday between February 3 and March 9. The quintessential New Orleans tradition, Mardi Gras has evolved over 300 years into the city's largest attraction, and indeed, into one of the greatest spectacles in all the world.

For as long as it lasts, Carnival practically turns the city inside out. Massive swaths of town, including the French Quarter and several major thoroughfares, become congested knots. Public transportation grinds to a halt, as does public

schooling and even postal service. Thousands pour out onto the streets wearing their favorite faces, ready to unburden their spirits with a little good-natured debauchery. And every year, on the day before Mardi Gras, the mayor of the city steps down so that Rex, the King of Carnival, may rule New Orleans for 24 hours. This transfer of power is merely symbolic, but it does accurately represent the regard in which the city holds its favored holiday.

As an annual tradition, Carnival's roots can be traced much further back than many would at first believe. The practice's pagan origins lie in ancient Greece, which held coming-of-spring festivals during which people sought purification through flogging. These rites were passed along to the Romans, whose Lupercalia was an annual occasion of great saturnalian release. For a time, the Catholic Church tried to discourage the tradition, but after centuries of failure to suppress it finally gave up and did as it always had, incorporating the pagan rite into its own calendar. As a result, the name for the Roman rite changed to *carnevale*, meaning "farewell to the flesh," in reference to the fasting period that begins with Ash Wednesday.

During these times, the rite had a lewd and almost bestial air, as people spent a handful of days releasing a year's pent-up frustrations and inhibitions. Only come the 17th century did the festival come to adopt a more theatrical sensibility, involving a baroque masquerade during which people could find release by transforming themselves into anonymous figures of carefree revelry. Carnival experienced something of a downslide during the Victorian era, until it was ironically rejuvenated in 1857 by a group of wealthy residents of New Orleans' Garden District. This group, calling itself the Mistick Krewe of Comus, made a raucous entry into Mardi Gras, raising the overall level of the tradition by the sheer expense of their lavish costumes and fluorescent floats. The festival grew from then on, and though few old-line parades remain today (thanks to a city anti-discrimination law), the overall festival is bigger and brighter than ever.

The Lay of the Land

While the entirety of the Greater New Orleans Metropolitan Area is considered part of Prince Vidal's domain, the bulk of the region's Kindred reside in Orleans Parish, and it is this area with which most are understandably concerned. New Orleans sits at the southern end of the broad Mississippi floodplain, bordered by Lake Pontchartrain to the north and bisected to the south by the river. It occupies roughly seven miles by eight miles in area, and sits at the nexus of Routes I-10 and I-610. The city itself is slowly but steadily sinking due to the power of the river, the looseness of the region's soil and the height of the local water table. Erosion cuts away nearly 40 square miles of coastal march annually, advancing the gulf northward at a rate of one half-mile per year.

The following represents only a broad overview of the city's prominent districts, with some discussion of a few important highlights therein. Greater detail on these areas is provided in **City of the Damned: New Orleans**.

Central Business District

After the Louisiana Purchase of 1803, city planners aimed to create an American commercial sector, and this district (along with its sub-district, the Warehouse District) is the result of those efforts. Once Americans took over, a pleased Prince Vidal welcomed a whole host of merchants, bankers and manufacturers whose entrepreneurialism transformed the area into a bustling port. In its earlier incarnation as the Faubourg St. Mary, this district developed into a network of banks, government buildings, private offices and warehouses, all centered around the central locus of Lafayette Square. In those days, Canal Street was the dividing line between the American and French parts of the city, and it still marks the boundary between Downtown and Uptown.

Prince Vidal has spared little expense in bringing those desirable elements to the fore in this, "his" district, while sparing an equally small amount of expense in the crushing of those intrusions he would not tolerate. To wit, most of this area was once an African-American neighborhood called "Back o' Town," and it acted as an extension of the seedy red-light district. Over time, Vidal and his mortal cohorts (both known and unknown) pushed, bought and bulldozed their vision into reality. Tonight, the CBD is the site of several important structures, including City Hall and the Louisiana Superdome, host to several Super Bowls.

The CBD's sub-district, the Warehouse District, was once the hub of much city activity, but as the port shrank, so did the sector's fortunes. The 1984 Louisiana World Expo focused some much-needed attention on the area, leading to a number of warehouses being converted into apartments and exhibit spaces for artists. With the addition of some notable restaurants, shops and a convention center, the Warehouse District has returned to life.

On a political level, the Prince likes to use the district as a bargaining chip with those who entreat him for acknowledgement in the city. Kindred know that the Prince could make their unlives difficult simply by carving up an established resident's domain on their behalf, so many new arrivals request space in the only area that has not already been claimed by another Kindred (or krewe of Kindred, as certain coteries call themselves). In this way, the Prince extorts favors (and often money or negotiable influences) from those whom he would set up with "low-cost Kindred housing." His strategy has worked, for the most part, and the CBD is now full of Kindred who owe the Prince a debt. Prince Vidal takes no haven for himself in this characterless district, of course.

Lower Garden District

Bordering the CBD to the southwest is the Lower Garden District, the old and faded sibling to the younger Garden District. In earlier nights, this area was one of the most elegant suburbs in the entire country. It was designed in a Greek-revival style, with tree-lined streets and homes that were built to hew to a classic faubourg aesthetic. When the district was

ST. LOUIS CEMETERY NO. 2

N. Villere St

ST. LOUIS CEMETERY NO. 1

St. Ann St

N. Robertson St

St. Philip St

N. Villere St

NEW ORLEANS THEATRE OF THE PERFORMING ARTS

Marais St

Treme St

MUNICIPAL AUDITORIUM

LOUIS ARMSTRONG PARK

Lafitte Av

Orleans Av

Basin St

SAENGER PERFORMING ARTS CENTER

BEAUREGARD SQUARE

St. Claude Av

St. Claude St

N. Rampart St

Burgundy St

Burgundy St

Dauphine St

Dauphine St

St. Peter St

Orleans Av

St. Ann St

Dumaine St

St. Philip St

Ursulines Av

Governor Nicholls St

6

Bourbon St

10

16

LAFITTES BLACKSMITH SHOP

Bourbon St

2 **11**

St. Louis St

ST. ANTHONY'S GARDEN

7

Royal St

4

GALLIER HOUSE

Royal St

VOODOO MUSEUM

Esplanade Av

8

ST. LOUIS CATH.

Exchange Pl

9

12

Chartres St

14

3

15

Chartres St

13

Dorsiere

1

OLD URSULINE CONVENT

Wilkinson St

5

JACKSON SQUARE

OLD CUSTOM HOUSE

Decatur St

Decatur St

Clinton St

JACKSON BREWERY

WASHINGTON ARTILLERY PARK

N. Peters St

OLD U.S. MINT

N. Peters St

Clay St

N. Front St

MOON WALK

RIVERFRONT STREETCAR

CANAL PLACE

THE NATCHEZ

WOLDENBERG RIVERFRONT PARK

WORLD TRADE CENTER

AQUARIUM OF THE AMERICAS

MISSISSIPPI RIVER

SPANISH PLAZA

Canal St. Ferry

The French Quarter

planned in the 19th century, surveyor Barthélémy Lafon intended for it to be the ultimate in urban design. The streets were all named after Greek gods — including a series of intersecting blocks named after the Muses — and the elite who came to live here added their own Greek appreciation to the mix, constructing columned galleries, cultivated gardens and prettified gazebos.

The district's glory days are long gone, however. The same wealthy elite that had so long supported the growth of the area soon moved uptown, to the newer Garden District, where all the real action was. Many of the beautiful homes left behind were divided into rental units for the many immigrants who drifted into the city in hopes of finding work. Housing projects further eroded the area's former charm, and with the opening of the Mississippi River Bridge, traffic and noise came to the once quiet neighborhood. Only recently, following the closure of the bridge ramp, have investors and shop owners once again taken an interest in the area, but the district's reinvigoration is an uphill battle, to say the least.

For decades upon decades, the Lower Garden District has been the home of the eldest member of Prince Vidal's Primogen council, the Daeva Pearl Chastain. She claims to have been instrumental in the original development of the region, and when it skyrocketed in wealth and prestige, drawing in the rich and famous from all over the country, she basked in the appreciation of both herself and her kind. When the sector's star fell, she remained, head held high. Among the Kindred, Pearl has come to be synonymous with the Lower Garden District, and many believe that nothing and no one could ever get her to abandon it now.

Garden District

Perhaps the largest, most obvious contrast in the Crescent City is the style and appearance of the area known as Uptown as compared to the French Quarter to the east. The Garden District (and Uptown to its west) is a spacious and clean architectural marvel, formerly made up of several different towns, namely Lafayette, Jefferson and Carrollton. These separate towns were gradually annexed into New Orleans proper over the course of about 20 years during the mid to late 19th century, leading to the single area it is tonight: Uptown. In addition to the commercial and residential developments, Uptown is also the site of two of Louisiana's premier learning institutions, Tulane University and Loyola University. The area in and around the two campuses is often referred to as University District.

Again the parallels provide juxtaposition. Despite their obvious differences, Garden District shares much in common with the Quarter. Both are National Historic Districts, where preservation laws attempt to maintain the architectural integrity and personality of the areas. While the French Quarter is given much more credit for being dangerous at night, certain sections of Garden District are just as unsafe after dark, if not more so. Prince Vidal, who maintains several havens in the area, would be quick to dispute that claim, but the facts remain, and anyone wise enough to pay attention to them sees the truth of it.

Garden District is not particularly large on its own (not taking into account the rest of Uptown). In fact, it is smaller than the French Quarter and the Lower Garden District, stretching only from St. Charles Avenue to Magazine Street, between Jackson and Louisiana Avenues. The area is primarily residential, and many of its prominent features are either extant personal homes or former personal residences, including the Charles Briggs House and Colonel Short's Villa, the former home of a confederate officer in the Civil War. Garden District is also home to Lafayette Cemetery, established in 1833, which is one of the city's most fascinating visual treats.

Mid-City

The part of New Orleans that is considered the most "urban" and the least historic is the district known as Mid-City. Easily the largest district in town, Mid-City is a general catchall term for what most people consider the north part of downtown New Orleans. It runs roughly from North Claiborne Avenue in the south to City Park Avenue in the north, with its northern border defined by the New Orleans Country Club to the west and the City Park to the east.

Mid-City is the least characteristically defined of New Orleans' districts, and the greatest mix of cultures and ethnicities can be found here. The majority of the city's Asian and Hispanic immigrants live and work in Mid-City, and few sites of any import or interest to either Kindred or kine are located here. The district has seen extensive development in recent years, but the work has been hyper-localized, without any broader sense of urban planning, and the area has suffered as a result. The district is riddled with crime of all varieties, making feeding that much easier. Given its age and condition, Mid-City is home to a number of young Kindred who could not hope for feeding rights in better parts of town. Still, the young Mekhet Primogen Coco Duquette has roots here, and she still strives to represent the Kindred of Mid-City as though she were their agent.

Esplanade Ridge

Like St. Charles Avenue in Uptown, Esplanade Avenue is a beautiful residential area, dotted with lovely homes and shaded by a continuous oak canopy running up and down its length. Set against the side of the city's biggest park, Esplanade Ridge boasts a number of interesting features, including its own pleasant bayou and a massive racetrack. The homes here are less extravagant than those Uptown, lending the area a quiet dignity lacking in the former area. The ridge itself is a strip of high ground extending from the Quarter to Bayou St. John, the ridge's sub-district and the oldest part of New Orleans. Settlers recognized the advantages of erecting homes up here, away from the ravages of the seasonal floods. Aside from the homes, the only notable landmarks in this area are City Park and Bayou St. John. The City Park is impressive. At 1,500 acres, it is the country's fifth-largest urban park. It boasts bayou lagoons and live oaks draped in Spanish moss. When Interstate 610 was directed through the park, ruining its peace and habitat, a number of concerned Kindred cried foul and tried to get the Prince to pull strings to have the interstate rerouted. According to the Prince, he tried and failed.

Bayou St. John, the old sub-district to the west of the ridge, abuts Mid-City to the south, the park to the north and the bayou itself to the east. French-Canadians settled the region long before New Orleans was founded, and long before that, Native Americans used the bayou waterway as the shortest link between Lake Pontchartrain and the Mississippi River. When French explorers caught onto this pathway, they recognized the area as ripe for settlement. Some classic houses can be found here, including Mullen House, Dabezies House and Luling Mansion. Some years back, the Prince forbade any Kindred from settling or feeding in Bayou St. John, but has not to this night explained the reason for the edict. This stony silence only furthers rumors about Vidal.

Tremé District

Traditionally populated by black Creoles, this small district bears the distinction of being New Orleans' first true suburb. Situated lakeside of the French Quarter's old walls, now North Rampart Street, this mostly poor neighborhood is but a shadow of the quaint area it once was. The rundown (and often derelict) condition of many of the district's once beautiful buildings has caused some residents to rally of late, in an attempt to revive the area. Progress is slow, much as it is in the Lower Garden District, for many consider the Tremé nothing but a lost cause.

Still, a number of important sites are located here, amid and beneath all the crime and grime. One of the most wondrous churches in the region, St. Augustine's, is located here. Built by the same architect who rebuilt the St. Louis Cathedral, St. Augustine's opened in 1842, making it the second-oldest African-American Catholic church in the nation. Down the road sits Louis Armstrong Park, the place commemorating the legendary jazz cornetist and singer. In the mid-19th century, the area was just outside the city walls and was the location for a slave and freed-blacks market called Congo Square. In the early 20th century, the infamous Storyville occupied the adjacent area. Once Storyville was razed, its stigma seemed to linger and few business or personal (or Kindred) interests were drawn to the area. Still, enough interest (or respect) endured for places like the Mahalia Jackson Theater and the Municipal Auditorium to emerge, and thanks to the efforts of some determined citizens (some of whom were Kindred), the area just won't go away for good. Tonight, there's even a radio station that broadcasts from the park itself.

Tremé District is known for being a gathering place of Kindred at certain times of the year. Many believe that some kind of a vampiric system of barter or debate has arisen between the various Kindred krewes in the city, while others think it is nothing more than a convenient, out-of-the-way spot for hip neonates to congregate in relative peace. Whatever the truth, the activities of these Kindred don't cause enough of a problem to draw the Prince's attention… yet.

The Vieux Carré

The jewel in the crown of the Big Easy, this relatively small section of New Orleans has risen to surpass all others in popularity and renown. The Vieux Carré, meaning the "old quarter," measures only six blocks by 13 blocks, yet it is one of the most densely packed districts of any city. The French Quarter, as it has come to be known, claims many of New Orleans' finest hotels, restaurants and sites of interest, all within walking distance of one another. Called simply the Quarter by the locals, the district is centered on Jackson Square and abuts the river to the east, the Faubourg Marigny to the north and the Warehouse District to the south. It claims less than 20,000 permanent residents in even the busiest months, but each of them is a potential vessel for its lord, Antoine Savoy.

One of the only effective methods of reining in the spread of Savoy's influence has been through the practice of establishing Elysium. When Savoy grew clever and worked toward making the French Quarter an historic tourist destination, the Prince responded by fighting fire with fire, declaring a great many buildings in the Vieux Carré to be Elysium. The move was pure genius. No one questioned the Prince's stated motivations: to protect the area's priceless pieces of living history from the depredations of violent Kindred, while providing for both the buildings' continued upkeep and the Kindred's mutual enjoyment. Safeguarding the Quarter seemed an obvious notion, and therein lay the genius, for when everyone sees the wisdom of a thing, then the true reasons for doing it become unimportant — even if they are underhanded in nature.

The act of establishing Elysium throughout the Quarter accomplished two major things. First, it intruded on the hegemony of the so-called lord of the domain. The city's Master of Elysium is, by decree, permitted to travel freely to and between sites that are declared Elysium, and when so many buildings within a certain domain are under his purview, he effectively has carte blanche with regard to movement within the domain of another vampire. Given the fact that the Master of Elysium is an officer of the Prince, one can see the wisdom in the move. The other thing that the Prince's strategy has accomplished is to embarrass Savoy. For every Elysium violation that takes place in his domain, Savoy loses some small measure of status. And given the Prince's stern punishment of Elysium violators, he appears to be forever meting out justice to the "upstarts" and "criminals among the Kindred" who dwell or revel within Savoy's domain. Savoy wanted the action so badly, now he must deal with the consequences.

FRENCH QUARTER ELYSIUM

The Prince has declared the following sites to be Elysium. Under his decree, all who violate their sanctity (directly or indirectly) are subject to censure. Most of these sites are historic hotels, restaurants or drinking establishments, but some, such as LeMonnier, were private homes at one point.

- 1850 House
- Antoine's
- Cabildo
- Cornstalk Hotel
- French Market

- Galatoire's
- Historic New Orleans Collection
- Hotel Monteleone
- Hotel Villa Convento
- Jean Lafitte's Old Absinthe House
- LeMonnier Mansion
- Maspero's Exchange
- Napoleon House
- Omni Royal Orleans
- Presbytère
- Preservation Hall

The Damned of New Orleans

Orleans Parish crawls with nearly 100 vampires on any given night, but only around 60 of these nocturnal revelers are true permanent residents, with havens and feeding rights in one of the city's various districts. What follows is merely a sampling of the more involved or entrenched of New Orleans' Kindred — those with the biggest political axe to grind and/or clout to wield.

Augusto Vidal, Prince of New Orleans

Clan: Ventrue

Covenant: Lancea Sanctum

Embrace: 1701

Apparent Age: Mid to late 30s

Mental Attributes: Intelligence 3, Wits 4, Resolve 6

Physical Attributes: Strength 5, Dexterity 5, Stamina 6

Social Attributes: Presence 4, Manipulation 5, Composure 4

Mental Skills: Academics (Catholic Dogma) 3, Computer 1, Investigation 4, Medicine 2, Occult 3, Politics 6, Science 3

Physical Skills: Athletics 3, Brawl 4, Drive 1, Firearms 3, Stealth 2, Survival 4, Weaponry 4

Social Skills: Animal Ken 2, Empathy 3, Expression 2, Intimidation 5, Persuasion 3, Socialize (Etiquette) 6, Streetwise 3, Subterfuge 5

Merits: Allies (Local Government) 3, Allies (High Society) 3, Allies (Police) 3, City Status 5, Clan Status (Ventrue) 4, Contacts 2, Covenant Status (Lancea Sanctum) 5, Haven 4, Herd 2, Language (English 2, French 3, Latin 2), Retainer 3, Resources 4

Willpower: 9 (reduced from the proper 10 by unlife activities)

Humanity: 5

Virtue: Faith

Vice: Pride

Health: 11

Initiative: 9

Defense: 4

Speed: 15

Blood Potency: 7

Disciplines: Auspex 3, Dominate 5, Resilience 5, Vigor 4, Majesty 3

Derangements: Narcissism (mild; 5), Suspicion (mild; 6)

Vitae/per Turn: 20/5

Among the Kindred, the name of Augusto Vidal has come to be synonymous with two things: the city of New Orleans and the determination of Ventrue superiority. Few cities in the New World can claim so many trials and tribulations as can New Orleans, and yet through it all, Vidal has endured. He is the first and only Prince the region has ever recognized, and as a result, he has come to be seen as something of an icon among young clan members across the United States and beyond. Sadly, few realize the toll that unceasing dominion has taken on Vidal.

Valencian by birth and Cordoban by marriage, Augusto Vidal was a petty Spanish noble who believed that his only hope for greatness was to earn it in battle. He entered the military and aspired to attain the rank of general, hoping that he might eventually amass enough power to sway national politics. Yet his military successes, while consistently solid, came few and far between. Therefore, in an ironic twist, Vidal was ultimately forced to marry into greatness. He was betrothed to a land-owning Andalusian noblewoman whose father sought to legitimize her through marriage.

When his bride died under mysterious circumstances, Vidal was approached by an ancestor of hers who, in a single violent night, removed him from public noble life and indoctrinated him into the private world of the Damned. In addition to being subjected to the Vinculum, Vidal owed both his holdings and his Kindred reputation to his sire (an elder of some regard), and he found himself the subject of an unending series of tests of worthiness and loyalty to both family and country.

The last and greatest of these tests came during the Seven Years War, when Vidal's sire bade him to take a direct role in the Spanish victory over France. Although Spain did indeed win Louisiana as a result of the war, the region's French citizens revolted in 1768 and Spanish soldiers were dispatched to restore order. Vidal's sire asked that he go along and represent Spanish interests in the French-dominated city of New Orleans. Vidal saw his chance at freedom and accepted, knowing that it would mean an end to both the Vinculum and the infuriating tether that kept him tied to his sire. The sense of duty he'd shown his sire, however, would be replaced by a sense of duty to his clan and the Catholic faith.

At every turn during his reign, Vidal has done whatever was necessary to keep his hands firmly gripped on the reins of power in New Orleans. He was always known for his disapproval of vodoun, but this impatience has grown feverish of late. His crackdown on the rising numbers of Kindred within his domain has led many to question the Prince's motives (and some his sanity). Many believe, and rightly so, that he is simply running out of time. Vidal must take his rest soon, and with no immediate heir apparent, many wonder what he will leave behind.

Vidal is tall for a Spaniard, with crisp, Mediterranean features and broad shoulders. His slick, black hair always appears wet, and he still wears the neatly trimmed Van Dyke he kept as a mortal. Unfortunately, the maintenance of this perfect facial hair takes up a considerable portion of the first hour of every night when Vidal rises, due to the fact that he was Embraced scraggly, without being given the chance to first tidy his appearance. Vidal dresses to impress, but he never forgets the lesson of function before form. He speaks with the sharp, authoritative staccato that characterizes his countrymen, and even after so many decades in the New World, has never shed his thick accent… or even cared to.

It is rumored that Prince Vidal may gain nourishment only from the blood of other Catholics. Then again, since his Blood Potency is so high he might feed only on Kindred….

Antoine Savoy,
Lord of the French Quarter

Clan: Daeva

Covenant: Lancea Sanctum

Embrace: Savoy claims his Embrace was in the early 1700s. New Orleans Kindred who have reason to believe otherwise suspect that it was closer to 1840.

Apparent Age: Mid-30s

Mental Attributes: Intelligence 3, Wits 3, Resolve 4

Physical Attributes: Strength 2, Dexterity 3, Stamina 2

Social Attributes: Presence 3, Manipulation 4, Composure 5

Mental Skills: Academics (Church History) 3, Crafts 1, Investigation 2, Occult (Vodoun) 4, Politics 5

Physical Skills: Athletics 1, Firearms 1, Stealth 1, Weaponry 3

Social Skills: Empathy 3, Expression 4, Intimidation 3, Persuasion (Guile) 3, Socialize 3, Streetwise 3, Subterfuge (Con Jobs) 4

Merits: Allies (Local Government) 2, Allies (Occult) 2, Allies (Criminal) 1, Clan Status (Daeva) 3, City Status 4, Contacts 3, Covenant Status (Lancea Sanctum) 4, Fame 1, Haven 3, Herd 3, Language (English 3, Spanish 3), Resources 4

Willpower: 9

Humanity: 5

Virtue: Justice

Vice: Envy

Health: 7

Initiative: 8

Defense: 3

Speed: 10

Blood Potency: 4

Disciplines: Auspex 4, Celerity 2, Majesty 5, Resilience 1, Theban Sorcery 3

Theban Sorcery Rituals: Vitae Reliquary (1), Liar's Plague (2), Blandishment of Sin (3)

Vitae/per Turn: 13/2

Antoine Savoy claims to have been an established elder in New Orleans when the Spanish took over in 1762. He also claims to have been a companion and ally of the former French Quarter lord, Maria Pascual, until her destruction in the late 1800s. In neither case has anyone found evidence to back his claims. He appears in no records nor in the memories of any elder Kindred — including those who knew Lady Maria well — before 1848. Even after Savoy's first noted appearance, none of Maria's allies recall that they had any substantial contact. Regardless, Antoine Savoy succeeded in exerting dominion over New Orleans' French Quarter not long after Maria's death, partially because he did indeed seem to have access to her knowledge and the backing of many of her most potent allies. He maintains that his apparent nonexistence before 1848 is simply a testament to his ability to keep his activities secret.

Ever since the Quarter developed into the tourist locale that it is tonight, Savoy has used his dominance over it to expand his influence. Engaged in a constant, bitter struggle with Prince Vidal, who refuses to recognize his legitimacy to grant territory and feeding rights, Savoy has actually used the cold war as a means of cementing his own authority. A native Creole (or so he appears), he plays upon the historical, racial and religious concerns of the locals. Savoy portrays himself as Catholic, but he is accepting of the precepts of vodoun. He even incorporates vodoun practices into his Catholic rites, a melding uncommon but not unheard of in New Orleans. In so doing, he increases the enmity of Prince Vidal (for "polluting" the faith) and Baron Cimitiere (who believes that Savoy uses vodoun purely as a tool to gain support among its followers).

Savoy paints himself as a protector of black, Creole and vodoun culture and Kindred. Many of Savoy's detractors — Baron Cimitiere is far from the only one — paint him as a pretender who uses these causes purely to advance his own agenda. Rumor even suggests that Savoy's allegiance to the Lancea Sanctum is pure show, that he joined that covenant because it conveys the image he desires, rather than for legitimate beliefs. The French Quarter and other poor districts of the city, already tense due to severe overpopulation (at least in Kindred terms), have more than once verged on open war between Savoy's supporters and enemies.

Savoy is remarkably open and approachable for a Kindred lord, holding an open court to which anyone may come and speak, and also making proclamations and speeches at Elysium like a politician seeking reelection. How genuinely sincere he is is anyone's guess, but he has gathered a sufficient number of supporters and followers to stand fast against the efforts of both Prince Vidal and Baron Cimitiere to unseat him.

Savoy is a short, thin man with strong European features. His hair is dark, as is the perpetual facial hair that hovers just between a five-o'clock shadow and a true beard. He prefers casual suits or sport coats and is rarely seen without a smile on his face. When he is emotional or emphatic, the faintest trace of a French accent emerges in his voice.

Baron Cimitiere, Circumstantial Regent

Clan: Nosferatu

Covenant: Circle of the Crone

Embrace: Unknown

Apparent Age: Indeterminate

Mental Attributes: Intelligence 5, Wits 4, Resolve 5

Physical Attributes: Strength 3, Dexterity 3, Stamina 4

Social Attributes: Presence 4, Manipulation 3, Composure 4

Mental Skills: Academics (History) 3, Crafts 2, Investigation (Research) 5, Medicine 3, Occult (Vodoun) 5, Politics 4

Physical Skills: Athletics 2, Brawl 1, Stealth 4, Survival 5, Weaponry 1

Social Skills: Animal Ken 2, Empathy 3, Expression 2, Intimidation (Staredowns) 4, Persuasion 3, Streetwise 5, Subterfuge 3

Merits: Allies (Vodouisants) 5, Allies (Occult) 2, Allies (Mainstream Religion) 1, City Status 3, Clan Status (Nosferatu) 2, Contacts 2, Covenant Status (Circle of the Crone) 4, Fame 1, Fast Reflexes 2, Haven (Security) 3, Herd 5, Language (English 1)

Willpower: 8 (reduced from the proper 9 by unlife activities)

Humanity: 6

Virtue: Faith

Vice: Wrath

Health: 9

Initiative: 9

Defense: 3

Speed: 11

Blood Potency: 5

Disciplines: Animalism 3, Auspex 2, Crúac 5, Nightmare 3, Obfuscate 4, Resilience 3, Vigor 1

Crúac Rituals: Appetite of Limba (Pangs of Proserpina) (1), Rigor Mortis (1); Cheval (2); Touch of Sousou Panman (Touch of the Morrigan) (3); Blood Price (4); Feeding the Loa (Feeding the Crone) (5), Blood Blight (5)

Vitae/per Turn: 14/2

Perhaps the most enigmatic figure in New Orleans, Baron Cimitiere is a savior to some, a threat to others, and a mystery to all. This strange Kindred arrived in the city in 1799, having left Haiti during the revolt against French colonial occupation. Of his time before, he speaks little, even to his most trusted followers. No one knows if he was native to Haiti or he traveled there at some point from elsewhere. He says only that he faced Final Death in Haiti and was restored to his current incarnation through the aid of the great loa Baron Samedi. Whether he speaks metaphorically or literally is another detail of which he does not speak, but he attributes his devotion to vodoun to that event.

Combining traditional vodoun rites with the powerful undead magics of his covenant, Baron Cimitiere made a powerful *houngan*. For many years after arriving in New Orleans, he was content to be left alone to participate in the growth of vodoun culture. It was at this time that he gained his small but devoted group of Kindred followers in the city, as well as his far more substantial mortal congregations. Slowly, he began to realize that both New Orleans' Kindred authorities posed a threat to his people — Prince Vidal because of his intolerant religious beliefs and his growing fear of Baron Cimitiere's power and influence; and Antoine Savoy through his manipulation of vodoun and its practitioners for purely political ends. Baron Cimitiere uses his considerable influence among the kine and his small but influential group of Kindred supporters in order to oppose both threats. On occasion, necessity has forced him to cooperate with Savoy against Vidal — as much as Baron Cimitiere despises Savoy's misuse of vodoun, it's better than Vidal's overt hostility toward it — but these alliances have always been short-lived arrangements.

When he is not reluctantly involved in politics, Baron Cimitiere dwells in one of several havens located throughout poorer, predominantly black neighborhoods — the heart of vodoun in New Orleans. He conducts frequent *ceremonis* for Kindred and kine alike. Most of his mortal followers believe him to be solely a powerful *houngan*, and they remain unaware of his undead nature. Baron Cimitiere has occasionally alluded to the existence of other groups of Kindred vodouisants beyond his followers in New Orleans (in Haiti, Central and South America, the Caribbean islands and across the United States). His followers believe that one of his objectives is to eventually unite them formally in a covenant to rival the primary five.

Many people mistake Baron Cimitiere for a costumed mummer upon first meeting him. He appears to be a walking corpse, his flesh gray and sunken, his teeth and eyes yellowed, his hair falling to his shoulders in stringy clumps. He dresses in the traditional fashion of Baron Samedi himself — an old black suit, cane, top hat and sunglasses. Baron Cimitiere naturally smells of rot, but he takes great pains and uses a variety of cleansers and scents to hide that fact. He claims his corpselike appearance came about when Baron Samedi raised him from Final Death.

Philip Maldonato, Advisor and Priscus

Clan: Mekhet
Covenant: Lancea Sanctum
Embrace: 1752
Apparent Age: Early 40s
Mental Attributes: Intelligence 5, Wits 5, Resolve 3
Physical Attributes: Strength 4, Dexterity 6, Stamina 4
Social Attributes: Presence 4, Manipulation 3, Composure 5
Mental Skills: Academics (Humanities) 5, Computer 3, Crafts 2, Investigation 5, Medicine 2, Occult 5, Politics 4, Science (Mathematics) 4
Physical Skills: Athletics 4, Brawl 3, Drive 1, Firearms 2, Stealth 5, Survival 5, Weaponry (Sword) 6
Social Skills: Empathy 4, Expression 3, Intimidation 4, Persuasion 3, Streetwise 5, Subterfuge 5
Merits: Allies (Police) 4, Allies (High Society) 3, Allies (City Hall) 1, City Status 3, Clan Status (Mekhet) 1, Contacts 4, Covenant Status (Lancea Sanctum) 2, Danger Sense, Disarm, Haven 3, Herd 1, Language (Arabic 2, English 3, French 3, Latin 3), Meditative Mind, Mentor 3, Resources 4

Willpower: 8
Humanity: 6
Virtue: Temperance
Vice: Wrath
Health: 9
Initiative: 11
Defense: 5
Speed: 15
Blood Potency: 6
Disciplines: Auspex 4, Celerity 5, Majesty 2, Obfuscate 2, Resilience 3, Vigor 1
Vitae/per Turn: 15/3

In the year 1602, the Archbishop of Valencia embarked on a personal crusade to rid "Christian Spain" of the noxious presence of non-Christians, especially those who had ruled the region for 700 years before he was even born — the Muslims. Although many wanted Arab and Muslim influence to wane now that Spain was ruled by Spaniards once again, few counseled the complete expulsion of the "Moriscoes" as did the archbishop. In making his case, he is known to have said that the Saracens "commended nothing so much as that liberty of conscience in all matters of religion, which all Mohammedans suffer their subjects to enjoy." Although the remark is perhaps the greatest compliment that could be paid to Spain's Muslim forebears, it was intended nonetheless as a stark disparagement.

One Spanish Saracen, a Mekhet named Al-Mohager, found the archbishop's words striking. As a scholar in the world-famous center of learning that was the marvelous city of Cordoba, Al-Mohager could not understand whence such hatred and intolerance could come and he found the entire affair morbidly fascinating. He'd never been a particularly religious man in life. In death, the only religion he knew was the moral code he adopted upon being brought into the fellowship of Clan Mekhet. Therefore, when the Spanish began forcing Spain's Muslims to convert or face exile, he voluntarily sank into torpor.

A century-and-a-half later, Al-Mohager awoke to find his home a place much changed. Christian Spain had followed through on its threats, and millions of Arabs had been forcibly evicted during his long rest. Spain had grown both fat and ambitious and had made numerous enemies for herself throughout Europe and in the burgeoning New World. With Spain on the brink of war, Al-Mohager decided that it was time to pass the torch. He could no longer deal with the place his own home had become, but with so much at stake, he needed to ensure his legacy's survival. And so he took a childe — an honorable Cordoban warrior-scholar by the name of Philip Maldonato.

One of Al-Mohager's former allies, a Cordoban Ventrue of considerable honor and traditional ethics, was delighted to see that his colleague had finally taken a childe. Cordoba's star was no longer the brightest in the Spanish crown, now that war was the order of the day, and many Spanish Ventrue found themselves caught up in the frenzy surrounding Spain's world ambitions. The Ventrue asked if Philip would watch over his own childe, a military man named Vidal, in whom he had placed much of his hopes for Spain. Philip was eager to oblige, and all throughout the Seven Years War, Philip remained at Vidal's side, eager to advise and protect.

After the war, Vidal was sent to administrate the province of Louisiana, and although his official duty had been fulfilled, Philip, who had developed a fondness for the Spaniard, decided to accompany Vidal to the New World to continue in his capacity as advisor. The Mekhet would never again leave Vidal's side.

Philip Maldonato is a very tall fellow. His skin is dusky and smooth, with only the merest hint of the wrinkles of age around his deep-set eyes, which sparkle faintly whenever he thinks hard on something. He favors hand-tailored business suits (black and gray, mostly) when seen in public or by the Prince's side. In private, Philip occasionally indulges the static habits of times before his Requiem, wearing anachronistic clothing and collecting fine furniture that is now considered "antique."

Pearl Chastain, Primogen

Clan: Daeva
Covenant: Invictus
Embrace: 1726
Apparent Age: 30-something
Mental Attributes: Intelligence 4, Wits 4, Resolve 2
Physical Attributes: Strength 2, Dexterity 3, Stamina 3
Social Attributes: Presence 2, Manipulation 4, Composure 5
Mental Skills: Academics 2, Crafts 3, Investigation 3, Occult 2, Politics (New Orleans) 4
Physical Skills: Athletics 1, Brawl 2, Drive 1, Firearms 3, Larceny 4, Stealth 2, Survival 3, Weaponry 2
Social Skills: Empathy 4, Expression 3, Intimidation 2, Persuasion 4, Socialize (Etiquette) 5, Streetwise 3, Subterfuge 5

Merits: Allies (Old Money) 4, Allies (High Society) 3, City Status 3, Clan Status (Daeva) 4, Common Sense, Contacts 2, Covenant Status (Invictus) 2, Fame 1, Haven 4, Resources 4, Retainer 3
Willpower: 7
Humanity: 6
Virtue: Prudence
Vice: Sloth
Health: 8
Initiative: 8
Defense: 3
Speed: 10
Blood Potency: 5
Disciplines: Auspex 4, Dominate 3, Celerity 2, Majesty 5, Resilience 2, Vigor 2
Derangements: Depression (mild; 6)
Vitae/per Turn: 14/2

As much as she would hate to admit it, Pearl Chastain is a relic of an age gone by. As one of the oldest active members of Prince Vidal's Primogen council, Pearl has seen and weathered a great deal. She's watched the city blossom into the jewel it is tonight, but as a result, she knows the sadly high price paid for that transformation.

Pearl remembers little of her days as a mortal woman, and that fact has troubled her more and more of late, especially while she sleeps. During the city's booming period in the mid-to-late 19th century, Pearl was one of the most active and influential Kindred in the city. She had the respect of nearly every Kindred, and worked very hard to ingratiate herself with even the most reticent of souls. In her time, Pearl made allies of bitter enemies and princes out of paupers. She led her clan to estimable achievements, always coming off as the soul of modesty, and even managed to make a lasting ally out of an ideologically opposed Prince. But that time is gone... *her* time is gone. The arrival of

Antoine Savoy signaled the dawn of a dark age for not only the city, but for the elderly matron of his clan.

Come the 21st century, Pearl is but an echo of her former self, bereft of vibrancy or even motivation. She still holds the power and prestige she has amassed, but only by virtue of not wishing to see it taken from her. Pearl is a Kindred who has passed her prime, but like all the undead, she has been forced to continue on into perpetuity, denied even the dignity of retiring quietly from view.

Among her clanmates, Pearl is considered somewhat gauche in her tastes. She ceased trying to keep up with the various fashions and cultural trends a long time ago, and in her attempt to go for a "timeless" and "classic" look, she ends up coming off as antiquated and dated. Although she was Embraced in her late 30s ("early" 30s, she says), she has a dusty, forgotten air about her that betrays the decades she has endured. Although trapped at the moment of death, it is as though her body has continued to bear the weight of its passing years. Yet the sagging jowl, the twin fans of wrinkles around her cloying eyes... these are products of her aged spirit, not reflections of physiological change.

Miss Opal, Primogen

Clan: Nosferatu
Covenant: Carthians
Embrace: 1848
Apparent Age: Middle aged
Mental Attributes: Intelligence 4, Wits 2, Resolve 4
Physical Attributes: Strength 5, Dexterity 2, Stamina 4
Social Attributes: Presence 1, Manipulation 3, Composure 3
Mental Skills: Academics 2, Computer 2, Crafts 2, Investigation (Body Language) 3, Occult 2, Politics 4
Physical Skills: Brawl 4, Drive 1, Stealth 3, Survival (Urban) 3
Social Skills: Animal Ken 3, Empathy 3, Intimidation (Physical Threats) 4, Persuasion (Rhetoric) 3, Streetwise 5, Subterfuge 3

Merits: Allies (Labor Organizations) 3 Allies (Local Government) 3, City Status 2, Clan Status (Nosferatu) 3, Contacts 3, Covenant Status (Carthians) 4, Giant (Note: Miss Opal is actually only 5'6" or so; it is her vast bulk that grants her the benefits of this Merit), Haven 2, Herd 3, Resources 2
Willpower: 7
Humanity: 7
Virtue: Prudence
Vice: Wrath
Health: 10
Initiative: 5
Defense: 2
Speed: 12
Blood Potency: 3
Disciplines: Nightmare 3, Obfuscate 4, Resilience 3, Vigor 3
Vitae/per Turn: 12/1

Miss Opal — she goes by no other name — is the self-appointed conscience of Prince Vidal's court. The child and childe of former slaves, she first gained real status during Reconstruction, when she led a campaign to make sure that the Nosferatu had a place in the new order. The clan's Priscus for many years, she disappeared into torpor during the middle decades of the 20th century. Reemerging around 1978, she has spent the years since attempting to both regain her previous status — in which she has largely been successful, due to the efforts of many Nosferatu who remember her from before — and sway the direction of Prince Vidal's political alignment. She is one of the eldest of the city's Primogen, as well as a constant irritant to the Prince. She recently turned down the honor of becoming Priscus for the Nosferatu once more, determining that another title, even an informal one, might interfere with her duties and efforts as Primogen.

Miss Opal is a great believer in the Carthian cause, and she constantly works from within not merely to encourage Prince Vidal and the Primogen to act accordingly, but in hopes of convincing them that granting more power and freedom to the "common Kindred" is in their best interest. She has not had much luck. Miss Opal abhors using violence for political ends, but she has no qualms about using physical intimidation on a personal level. (In fact, she has more than once expressed her displeasure at the "disgraceful" behavior of young Kindred by beating the tar out of them.)

Heavily obese, Miss Opal looks like a normal (if grossly overweight) dark-skinned woman until one sees her face — a sagging mass of lines and wrinkles so deep and heavy it's a wonder she can see. She dresses primarily in loose-fitting dresses and prefers to wear a shawl. She speaks with a thick drawl, and has a tendency (which many elders find irritating in the extreme) to call people pet names like "Sugar" and "Honey." Other Kindred who have seen her feed were particularly disturbed to learn that she treats her vessels with equal exuberance, often talking to them in the friendliest tones before and after the deed, regardless of whether they survive the process.

Coco Duquette, Primogen

Clan: Mekhet
Covenant: Carthians
Embrace: 1892
Apparent Age: Early 20s
Mental Attributes: Intelligence 3, Wits 3, Resolve 4
Physical Attributes: Strength 2, Dexterity 4, Stamina 3
Social Attributes: Presence 5, Manipulation 3, Composure 4
Mental Skills: Academics 1, Computer 1, Investigation 4, Medicine 2, Occult 1, Politics (Kindred) 4, Science 2
Physical Skills: Athletics 3, Brawl 4, Drive 1, Firearms 3, Stealth 3, Survival 2, Weaponry 3
Social Skills: Empathy 3, Intimidation 2, Persuasion 4, Socialize 4, Streetwise 5, Subterfuge 3
Merits: Allies (City Hall) 3, Allies (Political Activists) 3, City Status 3, Clan Status (Mekhet) 3, Contacts 4, Covenant Status (Carthians) 3, Haven 3, Herd 1, Inspiring, Resources 3, Striking Looks 2
Willpower: 8
Humanity: 8
Virtue: Hope
Vice: Lust
Health: 8
Initiative: 8
Defense: 3
Speed: 11
Blood Potency: 3
Disciplines: Auspex 2, Celerity 3, Dominate 1, Majesty 1, Obfuscate 3, Vigor 1
Vitae/per Turn: 12/1

Although Coco Duquette was born during the height of the Victorian era, she considers herself a child of the 21st century. She was rescued from a life of prostitution by an elderly gentleman who seemed to want nothing more than the pleasure of her company. Given the fate of some other prostitutes of the day, Coco was more than a little apprehensive when the man offered her his hand, but something in his demeanor put her at ease and she found herself stepping happily into his carriage and out of her former life.

The elderly gentleman, an aged Mekhet by the name of Starkweather, waited nearly two years before bestowing everlasting death upon his ward. During that time, he engaged her very plainly — nearly as an equal — on a wide host of issues, the majority of which revolved around politics and the role of humankind in the natural world. It was not until many years later that Coco would realize that her sire had been testing her. Only when her sire-to-be was satisfied with her responses and the progress they had made did he elect to Embrace her, and in so doing cause her to reevaluate not only everything he had just taught her, but everything she ever thought she knew. Rather than break her, however, the Embrace challenged her. Just as her sire intended, Coco found purpose in the cause of the Carthian dream, where every belief she held as a mortal was paralleled in the world of the Damned.

Once the protégé had once again reached her sire's predetermined level of wisdom and preparedness, he released her from her tutelage and left her to pursue her dream. Toward the end of the 20th century, Coco made her way onto the Prince's Primogen council by proving her worthiness as one who not only knew the hopes and dreams of the city's neonates, but as one who would always provide honest counterpoints at the debate table. Coco has never been pleased by the fact that the eldest of her clan is largely apolitical, but she respects his power, and more importantly, his importance to the Prince. She knows that she is no match for the Priscus, neither physically nor politically, but she hopes that by making herself nearly as indispensable to the Prince as is her rival, she might be able to have more of an impact on the city's power structure once he is asleep. If this is the game, then Coco Duquette intends to play it well.

One would need no magic mirror to know that, among the members of New Orleans' Primogen council, Coco Duquette is the fairest of them all. Her beauty is striking to be sure, but what gives it a quality all its own is the undeniable fire behind her eyes and the rousing stir in her velvet voice whenever she is engaged in the act of oratory or philosophical debate. Her cause is her passion and her passion fuels her cause, and few who give her leave to speak upon it are ever anything but utterly enthralled (especially among mortals and young Kindred). In her bid for respect, Coco has sworn off traditional "feminine attire," preferring a very carefully constructed outfit that normally consists of a tight black turtleneck (unimposing, yet suggestive) and a pair of black paratrooper pants. She regularly dyes her hair a deep red to provide contrast to her piercing blue eyes.

Sundown, the Afterhours King

Clan: Nosferatu
Covenant: Independent
Embrace: 1915
Apparent Age: Late 20s
Mental Attributes: Intelligence 3, Wits 5, Resolve 3
Physical Attributes: Strength 3, Dexterity 3, Stamina 4
Social Attributes: Presence 4, Manipulation 4, Composure 5
Mental Skills: Academics (Business) 2, Computer 3, Investigation 2, Occult 3, Politics 3, Science 2
Physical Skills: Athletics 3, Brawl 3, Drive 4, Firearms 3, Stealth 5, Survival 4, Weaponry 2
Social Skills: Empathy 3, Intimidation 3, Persuasion 3, Socialize (Hospitality) 5, Streetwise (The Rumor Mill) 5, Subterfuge 4
Merits: Allies (Nightlife) 4, Allies (City Bureaucracy) 2, Barfly, City Status 5, Clan Status (Nosferatu) 3, Contacts 5, Fame 3, Haven 3, Herd 5, Resources 3, Stunt Driver
Willpower: 8
Humanity: 7
Virtue: Prudence
Vice: Gluttony
Health: 9
Initiative: 8
Defense: 3
Speed: 11
Blood Potency: 3
Disciplines: Auspex 3, Majesty 2, Nightmare 3, Obfuscate 4, Resilience 2, Vigor 2
Vitae/per Turn: 12/1

One of the most well-known figures in all of New Orleans is also the one with the least active interest in the Byzantine power struggles at work. Indeed, this independent spirit has

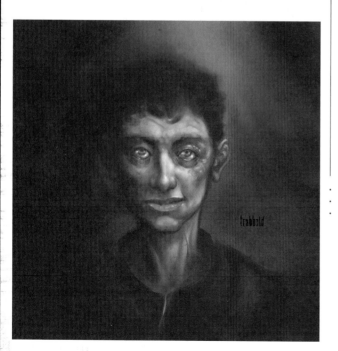

earned for himself no small measure of respect (albeit grudging, on some occasions) for his staunch refusal to venture into the political arena. This respect, in turn, only further increases his fortunes.

The reason the views of this one Kindred, who calls himself Sundown, are of such consequence is due to his remarkable influence over the mortal nightlife in New Orleans, and thus, over the mortal pulse of the city. If he were to lend his support to any of the three major Kindred players, the results would likely turn the tide in favor of the beneficiary. For this reason, it serves the purposes of everyone involved that he remain politically neutral, and thus far, Sundown — the patron of New Orleans revelry — has disappointed no one.

Sundown is perhaps best known for his ownership and management of several Kindred-hospitable bars and nightclubs in and around downtown New Orleans. The largest and most successful of these, the Carnival Club, was even declared Elysium some years back and has since become known as part of the local Rack among the city's hip neonates. The trademarks of a Sundown club include tinted glass (when the structure isn't below street level), moodlit rooms and mirrors only in the bathrooms. Even the Prince calls upon Sundown's establishments from time to time, and he can easily claim the most consistently amicable relations with the Nosferatu of the city's three major Kindred figures.

As a Nosferatu, Sundown goes against type on just about all fronts. He's sociable, approachable and stylish, and he clearly prefers lavish penthouse apartments to the dank and homely quarters often associated with his clanmates. His social and economic power disturbs more than a few traditionalist types in the city, and most of all Antoine Savoy, who abides the Nosferatu's power and presence only because not doing so would put the Prince at even greater advantage. Many believe that Savoy plans to use Sundown as a stepping stone to Princedom, though no one can say with any surety how or when the would-be usurper might accomplish such a feat.

In truth, Sundown is not so committed to neutrality as he claims. Rather, he has seen the tides of Kindred fortune rise and fall, and knows the price of failure intimately; he has helped ruin Kindred on more than one occasion. Sundown bides his time, waiting to see which faction will emerge as a favorite in the balance of power. Then and only then will he even consider lending support to that side — unless his participation isn't necessary, allowing him to still enjoy the benefits of remaining apart from whatever established institution emerges at the forefront.

The man who is now known as Sundown was once a fair-skinned boy of Creole extraction. Now he appears as a racially indistinct gentleman of considerable good looks — not so attractive as to be threatening, but more than handsome enough to put everyone around him at ease. He dresses in popular fashions and always tailors his attire to suit whatever club he's in, even if that means changing clothes on the way from one club to another. Still, even the most casual conversationalist notices something... off about Sundown. The aura of a predator veritably oozes off him, but those unaware of the Kindred don't know how valid their agitated nerves are. Despite all of his influence and esteem, few really want to get to know Sundown personally.

Lidia Kendall

Clan: Gangrel
Covenant: Ordo Dracul
Embrace: 1869
Apparent Age: Mid-teens
Mental Attributes: Intelligence 2, Wits 4, Resolve 3
Physical Attributes: Strength 2, Dexterity 4, Stamina 3
Social Attributes: Presence 4, Manipulation 4, Composure 3
Mental Skills: Academics 2, Crafts 3, Investigation 4, Occult 4, Science 1
Physical Skills: Athletics 2, Brawl 2, Drive 3, Larceny 3, Survival 4
Social Skills: Empathy 3, Expression (Acting) 4, Persuasion 2, Streetwise (Kindred Activity) 4, Subterfuge (Misdirection) 4
Merits: Allies (Vodouisants) 2, City Status 1, Contacts 2, Covenant Status (Ordo Dracul) 1, Danger Sense, Fleet of Foot 3
Willpower: 6
Humanity: 6
Virtue: Faith
Vice: Envy
Health: 8
Initiative: 7
Defense: 4
Speed: 14
Blood Potency: 3
Disciplines: Animalism 3, Celerity 2, Protean 3, Resilience 3, Vigor 1
Coils of the Dragon: Blood Seeps Slowly, Conquer the Red Fear
Vitae/per Turn: 12/1

Born in 1853, Lidia was the product of the rape of a young white woman by one of her uncle's slaves. Her mother treated her as a burden and a mark of shame, and Lidia grew up with a neurotic mixture of hatred and fascination for slaves and their culture. Hers would likely have been a short and inconsequential life had the child not caught the eye of Roger Halliburton, a northern Gangrel who arrived in New Orleans after its surrender to the Union in May of 1862. A pedophile since before he was a vampire, Halliburton intended to keep Lidia as a ghoul and vessel, but when she was trampled by a maddened horse in 1869, her patron — in a paroxysm of what he thought was love — chose to Embrace her.

Despite being trapped physically at age 16, Lidia soon developed a cunning and intellect that allowed her to use her apparent age and ignorance to her advantage. She eventually surpassed her sire's political acumen and status in the region. Decades later, when Halliburton was destroyed by a group of vodouisants in retaliation for the deaths of several local children, Lidia was easily able to continue on her own. Further, the destruction of her sire, with whom she had an intense love-hate relationship (leaning toward hate) re-inflamed her fascination with local black culture.

Her fascination swiftly became reverence during her studies, and Lidia become a practicing vodouisant and follower of the Ordo Dracul's transcendental philosophies during the Great Depression. Further, it was through her fellow Dragons that she was first introduced to Baron Cimitiere, whom she has since followed with a zealous — perhaps fanatical — devotion. Although Baron Cimitiere suspects that Lidia sees him as some sort of surrogate father/sire rather than a religious leader, her devout adherence to vodoun and her usefulness to his cause has encouraged him to overcome his reluctance and bestow upon her a fairly high-ranking position among his followers.

In truth, he's half right. Lidia does indeed look up to Cimitiere as a father figure and personal icon, but she's also devoted to her religion, her covenant members and her fellow practitioners — the first place she's ever really fit in. The fact that Baron Cimitiere does not share her covenant affiliation bothers her, as it is the only mark on what she considers his otherwise flawless judgment.

Lidia still makes use of her apparent youth as a tool, allowing others to underestimate her knowledge, experience and determination. In truth, despite her rather stunted emotional development when it comes to her father figures, she's normally very calculating, willing to show inhuman patience and take whatever actions are necessary for the advancement of her goals (which are, for the most part, the goals of Baron Cimitiere and his followers). Unless she attends a rite or formal occasion (in which case she prefers white flowing gowns), she usually dresses the part of the flighty teen, preferring T-shirts, low-cut jeans and brightly colored clips or cornrows in her black hair.

Natasha Preston

Clan: Ventrue (Malkovian)
Covenant: Invictus
Embrace: 1967
Apparent Age: Late 20s
Mental Attributes: Intelligence 4, Wits 3, Resolve 3
Physical Attributes: Strength 1, Dexterity 2, Stamina 3
Social Attributes: Presence 2, Manipulation 3, Composure 4
Mental Skills: Academics 4, Computer 3, Medicine 1, Politics 4, Science 2
Physical Skills: Drive 1, Larceny 1, Stealth 1, Survival 1
Social Skills: Animal Ken 1, Intimidation 3, Socialize 3, Streetwise 2, Subterfuge 1
Merits: City Status 1, Contacts 1, Covenant Status (Invictus) 2, Eidetic Memory, Haven 1, Resources 3
Willpower: 7
Humanity: 6
Virtue: Fortitude
Vice: Greed
Health: 8
Initiative: 6
Defense: 2
Speed: 8
Blood Potency: 2
Disciplines: Animalism 1, Dominate 4, Majesty 2
Derangements: Obsessive Compulsion (severe; bloodline), Irrationality (mild; 6)
Vitae/per Turn: 11/1

A relative newcomer to both New Orleans and the world of the Kindred in general, Natasha Preston was a typical daughter of wealth in post-WWII New England. Her family — which dated from colonial times and never let anyone forget it — sent all their children to college, despite the fact that women's selection of university programs in the 1960s were largely restricted. Natasha, who had a mind and fascination for business and politics, became one of the growing numbers of women to buck tradition and graduated with dual degrees in business and political science. Given her combination of skills, education and absolutely merciless and cutthroat practices, Preston had a promising career in politics ahead of her. At least, until she and her candidate of choice found themselves caught up with the sorts of "businessmen" who take rather more direct action than litigation when they believe they've been cheated. It was then, as the life ebbed from her, that Preston met one of her employer's other illicit patrons — a Ventrue named Constance. First as a simple pawn, then as a ghoul, and finally as a childe, Preston served her sire as a liaison to the world of modern business and politics, something she understood far better than a vampire whose Requiem began before the nights of American democracy.

What happened in the few decades after that remains unknown, as Preston does not speak of it. Whatever happened, she left (or was dismissed from) Constance's service, and somehow convinced Antoine Savoy to take her on in a similar capacity, despite her unfamiliarity with New Orleans and her relative youth (and certainly without telling him about the madness that tainted her Blood). However she did it, it has proven a worthwhile decision on Savoy's part. In the past few years, Preston has immersed herself in all aspects of New Orleans society, learned many intricacies of local Kindred politics, and become one of Savoy's most trusted political advisors and his primary eyes and ears in those territories that are still firmly controlled by Prince Vidal. For the most part, she seems to get along fairly well with her new patron, though she has berated him (or anyone who would listen) on more than one occasion about the male-dominated Kindred power structure, brought about by the fact that most Kindred leaders hail from a time when women were considered second-class citizens. It appears to be the only topic about which she is truly passionate.

Though she can be charming, Natasha Preston is primarily a severe, no-nonsense sort of woman. She is largely humorless, and never appears to consider herself "off duty." She prefers suits in muted colors and wears her dusky blonde hair in the latest conservative fashions.

"Are you the Devil?" she asked, and her voice was all hope.

"I have been called his son," I said, and brought forth gold to purchase her.

— Rites of the Dragon

Today I dreamed that I was down in that cellar again.
I could smell the rot lingering in the air. I heard a
rushed, sniffling, breathing sound, like a dog trying to
pick up a scent.

This is my last night, whelp. The things that I've seen,
they're bigger than me, and I'm not going to give them
the satisfaction of catching up with me. Neither am I
going to go mad trying to avoid them. I'm here now only
because I want to set the details of this unlife in order.
I have to tell old... allies that I'm not going to be part
of the program anymore.

I'm meeting the sunrise tomorrow. It's the only way to be
sure. And when that sun comes up, I'm setting fire to the
vestibule where I rest. If you want it to settle its gaze on
you next, come scrounging around my haven tomorrow night.
See what survives the fire and the rays of the sun.

If you're smart, though, you'll leave well enough alone.

Sweet fucking Jesus, it burns like there's no motherfucking tomorrow.
Blood coming down, running out of the holes where my hands used
to be — fuck! Can't hold onto anything and the pain is driving me
blind and I feel that red rage take over but there's nothing I can do
because they have me chained and hanging upside down. Blood's
spattering on a table underneath me. What the fuck is this, some
kind of dungeon? There's torches on the walls.
Little fucking pindick, the guy whose face I broke, standing next
to me and a guy looking like a priest except he has my blood making
an upside-down cross on his forehead standing next to him and
talking shit about sins and threats. Fuck them both.
And then they lower me — I'm still fucking chained — onto the
table. Burning my mutilated arms shut, and I go blind and berserk
again and when I know what's going on, I can see ashes floating in
the air that came from where my fucking dead flesh caught fire.
The priest takes a hammer and a stake and prays over it, and it's
above my chest and one angry blow sends it in.
I hear my screaming stop. The only noise after that is the rats,
the whoosh of the torches going out and a heavy door closing. I can't
see anything. I'm blind for real now.

I find it almost comical, how naive I was back then. I saw the Kindred as disparate groups, each vying against the next. The bloody terrors against the aristos, the brutish cult against the eldritch theosophists. My own group of idealists against them all.

A cold heart fosters treachery, however, and my time among the Damned has been productive. Matters of philosophy pale beside the personal ambitions each of us harbors.

My juvenile fascination with Lindsay has faded, and indeed had long before the witch-hunters found her haven with her still asleep in it. I wonder how they found her secret lair? The mind reels with possibilities.

Mr. Bennett has fallen far, his coarse ways too uncivilized for our court of night-fiends. It seems that everyone used him to get what they wanted, but no one made good on the promises they pledged.

Mr. Audelia I trust implicitly, but more out of respect for our mutual secrets best kept hidden than any altruism or affection. He is a disgusting creature, but a valuable one, and I would rather he inform me of others' deeds than inform others of my own doings.

It truly was in Lady Moltis' best interests to return whence she came. There was nothing here for her, and as much as I loathe the way she treated me when I labored under her mesmerism, I respect the skill with which she did so.

And Maxwell... well, we all know what became of Maxwell, don't we?

The city spread out beneath us, its lights twinkling like the flames of a thousand faraway candles.

"One night," she said, "All of this below us will be yours.

"For now, though, would you like to dance?"

And I heard the strings and piano.

Vampire
THE REQUIEM

Name: _____ Concept: _____ Clan: _____

Player: _____ Virtue: _____ Covenant: _____

Chronicle: _____ Vice: _____ Coterie: _____

Attributes

Intelligence ●○○○○		Strength ●○○○○		Presence ●○○○○	
Wits ●○○○○		Dexterity ●○○○○		Manipulation ●○○○○	
Resolve ●○○○○		Stamina ●○○○○		Composure ●○○○○	

Skills

Mental
(-3 unskilled)

Academics _____ ○○○○○
Computer _____ ○○○○○
Crafts _____ ○○○○○
Investigation _____ ○○○○○
Medicine _____ ○○○○○
Occult _____ ○○○○○
Politics _____ ○○○○○
Science _____ ○○○○○

Physical
(-1 unskilled)

Athletics _____ ○○○○○
Brawl _____ ○○○○○
Drive _____ ○○○○○
Firearms _____ ○○○○○
Larceny _____ ○○○○○
Stealth _____ ○○○○○
Survival _____ ○○○○○
Weaponry _____ ○○○○○

Social
(-1 unskilled)

Animal Ken _____ ○○○○○
Empathy _____ ○○○○○
Expression _____ ○○○○○
Intimidation _____ ○○○○○
Persuasion _____ ○○○○○
Socialize _____ ○○○○○
Streetwise _____ ○○○○○
Subterfuge _____ ○○○○○

Other Traits

Merits
_____ ○○○○○
_____ ○○○○○
_____ ○○○○○
_____ ○○○○○
_____ ○○○○○
_____ ○○○○○
_____ ○○○○○
_____ ○○○○○
_____ ○○○○○

Flaws
_____
_____
_____

Disciplines
_____ ○○○○○
_____ ○○○○○
_____ ○○○○○
_____ ○○○○○
_____ ○○○○○
_____ ○○○○○
_____ ○○○○○
_____ ○○○○○
_____ ○○○○○

Health
○○○○○○○○○○○
□□□□□□□□□□□

Willpower
○○○○○○○○○○
□□□□□□□□□□

Vitae
□□□□□□□□□□
□□□□□□□□□□

Blood Potency
○○○○○○○○○○

Humanity
10 _____ O
9 _____ O
8 _____ O
7 _____ O
6 _____ O
5 _____ O
4 _____ O
3 _____ O
2 _____ O
1 _____ O

Size _____
Defense _____
Initiative Mod _____
Speed _____
Experience _____
Armor _____

Equipment
_____
_____
_____
_____
_____
_____

Attributes 5/4/3 • Skills 11/7/4 (+3 Specialties) • Clan (+1 bonus Attribute; see p. 92) • Covenant • Blood Potency 1 (May be increased with Merit points) • Disciplines 3 (Two dots must be in-clan) • Merits 7 • (Buying the fifth dot in Attributes, Skills or Merits costs two points) • Health = Stamina + Size • Willpower = Resolve + Composure • Size = 5 for adult human-sized Kindred • Defense = Lowest of Dexterity or Wits • Initiative Mod = Dexterity + Composure • Speed = Strength + Dexterity +5 • Starting Humanity = 7 • Vitae = d10 roll

I rose up among the dead, and I was dead with them.
— *Rites of the Dragon*